TEMPERATURE

MEASUREMENT

IN

ENGINEERING

TEMPERATURE MEASUREMENT IN ENGINEERING

VOLUME II

H. DEAN BAKER, Ph.D.

Professor of Mechanical Engineering
Columbia University

E. A. RYDER, M.E.

Former Consulting Engineer
Pratt & Whitney Aircraft Division
United Aircraft Corporation
East Hartford, Connecticut

N. H. BAKER, M.A.

Former Research Assistant in the
    Department of Mechanical Engineering
Columbia University

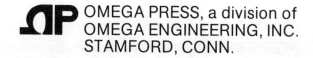 OMEGA PRESS, a division of
OMEGA ENGINEERING, INC.
STAMFORD, CONN.

PREFACE

The circumstances in which it is desired to measure temperature are so infinitely varied and the sorts of problems which arise are so numerous that any attempt at an entirely systematized discussion of the subject is bound to lead to inconsistencies, omissions, and repetitions. Not only do the situations differ, but the objectives vary in terms of what use is to be made of the temperature-measurement data. Only occasionally is the number on a standard scale of primary interest. Commonly, it is of equal concern to know when a certain temperature rise has occurred or to be notified at the instant of its arrival. The important factor may be to know where in a medium certain peak values occur. Perhaps the values themselves may be of less interest than their rates of change in space or time, i.e., space- and time-temperature gradients. More often than not, the difficulties of the situation determine what is attempted or sought. It is then recognized that such information as may be obtainable would be desirable to have, even if incomplete. Thereby, ingenuity is directed to devising means to obtain whatever data are possible under the limitations set for expendable effort as measured in time and money.

Usually, the means of measurement center on the problem itself and on its peculiar difficulties. The vast reserve of modern technology is brought to bear on the case, and the clever worker finds a combination of techniques which yields useful results. The same procedure may or may not be adaptable to an appreciable scope of other problems. However, despite the diversity and complexity of the array of such methods developed, there are three techniques which in their various modifications are used much more frequently than any others. They are the *thermocouple*, the *resistance thermometer*, and the *radiation pyrometer*. The present volume is divided so that, before any attempt is made to deal with actual problems, the resistance thermometer and the radiation pyrometer are thoroughly described in a systematic manner; thermocouples were so described in Volume I. Thus, in Part I, two chapters each are devoted to resistance thermometry and to radiation pyrometry: one a descriptive chapter and the other an analytical chapter. In the descriptive chapter, a survey is made of the available components, useful materials, and standard unit designs. In the analytical chapter, a systematized design procedure is developed. This design procedure is similar to that followed in purely mechanical design, such as, for example, that of machinery, where motions, stresses, and deflections are computed and members proportioned accordingly. By executing the described design-calculation procedure and applying the resulting choice of materials and components, a temperature-measurement installation is devised that can be hoped to be optimum for the particular case. And the basic character of the resistance and radiation technique results in a large scope of problems able to be solved in this manner.

However, it is not to be fancied that all problems lend themselves to being fitted into any such formulisms. For this reason, the second and larger part of this volume, i.e., Part II, is devoted to a selected assortment of actual problems. The peculiarities of the almost endless variety of situations are outlined in their essential features as far as space permits, and concrete examples are given of successful techniques worked out to perform measurements in these diverse circumstances. Some notion of the scope of temperature measurement may be suggested by cases ranging from the interior of the human body to interstellar space, the immediate vicinity of absolute zero to the internal temperatures of stars, or the temperatures in rotors of ultracentrifuges to those in precision thermostats, flames, and explosions.

Our objective in Volume II has been to complete the task outlined in the preface to Volume I. The form of treatment and organization of material have been essentially the same. However, the nature of the methods and problems discussed has resulted in this volume's being technically more advanced in character. To such extent as has seemed possible, the resulting limitation of the number of qualified readers has been reduced by presupposing only the barest minimum of previous knowledge. Each term or principle used is explained or defined, at least by context, at the point where it is introduced. The point of such first usage can be located by reference to the index. Likewise, all equations are stated in form suitable for direct application. In each case, the symbols are defined in the text following the particular equation, or group of equations relating to one topic. The appropriate units are given so that no difficulty should arise in substituting in numbers for practical computations. Derivations are not provided, because we did not regard them to be essential to engineering applications.

Very few worked-out examples are given. This omission arises partly from lack of space, since a full assortment of such sample calculations would outweigh the text itself. However, the principal reason is that such computations are to be looked upon as leading only to trial designs, and we do not wish them to be confused with our recommendations for final construction. To avoid any such misunderstanding, we have preferred to use the tried and tested designs of other scientists almost exclusively for application illustrations. These designs are included mostly in Part II.

The references, while numbering over a thousand, are not intended as a complete list. They represent the items from among those assembled in our personal libraries which we have found useful and therefore recommend to the reader's attention. We feel that a careful study of the text will usually provide a sufficient introductory grasp, whereas investigating any topic of particular interest by a reading of the references, marked by superior numbers at that topic, will yield a more detailed knowledge. Many of the references themselves contain extensive bibliographies, thereby providing access to further information.

Since our objective is that of application, we have not made a systematic attempt to achieve balanced perspectives of historical origins and fundamental contributions of individual scientists. While we consider distortions in these respects to be truly regrettable, we do not feel that their bearing on application will be essential. On the other hand, we have not made an attempt to reveal the very latest developments. Devices chosen for description are merely those considered best suited to illustrate essential design principles.

Aside from the references listed, we have drawn freely from all available sources of information, including a large collection of manufacturers' bulletins and catalogues and many letters in response to specific inquiries. Although these sources are rarely directly mentioned, we usually have in mind the actual equipment described.

Much of the hope that the book may prove to be reasonably free of errors rests on the diligent assistance of the graduate students in the Mechanical Engineering Department of Columbia University, including G. Srikantiah, K. Mohan, and D. Raichel, who read the entire text, A. Baldo, who read Chapters 13 and 14, and H. Brandmaier, who read Chapters 10 and 11. We also owe much to the care taken by R. W. Dodge and S. Battistessa in typing the manuscript.

H. DEAN BAKER
E. A. RYDER
N. H. BAKER

New York
May, 1961

CONTENTS

part I

TECHNIQUE

1

RESISTANCE THERMOMETERS

1·1 INTRODUCTION

The resistance thermometer was discussed, in terms of the general scope of its possibilities and applications, in the first two chapters of Volume I. It was there described as the basis of the International Temperature Scale for the range −297.35 to 1166.9°F and of the Provisional Temperature Scale from 11 to 90.19°K. The present chapter and that following will deal with the technique of its use. Applications to specific problems will be developed in relation to these problems as they are discussed in subsequent chapters.*

1·2 THE RESISTANCE THERMOMETER

The resistance thermometer is based on the fact that the resistance any material offers to the passage of an electric current is dependent on its temperature. Thus, the electric resistances of metallic conductors increase, whereas those of nonmetallic semiconductors decrease with rising temperature. The resistance of the sensitive element is compared, by means of suitable circuit arrangements, with that of a unit whose resistance is assumed to remain constant. The comparison is first made at the fixed points of the temperature scale to effect a calibration. Subsequent comparisons are made with the sensitive element in thermal communication with that portion of matter, the temperature of which it is desired to measure. Comparison of the electric resistances requires current flow in the sensitive-element resistance. The resulting heating effect tends to raise its temperature above that of its surroundings. In other respects, the problem of the relation between the temperature of the sensitive element and that which it is desired to measure is the same as for the thermocouple discussed in Volume I.

---

* By the 1954 agreement, °R = °F + 459.67 and °K = °C + 273.15, see Eq. 1·5 and footnotes on pages 4 and 5 of Volume I. For a full discussion, the reader is advised to consult H. F. Stimson, "Heat Units and Temperature Scales for Calorimetry," *Amer. J. Phys.*, **23**, no. 9, pp. 614–619 (December, 1955).

1·3 METALLIC SENSITIVE-ELEMENT MATERIALS

Choice of metal has little effect on the sensitivity of the element. Thus, the temperature coefficients of resistance for metals do not differ greatly, usually being around 0.0022 and rarely exceeding 0.0033 per °F.

Platinum wire of the highest available purity, 0.001- to 0.025-in. diameter, mounted as nearly as possible strain-free, annealed, and protected against contamination, is almost universally used in precision resistance thermometry. It is also widely used in nonprecision work for temperatures above 250°F, up to 2375°F and down to 20°R; however, evaporation tends to cause zero drifts above 1800°F, and 2000°F is the usual limit. Platinum wire is easily worked, relatively immune to corrosion, available in a highly pure and reproducible state, and of a relatively simple resistance-temperature relationship. Dry clean air or helium serves as an atmosphere in Pyrex, quartz, glass, suitable ceramic, or platinum protecting tubes. Mica, glass, quartz, or Pyrex insulation is used in coil mountings.[1-4]

Platinum can also be fused into glass, quartz, or Pyrex rods or tubes, but it is not then strain-free and is more subject to contamination with corresponding decreases in precision. Embedding the wire in pure alumina results in less contamination with increase in serviceability, the upper limit extending to 2900°F. Heavy wire, i.e., 0.025-in. diameter (No. 22 B & S gage) or larger, changes more slowly because of evaporation at high temperatures but results in either bulky and expensive or low-resistance elements. Fine wire, i.e., 0.001- to 0.004-in. diameter, permits achievement of a sufficient element resistance in a minimum of space.[1, 2, 4, 5-11]

Copper and nickel wire, being cheaper than platinum, are widely used in industrial resistance thermometers, at least for temperatures up to 250°F. Copper can be used down to −325°F; however, its low resistivity results in bulky or low-resistance elements. By joining lengths of nickel and copper or nickel and platinum wires in correct proportions, elements can be made of nearly linear response. Leaded phosphor-bronze can be used for temperatures below 13°R, provided that there is no magnetic field.[12, 13]

Tungsten or molybdenum wire fused into Pyrex, quartz, or ceramic rods or tubes is commercially available for use at temperatures up to 2200°F and in units as small as 0.025-in. diameter. The embedding material supports the wire against mechanical shock.[14, 15]

Metal-coated glass or ceramic rods can be made compactly with very high electric resistance and with much lower values of residual inductance and capacitance than is attainable in any wire-wound design.[16]

1·4   SEMICONDUCTING NONMETALLIC SENSITIVE-ELEMENT MATERIALS

Controlled compositions of sintered metallic oxides have electrical resistivities, at 77°F, of from 100 to 450,000 ohm cm, with temperature coefficients of resistance tenfold larger than those for metals, and negative in sign. Figure 1·1 suggests the wide range of resistances available in commercial thermistors. Strong compact ceramic units, i.e., thermistors, thus have large electrical resistances with low residual inductances and capacitances. Stock thermistors, after adjustment to "zero" error at one point, may conform to standard calibration curves to within 1°F. Preaged and sealed-in-glass beads, not heated above 212°F, may retain their calibrations for months to within less than 0.02°F variation, but drifts of up to a few per cent, i.e., of 0.1 to 1°F, occur if the beads are not sealed in glass, if aging is inadequate, or if temperatures higher than 212°F are used. Above 570°F, stability decreases; whereas, below around −150°F, resistances tend to become excessive. However, the resistance-temperature law holds to above 2300°F, and, with silver-soldered joints, elements can be used up to 1200°F.

Drifts due to pressure variations do not exceed 0.002°F/atm. Sporadic resistance fluctuations limit possible precision to ±0.004°F. Variations in manufacturing are substantial; however, by selective screening, standard specifications are maintained. Thus, tolerances on nominal resistances may be around ±10 per cent; whereas limiting variations to within ±1 per cent is difficult. This prevents close matching of thermistors in multiple-element circuits, as is so common and readily achieved with thermocouples. However, preaged thermistors rated as interchangeable to within ±0.2°F over limited ranges of temperature are commercially available. Typical commercial products are illustrated in Figs. 1·1 and 1·2.[17-32]

Electrolytic thermistors where bulb electrodes dip into solutions of metallic salts or waterglass are readily matched in resistance by adjusting electrode immersions and in temperature coefficient by varying solution concentrations. They are limited to a-c operation, but withstand high potentials without alteration, and are readily homemade in any required size or shape.[33-35]

Resistance curves for homemade carbon-composition elements and those of germanium with 0.0016 per cent of indium (see Fig. 1·3) are reproducible in the range 2 to 36°R to within 0.2 per cent, after heating to room temperature, and to within 1 per cent below 2°R.

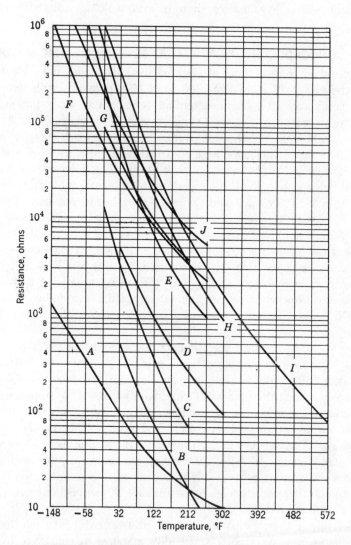

Fig. 1·1. Resistance-temperature curves for commercial thermistors. *A*, 0.140-in. diameter 0.75-in. long rod thermistor. *B*, 0.2-in. diameter 0.1-in. thick disk thermistor. *C*, 0.56-in. diameter 0.31 in. thick disk thermistor. *D*, 0.15-in. diameter 0.02-in. long bead thermistor. *E*, 0.26-in. diameter 0.03-in. wall 2-in. long tubular thermistor. *F*, 0.040-in. diameter 1.5-in. long rod thermistor. *G*, 0.05-in. diameter 1.2-in. long rod thermistor. *H*, 0.15-in. diameter 0.7-in. long rod thermistor. *I*, 0.1-in. diameter 0.6-in. long probe thermistor. *J*, 0.018-in. diameter 1.5-in. long rod thermistor.

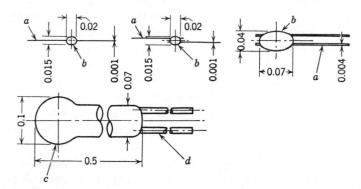

Fig. 1·2. Bead thermistors. *a*, Platinum-alloy leads; *b*, glass-coated semiconducting bead; *c*, semiconducting bead enclosed in solid glass cylinder; and *d*, tinned wire leads. All dimensions are in inches.

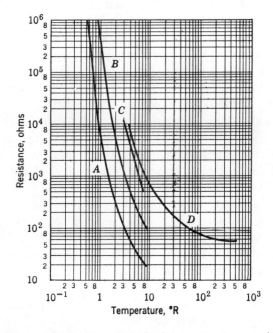

Fig. 1·3. Resistance-temperature curves for low-temperature sensitive elements. *A*, "2.7-ohm" carbon-composition sensitive element. *B*, "10-ohm" carbon-composition sensitive element. *C*, germanium with 0.0016 per cent indium sensitive element. *D*, "half-watt" carbon-composition sensitive element.

Carbon-composition elements are made from ordinary radio resistors by removing the paper and coating with baked-on Glyptal. Colloidal-carbon elements, of reproducibility subject to the condition of not being heated beyond the normal working range, result from coating paper or plastic strips with amorphous carbon such as India ink. Magnetic-field changes for carbon-composition elements are proportional to the square of the field intensity and may be as much as 2.3 per cent at 45,000 gauss. Temperature changes of less than 0.02°R can be observed with these elements at 36°R, and of less than 0.0002°R at 4°R.[13,36-45]

Thermometers of zinc oxide laid on a ceramic base are said to be more stable than those of colloidal carbon. They are accurate to within 0.02°R and have coefficients of around 0.055 per °R at 3.6°R.[46]

1·5 ELEMENT MOUNTING MATERIALS

Properties of available structural materials are discussed in Ch. 10 of Volume I. Precision-sensitive elements are mounted on mica spindles (see Figs. 1·4, 1·5, and 1·6). In Figs. 1·4 and 1·5 contact is limited to discrete points, minimizing strain and contamination. Susceptibility to dimensional changes straining the element and decline of insulation resistance in the direction of the cleavage planes in mica limit its use at higher temperatures. Mica is reliable up to 1100°F with 1800 or 2000°F as the upper limit.[4,10,11,47,48]

Glass insulation can be used in precision sensitive elements not intended for use above 575°F. Calibration at the sulfur point 444.6°C (832.28°F) is feasible, and a 0.02°F insulation-leakage error at this point does not cause errors exceeding ±0.01°F at temperatures below 575°F or ±0.0005°F in the range 32 to 212°F (see Fig. 1·7). At higher temperatures, errors rapidly increase as the glass-insulation resistance declines according to the semiconductor law (Eq. 1·1). Fused-in-quartz mounting, although rugged, strains the element, resulting in instability and much greater changes on heat treatment; thus α decreases and δ increases in Eq. 1·2 by several per cent. Such a mounting increases contamination and insulation leakage at higher temperatures, reducing precision. Embedding in less reactive ceramics for high-temperature insulation increases ranges and precision but decreases ruggedness. Within the temperature limits for the material, molded-plastic mountings can be used (see Fig. 1·8B) but with strain-reduced precision. Thermistors furnished insulated with glass coatings can be cemented in place as described for thermocouples in Ch. 11 of Volume I.[2,4,10,11,15,49,50]

1·6 PROTECTION

Clean moisture-free air or helium at half-atmospheric initial pressure is used in precision platinum-resistance thermometers. Base-metal elements must be protected against oxidation. Inner-tube-wall vapors must not react with any exposed sensitive-element surfaces. Thoroughly cleansed platinum, glass, fused-silica, and nonreactive impervious-ceramic inner tube walls are used in the precision thermometers. Low-conductivity nonvolatile nonreactive base-metal tubes are also used. The relatively high thermal resistances of nonmetallic protection tubes increase the temperature-rise errors corresponding to the heating effect of the measuring current. The time for response to temperature changes is also greater. Outer casings or tubes for embedded or fused-in sensitive elements are of metals chosen for suitable corrosion resistance under the operating conditions. Thermistor sensitive elements are furnished in forms adequately insulated and protected. Thus, they are commonly coated with or fused into glass. Carbon-composition low-temperature elements are protected and insulated with a coating of baked-on Glyptal varnish.[1, 2, 4, 7, 10, 11, 51]

1·7 LEADS

Junctions to the leads at the element, together with an initial length of the leads, must withstand the operating temperature, i.e., without corrosion or evaporation. In precision thermometers, an autogenous weld to a heavier strip of platinum is used. Silver solder is precluded for temperatures above 600°F. Gold is satisfactory up to 1800°F as being easily worked, inert, and of low resistivity. Copper can be used up to 400°F. Parasitic thermoelectric emfs are minimized by close spacing of junction pairs, shielding from heat waves, and avoiding of materials of large thermoelectric power (see Figs. 1·4 and 1·5). External leads, in lengths up to 1000 ft for d-c circuits, can be of heavy, i.e., No. 16 B & S gage (0.051 in.), single-strand copper wire, or for greater flexibility of three individually insulated strands of No. 26 or 28 B & S gage (0.016 or 0.013 in.) copper wire. Multiple-strand cable of the lamp-cord type is unsuitable because of the erratic variations in resistance to which it is subject. Two, three, or four leads may be required. Any unavoidable splices should be soldered, brazed, or welded. Compensating leads (see Fig. 2·2) must be equalized in resistance with the leads. Interchanged leads, marked r_l in Fig. 2·3, must be of equal resistance. Four-lead resistance thermometers (see Fig. 2·4) need not have equal lead resistances.

1·8 PRECISION ELEMENT DESIGNS

Precision element designs are indicated in Figs. 1·4, 1·5, 1·6, and 1·7. In Fig. 1·4B the classical construction, originally due to Callendar, is shown in the form described by Waidner and Burgess.[1] The platinum coil wound on a mica cross, touching only at discrete points, is intended to remain strain-free. It is not, however, entirely so, because of shifting in position with thermal-expansion changes and to swelling and warpage of the mica. The arrangements are for four leads (see Figs. 2·4 and 2·9) with head design suited to the minimization of parasitic thermoelectric emfs. The operating conditions are limited: (1), by the platinum and the mica, to upper temperatures of 1800 to 2000°F; (2), by response times of up to around 10 min; and (3) by its fragility, to laboratory use.[1, 2, 7, 47, 48, 52–55]

Roebuck's [56] modification (see Fig. 1·4A) eliminates most of the mechanical flimsiness by the introduction of a metal spindle in which the mica vanes are rigidly mounted and which is securely supported on the heavy lead wires. Warpage of the mica is greatly reduced; circular coil turns can shift with a minimum of straining; and no gravity or inertia loads are imposed on the fine lead wires. As shown, the upper temperature is limited to 575°F (which is Roebuck's requirement) by the brass, silver solder, and glass. An all-platinum construction with elimination of the glass would raise this limit to 1800 or 2000°F. The thermal capacity of the metal spindle tends to increase the lag time, whereas that of the metal tube tends to decrease it.[47, 48, 52, 56, 57]

The Meyers [59] coiled-filament feature (see Fig. 1·5A) by increasing the coil flexibility greatly reduces the wire strains resulting from coil deformations; it also permits a very small size. Barber [58] utilized this principle (see Fig. 1·5B) to attain a very simple compact construction while retaining high precision.[49, 58–61]

In the flat construction originally due to Dickinson and Mueller [62] (see Fig. 1·6), the thermal resistance is reduced between the coil wire and the ambient. This permits a larger measuring current for the same temperature-rise error, and also a reduced lag time. The metal case, rolled tightly against the platinum-wire–mica "sandwich," provides ruggedness; however, the wire is not strain-free and is subject to contamination by the mica throughout its length with consequent loss in precision.[4, 7, 10, 11, 50, 62, 63]

The construction of Fig. 1·5A and of a modification of Fig. 1·6 are commercially available; the others must usually be made specially. For detailed fabrication instructions in the various designs, the reader

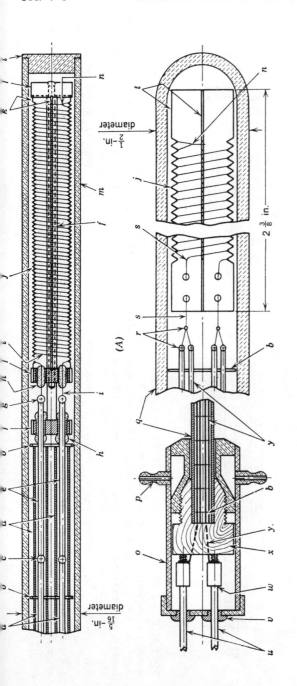

Fig. 1·4. (A) Roebuck-type and (B) classical Callendar-type precision elements. *a*, 0.032-in. diameter copper lead wires; *b*, 4-hole mica-disk spacers; *c*, silver-soldered junctions; *d*, tubular-nickel spacers; *e*, 0.032-in. diameter platinum leads; *f*, brass spindle assembly; *g*, silver-soldered junctions; *h*, lead-glass insulator sealed to wire; *i*, 0.002-in.-wire bifilar-wound 50-ohm-ice-point-resistance platinum sensitive element; *j*, double-thread notching; *k*, four mica vanes, mounted in spindle; *l*, silver-soldered brass end plug; *m*, brass tube; *n*, coil anchorage; *o*, copper housing; *p*, circulating-air connections; *q*, quartz, fused-silica, or ceramic tube; *r*, fused junctions; *s*, 0.004-in.-wire bifilar-wound 25-ohm-ice-point-resistance platinum sensitive element; *t*, four-vane dovetailed-construction mica-cross spindle; *u*, external copper lead wires; *v*, electric-insulation bushings; *w*, fusible-alloy connections in copper cups; *x*, paraffin-impregnated-wood split-screw head; *y*, 0.024-in. diameter platinum leads. (By permission J. R. Roebuck in J. Opt. Soc. Am., **6**, no. 8, 867, 871, October, 1922; C. W. Waidner and G. K. Burgess in Bulletin of the Bureau of Standards, **6**, no. 2, Fig. 1, November, 1909.)

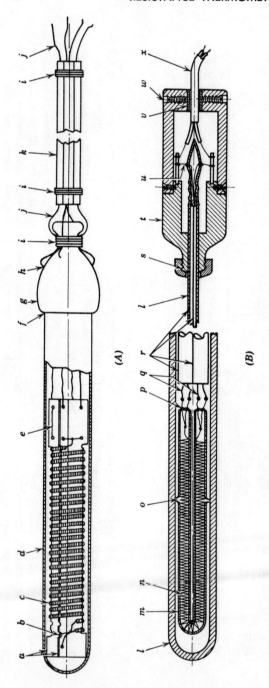

Fig. 1·5. Coiled-filament elements. (A) Meyer's design, (B) Barber's design. a, 0.004-in. thick mica, dovetailed-cross-construction spindle; b, end-loop anchoring; c, 0.004-in.-wire, 0.018-in. outside diameter helix, 25-ohm-ice-point-resistance, platinum sensitive element; d, 0.218-in. outside diameter 0.01-in.-wall helium-filled sealed platinum protecting tube; e, anchoring of leads; f, seal; g, glass head; h, leads emerging through seals; i, binding; j, 0.012-in. diameter platinum current and potential leads; k, insulating tubes; l, 7/32-in. outside diameter glass or Pyrex sheath; m, 0.06-in.-bore 0.008-in.-wall glass or Pyrex U-tube; n, 0.002-in.-wire, 0.06-in. outside diameter helix, 25.5-ohm-ice-point-resistance, platinum sensitive element; o, vents for evacuating, drying, and refilling with dried air; p, seals; q, 0.008- or 0.020-in. diameter platinum or gold current and potential leads; r, twin-bore, silica sheaths; s, chuck; t, Keramot head; u, platinum leads, sealed through lead glass painted with polystyrene solution; v, fiber split collar; w, grub screws; and x, four-strand cable. (By permission C. H. Meyers in RP 508, J. Research Natl. Bur. Standards, 9, no. 6, Figs. 1, 2, and 3, 808–811, December, 1932; C. R. Barber, J. Sci. Instr., 27, no. 2, 48, February, 1950.)

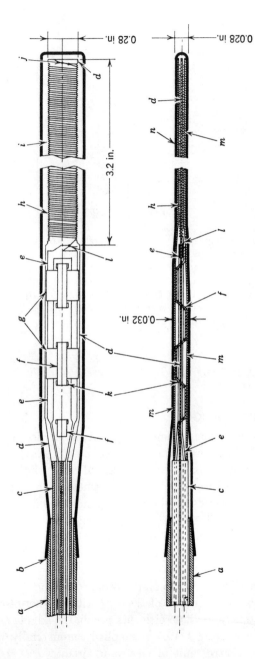

Fig. 1·6. Flat quick-response wire-wound element—Gittings' design. *a*, Glass tube; *b*, soldered joint; *c*, two twin-bore silica tubes; *d*, slotted and serrated 0.004-in. thick mica spindle; *e*, 0.02-in. diameter platinum leads rolled to 0.002 in. thickness; *f*, 0.004-in. thick by 0.12-in. wide mica lace; *g*, four 0.004-in. thick mica retaining strips; *h*, 0.004-in.-wire 25.6-ohm-ice-point-resistance biflar-wound platinum sensitive element; *i*, 0.02-in. pitch by 0.012-in. deep serrations; *j*, coil anchorage; *k*, five 0.04- by 0.12-in. slots; *l*, 0.004-in. thick flattened fused junctions; *m*, two 0.002-in. thick mica insulating strips; and *n*, silver or platinum sheath rolled down tight. (*By permission F. J. Gittings in J. Sci. Instr.*, **28**, *no. 8, 238, August, 1961*.)

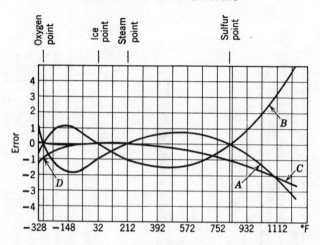

Fig. 1·7. Temperature-measurement error, per unit temperature error at the calibration points, for platinum sensitive elements. *A*, Error curve for calibration error at the ice point; *B*, error curve for calibration error at the steam point; *C*, error curve for calibration error at the sulfur point; and *D*, error curve for calibration error at the oxygen point. Curve *D* ends at the ice point. (*By permission E. F. Mueller in American Institute of Physics, Temperature, p. 175, Reinhold Publishing Corp., New York, 1941.*)

is referred to the original papers listed in the references at the end of this chapter.[1, 50, 56-59, 62-65]

1·9 INDUSTRIAL ELEMENT DESIGNS

Figure 1·9 indicates two typical commercially available designs for industrial elements. One of these, *A*, is equipped with a heavy outer immersion well. The various parts are substantial and solidly supported at all points, which results in great ruggedness. Thermal resistances between the wire coils and the cases are minimized by solid contacts. The wires are not strain-free and are subject to contamination from the embedding materials throughout their lengths, thus limiting precision. Very small-size platinum-wire elements are also commercially available.[4, 10, 11, 66]

Figure 1·10*A* due to Dowell,[19] *C* to Noltingk and Snelling,[67] and *D* to Karr [68] indicate industrial elements of the sort utilizing thermistors. The high electric resistances of these elements peculiarly adapts them to electronic indication. Figure 1·10*D* is supplied commercially with a package temperature-control unit of electronic circuitry.[19, 67-73]

1·10   OTHER SENSITIVE ELEMENTS

In Fig. 1·8A it is shown how the resistance wire can be spread out to indicate the average of the temperature throughout an extended space. Since no protection tube is provided, either the wire material must be immune to contamination from the ambient fluid, or it must be protected by a suitable coating. Precision will depend on these circumstances.[4, 10, 11, 74-78]

Figure 1·8B indicates a commercial product intended to be cemented on for measuring surface temperatures. Similar devices are available

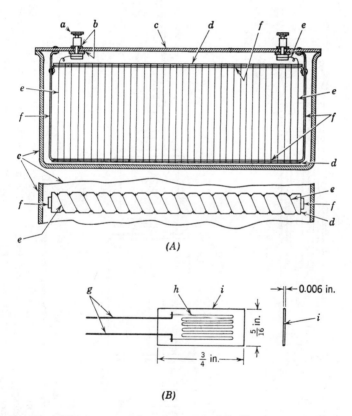

(A)

(B)

Fig. 1·8.   Special-purpose sensitive elements. (*A*) Space-average element per Knoblauch and Hencky, (*B*) surface-temperature element. *a*, Binding posts; *b*, electric-insulation washers; *c*, wall of duct; *d*, strip-mica electric insulation; *e*, sensitive-element resistance wire; *f*, metal frame; *g*, 0.01-in. tinned-wire leads; *h*, bonded-in 0.0008-in.-nickel-wire 50-ohm-nominal-resistance sensitive element; and *i*, molded-Bakelite wafer.

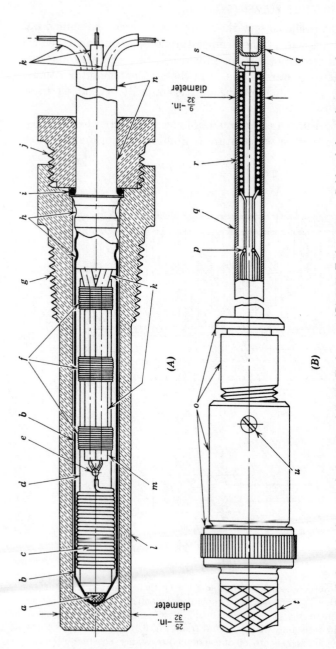

Fig. 1·9. Industrial wire-wound elements: (A) 250°F element, (B) 1000°F element. a, Soldered thermal contact; b, one-piece brass case; c, 100-ohm-ice-point-resistance oiled-silk-covered copper- or nickel-wire sensitive element; d, copper spindle; e, junctions to leads; f, lashings; g, ¾-in. standard pipe thread; h, crimping; i, gasket; j, threaded bushing; k, rubber-covered lead wires; l, corrosion-resistant-metal immersion well; m, flutes in spindle for leads; n, rubber-covered cable; o, mounting; p, junctions to leads; q, corrosion-resistant chromium-iron case; r, 25-ohm-ice-point-resistance cement-covered platinum-wire sensitive element; s, chromium-iron spindle; t, metal-braid-armored glass-braid-covered rubber-insulated or asbestos-insulated cable; and u, set screw. (By permission Leeds & Northrup Company, Philadelphia, Pa.)

from Arthur C. Ruge Associates, Inc. (Hudson, New Hampshire). The resulting low thermal resistance between the sensitive element and the parent surface material, together with the small thermal capacity of the element, makes it a sensitive indicator of the temperature of the portion of surface with which it is in contact. This temperature will, however, in general be altered by the disturbing effect of the element, on the heat-transfer coefficient over the surface area it covers.

Figure 1·10B indicates a catheter depending on a small bead thermistor as used by Benjamin and Horvath [79] for measuring internal temperatures in living animals including human beings. It is inserted into the tissue, carried inside a 19-gage hypodermic needle subsequently withdrawn leaving the catheter in position.[79-85]

1·11 CALIBRATION OF THERMISTOR, WIRE-WOUND, AND CARBON-GRANULE ELEMENTS

Wire-wound industrial sensitive elements (see Fig. 1·9) are furnished adjusted to conform, within specified limits, to standard curves. Common tolerances are ±0.5 to ±1.5°F in the range from −325 to 250°F and ±1 to ±3°F in the range from 250 to 1000°F. Pairs for measuring temperature differences may be matched to within tolerances of ±0.1°F.[86]

For low temperatures, i.e., below 36°R, carbon-composition sensitive elements are often used. Since they are manufactured for use as radio resistors and not for temperature measurement, they must be individually calibrated. The semiconductor law

$$\log_{10} r = A \log_{10} T + B/T + C \qquad (1·1)$$

(where $\log_{10}$ means logarithm to the base 10; T is the absolute temperature, °R; r is the resistance, ohms, at T, °R; and A, B, and C are constants) permits plotting the calibration curve by measuring r at three known temperatures. Although the element may be intended for use down to 1°R, the calibration temperatures can be at more conveniently accessible levels such as those in the liquid-helium, liquid-hydrogen, or liquid-oxygen regions, respectively. Simultaneous solution of the resulting three equations in A, B, and C then yields the values of these three constants. The most convenient method for solving these equations will be found clearly explained by Salvadori and Miller.[87] Substitution of the values for A, B, and C, thus found, into Eq. 1·1 provides a formula from which temperatures T, °R, can be computed directly from the measured values of r, ohms. Or, a curve can be plotted. Package cryostats producing temperatures down to 2°R are available from Arthur D. Little, Inc. (Cambridge, Massachusetts). These cryostats provide means to reproduce the helium, hydrogen, and oxygen points; i.e., the temperatures at which helium, hydrogen, and oxygen, respectively, boil at a pressure of 1 atm.[13, 19, 20, 36–41, 87–95]

Thermistor sensitive elements (see Figs. 1·1, 1·2 and 1·10) differ in initial resistance and must be adjusted by compensation to zero error at some one temperature. Thereafter, tolerances of from ±1 to $\pm1.5°F$ apply to standard curves furnished by the manufacturer. The precision of thermistors can be increased by individual calibration to within the limits set by their stability under the given operating conditions. The resistance r, ohms, is measured at three temperatures T, °R, within the desired working range. By substituting the corresponding values for temperature and resistance in Eq. 1·1, the constants A, B, and C are determined, and a curve is plotted. Depending on the precision sought, a calibrated liquid-in-glass thermometer, a calibrated thermocouple, a calibrated precision resistance thermometer, or fixed points can be used to determine these temperatures. The ice point and benzoic acid point, described in Volume I, are convenient. Triple-point cells are available from Transonics, Inc. (Burlington, Massachusetts). Package calibration units, each consisting of a thermostated furnace and a full sequence of fixed-point cells, are available from Weiller Instruments Corporation (New York, New York). Thermostated baths intended for comparison of the sensitive element to be tested with a certified thermometer or fixed-point cell are available from Hallikainen Instruments (Berkeley, California). Various other suitable furnaces and baths are commercially available.[96–105]

Metallized-ceramic resistors made as radio parts and not for temperature measurement must be individually calibrated. The precision of wire-wound industrial sensitive elements can be increased by individual calibration to within closer limits than those corresponding to the manufacturers' tolerances. The latter are set by the stability of the elements under the given operating conditions. Specially constructed sensitive elements must be calibrated. In operation at temperatures higher than those usually suitable for the given element materials, frequent recalibration may be necessary. Precision platinum-resistance sensitive elements require, for realization of their attainable precisions, the most careful calibration. The equation for pure strain-free annealed platinum, which also applies approximately to metals generally, is

$$t = (r_t/r_o - 1)/\alpha + \delta(t/100 - 1)t/100$$
$$+ \beta(t/100 - 1)(t/100)^3 \quad (1·2)$$

where t is the temperature, °C; r_t is the observed resistance, ohms, at t, °C; r_o is the resistance, ohms, at 0°C; α, β, and δ are constants for each

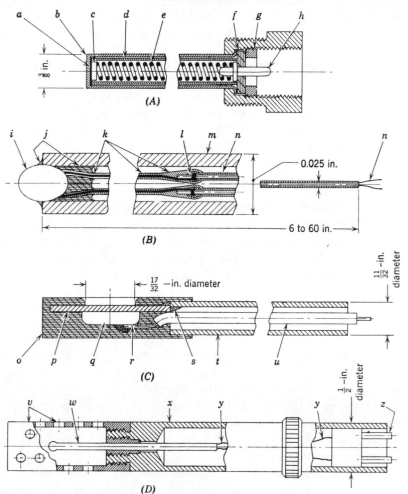

Fig. 1·10. Thermistor probes. (*A*) Disk-thermistor probe, (*B*) catheter, (*C*) plate-thermistor probe, (*D*) bead-thermistor probe. *a*, Tin-rolled-on-lead washer; *b*, copper tube; *c*, 0.2-in. diameter disk thermistor; *d*, insulating tube; *e*, stiff spring; *f*, insulating washer; *g*, locking collar; *h*, connection pin; *i*, 0.015-in. diameter 0.02-in. long glass-coated bead, thermistor (see Fig. 1·2); *j*, polystyrene cement; *k*, Bakelite-dipped rayon-wound 0.001-in. diameter platinum leads; *l*, conducting-silver-paste junction; *m*, 0.025-in. outside diameter 0.014-in. inside diameter radio-opaque plastic tube; *n*, 0.003-in. diameter enamel-covered copper wire; *o*, molded-Araldite block; *p*, embedded brass plate; *q*, disk thermistor soldered to brass plate *p*; *r*, soldered joint, of copper lead to thermistor; *s*, brazed joint; *t*, brass tube; *u*, insulated lead; *v*, shield; *w*, glass-coated bead thermistor (see Fig. 1·2); *x*, body shell; *y*, lead wires; and *z*, cable-connecting plug. (*By permission K. P. Dowell in Electrical Manufacturing,* **42**, *no. 2, pp. 84–91, August, 1948; R. J. Karr in Scientific Apparatus and Methods,* **6**, *no. 1, 6, Winter, 1954.*)

sensitive element. For precision platinum sensitive elements, satisfying the conditions of the International Temperature Scale, $\beta = 0$ above $0°C$.[61, 93, 106–110]

For metallized-ceramic and wire-wound industrial sensitive elements, the resistance r_o, ohms, is measured at the ice point and r_t is measured at three other temperatures t, °C, in the working range, by means of which temperature-resistance data the constants α, β, and δ in Eq. 1·2 are determined and a curve plotted. Depending on the precision sought, a calibrated liquid-in-glass thermometer, a calibrated thermocouple, a calibrated precision resistance thermometer, or fixed points can be used to determine these temperatures.[87]

1·12 CALIBRATION OF PRECISION ELECTRIC-RESISTANCE THERMOMETERS

The precision electric-resistance thermometer is used in the most serious scientific work and for the reproduction of the International Temperature Scale. Examples of the kinds of construction used are illustrated in Figs. 1·4 and 1·5.

A precision platinum-resistance sensitive element may be calibrated by measuring the resistance r_t in ohms at the oxygen point $-182.97°C$, ice point $0°C$, steam point $100°C$, and sulfur point $444.6°C$. Substitutions of pairs of values for t and r_t into Eq. 1·2 and simultaneous solution of the resulting three equations yields values for the constants α, β, and δ. The value of r_o is given directly.

The thermometer may also be furnished with a certificate from the manufacturer or from the National Bureau of Standards (Washington, D. C.) stating the values of α, β, δ, and r_o directly. Also available are tables of corresponding values of r_t/r_o or of $r_t - r_o$ at one-degree intervals over the calibration range of the thermometer. A thermometer of suitable construction can also be recalibrated at any time by sending it to the National Bureau of Standards (Washington, D. C.). A charge is usually made sufficient to compensate for costs.

Tables 1·1, 1·2, and 1·3 are then used to determine the temperature t, °C, corresponding to any observed resistance r_t, ohms.[87, 93] Thus r_t'/r_o' is found from

$$r_t'/r_o' = 0.004\,(r_t/r_o\alpha - 1/\alpha) + 1 \tag{1·3}$$

where r_t is the observed resistance, ohms, at t, °C; r_o is the calibration value for the resistance, ohms, at $0°C$; and α has the value found from the calibration data. The two values nearest to r_t'/r_o', i.e., $(r_t'/r_o')_1$ and $(r_t'/r_o')_2$ are then located in Table 1·1, and the corresponding tempera-

Table 1·1. Standard table of resistance ratio, r_t'/r_0', vs temperature, t', °C

				−190 to −1°C							
t'	r_t'/r_0'	diff	t'	r_t'/r_0'	diff	t'	r_t'/r_0'	diff	t'	r_t'/r_0'	diff
...	...	...	−150	0.373926	4326	−100	0.587183	4209	−50	0.795439	4124
...	...	...	−149	0.378252	4323	−99	0.591392	4207	−49	0.799563	4123
...	...	...	−148	0.382575	4320	−98	0.595599	4205	−48	0.803686	4121
...	...	...	−147	0.386895	4318	−97	0.599804	4203	−47	0.807807	4120
..	...	...	−146	0.391213	4315	−96	0.604007	4201	−46	0.811927	4119
...	...	...	−145	0.395528	4312	−95	0.608208	4199	−45	0.816046	4117
...	...	...	−144	0.399840	4310	−94	0.612407	4197	−44	0.820163	4115
...	...	...	−143	0.404150	4307	−93	0.616604	4195	−43	0.824278	4114
...	...	...	−142	0.408457	4304	−92	0.620799	4193	−42	0.828392	4113
...	...	...	−141	0.412761	4302	−91	0.624992	4191	−41	0.832505	4111
−190	0.198422	4451	−140	0.417063	4299	−90	0.629183	4190	−40	0.836616	4110
−189	0.202873	4449	−139	0.421362	4297	−89	0.633373	4188	−39	0.840726	4109
−188	0.207322	4444	−138	0.425659	4294	−88	0.637561	4186	−38	0.844835	4107
−187	0.211766	4441	−137	0.429953	4291	−87	0.641747	4184	−37	0.848942	4106
−186	0.216207	4438	−136	0.434244	4289	−86	0.645931	4182	−36	0.853048	4105
−185	0.220645	4434	−135	0.438533	4286	−85	0.650113	4181	−35	0.857153	4103
−184	0.225079	4431	−134	0.442819	4284	−84	0.654294	4179	−34	0.861256	4102
−183	0.229510	4427	−133	0.447103	4281	−83	0.658473	4177	−33	0.865358	4101
−182	0.233937	4424	−132	0.451385	4279	−82	0.662650	4175	−32	0.869459	4099
−181	0.238361	4420	−131	0.455664	4277	−81	0.666825	4173	−31	0.873558	4097
−180	0.242781	4418	−130	0.459941	4274	−80	0.670998	4171	−30	0.877655	4096
−179	0.247199	4413	−129	0.464215	4272	−79	0.675169	4170	−29	0.881751	4095
−178	0.251612	4411	−128	0.468487	4269	−78	0.679333	4169	−28	0.885846	4094
−177	0.256023	4407	−127	0.472756	4267	−77	0.683508	4167	−27	0.889940	4093
−176	0.260430	4404	−126	0.477023	4265	−76	0.687675	4165	−26	0.894033	4091
−175	0.264834	4401	−125	0.481288	4262	−75	0.691840	4163	−25	0.898124	4090
−174	0.269235	4397	−124	0.485550	4260	−74	0.696003	4162	−24	0.902214	4089
−173	0.273632	4394	−123	0.489810	4258	−73	0.700165	4160	−23	0.906303	4088
−172	0.278026	4391	−122	0.494068	4255	−72	0.704325	4158	−22	0.910391	4087
−171	0.282417	4388	−121	0.498323	4253	−71	0.708483	4156	−21	0.914478	4085
−170	0.286805	4385	−120	0.502576	4251	−70	0.712639	4155	−20	0.918563	4083
−169	0.291190	4381	−119	0.506827	4249	−69	0.716794	4153	−19	0.922646	4082
−168	0.295571	4379	−118	0.511076	4246	−68	0.720947	4152	−18	0.926728	4081
−167	0.299950	4375	−117	0.515322	4244	−67	0.725099	4150	−17	0.930809	4080
−166	0.304325	4372	−116	0.519566	4242	−66	0.729249	4148	−16	0.934889	4079
−165	0.308697	4369	−115	0.523808	4240	−65	0.733397	4147	−15	0.938968	4078
−164	0.313066	4366	−114	0.528048	4238	−64	0.737544	4146	−14	0.943046	4076
−163	0.317432	4363	−113	0.532286	4236	−63	0.741690	4144	−13	0.947122	4075
−162	0.321795	4360	−112	0.536522	4233	−62	0.745834	4142	−12	0.951197	4073
−161	0.326155	4357	−111	0.540755	4231	−61	0.749976	4140	−11	0.955270	4072
−160	0.330512	4354	−110	0.544986	4229	−60	0.754116	4139	−10	0.959342	4072
−159	0.334866	4352	−109	0.549215	4227	−59	0.758255	4138	−9	0.963414	4070
−158	0.339218	4349	−108	0.553442	4225	−58	0.762393	4136	−8	0.967484	4069
−157	0.343567	4346	−107	0.557667	4223	−57	0.766529	4134	−7	0.971553	4067
−156	0.347913	4343	−106	0.561890	4222	−56	0.770663	4133	−6	0.975620	4066
−155	0.352256	4340	−105	0.566112	4219	−55	0.774796	4132	−5	0.979686	4065
−154	0.356596	4337	−104	0.570331	4216	−54	0.778928	4130	−4	0.983751	4064
−153	0.360933	4334	−103	0.574547	4214	−53	0.783058	4129	−3	0.987815	4063
−152	0.365267	4331	−102	0.578761	4212	−52	0.787187	4127	−2	0.991878	4062
−151	0.369598	4328	−101	0.582973	4210	−51	0.791314	4125	−1	0.995940	4060

By permission F. D. Werner and A. C. Frazer in Rev. Sci. Instr., 23, no. 4, pp. 163–169 (April, 1952).

tures t_1' and $t_2' = t_1' + 1$, °C, are found opposite. Then t' is found by linear interpolation. Thus

$$t' = t_1' + [(r_t'/r_0') - (r_t'/r_0')_1]/[(r_t'/r_0')_2 - (r_t'/r_0')_1] \quad (1·4)$$

The tabular difference $(r_t'/r_0')_2 - (r_t'/r_0')_1$ is given in the third column of Table 1·1.[111]

The temperature determination t, °C, corresponding to the observed resistance r_t, ohms, is then given by

$$t = t' + \Delta t' \qquad (1·5)$$

where t', °C, is the value thus found by interpolation from Table 1·1; and $\Delta t'$ is found, in Table 1·2 for t' above 0°C or from Table 1·3 for t'

below 0°C, corresponding to the value of t' and the values for β and δ resulting from the calibration. Intermediate values of δ, β, and t' can be used by linear interpolation in Tables 1·2 and 1·3.

There is, of course, no point in attempting to calibrate any element to greater precision than that to which it is susceptible or which is required (see Ch. 3 of Volume I).[111]

Example. The observed resistance r_t is 22.1695 ohms for a sensitive element of calibration values: $r_0 = 25.2550$ ohms, $\alpha = 0.003925$ per °C, $\delta = 1.491$, and $\beta = 0.1120$. Equation 1·3 gives

$$r_t'/r'_0 = 0.004(22.1695/25.2550 \times 0.003925 - 1/0.003925) + 1 = 0.8754916$$

The two values in Table 1·1 nearest to 0.8754916 are 0.873558 corresponding to $t' = -31°C$ and 0.877655 corresponding to $t' = -30°C$. The tabular difference is given as 4097, i.e., 0.004097. Then by Eq. 1·4,

Table 1·1 (Continued)

0 to 199°C

t'	r_t'/r_0'	diff	t'	r_t'/r_0'	diff	t'	r_t'/r_0'	diff	t'	r_t'/r_0'	diff
0	1.000000	4059	50	1.201493	4000	100	1.400000	3940	150	1.595521	3880
1	1.004059	4058	51	1.205493	3998	101	1.403940	3938	151	1.599401	3879
2	1.008117	4057	52	1.209491	3997	102	1.407878	3937	152	1.603280	3878
3	1.012174	4056	53	1.213488	3996	103	1.411815	3936	153	1.607158	3876
4	1.016230	4054	54	1.217484	3995	104	1.415751	3935	154	1.611034	3875
5	1.020284	4053	55	1.221479	3993	105	1.419686	3934	155	1.614909	3874
6	1.024337	4052	56	1.225472	3992	106	1.423620	3933	156	1.618783	3873
7	1.028389	4051	57	1.229464	3991	107	1.427553	3931	157	1.622656	3872
8	1.032440	4049	58	1.233455	3989	108	1.431484	3930	158	1.626528	3870
9	1.036489	4048	59	1.237446	3988	109	1.435414	3929	159	1.630398	3869
10	1.040537	4047	60	1.241434	3987	110	1.439343	3928	160	1.634267	3868
11	1.044584	4046	61	1.245421	3986	111	1.443271	3927	161	1.638135	3867
12	1.048630	4045	62	1.249407	3985	112	1.447198	3925	162	1.642002	3866
13	1.052675	4044	63	1.253392	3984	113	1.451123	3924	163	1.645868	3864
14	1.056719	4043	64	1.257376	3983	114	1.455047	3923	164	1.649732	3863
15	1.060762	4041	65	1.261359	3981	115	1.458970	3922	165	1.653595	3862
16	1.064803	4040	66	1.265340	3980	116	1.462892	3921	166	1.657457	3861
17	1.068843	4039	67	1.269320	3979	117	1.466813	3919	167	1.661318	3860
18	1.072882	4038	68	1.273299	3978	118	1.470732	3918	168	1.665178	3858
19	1.076920	4036	69	1.277277	3977	119	1.474650	3917	169	1.669036	3857
20	1.080956	4035	70	1.281254	3976	120	1.478567	3916	170	1.672893	3856
21	1.084991	4034	71	1.285230	3974	121	1.482483	3915	171	1.676749	3855
22	1.089025	4033	72	1.289204	3973	122	1.486398	3913	172	1.680604	3854
23	1.093058	4032	73	1.293177	3972	123	1.490311	3912	173	1.684458	3853
24	1.097090	4030	74	1.297149	3971	124	1.494223	3911	174	1.688311	3851
25	1.101120	4029	75	1.301120	3969	125	1.498134	3910	175	1.692162	3850
26	1.105149	4028	76	1.305089	3968	126	1.502044	3909	176	1.696012	3849
27	1.109177	4027	77	1.309057	3967	127	1.505953	3907	177	1.699861	3848
28	1.113204	4026	78	1.313024	3966	128	1.509860	3906	178	1.703709	3846
29	1.117230	4024	79	1.316990	3965	129	1.513766	3905	179	1.707555	3845
30	1.121254	4023	80	1.320955	3964	130	1.517671	3904	180	1.711400	3844
31	1.125277	4022	81	1.324919	3962	131	1.521575	3903	181	1.715244	3843
32	1.129299	4021	82	1.328881	3961	132	1.525478	3901	182	1.719087	3842
33	1.133320	4020	83	1.332842	3960	133	1.529379	3900	183	1.722929	3842
34	1.137340	4019	84	1.336802	3959	134	1.533279	3899	184	1.726770	3841
35	1.141359	4017	85	1.340761	3958	135	1.537178	3898	185	1.730609	3839
36	1.145376	4016	86	1.344719	3956	136	1.541076	3897	186	1.734447	3838
37	1.149392	4015	87	1.348675	3955	137	1.544973	3895	187	1.738284	3837
38	1.153407	4014	88	1.352630	3954	138	1.548868	3894	188	1.742120	3836
39	1.157421	4013	89	1.356584	3953	139	1.552762	3893	189	1.745955	3835
40	1.161434	4011	90	1.360537	3952	140	1.556655	3892	190	1.749788	3833
41	1.165445	4010	91	1.364489	3951	141	1.560547	3891	191	1.753620	3832
42	1.169455	4009	92	1.368440	3949	142	1.564438	3890	192	1.757451	3830
43	1.173464	4008	93	1.372389	3948	143	1.568328	3888	193	1.761281	3830
44	1.177472	4006	94	1.376337	3947	144	1.572216	3887	194	1.765110	3829
45	1.181478	4005	95	1.380284	3946	145	1.576103	3886	195	1.768937	3827
46	1.185483	4004	96	1.384230	3944	146	1.579989	3885	196	1.772763	3826
47	1.189487	4003	97	1.388174	3943	147	1.583874	3884	197	1.776588	3825
48	1.193490	4002	98	1.392117	3942	148	1.587758	3882	198	1.780412	3824
49	1.197492	4001	99	1.396059	3941	149	1.591640	3881	199	1.784235	3823

Table 1·1 (Continued)

t'	r_t'/r_0'	diff	t'	r_t'/r_0'	diff	t'	r_t'/r_0'	diff	t'	r_t'/r_0'	diff
					200 to 399°C						
200	1.788056	3820	250	1.977605	3761	300	2.164167	3701	350	2.347745	3641
201	1.791876	3819	251	1.981366	3759	301	2.167868	3700	351	2.351386	3640
202	1.795695	3818	252	1.985125	3758	302	2.171568	3699	352	2.355026	3639
203	1.799513	3817	253	1.988883	3757	303	2.175267	3697	353	2.358665	3637
204	1.803330	3815	254	1.992640	3756	304	2.178964	3696	354	2.362302	3636
205	1.807145	3814	255	1.996396	3755	305	2.182660	3695	355	2.365938	3635
206	1.810959	3813	256	2.000151	3753	306	2.186355	3694	356	2.369573	3634
207	1.814772	3812	257	2.003904	3752	307	2.190049	3692	357	2.373207	3633
208	1.818584	3811	258	2.007656	3751	308	2.193741	3691	358	2.376840	3632
209	1.822395	3810	259	2.011407	3750	309	2.197432	3690	359	2.380472	3630
210	1.826205	3808	260	2.015157	3748	310	2.201122	3689	360	2.384102	3629
211	1.830013	3807	261	2.018905	3747	311	2.204811	3688	361	2.387731	3628
212	1.833820	3806	262	2.022652	3746	312	2.208499	3686	362	2.391359	3627
213	1.837626	3805	263	2.026398	3745	313	2.212185	3685	363	2.394986	3626
214	1.841431	3803	264	2.030143	3744	314	2.215870	3684	364	2.398612	3624
215	1.845234	3802	265	2.033887	3743	315	2.219554	3683	365	2.402236	3623
216	1.849036	3801	266	2.037630	3741	316	2.223237	3682	366	2.405859	3622
217	1.852837	3800	267	2.041371	3740	317	2.226919	3681	367	2.409481	3621
218	1.856637	3799	268	2.045111	3739	318	2.230600	3679	368	2.413102	3620
219	1.860436	3798	269	2.048850	3738	319	2.234279	3678	369	2.416722	3618
220	1.864234	3796	270	2.052588	3737	320	2.237957	3677	370	2.420340	3617
221	1.868030	3795	271	2.056325	3736	321	2.241634	3676	371	2.423957	3616
222	1.871825	3794	272	2.060061	3734	322	2.245310	3674	372	2.427573	3615
223	1.875619	3793	273	2.063795	3733	323	2.248984	3673	373	2.431188	3614
224	1.879412	3792	274	2.067528	3732	324	2.252657	3672	374	2.434802	3612
225	1.883204	3790	275	2.071260	3731	325	2.256329	3671	375	2.438414	3611
226	1.886994	3789	276	2.074991	3729	326	2.260000	3670	376	2.442025	3610
227	1.890783	3788	277	2.078720	3728	327	2.263670	3669	377	2.445635	3609
228	1.894571	3787	278	2.082448	3727	328	2.267339	3667	378	2.449244	3608
229	1.898358	3786	279	2.086175	3726	329	2.271006	3666	379	2.452852	3606
230	1.902144	3784	280	2.089901	3725	330	2.274672	3665	380	2.456458	3605
231	1.905928	3783	281	2.093626	3723	331	2.278337	3664	381	2.460063	3604
232	1.909711	3782	282	2.097349	3722	332	2.282001	3663	382	2.463667	3603
233	1.913493	3781	283	2.101071	3721	333	2.285664	3661	383	2.467270	3602
234	1.917274	3780	284	2.104792	3720	334	2.289325	3660	384	2.470872	3600
235	1.921054	3778	285	2.108512	3719	335	2.292985	3659	385	2.474472	3599
236	1.924832	3777	286	2.112231	3718	336	2.296644	3658	386	2.478071	3598
237	1.928609	3776	287	2.115949	3716	337	2.300302	3657	387	2.481669	3597
238	1.932385	3775	288	2.119665	3715	338	2.303959	3655	388	2.485266	3596
239	1.936160	3774	289	2.123380	3714	339	2.307614	3654	389	2.488862	3595
240	1.939934	3773	290	2.127094	3713	340	2.311268	3653	390	2.492457	3593
241	1.943707	3771	291	2.130807	3712	341	2.314921	3652	391	2.496050	3592
242	1.947478	3770	292	2.134519	3710	342	2.318573	3651	392	2.499642	3591
243	1.951248	3769	293	2.138229	3709	343	2.322224	3649	393	2.503233	3590
244	1.955017	3768	294	2.141938	3708	344	2.325873	3648	394	2.506823	3588
245	1.958785	3766	295	2.145646	3707	345	2.329521	3647	395	2.510411	3587
246	1.962551	3765	296	2.149353	3705	346	2.333168	3646	396	2.513998	3586
247	1.966316	3764	297	2.153058	3704	347	2.336814	3645	397	2.517584	3585
248	1.970080	3763	298	2.156762	3703	348	2.340459	3644	398	2.521169	3584
249	1.973843	3762	299	2.160465	3702	349	2.344103	3642	399	2.524753	3583

$$t' = -31 + (0.8754916 - 0.873558)/0.004097 = -30.52804°C$$

For $t' = -40°C$, $\delta = 1.491$, and $\beta = 0.1120$; Table 1·3 gives $\Delta t' = -0.00083°C$. The observed temperature is then given by Eq. 1·5 as $t = -30.52804 - 0.00083 = -30.5289°C$. However, if α is known only to four significant figures, t can be stated to but one decimal place, i.e., $t = -30.5°C$.

Temperatures thus computed correspond to the observed resistance and given values for the constants r_o, α, β, and δ to within a calculation uncertainty slightly exceeding 0.0001°C, provided that r_t, r_o, and α are given to a sufficient number of significant figures. Under ideal conditions, temperature determinations with precision platinum-resistance thermometers may be reproducible to within approximately 0.0001°C. This figure represents about the ultimate in reproducibility.

Table 1·1 (Continued)

					400 to 600°C						
t'	r_t'/r_0'	diff	t'	r_t'/r_0'	diff	t'	r_t'/r_0'	diff	t'	r_t'/r_0'	diff
400	2.528336	3581	450	2.705941	3522	500	2.880560	3462	550	3.052193	3402
401	2.531917	3580	451	2.709463	3520	501	2.884022	3461	551	3.055595	3401
402	2.535497	3579	452	2.712983	3519	502	2.887483	3459	552	3.058996	3400
403	2.539076	3578	453	2.716502	3518	503	2.890942	3458	553	3.062396	3399
404	2.542654	3577	454	2.720020	3517	504	2.894400	3457	554	3.065795	3397
405	2.546231	3575	455	2.723537	3516	505	2.897857	3456	555	3.069192	3396
406	2.549806	3574	456	2.727053	3514	506	2.901313	3455	556	3.072588	3395
407	2.553380	3573	457	2.730567	3513	507	2.904768	3454	557	3.075983	3394
408	2.556953	3572	458	2.734080	3512	508	2.908222	3452	558	3.079377	3393
409	2.560525	3571	459	2.737592	3511	509	2.911674	3451	559	3.082770	3391
410	2.564096	3569	460	2.741103	3510	510	2.915125	3450	560	3.086161	3390
411	2.567665	3568	461	2.744613	3509	511	2.918575	3449	561	3.089551	3389
412	2.571233	3567	462	2.748122	3507	512	2.922024	3448	562	3.092940	3388
413	2.574800	3566	463	2.751629	3506	513	2.925472	3446	563	3.096328	3387
414	2.578366	3565	464	2.755135	3505	514	2.928918	3445	564	3.099715	3386
415	2.581931	3564	465	2.758640	3504	515	2.932363	3444	565	3.103101	3384
416	2.585495	3562	466	2.762144	3503	516	2.935807	3443	566	3.106485	3383
417	2.589057	3561	467	2.765647	3501	517	2.939250	3442	567	3.109868	3382
418	2.592618	3560	468	2.769148	3500	518	2.942692	3440	568	3.113250	3381
419	2.596178	3559	469	2.772648	3499	519	2.946132	3439	569	3.116631	3379
420	2.599737	3557	470	2.776147	3498	520	2.949571	3438	570	3.120010	3378
421	2.603294	3556	471	2.779645	3497	521	2.953009	3437	571	3.123388	3377
422	2.606850	3555	472	2.783142	3495	522	2.956446	3436	572	3.126765	3376
423	2.610405	3554	473	2.786637	3494	523	2.959882	3434	573	3.130141	3375
424	2.613959	3553	474	2.790131	3493	524	2.963316	3433	574	3.133516	3374
425	2.617512	3551	475	2.793624	3492	525	2.966749	3432	575	3.136890	3372
426	2.621063	3550	476	2.797116	3491	526	2.970181	3431	576	3.140262	3371
427	2.624613	3549	477	2.800607	3489	527	2.973612	3430	577	3.143633	3370
428	2.628162	3548	478	2.804096	3488	528	2.977042	3429	578	3.147003	3369
429	2.631710	3547	479	2.807584	3487	529	2.980471	3427	579	3.150372	3368
430	2.635257	3546	480	2.811071	3486	530	2.983898	3426	580	3.153740	3366
431	2.638803	3544	481	2.814557	3485	531	2.987324	3425	581	3.157106	3365
432	2.642347	3543	482	2.818042	3483	532	2.990749	3424	582	3.160471	3364
433	2.645890	3542	483	2.821525	3482	533	2.994173	3423	583	3.163835	3363
434	2.649432	3541	484	2.825007	3481	534	2.997596	3421	584	3.167198	3362
435	2.652973	3540	485	2.828488	3480	535	3.001017	3420	585	3.170560	3360
436	2.656513	3538	486	2.831968	3478	536	3.004437	3419	586	3.173920	3359
437	2.660051	3537	487	2.835447	3477	537	3.007856	3418	587	3.177279	3358
438	2.663588	3536	488	2.838924	3476	538	3.011274	3416	588	3.180637	3357
439	2.667124	3535	489	2.842400	3475	539	3.014690	3415	589	3.183994	3356
440	2.670659	3534	490	2.845875	3474	540	3.018105	3414	590	3.187350	3354
441	2.674193	3532	491	2.849349	3473	541	3.021519	3413	591	3.190704	3353
442	2.677725	3531	492	2.852822	3471	542	3.024932	3412	592	3.194057	3352
443	2.681256	3530	493	2.856293	3470	543	3.028344	3411	593	3.197409	3351
444	2.684786	3529	494	2.859763	3469	544	3.031755	3409	594	3.200760	3350
445	2.688315	3528	495	2.863232	3468	545	3.035164	3408	595	3.204110	3348
446	2.691843	3526	496	2.866700	3467	546	3.038572	3407	596	3.207458	3347
447	2.695369	3525	497	2.870167	3466	547	3.041979	3406	597	3.210805	3346
448	2.698894	3524	498	2.873633	3464	548	3.045385	3405	598	3.214151	3345
449	2.702418	3523	499	2.877097	3463	549	3.048790	3403	599	3.217496	3344
									600	3.220840	

Table 1·2. $\Delta t'$, the correction to be added to t' from Table 1·1, for various values of δ and t'. For use above 0°C

t'	$\delta = 1.490$	$\delta = 1.491$	$\delta = 1.492$	$\delta = 1.494$	$\delta = 1.495$
0	0	0	0	0	0
50	+0.00075	+0.00050	+0.00025	−0.00025	−0.00050
100	0	0	0	0	0
150	−0.00232	−0.00155	−0.00077	+0.00077	+0.00155
200	−0.00628	−0.00419	−0.00209	+0.00209	+0.00419
250	−0.01196	−0.00798	−0.00399	+0.00399	+0.00798
300	−0.01945	−0.01297	−0.00648	+0.00648	+0.01297
350	−0.02883	−0.01922	−0.00961	+0.00961	+0.01922
400	−0.04020	−0.02680	−0.01340	+0.01340	+0.02680
450	−0.05366	−0.03577	−0.01789	+0.01789	+0.03577
500	−0.06931	−0.04621	−0.02310	+0.02310	+0.04621
550	−0.08727	−0.05818	−0.02909	+0.02909	+0.05818
600	−0.10743	−0.07162	−0.03581	+0.03581	+0.07162

Table 1·3. $\Delta t'$, the correction to be added to t' from Table 1·1, for various values of δ, β, and t'. For use below 0°C

For $\delta = 1.490$

β	$t' = -40$	$t' = -80$	$t' = -100$	$t' = -140$	$t' = -170$	$t' = -190$
0.1090	−0.00163	−0.00414	−0.00570	−0.00938	−0.01256	−0.01485
0.1095	−0.00159	−0.00370	−0.00475	−0.00631	−0.00651	−0.00591
0.1100	−0.00154	−0.00326	−0.00380	−0.00326	−0.00046	+0.00302
0.1105	−0.00150	−0.00281	−0.00285	−0.00019	+0.00559	+0.01195
0.1110	−0.00146	−0.00237	−0.00190	+0.00287	+0.01163	+0.02088
0.1115	−0.00141	−0.00193	−0.00095	+0.00593	+0.01769	+0.02981
0.1120	−0.00136	−0.00149	0	+0.00900	+0.02373	+0.03875
0.1125	−0.00132	−0.00105	+0.00095	+0.01206	+0.02978	+0.04768

For $\delta = 1.491$

β	$t' = -40$	$t' = -80$	$t' = -100$	$t' = -140$	$t' = -170$	$t' = -190$
0.1090	−0.00109	−0.00276	−0.00380	−0.00625	−0.00837	−0.00990
0.1095	−0.00105	−0.00232	−0.00285	−0.00319	−0.00232	−0.00097
0.1100	−0.00100	−0.00188	−0.00190	−0.00012	+0.00373	+0.00797
0.1105	−0.00096	−0.00144	−0.00095	+0.00294	+0.00978	+0.01690
0.1110	−0.00092	−0.00099	0	+0.00600	+0.01582	+0.02583
0.1115	−0.00087	−0.00055	+0.00095	+0.00906	+0.02188	+0.03476
0.1120	−0.00083	−0.00011	+0.00190	+0.01213	+0.02792	+0.04370
0.1125	−0.00078	+0.00033	+0.00285	+0.01519	+0.03397	+0.05263

For $\delta = 1.492$

β	$t' = -40$	$t' = -80$	$t' = -100$	$t' = -140$	$t' = -170$	$t' = -190$
0.1090	−0.00054	−0.00138	−0.00190	−0.00313	−0.00419	−0.00495
0.1095	−0.00050	−0.00094	−0.00095	−0.00007	+0.00186	+0.00398
0.1100	−0.00045	−0.00050	0	+0.00300	+0.00791	+0.01292
0.1105	−0.00041	−0.00005	+0.00095	+0.00606	+0.01396	+0.02185
0.1110	−0.00037	+0.00039	+0.00190	+0.00912	+0.02000	+0.03078
0.1115	−0.00032	+0.00083	+0.00285	+0.01218	+0.02606	+0.03971
0.1120	−0.00028	+0.00127	+0.00380	+0.01525	+0.03210	+0.04865
0.1125	−0.00023	+0.00171	+0.00475	+0.01831	+0.03815	+0.05758

For $\delta = 1.493$

β	$t' = -40$	$t' = -80$	$t' = -100$	$t' = -140$	$t' = -170$	$t' = -190$
0.1090	0	0	0	0	0	0
0.1095	+0.00004	+0.00044	+0.00095	+0.00306	+0.00605	+0.00893
0.1100	+0.00009	+0.00088	+0.00190	+0.00613	+0.01210	+0.01787
0.1105	+0.00013	+0.00133	+0.00285	+0.00919	+0.01815	+0.02680
0.1110	+0.00017	+0.00177	+0.00380	+0.01225	+0.02419	+0.03573
0.1115	+0.00022	+0.00221	+0.00475	+0.01531	+0.03025	+0.04466
0.1120	+0.00026	+0.00265	+0.00570	+0.01838	+0.03629	+0.05360
0.1125	+0.00031	+0.00309	+0.00665	+0.02144	+0.04234	+0.06253

For $\delta = 1.494$

β	$t' = -40$	$t' = -80$	$t' = -100$	$t' = -140$	$t' = -170$	$t' = -190$
0.1090	+0.00054	+0.00138	+0.00190	+0.00313	+0.00419	+0.00495
0.1095	+0.00058	+0.00182	+0.00285	+0.00619	+0.01024	+0.01388
0.1100	+0.00063	+0.00226	+0.00380	+0.00926	+0.01629	+0.02282
0.1105	+0.00067	+0.00271	+0.00475	+0.01232	+0.02234	+0.03175
0.1110	+0.00071	+0.00315	+0.00570	+0.01538	+0.02838	+0.04068
0.1115	+0.00076	+0.00359	+0.00665	+0.01844	+0.03444	+0.04961
0.1120	+0.00080	+0.00403	+0.00760	+0.02151	+0.04048	+0.05855
0.1125	+0.00085	+0.00447	+0.00855	+0.02457	+0.04743	+0.06748

For $\delta = 1.495$

β	$t' = -40$	$t' = -80$	$t' = -100$	$t' = -140$	$t' = -170$	$t' = -190$
0.1090	+0.00109	+0.00276	+0.00380	+0.00625	+0.00837	+0.00990
0.1095	+0.00113	+0.00320	+0.00475	+0.00931	+0.01442	+0.01883
0.1100	+0.00118	+0.00364	+0.00570	+0.01238	+0.02047	+0.02777
0.1105	+0.00122	+0.00409	+0.00665	+0.01544	+0.02652	+0.03670
0.1110	+0.00126	+0.00453	+0.00760	+0.01850	+0.03256	+0.04563
0.1115	+0.00131	+0.00497	+0.00855	+0.02156	+0.03862	+0.05456
0.1120	+0.00135	+0.00541	+0.00950	+0.02463	+0.04466	+0.06350
0.1125	+0.00140	+0.00585	+0.01045	+0.02769	+0.05071	+0.07243

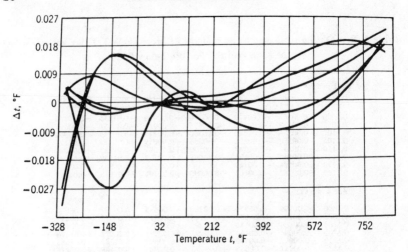

Fig. 1·11. Variations Δt, °F, among the readings on a group of precision sensitive elements, each satisfying the conditions of International Temperature Scale. (*By permission H. J. Hoge, and F. G. Brickwedde in RP 1454, J. Research Natl. Bur. Standards, 28, no. 2, 224, February, 1942.*)

It is not to be supposed, however, that thermodynamic temperatures can be determined with this precision   Figure 1·11 indicates that determinations by sensitive elements, satisfying the conditions of the International Temperature Scale, may differ from one another by more than 0.01°C (0.018°F).   The uncertainty in knowledge of the thermodynamic temperature will be by at least this amount and may be greater.[5, 61, 109, 111-124]

REFERENCES *

1. C. W. Waidner and G. K. Burgess, "Platinum Resistance Thermometry at High Temperatures," *Bulletin of the Bureau of Standards*, 6, no. 2, pp. 152–158, 178–181, 198–199, 222–230 (November, 1909); contains bibliography of 138 references.

2. G. K. Burgess and H. LeChatelier, *The Measurement of High Temperatures*, pp. 202–207, 231–234, 3rd ed. John Wiley & Sons, New York, 1912.

3. R. J. Corruccini, "Annealing of Platinum for Thermometry," RP 2232, *J. Research Natl. Bur. Standards*, 47, no. 2, pp. 94–103 (August, 1951).

---

* Where abbreviated journal titles are given, the full title can usually be obtained from *Chemical Abstracts Index for Periodicals,* which also gives the libraries in which these periodicals can be found. Abbreviations not found in *Chemical Abstracts Index* may be found in *World List of Scientific Periodicals.*

4. The Liquid Steel Temperature Subcommittee, "A Symposium on the Contamination of Platinum Thermocouples," *J. Iron Steel Inst. (London),* **155,** Part 2, pp. 213–234 (February, 1947).

5. H. J. Hoge and F. G. Brickwedde, "Intercomparison of Platinum Resistance Thermometers between −190° and 445°C," *RP* 1454, *J. Research Natl. Bur. Standards,* **28,** no. 2, pp. 217–240 (February, 1942).

6. R. F. Vines, *The Platinum Metals and Their Alloys,* 141 pp., The International Nickel Co., New York, 1941.

7. E. F. Mueller, "Precision Resistance Thermometry," American Institute of Physics, *Temperature,* pp. 162–179, Reinhold Publishing Corp., New York, 1941; contains bibliography of 40 references.

8. P. G. Weiller, "Platinum Thermometer," *Rev. Sci. Instr.,* **21,** no. 9, p. 819 (September, 1950).

9. P. G. Weiller, "Platinum Resistance Thermometer," *Rev. Sci. Instr.,* **20,** no. 12, p. 971 (December, 1949).

10. H. E. Stauss, "Platinum and Pyrometry," American Institute of Physics, *Temperature,* pp. 1267–1271, Reinhold Publishing Corp., New York, 1941.

11. B. Brenner, "Changes in Platinum Thermocouples Due to Oxidation," American Institute of Physics, *Temperature,* pp. 1281–1283, Reinhold Publishing Corp., New York, 1941.

12. J. E. Dinger and R. E. Ruskin, "Resistance Thermometer with a Linear Response," *Rev. Sci. Instr.,* **24,** no. 12, p. 761 (December, 1952).

13. A. Brown, M. W. Zemansky, and H. A. Boorse, "A Sensitive and Reproducible Thermometer in the Range 2° to 20°K," *Phys. Rev.,* **84,** no. 5, p. 1050 (December, 1951).

14. Weiller Instruments Corporation, "Fuse-Din Long Stem Quartz Thermometer," *Rev. Sci. Instr.,* **23,** no. 2, p. 108 (February, 1952).

15. Emil Greiner Co., "Electronic Resistance Thermometer," *Rev. Sci. Instr.,* **22,** no. 2, p. 121 (February, 1952).

16. P. G. Weiller, "Temperature Instruments of the Future," *Instruments,* **20,** no. 3, pp. 231–233 (March, 1947).

17. B. M. Zeffert and S. Hormats, "Application of Thermistors to Cryoscopy," *Anal. Chem.,* **21,** pp. 1420–1422 (November, 1949).

18. Yellow Springs Instrument Co., *YSI Thermistemp Temperature Probes,* 6 pp., Yellow Springs Instrument Co., Yellow Springs, Ohio, June, 1959.

19. K. P. Dowell, "Thermistors as Components Open Product Design Horizons," *Elec. Mfg.,* **42,** no. 2, pp. 84–91 (August, 1948).

20. J. A. Becker, C. B. Green, and G. L. Pearson, "Properties and Uses of Thermistors—Thermally Sensitive Resistors," *Electrical Engineering,* **65,** no. 711, pp. 711–725 (November, 1946).

21. C. F. Rothe, "Simple Surface Thermometer," *Rev. Sci. Instr.,* **29,** no. 5, pp. 436–437 (May, 1958).

22. M. J. Rand and L. P. Hammett, "Reaction Rates and Heats by the Temperature Rise in a Stirred Flow Reactor," *J. Am. Chem. Soc.,* **72,** no. 1, pp. 287–293 (January, 1950).

23. A. Beck, "The Stability of Thermistors," *J. Sci. Instr.,* **33,** no. 1, pp. 16–18 (January, 1956).

24. P. R. Malmberg and C. G. Matland, "Thermistor Temperature Control," *Rev. Sci. Instr.,* **27,** no. 3, pp. 136–139 (March, 1956).

25. J. A. McLean, "A Method for Constructing Direct Reading Thermistor Thermometers," *J. Sci. Instr.,* **31,** no. 12, pp. 455–457 (December, 1954).

26. R. W. Woods, "Thermistor Electronic Thermometer," *Science,* **121,** no. 3140, pp. 337–338 (March, 1955).

27. R. H. Muller and H. J. Stolten, "Use of Thermistors in Precise Measurement of Small Temperature Differences," *Anal. Chem.,* **25,** no. 7, pp. 1103–1106 (July, 1953).

28. R. P. Benedict, "Thermistors vs. Thermocouples," *Elec. Mfg.,* **54,** no. 2, pp. 120–125 (August, 1954).

29. R. L. Burwell, Jr., A. H. Peterson, and G. B. Rathmann, "A Temperature Control Device Employing Thermistors and a Saturable Reactor," *Rev. Sci. Instr.,* **19,** no. 9, pp. 608–609 (September, 1948).

30. Y. Doucet, "Sur l'emploi des thermistors" (The Use of Thermistors), *J. de physique et le radium,* **12,** no. 8, p. 823 (October, 1951).

31. A. D. Misener and L. G. D. Thompson, "The Pressure Coefficient of Resistance of Thermistors," *Canadian J. Technol.,* **30,** pp. 89–94 (April, 1952).

32. W. T. Gibson, "Thermistor Production," *Electrical Communication,* **30,** no. 4, pp. 263–270 (December, 1953).

33. F. Gutmann and L. M. Simmons, "Electrolytic Thermistors," *Rev. Sci. Instr.,* **20,** no. 9, pp. 674–675 (September, 1949).

34. P. G. Weiller and I. H. Blatz, "Electronic Thermometer," *Electronics,* **17,** pp. 138–139, 362–363 (July, 1944).

35. D. N. Craig, "Electrolytic Resistors for Direct-Current Applications in Measuring Temperatures," *RP* 1126, *J. Research Natl. Bur. Standards,* **21,** no. 2, pp. 225–233 (August, 1938).

36. J. R. Clement, E. H. Quinnell, M. C. Steele, R. A. Hein, and R. L. Dolecek, "Carbon-Composition Thermometers at Very Low Temperatures," *Rev. Sci. Instr.,* **24,** no. 7, pp. 545–546 (July, 1953).

37. J. R. Clement and E. H. Quinnell, "The Low Temperature Characteristics of Carbon-Composition Thermometers," *Rev. Sci. Instr.,* **23,** no. 5, pp. 213–216 (May, 1952).

38. R. Berman, "A Note on the Current Sensitivity of Carbon Resistance Thermometers at Liquid Helium Temperatures," *Rev. Sci. Instr.,* **25,** no. 1, pp. 94–95 (January, 1954).

39. I. Estermann, S. A. Friedberg, and J. E. Goldman, "The Specific Heats of Several Metals between $1.8°$ and $4.2°K$," *Phys. Rev.,* **87,** no. 4, pp. 584–585 (August, 1952).

40. H. A. Fairbank and C. T. Lane, "A Simple Carbon-Resistance Thermometer for Low Temperatures," *Rev. Sci. Instr.,* **18,** no. 7, p. 525 (July, 1947).

41. N. Kurti, "The Lowest Temperature in the World," *Physics Today,* **13,** no. 10, pp. 26–29 (October, 1960).

42. D. C. Pearce, A. H. Markham, and J. R. Dillinger, "Carbon Resistor Thermometry Between 0.3 and $0.2°K$," *Rev. Sci. Instr.,* **27,** no. 4, p. 240 (April, 1956).

43. F. E. Hoare, J. C. Matthews, and B. Yates, "Carbon Resistor Thermometers," *Proc. Phys. Soc. London B,* **68,** Part 6, pp. 388–389 (June, 1955).

44. T. H. Geballe, D. N. Lyon, J. M. Whelan, and W. F. Giauque, "Carbon Thermometer-Heaters for Use at Low Temperatures. Effects of Particle Size and Adsorption of Hydrogen or Helium," *Rev. Sci. Instr.,* **23,** no. 9, pp. 489–492 (September, 1952).

45. B. J. Sandlin and J. C. Thompson, "Precision Thermometer System for the Liquid Helium Region," *Rev. Sci. Instr.*, **30**, no. 8, pp. 659–661 (August, 1959).

46. L. Weil, J. Peretti, and A. Locaze, "Thermomètre à résistance en oxyde de zinc" (A Zinc Oxide Resistance Thermometer), *Compt. rend.*, **237**, no. 17, pp. 974–975 (October, 1953).

47. P. Hidnert and G. Dickson, "Some Physical Properties of Mica," *RP* 1675, *J. Research Natl. Bur. Standards*, **35**, no. 4, pp. 309–353 (October, 1945).

48. A. B. Lewis, E. L. Hall, and F. R. Caldwell, "Some Electrical Properties of Foreign and Domestic Micas and the Effect of Elevated Temperatures on Micas," *RP* 347, *J. Research Natl. Bur. Standards*, **7**, no. 2, pp. 403–418 (August, 1931).

49. H. J. Hoge, "Electrical Conduction in the Glass Insulation of Resistance Thermometers," *RP* 1466, *J. Research Natl. Bur. Standards*, **28**, no. 4, pp. 489–498 (April, 1942).

50. T. S. Sligh, Jr., "Recent Modifications in the Construction of Platinum Resistance Thermometers," *Sci. Papers Bur. Standards*, **17**, no. 407, pp. 49–63 (January, 1921).

51. R. I. Schiff, "Thermistors," *Instruments*, **33**, no. 1, p. 83 (January, 1960).

52. D. R. Harper 3rd, "Thermometric Lag," *Bulletin of the Bureau of Standards*, **8**, no. 4, pp. 694–714 (March, 1912).

53. H. C. Dickinson and E. F. Mueller, "Calorimetric Resistance Thermometers and the Transition Temperature of Sodium Sulphate," *Bulletin of the Bureau of Standards*, **3**, no. 4, pp. 641–661 (October, 1907).

54. W. H. Keesom and B. G. Dammers, "Comparison of Some Platinum Thermometers with the Helium Thermometer between 0° and −183°C," *Physica*, **2**, no. 10, pp. 1080–1090 (1935).

55. J. Rolinski and Z. Gajewski, "Réalisation de l'échelle intérnationale de température entre 0° et 660°C" (Realization of the International Scale of Temperature between 0° and 660°C), *Acta Physica Polonica*, **7**, no. 4, pp. 305–309 (1939).

56. J. R. Roebuck, "On Construction of Platinum Thermometers and of Resistance Coils, *J. Opt. Soc. Am. and Rev. Sci. Instr.*, **6**, no. 8, pp. 865–874 (October, 1922).

57. J. R. Roebuck, "A Porous Plug Method for the Mechanical Equivalent of Heat," *Phys. Rev.*, **2**, no. 2, pp. 89–91 (August, 1913).

58. C. R. Barber, "Platinum Resistance Thermometers of Small Dimensions," *J. Sci. Instr.*, **27**, no. 2, pp. 47–49 (February, 1950).

59. C. H. Meyers, "Coiled Filament Resistance Thermometers," *RP* 508, *J. Research Natl. Bur. Standards*, **9**, no. 6, pp. 807–813 (December, 1932).

60. D. R. Stull, "Application of Platinum Resistance Thermometry to Some Industrial Physicochemical Problems," *Ind. Eng. Chem. Anal. Ed.*, **18**, no. 4, pp. 234–242 (April, 1946).

61. H. J. Hoge and F. G. Brickwedde, "Establishment of a Temperature Scale for Calibration of Thermometers between 14° and 83°K," *RP* 1188, *J. Research Natl. Bur. Standards*, **22**, no. 3, pp. 351–373 (March, 1939).

62. H. C. Dickinson and E. F. Mueller, "New Calorimetric Resistance Thermometers," *Bulletin of the Bureau of Standards*, **9**, no. 4, pp. 483–492 (October, 1913).

63. F. J. Gittings, "A Modification in the Construction of Calorimetric Resistance Thermometers," *J. Sci. Instr.*, **28**, no. 8, p. 238 (August, 1951).

64. J. A. Hall, "Portable Precision Resistance Thermometer Equipment for Mains Operation," *J. Sci. Instr.,* **26,** no. 12, pp. 392–396 (December, 1949).

65. H. S. Eisner, "A Simple Resistance Thermometer," *J. Sci. Instr.,* **29,** no. 5, p. 166 (May, 1952).

66. E. W. Hayes, "Resistance Thermometry," *Petrol. Refiner,* **25,** no. 12, pp. 139–140 (December, 1946).

67. B. E. Noltingk and M. A. Snelling, "An Electronic Temperature Controller," *J. Sci. Instr.,* **30,** no. 10, pp. 349–351 (October, 1953).

68. R. J. Karr, "Thermistor Actuated Temperature Regulation," *Scientific Apparatus and Methods,* **6,** no. 1, pp. 1–12 (Winter, 1954).

69. E. F. G. Herrington and R. Handley, "The Use of Thermistors for the Automatic Recording of Small Temperature Differences," *J. Sci. Instr.,* **25,** no. 12, pp. 434–437 (December, 1948).

70. W. O. Pruit, "A Method of Mounting Thermistors for Field Use," *Ecology,* **33,** no. 4, p. 550 (October, 1952).

71. E. B. Greenhill and J. R. Whitehead, "An Apparatus for Measuring Small Temperature Changes in Liquids," *J. Sci. Instr.,* **26,** no. 3, pp. 92–95 (March, 1949).

72. The Yellow Springs Instrument Company, Inc., "Tele-Thermometer," *Rev. Sci. Instr.,* **24,** no. 11, pp. 1077–1078 (November, 1953).

73. Beckman & Whitley, "Temperature Indicator," *Rev. Sci. Instr.,* **23,** no. 2, p. 104 (February, 1952).

74. J. S. Clark and L. O. C. Johnson, "Resistance Thermometers in the 50 Meter Comparator at the N.P.L.," *The Engineer,* **196,** no. 5092, pp. 260–261 (August, 1953).

75. W. P. Hutchinson, E. W. Pulsford, A. G. White, "Temperature Control of a Large Water Bath Using a Resistance Thermometer," *J. Sci. Instr.,* **31,** no. 11, pp. 420–424 (November, 1954).

76. F. B. Keyes and F. W. Sears, "Recent Measurements of the Joule Effect for CO_2," *Proc. Natl. Acad. Sci. U. S.,* **11,** no. 1, pp. 38–41 (January, 1925).

77. J. H. Berglund and R. T. Pierce, "An Accurate Method for Determining Average Temperatures in Storage Tanks," *Petroleum Engineer,* **23,** no. 1, pp. A39–A46 (January, 1951).

78. O. Knoblauch and K. Hencky, *Anleitung zu genauen technischen Temperaturmessungen* (Introduction to Precision, Technical Temperature Measurement), pp. 159–160, Druck und Verlag von R. Oldenbourg, Munich and Berlin, 1926.

79. J. M. Benjamin, Jr., and S. M. Horvath, "Temperature Measurement inside the Body Using a Thermistor," *Science,* **109,** no. 2841, pp. 592–593 (June, 1949).

80. L. F. Drummeter, Jr., and W. G. Fastie, "A Simple Resistance Thermometer for Blood-Temperature Measurements," *Science,* **105,** no. 2716, pp. 73–75 (January, 1947).

81. J. Krog, "Thermistor Hypodermic Needle for Subcutaneous Temperature Measurement," *Rev. Sci. Instr.,* **27,** no. 6, pp. 408–409 (June, 1956).

82. J. Krog, "Improved Needle Thermocouple for Subcutaneous and Intramuscular Temperature Measurements in Animals and Man," *Rev. Sci. Instr.,* **25,** no. 8, pp. 799–800 (August, 1954).

83. H. Eiber, "Heissleiter-Widerstandsthermometer in Injektionsnadelform zur Messung sehr kleiner Temperatur-Differenzen im menschlichen Körper" (Hy-

podermic Needle Thermistor Resistance Thermometer for the Measurement of Very Small Temperature Differences in the Human Body), *Z. angew. Phys.*, **10**, no. 8, pp. 379–382 (August, 1958).

84. R. W. Stow, "Rapid High-Sensitivity Recording Thermometer," *Rev. Sci. Instr.*, **29**, no. 9, pp. 774–775 (September, 1958).

85. J. A. McLean, "A Method for Constructing Direct Reading Thermistor Thermometers," *J. Sci. Instr.*, **31**, no. 12, pp. 455–457 (December, 1954).

86. E. W. Hayes, "Resistance Thermometry, *Instruments*, **25**, no. 5, pp. 629–631 (May, 1952).

87. M. G. Salvadori and K. S. Miller, *The Mathematical Solution of Engineering Problems*, pp. 114–146, McGraw-Hill Book Co., New York, 1948.

88. W. S. Boyle and J. B. Brown, "Thermoregulator for a Liquid Helium Bath," *Rev. Sci. Instr.*, **25**, no. 4, pp. 359–360 (April, 1954).

89. N. S. Rasor, "Simple Equipment and Techniques for a Small Cryogenics Laboratory," *Rev. Sci. Instr.*, **25**, no. 4, pp. 311–318 (April, 1954).

90. A. L. Smith and H. L. Johnston, "A Cryostat for Magnetic Susceptibility Measurements at Low Temperatures," *Rev. Sci. Instr.*, **24**, no. 6, pp. 420–423 (June, 1953).

91. G. Seidel and P. H. Keesom, "He^3 Cryostat for Measuring Specific Heat," *Rev. Sci. Instr.*, **29**, no. 7, pp. 606–611 (July, 1958).

92. R. A. H. Pool, B. D. C. Shields, and L. A. K. Stavesley, "The Triple Point of Argon as a Thermometric Fixed Point," *Nature*, **181**, no. 4612, p. 831 (March, 1958).

93. A. B. Kaufman and W. E. Drees, "How Accurate Are Your Temperature Transducer Calibrations?" *Instruments*, **32**, no. 11, pp. 1682–1685 (November, 1959).

94. O. V. Lounasma, "A Simple Formula for Use with Carbon Thermometers at Low Temperatures," *Phil. Mag.*, Series 8, **3**, no. 30, pp. 652–653 (June, 1958).

95. G. Bosson, F. Gutmann, and L. M. Simmons, "A Relationship between Resistance and Temperature of Thermistors," *J. Appl. Phys.*, **21**, no. 12, pp. 1267–1268 (December, 1950).

96. Hallikainen Instruments, "Calibration Baths," *Instruments*, **26**, no. 3, pp. 360, 362 (March, 1953).

97. R. E. Wilson, "Standards of Temperature," *Phys. Today*, **6**, no. 1, pp. 10–13 (January, 1953).

98. E. F. Mueller and T. S. Sligh, "A Laboratory Hypsometer," *J. Opt. Soc. Am.*, **6**, no. 9, pp. 958–964 (November, 1922).

99. A. B. Kaufman and P. R. Mitchell, "How Accurate Are Your Reference Baths?" *Instruments*, **28**, no. 3, pp. 450–451 (March, 1955).

100. E. H. McLaren, "The Freezing Points of High Purity Metals as Precision Temperature Standards. II. An Investigation of the Freezing Temperatures of Zinc, Cadmium, and Tin," *Can. J. Phys.*, **35**, no. 9, pp. 1086–1106 (September, 1957).

101. W. G. Kannuluik and P. G. Law, "Note on the CO_2-point in Thermometry," *J. Sci. Instr.*, **23**, no. 7, pp. 154–155 (July, 1946).

102. H. H. Plumb and M. H. Edlow, "Constant Temperature Liquid Helium Bath and Reproducibility of Resistance Thermometers," *Rev. Sci. Instr.*, **30**, no. 5, pp. 376–377 (May, 1959).

103. R. P. Benedict, "The Calibration of Thermocouples by Freezing-Point Baths and Empirical Equations," *Paper* 58-A-175, American Society of Mechanical Engineers, New York (1950).

104. J. A. Hall and V. M. Leaver, "The Emergent Column Correction in Mercury Thermometry," *J. Sci. Instr.*, **35**, no. 3, pp. 93–96 (March, 1958).

105. J. F. Swindells, "Calibration of Liquid-in-Glass Thermometers," *Natl. Bur. Standards Circ.* 600, 21 pp., Government Printing Office, Washington (1959).

106. H. J. Hoge, "A Resistance-Temperature Relation for Low Temperature Thermometry," *Rev. Sci. Instr.*, **21**, no. 9, pp. 815–816 (September, 1950).

107. J. M. Los and J. A. Morrison, "The Calibration of Platinum Resistance Thermometers in the Temperature Range 11° to 90°K," NRC 2339, *Can. J. Phys.*, **29**, no. 3, pp. 142–150 (March, 1951).

108. American Society of Mechanical Engineers, "Resistance Thermometers," *Power Test Codes ASME 1945*, "Supplement on Instruments and Apparatus," PTC 19.3.4–1945, Part 3, "Temperature Measurement," Ch. 4, pp. 5–17, New York (1945).

109. E. H. McLaren, "Intercomparison of 11 Resistance Thermometers at the Ice, Steam, Tin, Cadmium, and Zinc Points," *Can. J. Research*, **37**, no. 4, pp. 422–432 (April, 1959).

110. H. F. Stimson, "The International Temperature Scale of 1948," *RP* 1962, *J. Research Natl. Bur. Standards*, **42**, no. 3, pp. 209–217 (March, 1949).

111. F. D. Werner and A. C. Frazer, "A New Method of Converting Platinum Resistance Values to Degrees Centigrade," *Rev. Sci. Instr.*, **23**, no. 4, pp. 163–169 (April, 1952).

112. J. A. Beattie and B. E. Blaisdell, "An Experimental Study of the Absolute Temperature Scale," *Proc. Am. Acad. Arts Sci.*, **77**, no. 8, pp. 255–336 (May, 1949).

113. "Misuse of the Average Deviation," *Natl. Bur. Standards U. S., Tech. News Bull.*, **34**, no. 1, pp. 9–10 (January, 1950).

114. S. J. Kline and F. A. McClintock, "Describing Uncertainties in Single-Sample Experiments," *Mech. Eng.*, **75**, no. 1, pp. 3–8 (January, 1953).

115. Y. Beers, *Introduction to the Theory of Error*, 65 pp., Addison-Wesley Publishing Co., Cambridge, Mass., 1953.

116. R. T. Leslie, "Over-estimation of Probable Errors," *Nature*, **160**, no. 4074, pp. 751–752 (November, 1947).

117. H. F. Stimson, "Heat Units and Temperature Scales for Calorimetry," *Amer. J. Phys.*, **23**, no. 9, pp. 614–619 (December, 1955).

118. R. J. Corruccini, "Interpolation of Platinum Resistance Thermometers, 20° to 273.15°K," *Rev. Sci. Instr.*, **31**, no. 6, pp. 637–640 (March, 1960).

119. T. M. Dauphinee and H. Preston-Thomas, "Direct Reading Resistance Thermometer Bridge. Part I," and T. M. Dauphinee, C. G. M. Kirby, and H. Preston-Thomas, Part II, *Rev. Sci. Instr.*, **31**, no. 3, pp. 253–257 and 258–263 (March, 1960).

120. G. C. Lowenthal, W. R. G. Kemp, and A. F. A. Harper, "A Temperature Scale Down to 20°K Using Platinum Resistance Thermometers," *Bulletin de l'institut international du froid*, no. 1, pp. 107–116, 1958.

121. H. van Dijk, "On the Use of Platinum Resistance Thermometers Between 90 and 4°K," *Bulletin de l'institut international du froid*, no. 1, pp. 103–105, 1958.

122. "High Temperature Resistance Thermometry," *Instrument Practice, Automation and Electronics*, **14**, no. 1, p. 62 (January, 1960).

123. E. H. McLaren and E. G. Murdock, "The Freezing Points of High Purity Metals as Precision Temperature Standards. V. Thermal Analyses on 10 Samples of Tin with Purities Greater than 99.99+%," *Can. J. Phys.,* **38,** no. 1, pp. 100–118 (January, 1960).

124. G. C. Lowenthal and A. F. A. Harper, "Resistance-Temperature Relationship of Platinum at Low Temperatures and Its Influence on Precision Thermometry," *British J. Appl. Phys.,* **11,** no. 5, pp. 205–208 (May, 1960).

2

RESISTANCE-THERMOMETER
DESIGN CALCULATIONS

2·1 INTRODUCTION

In the preceding chapter various designs of electric-resistance thermometers have been described. The kinds of errors to which these
alternative varieties are subject have been listed, and the constructional
problems related to coping with these and other difficulties have been
discussed. The present chapter is devoted to computational technique.
The objective of this technique is to enable the engineer to make in
advance quantitative estimates of the magnitudes of the various errors
to which a given construction will be subject. In this manner, he can
work out a design for which these errors will be within the limits set
by his requirements but for which the construction will be the simplest,
cheapest, and best suited mechanically to serve his purpose.

2·2 CIRCUITS

Invention has been abundant in circuit arrangements for the measurement of resistance. Although these arrangements are described in
various places, not all are commercially available in finished package
form. The most commonly used circuit is the *Wheatstone bridge* (see
Fig. 2·1). It is subject to the null-balance relation

$$r_e/r_b = r_1/r_2 \qquad (2·1)$$

where, for $r_1 = r_2$, the resistance r_e is read as equal to that of the balancing unit r_b. Arranged for use with equal compensating leads r_l, this
bridge appears as shown in Fig. 2·2. Here, r_e is still equal to r_b.
Figure 2·3 indicates the *Siemens 3-lead* variation, where again $r_e = r_b$,
provided that the lead resistances r_l are equal. To adapt the Wheatstone bridge to the 4-lead potential-terminal sensitive element a suitable switching arrangement is required. Figure 2·4 shows a 4-lead
circuit due to Mueller [12] where two settings r_b and r_b' are made for the
two positions of the switches shown as solid and dotted, respectively. Then $r_e = (r_b + r_b')/2$. A highly refined design known as the
Mueller [12] *bridge* is intended also to suppress the effects of contact

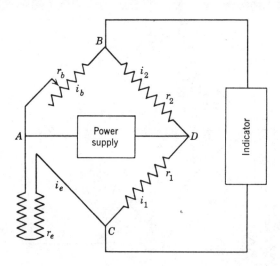

Fig. 2·1. Wheatstone bridge.

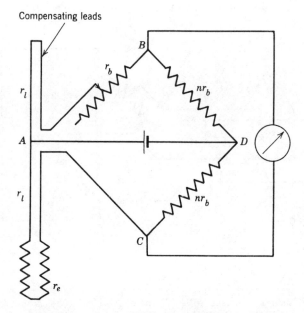

Fig. 2·2. Two-lead element with compensating leads and Wheatstone bridge.

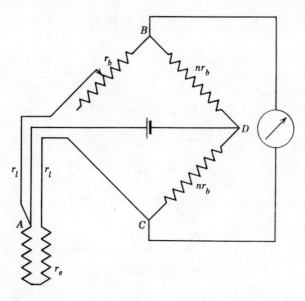

Fig. 2·3. Siemens 3-lead element with Wheatstone bridge.

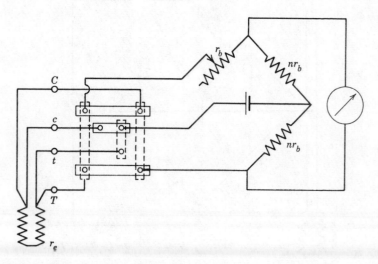

Fig. 2·4. Four-lead element with Wheatstone bridge. (*By permission E. F. Mueller in Bulletin of the Bureau of Standards,* **13,** *no. 4, 557, March, 1917.*)

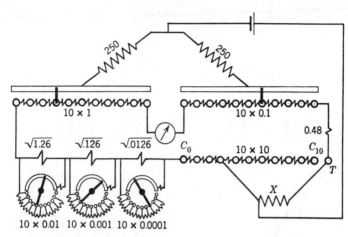

Fig. 2·5. Mueller bridge. All numbers refer to resistances in ohms. (*By permission E. F. Mueller in Bulletin of the Bureau of Standards*, **13**, *no. 4, 549, March, 1917.*)

resistance at the switches and terminals. An early form of this device is shown in Fig. 2·5. Bridges made according to the principles of these designs are commercially available in very precise constructions as well as in a wide assortment of broader tolerances. Commercial units are usually all intended for use with the "standard" 2.5- or 25-ohm sensitive elements. Figure 2.6 shows how an added decade can be externally connected to a commercial Mueller-type bridge to function as a 10^{-5}-ohm dial, extending the range to a tenfold smaller least count.[1-18]

The Kelvin or Thomson bridge shown in Fig. 2·7 is often used in the measurement of very small resistances. The equality $r_1/r_2 = r_3/r_4$ is maintained in all adjustments. Then, at balance $r_e = (r_1/r_2)r_b$, the resistances r_1 and r_3 can be made much larger than those of any leads which are effectively added to them. If r_e is small, its current can be made much greater than that through the arms r_1, r_2, r_3, and r_4, with a corresponding increase in its potential drop; whereas with a small ratio r_1/r_2, r_b can be much larger than r_e. In resistance thermometry with optimum design arrangements, i.e., with a suitable galvanometer, the limit is set by power dissipation in the sensitive element. Under these conditions the over-all sensitivity is the same for the Wheatstone and Kelvin bridges. The Kelvin bridge can be used as shown in Fig. 2·8 with electronic indicators in place of an unbalanced Wheatstone bridge when r_e is small and rapid or continuous readings are required. The power supply can then be d-c or a-c.[16, 19]

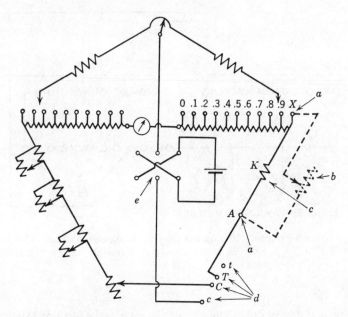

Fig. 2·6. Low-range-decade attachment for commercial, Mueller-type bridge. *a*, Connection to wires labeled X and A where these emerge from the temperature-controlled region inside the bridge; *b*, Waidner-Wolff-type resistance decade serving as a 10^{-5}-ohm dial; *c*, resistance of effective value K which includes resistances of lead wires to junctions A and X; *d*, labeled binding posts for connecting the four sensitive-element leads; and *e*, reversing switch. (*By permission R. M. LeLacheur in Rev. Sci. Instr.*, **23**, *no. 7, 383, July, 1952.*)

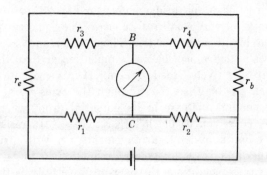

Fig. 2·7. Kelvin or Thomson bridge.

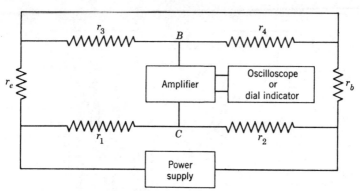

Fig. 2·8. Kelvin or Thomson bridge with electronic indication.

The 4-lead potential-terminal element is shown in Fig. 2·9 arranged for potentiometer indication. Since the same current flows through both r_e and r_b, the ratio r_e/r_b is equal to the ratio of the two potentiometer settings for the switch at the ee and bb positions, respectively. This circuit permits precision work with a type of instrument more often available than the Mueller [12] bridge. A modified form, intended for continuous electronic indication, is shown in Fig. 2·10. Here r is made large to stabilize the current as r_e varies with temperature. The power supply can be d-c or a-c.[20-22]

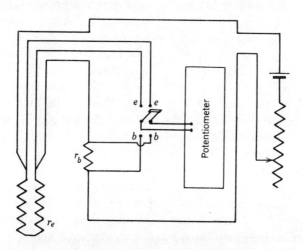

Fig. 2·9. Four-lead element with potentiometer.

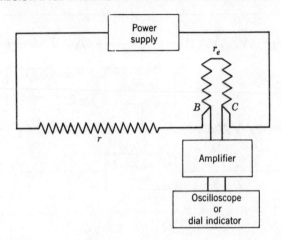

Fig. 2·10. Four-lead potentiometer circuit with electronic indication.

2·3 THE WHEATSTONE BRIDGE

This circuit is indicated in Fig. 2·1. For balance, i.e., when B and C are at the same electric potential and no current flows through the indicator,

$$r_e/r_b = r_1/r_2 \qquad (2·1)$$

The power supply can be either a-c or d-c; however, certain additional considerations discussed in Sec. 2·4 apply to a-c bridges. For unbalance, i.e., for r_e replaced by $r_e + \Delta r_e$, B and C are no longer at the same potential, and a current flows through the indicator. The size of this current depends on the magnitude of Δr_e. At balance, r_e and its variations Δr_e can be computed, using Eq. 2·1, from the corresponding values required in r_b, r_1, and r_2. In the unbalanced case, Δr_e can be measured by the corresponding current through the indicator. The relationship between Δr_e and the indicator current can be determined by over-all calibration, or it can be calculated.[23-29]

If the impedance of the indicator is very large in relation to those of the resistances r_e, r_b, r_1, and r_2, the current at unbalance through the indicator is very much smaller than those through r_e, r_b, r_1, and r_2. The effect then approximates that of open-circuit potential variations between B and C. This situation most often occurs when the indicator impedance is that of the input stage of an electronic amplifier.

For this case, the arm resistances r_1 and r_2 are best made equal to the initial value r of r_e; whereas, at balance, r_b is adjusted to equality with r_e.

In unbalanced-bridge operation, which is suited to electronic indication of rapidly changing effects, r_b is fixed at the initial value r, while r_e becomes r plus the change Δr_e. Then

$$\Delta V_{BC} = \Delta r_e V_{AD}/4r \qquad (2\cdot2)$$

where ΔV_{BC} is the potential difference imposed across the indicator, v (volts); V_{AD} is that maintained across A and D by the power supply, v; r is the resistance of the individual bridge arms, ohms; and Δr_e is the change in r_e, ohms.[11]

If the impedance of the indicator is not large relative to the resistances r_e, r_b, r_1, and r_2, different relations apply. This may occur with an electronic amplifier of comparatively low impedance in the input stage. Usually, however, it occurs with suspension-galvanometer indicators.

Then r_1 and r_2 are made equal but n times larger than r_b. The sensitivity of the bridge is proportional to the ratio $n/(n+1)$ and is maximum for n very large. If n is as small as unity, the sensitivity is reduced by one-half, and values of n less than unity should not be used. However, for $n = 10$, the sensitivity acquires ten-elevenths of its maximum value, and further increases effect diminishing improvements.[19]

With n thus larger than unity, attainment of maximum sensitivity requires that the galvanometer be connected across points B and C as indicated in Figs. 2·2, 2·3, and 2·4. The resistance of the bridge in series with the galvanometer is then [19, 30]

$$r_{BC} = 2nr_b/(1+n) \qquad (2\cdot3)$$

A galvanometer should be chosen for which the external resistance r_d required to produce the most favorable damping effect is equal to or greater than r_{BC}. If r_d is greater than r_{BC}, an additional resistance equal to $r_d - r_{BC}$ must be placed in series in the galvanometer arm to provide the required damping. If, however, r_d is less than r_{BC}, a shunt r_p parallel to the galvanometer must be placed in the galvanometer arm such that

$$r_p = r_d r_{BC}/(r_{BC} - r_d) \qquad (2\cdot4)$$

This shunt r_p, thus introduced to provide the required damping, reduces the sensitivity. Such sacrifice in sensitivity is avoided by proper selection of the galvanometer.[19, 31]

2·4   THE A-C WHEATSTONE BRIDGE

Well-developed a-c amplifiers do not have the tendency to drift commonly associated with d-c electronic amplifiers. Because of the tendency of d-c electron-tube circuits to drift, d-c amplifiers are often provided with internal arrangements for modulation at the input stage and rectification of the output. The mechanical "choppers" used are limited to low frequencies. In their most sensitive and highly stabilized forms, the response times may be of the order of seconds. Reliable commercial a-c amplifiers and power-supply units are available in ranges of from a few cycles per second to hundreds of megacycles per second.[32, 33]

In measuring *rapidly changing* effects the power-supply frequency should be at least ten times that of these effects. Thus, if the phenomenon is one of 10^{-4}-sec duration or of recurrence at the rate of 10^4 times per second, a power supply of 10^5 cycles/sec would be required.[11]

Since accurate measurements depend on the values of the various resistances in the bridge circuit, electrical phenomena peculiar to these frequencies may be important. Thus because of the *skin effect*, the resistances of conductors increase. For increases up to 10 per cent in solid circular wire, the increase is given by

$$r_f = r(1 + 8.5 \times 10^{-17} \times f^2 \mu^2 d_o^4 / \rho^2) \qquad (2·5)$$

where r_f is the actual resistance at frequency f, ohms; r is the d-c resistance, ohms; f is the frequency of the a-c supply, cycles/sec; d_o is the diameter of the wire, in.; ρ is the resistivity of the wire material, ohm cm; and μ is the magnetic permeability of the wire material ($\mu = 1$, approximately, for most nonferrous, i.e., nonmagnetic, materials).[34-37]

Skin effect can be reduced by using multiple strands of separately insulated wires to achieve the required cross section. It is usually unimportant at frequencies below 10,000 cycles/sec.[34-37]

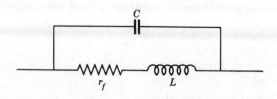

Fig. 2·11.   Residual inductance and capacitance.

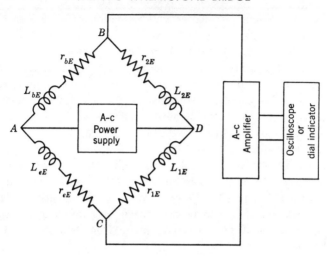

Fig. 2·12. A-c Wheatstone bridge.

Lead wires, resistance coils, sensitive elements, and other units unavoidably have small residual values of *inductance L*, h (henries), and *capacitance C*, f (farads). The inductance is in series, whereas the distributed capacitance may be represented by an equivalent "lumped" capacitor in parallel, as indicated in Fig. 2·11. In a-c operation the resistance then behaves as a frequency-dependent effective value r_E in series with an inductance L_E, and the Wheatstone-bridge circuit becomes that of Fig. 2·12. For estimated values of C and L, the approximate magnitudes of r_E and L_E can be computed from

$$r_E = r_f[1 + 4\pi^2 f^2(2LC - C^2 r_f^2)] \tag{2·6}$$

and

$$L_E = L - C r_f^2 \tag{2·7}$$

where r_E is the effective value of the resistance, ohms; L_E is the effective value of the inductance, h; r_f is the actual value of the resistance at frequency f, ohms; L is the residual inductance in series, h; C is the lumped residual capacitance effectively in parallel, f; and f is the frequency of the a-c power supply, cycles/sec.[34-37]

In wire-wound resistors, inductance is minimized by reducing the areas enclosed within the loops of the wire by placing portions with oppositely directed currents as close together as possible. Capacitance is minimized by arranging for minimum potential difference between adjacent strands. Since capacitance is also less for large separation between strands, a compromise or adjustment must be made between reduction of residual inductance and reduction of capacitance. The bifilar winding, usually used in coils and sensitive elements intended for d-c use (see Figs. 1·4 and 1·6), achieves a minimum of inductance, which reduces parasitic effects due to stray electromagnetic fields. This type of winding, however, results in relatively large residual capacitance and is thereby unsuitable for use at high frequencies where capacitance effects are those of most importance.[36, 38]

The deviation of the effective resistance r_E from the actual resistance r_f is proportional to $2LC - C^2 r_f^2$ (see Eq. 2·6). Design aims at equalizing the terms $2LC$ and $C^2 r_f^2$. Commercial wire-wound resistors are available with values of $2LC - C^2 r_f^2$ ranging from less than $\pm 10^{-10}$ to more than $\pm 10^{-7}$ sec². Similarly, the effective inductance $L - C r_f^2$ (see Eq. 2·7) can be minimized by equalizing the terms L and $C r_f^2$. Values of $(L - C r_f^2)/r_f$ range from less than $\pm 10^{-7}$ to $\pm 10^{-6}$ h/ohm.

Composition resistors, e.g., the carbon-granule and semiconductor or thermistor type, have negligible series inductance. The carbon-composition resistor decreases in resistance as increases in frequency operate on its residual capacitance. The effect is at a far greater rate than its increase in resistance due to the skin effect. Thus, decreases of 50 per cent may occur at 100,000 cycles/sec. In metalized-ceramic resistors, the two effects are of the same order of magnitude, and net changes may not exceed ± 10 per cent at up to 50×10^6 cycles/sec. Molded boron-carbon metallic-film plastic-housed resistors are rated as constant in resistance at up to nearly 20×10^6 cycles/sec.[36, 37]

The conditions for balance on an a-c Wheatstone bridge (see Fig. 2·12) are then

$$r_{1E}r_{bE} = r_{2E}r_{eE} - 4\pi^2 f^2 (L_{2E}L_{eE} - L_{1E}L_{bE}) \qquad (2·8)$$

$$r_{1E}L_{bE} + r_{bE}L_{1E} = r_{2E}L_{eE} + r_{eE}L_{2E} \qquad (2·9)$$

where r_{1E}, r_{2E}, r_{eE}, and r_{bE} are the effective values for the resistances in the four arms, respectively, ohms; and L_{1E}, L_{2E}, L_{eE}, and L_{bE} are the effective values for the inductances in the four arms, respectively, h.[34]

Substantial deviations from the d-c values may require calibration at the operating frequency. Similarly, changes in the effective inductances, occurring with changes in resistors in balancing, may require care. The high resistance values used in a-c circuits will usually render unimportant any frequency variations of resistance in the lead wires. Direct measurement of the residual inductance L and capacitance C will permit application of Eqs. 2·6 to 2·9 in calculating small corrections.[35]

Example. In Fig. 2·12, r_1 and r_2 are 1000-ohm coils of 0.05 in. manganin wire, and r_b is a variable decade. The sensitive element r_e is initially 1000 ohms. For operation at 10,000 cycles/sec, the resistance increase due to the skin effect is given by Eq. 2·5 as

$$r_f = r(1 + 8.5 \times 10^{-17} \times f^2 \mu^2 d_o^4/\rho^2)$$

where $f = 10,000$ cycles/sec, $\mu = 1$, $d_o = 0.05$ in., and $\rho = 44 \times 10^{-6}$ ohm cm. Then $r_f = r(1 + 2.8 \times 10^{-5})$ ohms.

The bridge coils r_1, r_2, and r_b are assumed to be wound so that $2LC - C^2r_f^2 = -10^{-10}$ sec^2 and $(L - Cr_f)/r_f = 10^{-7}$ h/ohm; whereas, for the sensitive element, it is estimated that $2LC - C^2r_f^2$ may be -0.5×10^{-10} sec^2 and $(L - Cr_f)/r_f$ may be 10^{-6} h/ohm, because of the more "open" winding. Then the effective values of the resistances are given by Eq. 2·6 as

$$r_E = r_f[1 + 4\pi^2f^2(2LC - C^2r_f^2)]$$

where $f = 10,000$ cycles/sec, and $(2LC - C^2r_f^2)$ is -10^{-10} sec^2 for the bridge arms r_1, r_2, and r_b and -0.5×10^{-10} sec^2 for the sensitive element r_e. Then

$$r_{1E} = r_{2E} = r_{bE} = 1000 \times [1 - 4\pi^2(10^4)^2 \times 10^{-10}] = 606 \text{ ohms}$$

while

$$r_{eE} = 1000 \times [1 - 4\pi^2(10^4)^2(0.5) \times 10^{-10}] = 803 \text{ ohms}$$

The effective values of the inductances are given by $L_E = L - Cr_f^2$ where $(L - Cr_f)/r_f$ is 10^{-7} h/ohm for the bridge arms and 10^{-6} h/ohm for the sensitive element. Then

$$L_{1E} = L_{2E} = L_{bE} = 10^{-7} \times 1000 = 10^{-4} \text{ h}$$

while $L_{eE} = 10^{-6} \times 1000 = 10^{-3}$ h.

If the bridge were balanced with d-c, the a-c condition (Eq. 2·8) $r_{1E}r_{bE} = r_{2E}r_{eE} - 4\pi^2f^2(L_{2E}L_{eE} - L_{1E}L_{bE})$ becomes $606 \times 606 \neq 606 \times 803 - 4\pi^2(10^4)^2 \times (10^{-4} \times 10^{-3} - 10^{-4} \times 10^{-4})$, or $367,000 \neq 487,000 - (394 - 39.4)$.

To produce a balance, r_b would have to be given a d-c value nearly one-third greater than that of r_e. Further adjustments would be required to rebalance Eq. 2·9. This tendency to change in balance at operating frequency can be minimized by making r_1 and r_2, and r_b and r_e, respectively, of as nearly identical constructions as feasible. Calibration at operating frequency and careful study of residuals will still be required. For higher frequencies, metalized-ceramic or composition resistors would be indicated. The skin effect would also then become important. If a frequency of 1000 cycles/sec will suffice, the discrepancies will be 100-fold smaller, and the effective resistances will differ from the actual by only a few per cent.

2·5 SENSITIVITY OF GALVANOMETER INDICATORS

The sensitivity of a galvanometer S_g is defined as the emf, v, in series with the galvanometer and the external damping resistance which will produce a deflection of one scale division, v/mm. The external damping resistance is that for which the deflection promptly reaches its final value with a minimum of "overshoot" and oscillation but without unnecessary sacrifice in sensitivity.[19, 23, 39]

By removing the scale to a sufficient distance from the swinging mirror on the galvanometer suspension or by employing one of the various galvanometer-deflection amplifiers such as those described by Strong, the sensitivity can be increased by any desired amount. The limit of useful amplification occurs when the signal emf ΔE_{lc}, v, is just resolved in relation to random effects. The quantity ΔE_{lc}, called the least-count emf, is thus the smallest increment which can be measured.[40, 43]

Common random effects result from drift in the elastic properties of the suspension, temperature variations in the coil circuit, mechanical vibrations, and stray electromagnetic waves. By elaborations in mechanical isolation, care in construction and operation, and thermal and electrical shielding, these effects can be reduced indefinitely. The ultimate limitation then results from the random thermal motion of the galvanometer-suspension unit.[40, 44-48]

The corresponding thermal-noise emf is given by

$$\Delta E_{tn} = 4.9 \times 10^{-12} (rT/\tau)^{1/2} \qquad (2 \cdot 10)$$

where Δ_{tn} is the *root-mean-square* (i.e., square root of the average square) value of the thermal-noise emf, v; r is the total electrical resistance in the galvanometer circuit (i.e., the sum of the external damping resistance and that of the galvanometer itself), ohms; T is the absolute temperature of the resistance r, °R; and τ is the open-circuit period of the galvanometer, sec.[40, 49]

2·6 THERMAL-NOISE LIMIT

Amplifications as great as 370 have been successfully used. Great care is required, however, to reduce other random deflections such as those from mechanical and electromagnetic disturbances to within the 1-mm limit.[46, 50-55]

To determine what amplifications can be used in a given system before the thermal-noise deflection will exceed one scale division, the following sample problem is worked out.

Example. Suppose, in Fig. 2·1, that resistances r_1 and r_2 are each 250 ohms while r_b is 2.5 ohms, all at 68°F, and that r_e is at 200°F and at that temperature has a resistance of 3.43 ohms. Then

$$1/r_{BC} = 1/(250 + 250) + 1/(2.5 + 3.43) = 0.171$$

or $r_{BC} = 5.85$ ohms. The galvanometer to be used has a coil-and-suspension resistance of 16 ohms and requires an external damping resistance of 40 ohms. The period is 5 sec, the sensitivity S_g is 0.2×10^{-6} v/mm for a scale distance of 1 m with this damping resistance in series. Since r_{BC} is less than the required external damping resistance, a 35-ohm resistor is placed in series in the galvanometer arm, resulting in a total resistance of 56.85 ohms in the galvanometer circuit. The thermal-noise emf is then computed from Eq. 2·10 as

$$\Delta E_{tn} = 4.9 \times 10^{-12} \times (rT/\tau)^{1/2} = 4.9 \times 10^{-12} \times (56.85 \times 527.69/5)^{1/2}$$
$$= 3.8 \times 10^{-10} \text{ v}$$

For the deflection due to this to equal 1 mm, a scale distance of $0.2 \times 10^{-6}/3.8 \times 10^{-10} = 527$ m, i.e., a deflection amplification of 527, is required.

2·7   THE SENSITIVITY OF ELECTRONIC INDICATORS

The sensitivity of an electronic indicator is usually given as a minimum limiting signal emf or *least count* ΔE_{lc} at the input terminals of the first stage. The ultimate indication can always be amplified to any desired magnitude by providing a sufficient number of stages. The minimum signal ΔE_{lc} is that which is just resolved in relation to random effects.

Common random effects result from drift in the amplification ratio, mechanical vibrations, atmospheric disturbances, variable contact resistances, supply-voltage fluctuations at the various tube elements, and inadequate grounding. By elaborations in design and care in construction and operation, these effects can be reduced indefinitely.[56]

What is called *tube noise* in the electron tubes used in amplifiers consists of fluctuations in tube output resulting from random emission of electrons (*Schottky*[58] effect) and random changes in surface conditions at the tube cathodes (*flicker* effect). With suitable design, this noise is important only in the first stage. An input transformer introduces noise only as Johnson[44] noise, which can be made small by choice of low-resistance transformer coils. Such transformer amplification can be usefully employed up to the point where the thermal or Johnson noise in the bridge circuit is amplified to equality with the tube noise in the first stage. Thus by matching the amplification ratio of the input transformer to the resistance of the thermometer-bridge circuit, the thermal-noise emf (Johnson noise) in the thermometer bridge becomes the ultimate limitation.[33, 44, 56–58]

This thermal noise consists of random emf fluctuations due to random thermal motions of the electrons in the thermometer-bridge circuit. It is computed from

$$\Delta E_{tn} = 5.54 \times 10^{-12} (rT \, \Delta f)^{1/2} \tag{2·11}$$

where ΔE_{tn} is the root-mean-square value of the thermal-noise emf, v; r is the electric resistance of the primary coil of the input transformer plus that of the thermometer-bridge circuit, i.e., plus r_{BC} in Figs. 2·1, 2·8, 2·10, and 2·12, ohms; T is the absolute temperature of the resistance r, °R; and Δf is the total width of the response curve of the indicator, i.e., amplifier or filter, at half the peak response, cycles/sec.[33],[44],[45],[56]

2·8   THERMAL-NOISE VOLTAGE

To illustrate the magnitudes which thermal-noise voltages may attain, a sample case is worked out.

Example. In Fig. 2·1, assume that resistances r_b, r_1, and r_2 are each 1000 ohms and are at 68°F and that r_e is at 600°F and has a resistance of 2170 ohms at that temperature. Also, suppose the indicator circuit to be one for which the resistance of the primary coil in the input transformer is small and $\Delta f = 1.2$ cycles/sec. Then

$$1/r_{BC} = 1/(1000 + 1000) + 1/(1000 + 2170) = 1/1226$$

or

$$r_{BC} = 1226 \text{ ohms}$$

The temperatures of r_b, r_1, and r_2 converted to °R are each $68 + 459.67 = 527.67$°R, and that of r_e is $600 + 459.67 = 1059.67$°R. The average of the square roots of these temperatures is 25.36(°R)$^{1/2}$. Using this average value for $T^{1/2}$, the thermal noise voltage is computed as

$$\Delta E_{tn} = 5.54 \times 10^{-12} \times (1226)^{1/2} \times 25.36 \times (1.2)^{1/2} = 5.4 \times 10^{-9} \text{ v}$$

Amplifiers are commercially available, both in a-c and d-c, for which the least count ΔE_{lc} due to the combination of drift and other random effects associated with the indicator itself does not exceed 5×10^{-9} v. Cheaper units, usually easier to maintain, have values of ΔE_{lc} ranging from 10^{-6} to 10^{-3} v. In computing the effective indicator sensitivity, one uses the value of ΔE_{tn} for the thermometer-bridge circuit, v, or ΔE_{lc} for the indicator, v, whichever is larger.[33],[47],[56],[59-61]

For any given amplification and scale arrangement on the final indicator dial, the *sensitivity* of an electronic indicator S_{ei} is defined as the emf, v, applied to the input terminals which will produce a deflection of one scale division.

2·9   TEMPERATURE SENSITIVITY OF THE ELEMENT

The *temperature sensitivity* of the sensitive element $S_e = \Delta V_{AC}/\Delta t$, v/°F, is measured by the change which occurs in the electric-potential difference ΔV_{AC}, v, between its terminals (see Fig. 2·1) for unit change in its temperature Δt, °F. The potential drop $V_{AC} = i_e r_e$, v, results from the flow of current i_e, amps, through the resistance r_e, ohms, of the sensitive element. Similarly, its change ΔV_{AC}, v, results from the resistance change Δr_e, ohms. The current i_e, amps, also dissipates electric power $W_e = i_e^2 r_e = V_{AC}^2/r_e$, w (watts), as heat. Thus the temperature sensitivity can be expressed in terms of the power dissipation, i.e.,

$$S_e = \alpha_e (r_e W_e)^{1/2} \qquad (2·12)$$

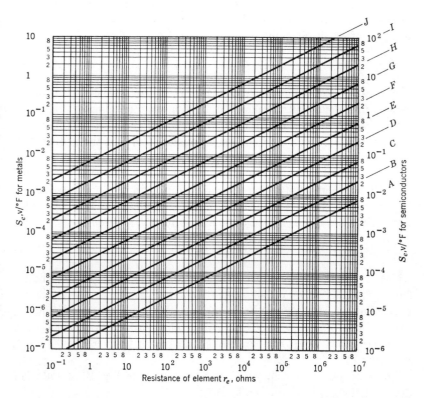

Fig. 2·13. Temperature sensitivity of the element, S_e, i.e., electric-potential drop across the sensitive element per unit change in temperature, v/°F, versus electric resistance of the sensitive element r_e ohms. Curves are for various electric-power dissipations W_e, w. Thus W_e is: A, 10^{-8} w (3.4×10^{-8} Btu/hr); B, 10^{-7} w (3.4×10^{-7} Btu/hr); C, 10^{-6} w (3.4×10^{-6} Btu/hr); D, 10^{-5} w (3.4×10^{-5} Btu/hr); E, 10^{-4} w (3.4×10^{-4} Btu/hr); F, 10^{-3} w (3.4×10^{-3} Btu/hr); G, 10^{-2} w (3.4×10^{-2} Btu/hr); H, 10^{-1} w (3.4×10^{-1} Btu/hr); I, 1 w (3.4 Btu/hr); and J, 10 w (34 Btu/hr). Left-hand scale is for metallic sensitive elements of temperature coefficient of resistance $\alpha_e = 0.0022$ per °F. Right-hand scale is for semiconducting sensitive elements of temperature coefficient of resistance $\alpha_e = -0.022$ per °F.

where S_e is the temperature sensitivity of the element, v/°F; α_e is the temperature coefficient of resistance of the sensitive element, per °F; r_e is the resistance of the sensitive element, ohms; and W_e is the power dissipation, w. For convenience in computations, this relationship is plotted graphically in Fig. 2·13.

2·10   THERMOMETER-BRIDGE-INDICATOR SENSITIVITY

For electronic indication, the arms r_1 and r_2 and the initial value of r_b (see Fig. 2·1) are best made individually equal to the initial value of the electric resistance r_e, ohms, of the sensitive element. Then, the least count Δt_{lc} is given by

$$\Delta t_{lc} = 2S_{ei}/S_e \qquad (2·13)$$

where Δt_{lc} is the temperature change, °F, in the sensitive element resulting in a deflection of one scale division on the indicator; S_{ei} is the emf, v, which applied to the input terminals of the electronic indicator will produce a deflection of one scale division; and S_e is the temperature sensitivity of the sensitive element, v/°F.

For galvanometer indication, the arms r_1 and r_2 are best made equal to each other but many times larger than r_b, and the bridge resistance in series with the galvanometer is made such that the most favorable damping is produced. Then the least count Δt_{lc} is given by

$$\Delta t_{lc} = S_g/S_e \qquad (2·14)$$

where Δt_{lc} is the temperature change, °F, in the sensitive element resulting in a deflection of one scale division; S_g is the sensitivity of the galvanometer, i.e., the emf, v, in series with the galvanometer and the external damping resistance that will produce a deflection of one scale division; and S_e is the temperature sensitivity of the sensitive element, v/°F.[19]

For convenience in computations the relations in Eqs. 2·13 and 2·14 are plotted graphically in Fig. 2·14.

2·11   ERROR DUE TO POWER DISSIPATION IN SENSITIVE ELEMENT

The electrical power dissipation causes the sensitive element to assume a steady-state temperature Δt, °F, above that of the adjacent parent-body material. Time must also elapse during approach to this steady-state condition. And, this delay may be an inconvenience in balancing a bridge which has its key in the battery circuit.

If the heat-transfer conditions to the parent-body material are steady, the effect of this Δt can be largely eliminated from the results

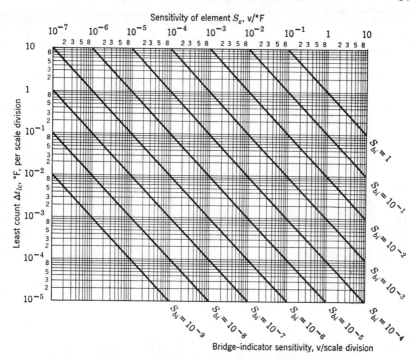

Fig. 2·14. Thermometer-bridge-indicator sensitivity. Least count Δt_{lc}, °F, is plotted vertically versus sensitivity of the element S_e, v/°F, for various bridge-indicator sensitivities S_{bi} v/scale division. For galvanometer indication, S_{bi} is equal to the sensitivity of the galvanometer S_g, v/scale division. For electronic indication, $S_{bi} = 2S_{ei}$, where S_{ei} is the sensitivity of the electronic indicator, v/scale division.

by taking successive readings at reduced power dissipations and extrapolating to zero power. In fact, since the power and thereby Δt are proportional to the square of the current, reducing the current to 0.707 of its value halves Δt. Thus, subtracting the difference from the lower reading provides the required correction.

If, however, the temperature, fluid-flow pattern, or other heat-transfer variables in the parent body are changing, it is difficult to perform this correction. Doubling the required number of readings may also be objectionable. In these circumstances, Δt becomes an error. This error is given by

$$\Delta t = q_e/UA \qquad (2·15)$$

where Δt is the error, °F; q_e/A is the electric-power dissipation in the sensitive element per unit of outer-surface area, Btu/hr ft²; and U is the thermal boundary conductance referred to the outer-surface area, Btu/hr ft² °F. For convenience in computations, this relationship is plotted graphically in Fig. 2·15. Also, q_e is given by

$$q_e = W_e/J \qquad (2 \cdot 16)$$

where W_e is the electric-power dissipation in the sensitive element, w; and $J = 0.293$ w hr/Btu.

For wire-wound sensitive elements, U is given by

$$U = 1/(1/U_i + 1/U_w + 1/U_o) \qquad (2 \cdot 17)$$

where U_i is the boundary conductance, referred to the outer-surface area, from the sensitive element to the inner surface of the casing, Btu/hr ft² °F; U_w is the boundary conductance, referred to the outer-surface area, of the casing wall, Btu/hr ft² °F; and U_o is the boundary

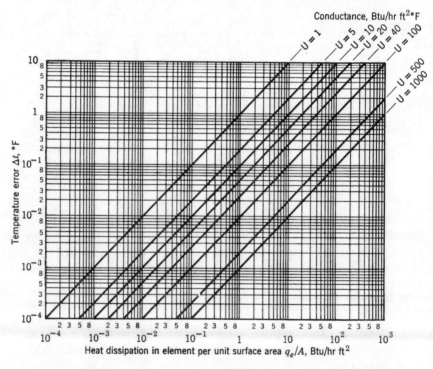

Fig. 2·15. Error in temperature determination Δt, °F, due to electric-power dissipation in the sensitive element per unit of outer-surface area q_e/A, Btu/hr ft². Curves are for conductances U, Btu/hr ft² °F, referred to the outer-surface area of the sensitive-element casing.

conductance over the outer-surface area to those portions of the parent-body material sufficiently distant to be undisturbed in temperature by the presence of the sensitive element.

U can be computed by using Eqs. 7·2, 7·3, 7·12 and 7·13 and Figs. 7·5 and 7·7 in Volume I and employing the procedures described in that chapter.

For an assortment of 28 gas-filled-bulb wire-wound sensitive elements, Lieneweg [62, 64–66] found the term $1/U_i$ to be unimportant. For bulbs immersed in water, he found $1/U_w$ to be the dominant term. The quantity Δt for the bulb immersed in still air ranged, for different constructions, from the same as that for the bulb immersed in water to values 25 times larger. Mueller [39] notes that, for a precision sensitive element immersed in water and operating at the rated dissipation of 10^{-4} w, Δt is a few thousandths of a degree. At 0.010-amp current in the sensitive element, Lieneweg found errors Δt to range, for different constructions, from 0.010 to 0.024°F in still water and from 0.030 to 0.550°F in still air.[13, 39, 62–66]

When the filament is embedded or fused into a rod of glass, quartz, or ceramic, the term $1/U_i$ vanishes, and U_w is computed for a cylinder of inner diameter d_1 equal to that of the wire and outer diameter d_2 equal to that of the rod (see Eqs. 7·3 and 7·13 of Volume I).

For semiconducting sensitive elements, i.e., thermistors as indicated in Fig. 1·2, $1/U_i$ vanishes, and U_w is the conductance of the body of semiconducting material referred to its outer-surface area, Btu/hr ft² °F. For spherical or bead thermistors (see Fig. 1·2), U_w is given by

$$U_w = 10k/d_2 \qquad (2·18)$$

where d_2 is the diameter at the bead, ft; and k is the thermal conductivity of the bead material, Btu/hr ft °F.

For the long cylindrical or rod thermistor, U_w is given by

$$U_w = 8k/d_2 \qquad (2·19)$$

where d_2 is the diameter of the rod, ft; and k is the thermal conductivity of rod material, Btu/hr ft °F.

For the thin-slab or disk thermistor (see Fig. 1·10C), U_w is given by

$$U_w = 6k/d_2 \qquad (2·20)$$

where d_2 is the thickness of the disk, ft; and k is the thermal conductivity of the disk material, Btu/hr ft °F.

U_o is the surface boundary conductance of the thermistor, Btu/hr ft² °F, referred to its diameter or thickness d_2.

Manufacturers' ratings for $W_e/\Delta t$, the power dissipation per unit temperature rise for thermistors immersed bare in still air, range from 0.00005 to 0.01 w/°F for thermistors of $\frac{1}{64}$-in. diameter beads or $\frac{9}{16}$-in. diameter by $\frac{5}{16}$-in. thick disks, respectively.[67-70]

2·12 ERROR DUE TO CONDUCTION OF HEAT ALONG THE STEM

This subject is discussed for thermocouple installations in Ch. 7 of Volume I. The design of resistance sensitive elements should be based on Sec. 7·12 in that chapter, making L the immersed-stem length, ft, measured along the leads to the junction of the internal leads with the sensitive element. In Eq. 7·9 of Volume I, $t_2' - t_2$ is then the discrepancy, °F, between the temperature of this junction and that to be measured. L should be large enough so that $t_2' - t_2$ does not exceed the allowable magnitude for a single contributing source of error.

Trueblood's [71] experimental studies on flat precision units (see Fig. 1·6) immersed in the vapor of boiling naphthalin (424.4°F) revealed stem-conduction errors ranging from 0.01 to 0.055°F.

2·13 ERROR DUE TO BRIDGE-TEMPERATURE DRIFT

The equal-ratio arms r_1 and r_2 of a bridge circuit (see Fig. 2·1) are usually wound on the same spool and of wire from the same original strand. The arms, being thus of the same and small temperature coefficient of resistance α, per °F, and at nearly the same temperature, any variation in the ratio of their resistance is small and is designed to remain within the tolerance accepted for the instrument.

The resistance changes Δr_e in the sensitive element r_e, by which temperature indication occurs, are measured as equal to those required for a setting in the balancing arm r_b. Thus, any changes in the resistance of the balancing arm, due to drift in the bridge temperature, will be attributed to the sensitive element and occur as errors. The resulting error in temperature measurement is given by

$$\Delta t = (t_2 - t_1)\alpha_b/\alpha_e \qquad (2·21)$$

where Δt is the error, °F; α_b is the temperature coefficient of resistance for the material in the balancing arm r_b of the bridge circuit, per °F; α_e is the temperature coefficient of resistance for the sensitive element r_e, per °F; and $t_2 - t_1$ is the drift from calibration temperature in the balancing arm of the bridge, °F. For convenience in computations this relationship is plotted graphically in Fig. 2·16.[72]

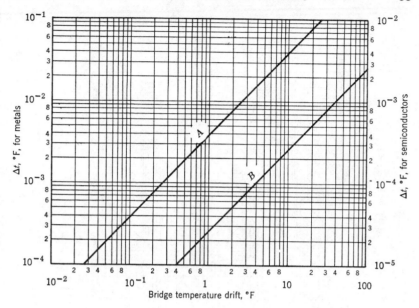

Fig. 2·16. Error in temperature determination Δt, °F, due to drift in the temperature of the balancing arm in the bridge circuit. Curves are for bridge coils of: A, manganin; and, B, gold with 2.1 per cent chromium. Left-hand scale is for metallic sensitive elements of temperature coefficient of resistance $\alpha_e = 0.0022$ per °F. Right-hand scale is for semiconducting sensitive elements of temperature coefficient of resistance $\alpha_e = -0.022$ per °F.

2·14 ERRORS DUE TO TEMPERATURE CHANGES IN THE RESISTANCES OF THE LEADS

In the four-wire arrangements shown in Figs. 2·4, 2·9, and 2·10, the resistance of the element r_e is measured independently of the leads. Consequently, variations in the resistance of the leads have no effect, provided that no change occurs during the time taken to make the two determinations.

For the two-, four-, and three-wire arrangements, however, shown in Figs. 2·1, 2·2, and 2·3, respectively, the lead resistances occur in the bridge arms; and their variations, not compensated by one another, are confused with the changes in the resistance of the sensitive element that serve to measure temperature. The error thus introduced in the determination of temperature is given by

$$\Delta t = (t_2 - t_1) r_l \alpha_l / r_e \alpha_e \qquad (2·22)$$

where Δt is the error, °F; α_e is the temperature coefficient of resistance of the sensitive element, per °F; α_l is the temperature coefficient of

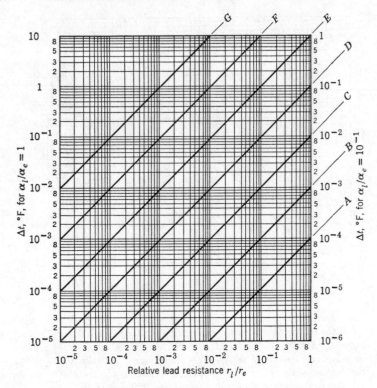

Fig. 2·17. Error in temperature determination Δt, °F, due to temperature variations in the resistances of the lead wires for various temperature differentials
$t_2 - t_1$, °F, in Eq. 2·22. Thus, $t_2 - t_1$ is for curves: A, 10^{-3}°F; B, 10^{-2}°F; C,
10^{-1}°F; D, 1°F; E, 10°F; F, 10^{2}°F; and, G, 10^{3}°F. Left-hand scale is for metallic
sensitive elements of the same temperature coefficient of resistance as the lead-
wire materials. Right-hand scale is for semiconducting sensitive elements of temperature coefficients of resistance 10 times those for the lead-wire materials.

resistance for the lead-wire material, per °F; and r_e is the resistance
of the sensitive element, ohms. It is to be noted that $t_2 - t_1$ and r_l
are given differently for the three cases:

1. For the two-wire arrangement shown in Fig. 2·1, $t_2 - t_1$ is the
mean change in the temperature of the lead wires from that at which
calibration was performed, °F; and r_l is the resistance of the pair of
lead wires, ohms.

2. For the four-wire arrangement shown in Fig. 2·2, $t_2 - t_1$ is the
mean difference in temperature between the two pairs of lead wires,

i.e., between the leads and the compensating leads, °F; and r_l is the resistance of one pair of leads, ohms.

3. For the three-wire arrangement shown in Fig. 2·3, $t_2 - t_1$ is the mean difference in temperature between the two lead wires r_l connected into the bridge arms, °F; and r_l is the resistance of a single lead wire, ohms.

For convenience in computations this relationship is plotted graphically in Fig. 2·17.

2·15 ERRORS DUE TO INSULATION LEAKAGE

Insulation leakage in the presence of moisture or another electrolyte usually results in parasitic voltaic emfs; the errors due to which are

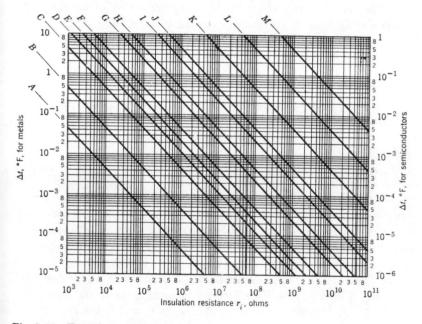

Fig. 2·18. Error in temperature determination Δt, °F, due to insulation leakage in the circuit of the sensitive element for various electric resistances r_e, ohms, of the element. Thus, r_e is for curves: A, 0.1 ohm; B, 1 ohm; C, 10 ohms; D, 25 ohms; E, 50 ohms; F, 100 ohms; G, 500 ohms; H, 1000 ohms; I, 5000 ohms; J, 10^4 ohms; K, 10^5 ohms; L, 10^6 ohms; and, M, 10^7 ohms. Left-hand scale is for metallic sensitive elements of temperature coefficient of resistance $\alpha_e = 0.0022$ per °F. Right-hand scale is for semiconducting sensitive elements of temperature coefficient of resistance $\alpha_e = -0.022$ per °F.

discussed in Sec. 2·16. Such leakage may, however, also occur in the absence of moisture, as, for example, between the leads inside the sensitive-element casing or within the cable. The indicating instruments are ordinarily provided with adequate insulation; however, in the branch of the circuit containing the sensitive element, it may be difficult to effect similar precautions.

Any insulation leakage between the leads, either directly or through leakage at more than one point to the parent-body material, changes the apparent resistance of the sensitive element and is attributed to a corresponding temperature change.

The resulting error in temperature measurement is given by

$$\Delta t = r_e / (r_e + r_i) \alpha_e \qquad (2·23)$$

where Δt is the error, °F; α_e is the temperature coefficient of resistance for the sensitive element, per °F; r_e is the resistance of the sensitive element, ohms; and r_i is the resistance of the insulation shunting the sensitive element, ohms. For convenience in computations this relationship is plotted graphically in Fig. 2·18.

2·16 ERRORS DUE TO PARASITIC VOLTAIC EMFS

Parasitic voltaic emfs were discussed in Sec. 5·4 of Volume I. It was noted that they may be of the order of magnitude of 1 v. For d-c circuits, the corresponding error in the determination of temperature is given by

$$\Delta t = 1/S_e \qquad (2·24)$$

where Δt is the possible error, °F; and S_e is the sensitivity of the sensitive element, v/°F. Except for high-voltage and a-c circuits, such errors are usually large and must be avoided by taking the precautions described for thermocouple circuits. Thus, for a thermistor element of $\alpha_e = 0.022$ per °F operating at $V_{AC} = 100$ v (see Fig. 2·1), i.e., for $S_e = \alpha_e V_{AC} = 2.2$ v/°F, the error $\Delta t = 1/2.2 = 0.45$°F. However, for a 25-ohm platinum sensitive element operating at 0.002 amp, i.e., for $S_e = \alpha_e i_e r_e = 0.0022 \times 0.002 \times 25 = 0.00011$ v/°F, the error $\Delta t = 1/0.00011 = 9100$°F. This error is obviously so large that it entirely masks the legitimate indication.

Since a voltaic emf produces only d-c components which are not passed by an a-c electron-tube amplifier, no appreciable error should ordinarily result in a-c circuits.

If a double-throw switch is introduced into the circuit, as, for example, to reverse the measuring current, parasitic voltaic emfs are canceled when the two successive readings are averaged. This technique is very useful when drifts are slow and steady enough so that their effects can also be eliminated.

2·17 ERRORS DUE TO PARASITIC THERMOELECTRIC EMFS

Parasitic thermoelectric emfs were discussed in Sec. 5·3 of Volume I. Careful design usually provides for minimizing their effects within an instrument. Thus, copper is used as much as possible, and other metals are chosen with regard to minimum thermoelectric power against one another and against copper. Opposing junctions are placed near to one another in good thermal communication and shielded from external heat sources. In d-c electron-tube amplifiers where filament heaters occur within the units, further precautions are taken. Thus, in the input (i.e., low-voltage) d-c stages, special "low-thermal" (i.e., low thermoelectric power, see Fig. 2·19) solders are used. For a given instrument in rated service, errors are usually intended to remain within the tolerance accepted for the unit.[9, 12, 33, 73–75]

In the branch of the circuit containing the sensitive element, it may be difficult to effect similar precautions. Joints must be made between resistance coils and leads. Soldered joints may occur with the solder in series with the materials joined. Switches, junction boxes, and brush contacts or commutators may occur. For each such pair of junctions in series in the circuit, a thermoelectric emf is introduced, given by

$$E_{AB} = e_{AB}(t_1 - t_2) \qquad (2·25)$$

where E_{AB} is the thermoelectric emf, v; e_{AB} is the thermoelectric power between the pair of metals A and B, v/°F; and t_1 and t_2 are the temperatures of the two opposing junctions. In accord with Sec. 5·2 of Volume I, the emf contributed by any one pair of junctions in a multiple-metal circuit may be considered independently of the other junction pairs in the circuit.

For d-c circuits, the error thus introduced in the determination of temperature for the junction pair AB is given by

$$\Delta t_{AB} = E_{AB}/S_e \qquad (2·26)$$

where Δt_{AB} is the error, °F; E_{AB} is the thermoelectric emf for the junction pair AB, v; and S_e is the sensitivity of the sensitive element, v/°F. For convenience in computations, this relationship is plotted graphically in Fig. 2·19 for various combinations which may occur as junction pairs and for $t_1 - t_2 = 1$°F, i.e., per unit of thermal nonuniformity between junctions A and B of a pair.

Since a thermoelectric emf produces only d-c components not passed

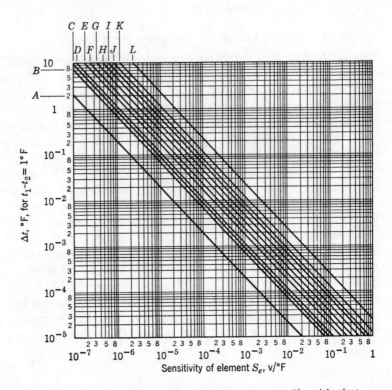

Fig. 2·19. Error in temperature determination due to nonuniformities in temperature in the thermometer circuit. Error Δt, °F, per unit temperature difference, i.e., $t_1 - t_2 = 1$°F in Eq. 2·25 for pairs of junctions between various materials, is plotted vertically against the sensitivity of the element S_e, v/°F. Curves are for junction pairs of: A, copper against cadmium, gold, silver, or zinc; B, copper, gold, or silver against manganin or tungsten; C, copper, gold, or silver against silver solder (50 per cent silver, 15.5 per cent copper, 16.5 per cent zinc, and 18 per cent cadmium); D, copper, gold, or silver against brass (copper with 10 to 40 per cent zinc) or phosphor bronze (copper with 1.25 to 10 per cent tin); E, copper, gold, or silver against molybdenum, lead, tin, or lead-tin solders; F, platinum against lead, tin, or lead-tin solders; G, platinum against brass (copper with 10 to 40 per cent zinc) or phosphor bronze (copper with 1.25 to 10 per cent tin); H, copper, gold, or silver against carbon, gold-chromium alloy (gold with 2.1 per cent chromium), or platinum; I, copper, gold, or silver against mercury; J, platinum against nickel; K, nickel against copper, gold, silver, or tungsten; and L, copper, gold or silver against constantan (copper with 40 to 45 per cent nickel).

by an a-c electron-tube amplifier, ordinarily no appreciable error should result in a-c circuits.

When temperatures are not rapidly changing with time, reversing the measuring current is a useful technique for canceling out parasitic thermoelectric emfs (see Sec. 2·16).

2·18 CONTACT RESISTANCE

When electric connections between circuit elements are made without soldering, brazing, or welding, *contact resistances* arise. Thus, (1), conductors may be pressed together as in the case of wires clamped under binding posts; (2), they may be slid into position under pressure as are the flat blocks of metal or tapered plugs in switching devices; or, (3), they may slide continuously as in *commutators* and *brush contacts* or *slip rings*.[76]

Contact resistances may range in magnitude from negligible values to amounts sufficient for insulation. In each of the three cases, the resistance will depend on: (1), the cleanness of the surfaces, (2), the thrust between them, (3), the *electrical potential difference* across the contact, and (4), the character of the participating materials.[76, 77]

Freedom from visible tarnish is indispensable to low contact resistance. This may be temporarily attained by cleaning with fine emery or crocus cloth. Sliding contacts often tend to retain a degree of cleanness by abrasion in service. Lubricating with oil or *epilamen* (a coating which forms an adherent monomolecular layer) tends to retard tarnishing but increases the contact resistance. Materials such as aluminum, which quickly develop tough tarnish layers thick enough for insulating effect, do not make good contacts. Good electric conductors, which slowly form brittle tarnish layers and are soft enough to mate to one another under pressure, have the lowest contact resistances. For repeated or continued motion, increased contact resistance may be accepted in attaining durability. The lowest resistances occur with copper, silver, and gold contacts. On silver, the oxide forms slowly and reduces to silver at points of local heating, whereas the rapidly forming sulfide is of low electrical resistivity. Bronze is a good contact material. Brass oxidizes too easily but is serviceable in sliding contacts. In brush contacts, one member is often of carbon to minimize wear, friction, and scoring. However, the black film that forms on the copper ring and limits wear is insulating at low voltages.[76, 78-81]

Generally, contact resistance varies inversely with the force or thrust between the contacting members. Thus, for clean copper surfaces, the contact resistance may be reduced from nearly an ohm at a thrust of a few milligrams to less than 10^{-6} ohm at a thrust of a ton. Surface crushing of contact materials under thrust may sufficiently crack up tarnish layers, permitting the formation of extruded *bridges* of metal through the cracks and thus reducing contact resistance. For rigid clamped connections, the materials must be such as to sustain this thrust and not gradually relieve it by creep.[76, 81]

For clean surfaces, the potential difference across the contact has no important effect up to such amperages as cause local heating. However, when there is a tarnish film unbroken by pressure or abrasion, a critical voltage occurs. Voltages exceeding this value cause *puncturing* which results from dielectric breakdown and effects a gross decrease in the contact resistance. The puncturing voltage usually ranges from 0.1 to 10 v, although some effect may occur at 0.01 v or less and some films may sustain as much as 100 v. Beyond the puncturing range, voltage has little effect.

Figure 2·20 shows a design due to Roebuck [82] for tapered-plug contacts intended to permit establishing large thrusts. Well-fitted plugs, clean and bright, gave resistances of around 10^{-5} ohm. Lubricated with mercury amalgamated to both surfaces, the contact resistance was less than 10^{-6} ohm, and varied by about 10^{-7} ohm in service. Roebuck felt that the reproducibility of such contacts could be trusted with certainty to within 10^{-6} ohm.

Contacts, which close with a sliding motion as in switches, may have resistances as low as 10^{-4} ohm for good contact materials, kept clean, and for constructions providing firm thrust between the sliding surfaces. Resistances in switches are usually, however, much larger, i.e., 10^{-3} to 10^{-2} ohm when care is taken. One official specification provides for

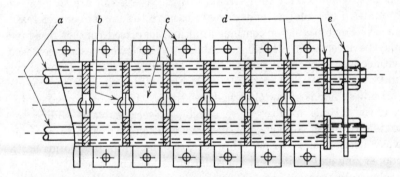

Fig. 2·20. Tapered-plug contacts—Roebuck's design. *a*, Tie bolts; *b*, tapered contact surfaces; *c*, copper blocks; *d*, insulating washers; and *e*, spacer. (*By permission J. R. Roebuck in J. Opt. Soc. Am., 6, no. 2, 175, March, 1922.*)

maintaining the contact resistances in thermocouple-pyrometer switches at less than 0.25 ohm.[76, 83, 84]

A silver brush sliding on a copper ring has been found to have a contact resistance as low as 0.0002 ohm where the thrust was 1 lb, and less than 0.01 ohm for a thrust of 10 g. Alloys, available from J. M. Ney Company (Hartford, Connecticut), consisting of combinations of platinum, palladium, gold, silver, copper, and zinc which are highly durable in sliding motion are rated at sliding-contact resistances of 0.1 ohm. The carbon or graphite brushes used in electric machinery, because of the lubricating black film, may have resistances ranging from 10 to 500 ohms at potential differences of less than 1 v across the contact, although at 2 or more volts this resistance may drop to 0.5 ohm or less. Contacts to the rotor of an ultracentrifuge, formed by axial steel needle points pressing against the ends of the shaft, were found to have a combined resistance of 10 ohms.[76, 85, 86]

Trueblood [71] found repeated polishing was required to maintain the resistance between copper lugs clamped under copper binding posts at less than 0.044 ohm. Silver or gold plating reduced this difficulty. Thomas [87] reported difficulty in avoiding an unknown contact resistance of the order of 10^{-4} ohm in clamped connections.[71, 83, 87, 88]

2·19 ERRORS DUE TO CONTACT RESISTANCE

Bridge circuits are usually so designed as to minimize the effects of contact resistances. Thus in Fig. 2·5, resistances at the contacts in the battery and galvanometer branches do not affect the balance but merely the sensitivity of the bridge. The remaining adjustable contacts are either in series with large resistances or shunted by small resistances, whereby the errors introduced are intended to be within the tolerance accepted for the instrument.[9, 12, 73, 74]

In the branch containing the sensitive element for the circuit arrangements shown in Figs. 2·1, 2·2, 2·3, 2·7, 2·8, and 2·12, binding posts, switches, and moving brush contacts may occur in series with the element. Contact resistances and their variations are thereby confused with the changes in the resistance of the sensitive element that serve to measure temperature. The error thus introduced in the determination of temperature is given by

$$\Delta t = r_c / \alpha_e r_e \qquad (2 \cdot 27)$$

where Δt is the error, °F; r_c is the unknown contact resistance or its unknown variations, ohms; r_e is the resistance of the sensitive element, ohms; and α_e is the temperature coefficient of resistance of the sensitive

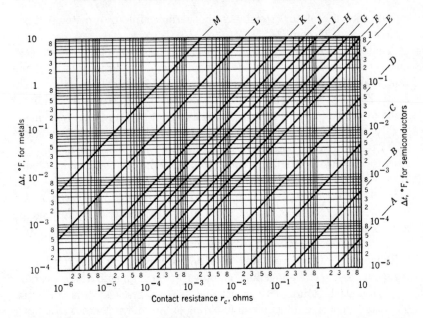

Fig. 2·21. Error in temperature determination Δt, °F, due to electric contact resistance r_c, ohms, in the circuit of the sensitive element for various electric resistances r_e, ohms, of the sensitive element. Thus, r_e is for curves: A, 10^7 ohms; B, 10^6 ohms; C, 10^5 ohms; D, 10^4 ohms; E, 10^3 ohms; F, 500 ohms; G, 250 ohms; H, 100 ohms; I, 50 ohms; J, 25 ohms; K, 10 ohms; L, 1 ohm; and M, 10^{-1} ohm. Left-hand scale is for metallic sensitive elements of temperature coefficient of resistance $\alpha_e = 0.0022$ per °F. Right-hand scale is for semiconducting sensitive elements of temperature coefficient of resistance $\alpha_e = -0.022$ per °F.

element, per °F. For convenience in computations, this relationship is plotted graphically in Fig. 2·21.

2·20   TESTING FOR CONTACT RESISTANCES

Since a contact resistance may depend on the total emf in the circuit in the critical range from 0.01 to 100 v, appropriate testing must be done. This can be either with the actual service emf or with an emf outside the critical range and corresponding to that of operation. The most reliable and usually the most convenient procedure is to make tests in the actual operating circuit. A contact resistance may be tested by alternately shorting it out and noting the effect on the instrument indications. For many industrial connections and switches, a heavy-duty knife switch may be considered to effect a short. For precision work a Roebuck [82]-type mercury-lubricated plug (see Fig. 2·20) can usually be used. Otherwise, a soldered shunt may be necessary.

If the resistance of the shunt and that of the metallic path shunted are found to differ, the circuit must be improved or the thus-calibrated difference used as a computed correction.   In the case of brush contacts to a moving body, where shorting the contacts is impossible, the remaining resistance in the circuit can be eliminated, and the residue due to the brush contacts measured at operating speed using the installed instrumentation.   To achieve this, a low-resistance shunt can be attached between contacts on the moving body, and similar shunts provided in the stationary portions of the circuit.[76, 82, 84]

Figure 2·22 shows an arrangement suitable for measuring contact resistances and their variations.   It is necessary here that the metallic path remain (as indicated) unbroken through the points at which the potentiometer taps in; however, elsewhere than through this section containing the test unit, ordinary switches and binding posts can be used.   Then

$$r_c = \Delta V_{AB}/i \qquad (2·28)$$

where r_c is the magnitude of the test resistance, ohms; ΔV_{AB} is the potential difference across the test unit as indicated on the potentiometer, v; and i is the current through the milliammeter, amps.   If the potentiometer is such as to indicate to within 10^{-7} v, small test resistances can be measured to within around 10^{-5} ohm.   If the test unit

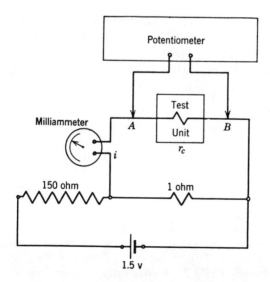

Fig. 2·22. Circuit for measuring electric contact resistances in switches, tapered-plug contacts, binding posts, and sliding or brush contacts.

contains appreciable resistance in addition to the contact resistance, this other resistance must be eliminated by shorting out or by subtracting the resistance of a similar unit without the contact. Repeated readings will reveal the magnitudes of random variations that cause most of the errors associated with contact resistances.[9]

2·21 ERRORS IN CALIBRATION

Obviously, no measurements can be made with greater precision than that to which the thermometers and indicating instruments have been calibrated. Similarly, changes in the characteristics of these devices after calibration result in errors of the same magnitudes. Methods for calibration of the thermometers have been discussed in Secs. 1·11 and 1·12. Methods for calibrating resistors, bridge circuits, potentiometers, galvanometers, and other indicators will be found in textbooks on electrical measurements. Rated accuracies are usually available from the manufacturer. Standard resistors and standard voltaic cells can be sent to the National Bureau of Standards (Washington, D. C.) for calibration. A convenient recourse is often that of over-all calibration of the installed circuit against a calibrated thermometer or fixed points.

2·22 CONCLUSION—SAMPLE DESIGN CALCULATION

In Ch. 1, a survey was given of the various established forms of apparatus available for temperature measurement by the electric-resistance method. In the present chapter, systematic procedures with formulas and charts have provided means for numerical determinations of each of the essential factors contributing to the over-all performance of an installation design. By suitable use of this technique, a design can be formulated to meet the requirements of a given problem. To illustrate how this procedure is applied in practice, a sample problem is worked out.[89, 90]

Example. It is required to measure changing local temperatures to within 12°F on a high-speed nickel-alloy rotor whose hottest portions are expected to approximate 1600°F. Space limitations permit only two brush–slip-ring contacts. Since only two leads are possible on the rotor, where temperature variations are greatest, it is decided to use a 2-lead construction throughout. Platinum brush and ring alloys for which the sliding-contact resistance is 0.1 ohm are used at ring radii such that the sliding speed permits adequate service lifetime. The element type selected as adapted to the conditions is of tungsten wire fused into quartz in 6°F accuracy. This leaves $12 - 6 = 6$°F allowable error elsewhere, i.e., 0.6°F allowable error or 0.2°F probable error, for individual contributions (see Eq. 3·4 in Volume I).

For probable error $\Delta t = 0.2$°F and total contact resistance $r_c = 0.2$ ohm, the required element resistance is determined from the chart, Fig. 2·21 (or

Eq. 2·27), as 455 ohms at 1600·F. This is found to be available in a size 0.125 in. diameter by 2 in. long with 0.001-in. wire.

To compute the sensitivity of the element in terms of the permissible dissipation q_e, Btu/hr, it is necessary first to find the over-all conductance U, Btu/hr ft^2 °F, from the tungsten wire to the rotor-body material using Eq. 2·17. For support against inertia forces, the element is to be cemented into a drilled hole as described in Sec. 11·2 of Volume I. The thermal conductivity of the rotor-body material is assumed to be 7.8, and that of the quartz, 0.57 Btu/hr ft °F. Then $1/U_i = 0$. Now, $U_o = U_b$ is given by Eq. 7·14 or Fig. 7·7 of Volume I as 540 Btu/hr ft^2 °F, and U_w is given by Eq. 7·13 (or Fig. 7·5 of Volume I) as 22.6 Btu/hr ft^2 °F. The likelihood of transparency in the quartz permitting appreciable further heat transfer by transmitted radiation is ignored. Then, $U = 1/(1/22.6 + 1/540) = 21.7$ Btu/hr ft^2 °F. For a probable error $\Delta t = 0.2$°F, q_e/A is determined from the chart, Fig. 2·15 (or Eq. 2·15), as 4.34 Btu/hr ft^2. Thus, for $A = \pi(2)(0.125)/144 = 0.00545$ ft^2, $q_e = (4.34)(0.00545) = 0.0237$ Btu/hr; or, by Eq. 2·16, $W_e = (0.0237)(0.293) = 0.00695$ w. The sensitivity of the element is then determined from the chart, Fig. 2·13 (or Eq. 2·12), as $S_e = 0.0039$ v/°F. The required bridge-indicator sensitivity is then determined from the chart, Fig. 2·14, for a probable error $\Delta t = 0.2$°F as 0.00078 v/scale division. In accord with Eqs. 2·13 and 2·14, this is the required sensitivity S_g for a galvanometer indicator, or twice the sensitivity S_{ei} for an electronic indicator. Thus, the required sensitivities are found to be $S_g = 0.00078$ v/scale division for galvanometer and 0.00039 v/scale division for electronic indicators. Thus, $E_{lc} = 0.00039$ v at the input terminals of the first stage of an electronic indicator. For these sensitivities, rugged self-balancing and recording instruments are commercially available.

Silver leads from the element, changing to copper at the brush-and-ring contacts, are found to have a total resistance $r_l = 0.3$ ohm. For 2-lead construction, the relative lead resistance is then $r_l/r_e = (0.3)/(455) = 0.000659$; and, for the tungsten element with silver or copper leads, it is assumed to be a sufficiently close approximation to take $\alpha_l/\alpha_e = 1$. Then, for a probable error $\Delta t = 0.2$°F, the permissible mean change $t_2 - t_1$ in temperature of the leads from that at calibration is determined from the chart, Fig. 2·17 (or Eq. 2·22), as 303°F. For the element resistance $r_e = 455$ ohms and a probable error $\Delta t = 0.2$°F, the required insulation resistance r_i between the leads is determined from the chart, Fig. 2·18 (or Eq. 2·23), as $r_i = (1.03)(10)^6$ ohms. For a manganin balancing arm r_b (see Fig. 2·1), a metallic sensitive element, and a probable error $\Delta t = 0.2$°F, the permissible drift in the bridge temperature $t_2 - t_1$ is determined from the chart, Fig. 2·16 (or Eq. 2·21), as $t_2 - t_1 = 52.8$°F. It is assumed that the thermoelectric power e_{AB} between the contact and lead materials approximates that between platinum and copper or silver, i.e., $e_{AB} = 4.2$ μv/°F, and that this is the largest thermoelectric power prevailing among the various combinations of materials occurring. Above, it was determined that the sensitivity of the element would be made $S_e = 0.0039$ v/°F (or greater). For a probable error

$\Delta t = 0.2°F$, the probable error for each junction pair Δt_{AB} is found from Eq. 3·3 of Volume I. Thus, $\Delta t = \Delta t_{AB}(N)^{1/2}$ where N is the number of pairs of parasitic junctions. If N is taken as $N = 4$, then $\Delta t_{AB} = \Delta t/(N)^{1/2} = (0.2)/(4)^{1/2} = 0.1°F$. Then, the chart, Fig. 2·19 (or Eqs. 2·25 and 2·26), indicates that 0.00108°F error will result from each 1°F difference in temperature between the junctions of a pair or that $t_2 - t_1 = \Delta t_{AB}/(0.00108) = (0.1)/(0.00108) = 92.7°F$. Thus, uniformity of temperature must be maintained to within 92.7°F between the junctions comprising each of the pairs.

No difficulty is to be anticipated in satisfying these requirements.

This installation requires a hole 0.125 in. in diameter and yields two-thirds response in 1 sec time. If space limitations had required a smaller hole, the calculation could have been attempted in accord with the properties of a smaller-diameter similar unit, or a metalized-ceramic resistor could have been substituted. In the latter case, the higher resistance r_e, ohms, would have permitted the smaller-diameter lead wires necessitated by the reduced hole diameter. The zero drift for such an element would be greater, requiring both broader limits on precision and frequent recalibration. If the temperature level were low enough to permit use of a semiconductor, i.e., thermistor element (see Fig. 1·2), small size could be attained with increased precision.[88]

Although the details of such a computation may seem numerous to anyone not accustomed to designing thermometer installations in this manner, they include no factors not essential to successful performance. By arranging a suitable combination in preliminary design, unsatisfactory constructions can be avoided. Furthermore, measurement problems which might not otherwise be attempted can thus be undertaken with assurance.

REFERENCES *

1. J. Lorenz, "Temperaturmessung mit dem Kreuzspulgerät" (Temperature Measurement with the Crossed-Coil Apparatus), *ATM Archiv für technisches Messen*, V212-1, T138 (November, 1939).

2. W. Geyer, "Temperaturdifferenz-Messung mit Widerstandsthermometern bei zwei veränderlichen Temperaturen" (Measurement of Temperature Differences with Resistance Thermometers at Two Changing Temperatures), *ATM Archiv für technisches Messen*, V2166-2, T66 (1931).

3. R. W. Troke, "The Direct-Reading D-C Strain-Gage Bridge," *Instruments*, **24**, no. 5, pp. 535, 536, 538, 540, 542, 544 (May, 1951).

4. H. J. Hoge, "A Two-Emf Method for the Comparison of Resistances," *Rev. Sci. Instr.*, **25**, no. 9, pp. 902–907 (September, 1954).

5. H. J. Hoge, "Comment on Comparison of Resistances," *Rev. Sci. Instr.*, **26**, no. 2, p. 233 (February, 1955).

6. N. C. Fick and N. A. Crites, "A Fifty-point Bridge Balance Unit for Use with a Baldwin SR-4 Strain Indicator," *Instruments*, **21**, no. 4, pp. 329, 330 (April, 1948).

---

* See footnote on page 26.

7. W. J. Worley, "Simplified Dynamic Strain Equipment," *Instruments*, **21**, no. 4, pp. 330–332 (April, 1948).

8. C. O. Fairchild, "Industrial Temperature Instruments Employing Electronic Methods and Devices," *Instruments*, **17**, no. 8, pp. 468–472, 496 (August, 1944).

9. M. Eppley, "Modifications of the Resistance Thermometer Bridge (Mueller Bridge) and of the Commutator Selector for Use with It," *Rev. Sci. Instr.*, **3**, no. 11, pp. 687–711 (November, 1932).

10. A. Meier, "Recording Rapidly Changing Cylinder-Wall Temperatures," *Technical Memorandum*, no. 1013, pp. 21–27, U. S. National Advisory Committee for Aeronautics, Washington (May, 1942); also *Forschung auf dem Gebiete des Ingenieurwesens*, **10**, no. 1, pp. 41–54 (January, 1939).

11. W. B. Dobie, *Electric Resistance Strain Gages*, pp. 17–23, 71–84, University of London Press Limited, London, 1948.

12. E. F. Mueller, "Wheatstone Bridges and Some Accessory Apparatus for Resistance Thermometry," *Bulletin of the Bureau of Standards*, **13**, no. 4, pp. 547–561 (March, 1917).

13. C. W. Waidner and G. K. Burgess, "Platinum Resistance Thermometers at High Temperatures," *Bulletin of the Bureau of Standards*, **6**, no. 2, pp. 152–158, 178–230 (November, 1909).

14. W. R. Beakley, "The Design of Thermistor Thermometers with Linear Calibration," *J. Sci. Instr.*, **28**, no. 6, pp. 176–179 (June, 1951).

15. G. T. Armstrong, P. K. Wong, and L. A. Krieger, "Use of a Direct Current Amplifier and Recorder to Balance a Mueller Resistance Bridge, *Rev. Sci. Instr.*, **30**, no. 5, pp. 339–343 (May, 1959).

16. M. H. Aronson, "Resistance Measurement," *Instruments*, **32**, no. 9, pp. 1350–1355 (September, 1959).

17. W. N. Hubbard, "On the Comparison of the Lower Decades of a Mueller Bridge," *Rev. Sci. Instr.*, **29**, no. 9, p. 784 (September, 1958).

18. R. M. LeLacheur, "A Low Range Decade for Resistance Thermometer Bridges," *Rev. Sci. Instr.*, **23**, no. 7, p. 383 (July, 1952).

19. F. Wenner, "Methods, Apparatus, and Procedures for the Comparison of Precision Standard Resistors," *RP* 1323, *J. Research Natl. Bur. Standards*, **25**, no. 2, pp. 232–241 (August, 1940).

20. J. B. Kelley and H. H. Marold, "Potentiometers," *Instruments*, **32**, no. 9, pp. 1361–1363 (September, 1959).

21. "Voltage References," *Instruments*, **32**, no. 9, pp. 1357–1359 (September, 1959).

22. J. E. Miller, "Precision Potentiometers—Use and Maintenance Tips," *Instruments*, **32**, no. 1, pp. 84–87 (January, 1959).

23. P. M. Andress, "I. Deflection Constants of the DC Galvanometer at a Specified Damping; II. Improved Solutions of the Unbalanced Bridge Circuit," *Rev. Sci. Instr.*, **24**, no. 2, pp. 172–177 (February, 1953).

24. K. S. Cole, "Thermistor Thermometer Bridge: Linearity and Sensitivity for a Range of Temperature," *Rev. Sci. Instr.*, **28**, no. 5, pp. 326–328 (May, 1957).

25. D. R. Stull, "An Automatic Recorder for Resistance Thermometry," *Rev. Sci. Instr.*, **16**, no. 11, pp. 318–321 (November, 1945).

26. D. M. Kerns, "Analysis of the Direct-Current Bolometer Bridge," *RP* 2051, *J. Research Natl. Bur. Standards*, **43**, no. 6, pp. 581–589 (December, 1949).

27. C. Blake, C. E. Chase, and E. Maxwell, "Resistance Thermometer Bridge for Measurement of Temperatures in the Liquid Helium Range," *Rev. Sci. Instr.*, **29**, no. 8, pp. 715–716 (August, 1958).

28. P. M. Hu and R. W. Parsons, "A Thermostat Using a Resistance Thermometer and a Galvanometer-Photocell Amplifier," *J. Sci. Instr.*, **34**, no. 7, pp. 283–285 (July, 1957).

29. H. Diesselhorst, "Methodisches zur Messung mit dem Widerstandsthermometer in der Wheatstonischen Brücke" (Procedure for Measurement with the Resistance Thermometer in the Wheatstone Bridge), *Zeitschrift für technische Physik*, **24**, no. 7, pp. 162–166 (1943).

30. F. R. Kotter, "Location of the Galvanometer Branch for Maximum Sensitivity of the Wheatstone Bridge," *RP* 1884, *J. Research Natl. Bur. Standards*, **40**, no. 5 (May, 1948).

31. T. M. Dauphinee, "Device for Matching a Galvanometer or dc Indicator to Its Associated Circuit," *Rev. Sci. Instr.*, **29**, no. 3, pp. 240–241 (March, 1958).

32. Shasta Division of Beckman Instruments, "High Resistance Bridge," *Industrial Laboratories*, **5**, no. 5, pp. 22–23 (May, 1954).

33. M. D. Liston, C. E. Quinn, W. E. Sargeant, and G. G. Scott, "A Contact Modulated Amplifier to Replace Sensitive Suspension Galvanometers," *Rev. Sci. Instr.*, **17**, no. 5, pp. 194–198 (May, 1946).

34. D. Owen, *Alternating Current Measurements*, rev. 3rd ed., pp. 17, 18, 54, 86, John Wiley & Sons, New York, 1953.

35. H. A. Brown, *Radio-Frequency Electrical Measurements*, pp. 23–28, McGraw-Hill Book Co., New York, 1938.

36. F. E. Terman, *Radio Engineers' Handbook*, pp. 28–37, 40–47, McGraw-Hill Book Co., New York, 1943.

37. F. Langford-Smith, *Radiotron Designer's Handbook*, pp. 186–191, Radio Corporation of America, New Jersey, 1953.

38. C. R. Barber, A. Gridley, and J. A. Hall, "A Design for Standard Resistance Coils," *J. Sci. Instr.*, **29**, no. 3, pp. 65–69 (March, 1952).

39. E. F. Mueller, "Precision Resistance Thermometry," American Institute of Physics, *Temperature*, pp. 162–179, Reinhold Publishing Corp., New York, 1941.

40. J. Strong, H. V. Neher, A. E. Whitford, C. H. Cartwright, and R. Hayward, *Procedures in Experimental Physics*, 642 pp., Prentice-Hall, Inc., New York, 1941.

41. T. M. Dauphinee, "Deflection Multiplier for Reflecting Galvanometers," *Rev. Sci. Instr.*, **26**, no. 9, pp. 873–875 (September, 1955).

42. H. O. Hoadley, "A Multiple-Reflection Optical Lever," *Rev. Sci. Instr.*, **20**, no. 1, pp. 30–35 (January, 1949).

43. W. Leo and W. Hübner, "Zur Strahlungsmessung mittels Thermoelementen und hochempfindlicher Photozellkompensation" (Thermocouples and High-Sensitivity Photocell Compensation for Radiation Measurement), *Zeitschrift für angewandte Physik*, **2**, no. 12, pp. 454–461 (1950).

44. J. B. Johnson, "Thermal Agitation of Electricity in Conductors," *Phys. Rev.*, **32**, no. 1, pp. 97–109 (January, 1928).

45. H. Nyquist, "Thermal Agitation of Electric Charge in Conductors," *Phys. Rev.*, **32**, no. 1, pp. 110–113 (January, 1928).

46. A. V. Hill, "Limit of Useful Amplification of a Galvanometer Deflexion," *Nature*, **163**, no. 4156, pp. 994–995 (June, 1949).

47. C. H. Cartwright, "Natural Observation Limit of Radiometric Measurements," *Physics*, **1**, no. 4, pp. 211–229 (October, 1931).

48. M. Surdin, "Sur la sensibilité limite des galvanomètres" (On the Sensitivity Limit of Galvanometers), *J. de physique et le radium,* Series 8, **10**, nos. 7-8-9, pp. 253–254 (July-August-September, 1949).

49. L. G. A. Sims, "Measurement of Temperature by Thermocouple & Galvanometer," *Engineering,* **177**, no. 4593, pp. 180–181 (February, 1954).

50. H. D. Baker, W. Claypoole, and D. D. Fuller, "Further Developments in the Measurement of the Coefficient of Static Friction," *Proceedings of First U. S. National Congress of Applied Mechanics,* American Society of Mechanical Engineers, New York (1951).

51. D. A. Lupfer, "Vibration-Free Galvanometer Support," *Rev. Sci. Instr.,* **24**, no. 11, p. 1073 (November, 1953).

52. W. H. Julius, "Über eine Vorrichtung um Messinstrumente gegen die Erschütterungen des Bodens zu schützen" (On an Arrangement to Protect Measuring Instruments from Earth Vibrations), *Annalen der Physik und Chemie,* **56**, Series 3, no. 9, pp. 151–160 (August, 1895).

53. G. M. Hobbs, "Vibration-Free Galvanometer Support," *Rev. Sci. Instr.,* **22**, no. 2, p. 118 (February, 1951).

54. R. C. Lewis and K. Unholtz, "A Simplified Method for the Design of Vibration-Isolating Suspensions," *Trans. ASME,* **69**, no. 8, pp. 813–820, American Society of Mechanical Engineers, New York (November, 1947).

55. "Vibration Control for Electronic Products," *Electronics,* **18**, no. 9, pp. 134–139 (September, 1945).

56. L. C. Roess, "Vacuum Tube Amplifier for Measuring Very Small Alternating Voltages," *Rev. Sci. Instr.,* **16**, no. 7, pp. 173–176 (July, 1945).

57. R. Aumont, J. Romand, and B. Vodar, "Mesure de la température absolue d'un conducteur métallique à partir de la tension électrique produite par l'agitation thermique des électrons dans ce conducteur" (The Measurement of the Absolute Temperature of a Metallic Conductor from the Electrical Tension Produced by the Thermal Agitation of the Electrons in the Conductor), *Compt. rend.,* **238**, no. 12, pp. 1293–1296 (March, 1954).

58. W. Schottky, "Über spontane Stromschwankungen in verschiedenen Elektrizitätleitern" (On Spontaneous Current Fluctuations in Various Electric Conductors), *Annalen der Physik,* **57**, Series IV, pp. 541–567 (1918).

59. T. M. Dauphinee, "Method of Reducing Zero Error and Drift in Breaker Type dc Amplifiers," *Rev. Sci. Instr.,* **26**, no. 4, pp. 401–402 (April, 1955).

60. I. Cederbaum and P. Balaban, "Automatic Drift Compensation in dc Amplifiers," *Rev. Sci. Instr.,* **26**, no. 8, pp. 745–747 (August, 1955).

61. T. M. Dauphinee and S. B. Woods, "Low-Level Thermocouple Amplifier and a Temperature Regulation System," *Rev. Sci. Instr.,* **26**, no. 7, pp. 693–695 (July, 1955).

62. F. Lieneweg, "Der Erwärmungsfehler von Widerstandsthermometern" (The Heating Error of Resistance Thermometers), *ATM Archiv für technisches Messen,* **165**, J023-4, T87-88 (October, 1949).

63. G. K. Burgess and H. LeChatelier, *The Measurement of High Temperatures,* 3rd ed., 510 pp., John Wiley & Sons, New York, 1912.

64. F. Lieneweg, "Die Bestimmung von Temperaturmessfehlen mittels Thermometer-Kennzahlen" (The Determination of Errors in Temperature Measurement in Terms of Thermometer Parameters), *Allgemeine Wärmetechnik,* **2**, no. 11–12, pp. 238–249 (1951).

65. F. Lieneweg, "Temperaturmessfehler durch Aufbau und Einbau von Thermometern" (Errors in Temperature Measurement due to the Construction and Location of Thermometers), *ATM Archiv für technisches Messen*, **196**, V2165-2, pp. 107–110 (May, 1952).

66. F. Lieneweg, "Angleichung von Widerstandsthermometern an andere Eichkurven" (Comparison of Resistance Thermometers with Other Calibration Curves), *ATM Archiv für technisches Messen*, J222-2 T115-116 (December, 1949).

67. K. P. Dowell, "Thermistors as Components Open Product Design Horizons," *Elec. Mfg.*, **42**, no. 2, pp. 84–91 (August, 1948).

68. J. A. Becker, C. B. Green, and G. L. Pearson, "Properties and Uses of Thermistors—Thermally Sensitive Resistors," *Electrical Engineering*, **65**, no. 711, pp. 711–725 (November, 1946).

69. O. J. M. Smith, "Thermistors. Part I Static Characteristics," *Rev. Sci. Instr.*, **21**, no. 4, pp. 344–350 (April, 1950).

70. R. R. Batcher, "Thermistors in Electronic Circuits," *Electronic Industries*, **4**, nos. 1–6, pp. 76–80 (January, 1945).

71. H. M. Trueblood, "The Joule-Thomson Effect in Superheated Steam: I. Experimental Study of Heat-Leakage," *Proc. Am. Acad. Arts Sci.*, **52**, no. 12, pp. 754–767 (June, 1917).

72. T. B. Godfrey, "Further Data on Gold-Chromium Resistance Wire," *RP* 1206, *J. Research Natl. Bur. Standards*, **22**, no. 5, pp. 565–571 (May, 1939).

73. S. S. Stack, "Resistance-Thermometer Bridge," *Gen. Elec. Rev.*, **51**, no. 7, pp. 17–21 (July, 1948).

74. C. W. Waidner, H. C. Dickinson, E. F. Mueller, and D. R. Harper 3d, "A Wheatstone Bridge for Resistance Thermometry," *Bulletin of the Bureau of Standards*, **11**, no. 4, 241, pp. 571–590 (May, 1915).

75. "Ultrasonic Solder Pot," *Ultrasonic News*, p. 28 (December, 1957).

76. R. Holm, *Electric Contacts*, pp. 41–49, 77–114, 214–234, Hugo Gebers Forlag, Stockholm, 1946.

77. D. G. Flom, "Contact Resistance Measurements at Low Loads," *Rev. Sci. Instr.*, **29**, no. 11, pp. 979–981 (November, 1958).

78. L. Addicks, *Silver in Industry*, pp. 297–342, Reinhold Publishing Corp., New York, 1940.

79. F. L. Jones, *The Physics of Electrical Contacts*, 219 pp., Clarendon Press, Oxford, 1957.

80. R. L. Powell and A. A. Aboud, "Electrical Contact Resistance of Copper-Copper Junctions at Low Temperatures," *Rev. Sci. Instr.*, **29**, no. 3, pp. 248–249 (March, 1958).

81. "Instrument Contacts," *Mech. Eng.*, **73**, no. 10, pp. 828, 829 (October, 1951).

82. J. R. Roebuck, "Mercury Lubricated Resistance Box Plugs," *J. Opt. Soc. Am.*, **6**, no. 2, pp. 169–176 (March, 1922).

83. Y. V. Baimakoff, "Resistance of Contact between Metals, and between Metals and Carbon Materials," *The Engineers' Digest N. Y.*, **4**, no. 4, p. 164 (April, 1947).

84. J. T. Cataldo and W. R. Dravneek, "Apparatus and Procedure for Testing Pyrometer Switches," *Instruments*, **21**, no. 11, pp. 1014, 1015 (November, 1948).

85. L. A. Nettleton and F. E. Dole, "Potentiometers," *Rev. Sci. Instr.*, **17**, no. 10, pp. 359–361 (October, 1946).

86. P. G. Ecker, J. Blum, and C. W. Hiatt, "A Device for the Measurement of Rotor Temperature in the Air-Driven Ultracentrifuge," *Rev. Sci. Instr.,* **20,** no. 11, p. 801 (November, 1949).

87. J. L. Thomas, "Precision Resistors and Their Measurement," p. 13, *Natl. Bur. Standards Circ.,* **470,** Government Printing Office, Washington (1948).

88. C. W. Hiatt, "Rotor Temperature in the Ultracentrifuge," *Rev. Sci. Instr.,* **24,** no. 2, pp. 182–183 (February, 1953).

89. D. A. Bell, *Electrical Noise,* 320 pp., D. Van Nostrand Co., Princeton (1960).

90. C. A. Swenson and A. G. Emslie, "Low-Temperature Electronics," *Proceedings of the IRE,* **42,** no. 10, pp. 408–413 (February, 1954), The Institute of Radio Engineers, New York.

3

RADIATION DETECTORS

3·1 INTRODUCTION

In Volume I, the principles of thermoelectric thermometry were explained and applied. Chapters 1 and 2 of the present volume have been devoted to a discussion of electric-resistance thermometry, viewed as a generally applicable technique. The present chapter and Ch. 4 are intended to effect a similar treatment of radiation pyrometry. Chapter 3 will consist of a descriptive survey of the various materials and apparatus available for incorporation into an installation design of the radiation category, and Ch. 4 will consist of a systematic compilation of the calculation techniques required to predict performance for any selected arrangement of components. By carrying out the sort of calculations indicated, rational design becomes a routine procedure.

Measurement of the temperature of the surface of a body by means of the radiation emitted from it is an attractive method in many circumstances. Since it is not necessary for any part of the apparatus employed to be at the body's temperature or even in physical proximity to the body, surfaces at very high temperatures, moving bodies, corrosive liquids, and distant objects such as stars can be studied. Since radiation phenomena occur with great rapidity, highly transient temperatures can also be observed.

The present chapter is devoted to a description of the essential varieties of equipment available. The most important of them are the *radiation detectors*. Thus, most of what follows is intended to provide a survey of the essential types and designs of thermocouples, bolometers, photo-cells, etc., as introductory to the extensive literature in which these devices are discussed in full.

3·2 THE HUMAN EYE

The responsivity of the human eye to dim radiation is as remarkable as its ability to withstand intense radiation unharmed. When the eye is adapted by becoming "accustomed," as we would say, to receiving radiation of a given mean intensity, radiations of substantially lower or greater magnitudes appear as zero and infinite, i.e., as total darkness and brilliant luminosity, respectively. Thus, absolute intensity is not sensed directly and can be "judged," even to within an accuracy of a factor of two, only with the greatest difficulty and by the employment of extraneous reasoning processes. Near to the mean, however, relative intensities are differentiated in a continuous scale for a range of many decibels. As a *photo element*, the responsivity of the eye is appreciable only in a narrow wavelength range beginning at about 0.4 μ and ending at about 0.7 μ. The wavelength of maximum sensitivity for normal vision is around 0.55 μ; at this wavelength, the *responsivity* is tenfold that at either 0.45 μ or 0.65 μ. Individuals differ markedly in color vision, an appreciable percentage being classed as deficient.[1-9]

The minimum distinguishable intensity difference depends on many factors besides the individual observer, his state of mind, degree of fatigue, nutrition, and distraction by varied background intensities. Thus, the mean absolute intensity, the wavelength range, and the geometrical relations provided have gross effects. Minimum-distinguishable intensity differences, under conditions considered suitable, may be several per cent; however, 0.5 to 1 per cent is feasible.[1-7, 9, 10]

It had long been supposed that the minimum temperature at which a body emits visible radiation is about 800°C (1472°F). However, a human eye, if first accustomed to total darkness, becomes more sensitive. In *scotopic* vision, i.e., for an eye in darkness for the previous hour, the threshold has been found to lie below 400°C (752°F). The sensitive wavelength range does not include that for the usual red filter employed in optical pyrometers. However, it is only about twice as broad. It thus extends from about 5400 to 6100 Å (0.54 to 0.61 μ). In this range the minimum-distinguishable difference in brightness may be around 2 per cent.[9, 10]

3·3 OPTICAL PYROMETERS

The human eye is the radiation detector used in *optical pyrometers*. Here the capacity of the eye to distinguish relative brightnesses is exploited by arranging that the brightness of the *source-body surface* be presented for comparison in juxtaposition to that of a calibrated *reference* surface whose temperature is adjustable. This may be effected by projecting the images alongside one another, the one surrounding the other, or the image of the source-body surface area superimposed on the actual reference surface. Intensities and wavelength ranges may be regulated by calibrated filters and *choppers*. Portable package instruments, commercially available, are numerous and extensively illustrated in the various catalogs and textbooks. These instruments may include lenses, windows, and prisms to direct the radiation as required.[1-3, 5, 6, 8, 11-16]

When adequate care is taken in their design and construction, the precision of such instruments depends on the responsivity of the human eye. Under optimum conditions, the eye can distinguish between two fields to within 0.5 per cent of the intensity of either. However Euler [17-19] and Schneider [17] have shown that, by employing multiple fields of suitably spaced brightnesses superimposed on an incandescent-wire reference surface, this difference can be reduced to 0.1 per cent (w/in.^{2}). Thus, they find accuracies in settings to within 0.1°K (0.18°F) at 1500°K (2240°F) and 0.5°K (0.9°F) at 4000°K (6740°F). In the range 800 to 4000°C (1472 to 7232°F), a mean deviation of 1°C (1.8°F) has been observed.[1, 5, 6, 9-13, 16-25]

In scotopic vision for the dark-adapted eye, a blue filter can be used, or the natural limits of the human eye to the wavelength range from 5400 to 6100 Å (0.54 to 0.61 μ) may be a sufficient restriction. Pyrometer measurements can then be made at temperatures as low as 400 or 500°C (752 to 932°F). Settings to within 5 or 6°C (9 to 10.8°F) are possible.[9, 10]

3·4 ARTIFICIAL REFERENCE BLACKBODIES

For calibrating optical pyrometers and other radiation-sensitive instruments, it is necessary to have a source of blackbody radiation with precise means of controlling and measuring the temperature of this source. The interior surface of a heated cavity constitutes a convenient form, since the intensity of radiation from it is essentially independent of the actual material and its surface condition.

Various designs for artificial reference sources of blackbody radiation are shown in Fig. 3·1. Figure 3·1A is a precision arrangement intended for insertion into the cylindrical cavity of a furnace. It is essential that the furnace be so built as to maintain the most uniform possible temperature over its inner surface. The size of the blackbody unit and the desired operating temperature range will dictate the choice of furnace. Thus, in the blackbody unit, the proportions shown should be maintained, but the actual size can be varied and has been successfully adapted to cylindrical furnace cavities ranging from 0.67 to 1.57 in. diameter. The various parts should preferably be made of the same material, metallic or nonmetallic, chosen from among those suited to the operating temperatures and to the fabrication requirements. The inner surfaces should be diffusely reflecting, i.e., mat, and may be blackened. However, unblackened surfaces can also be used. Adequate means should be taken to insure a sufficiently close approxima-

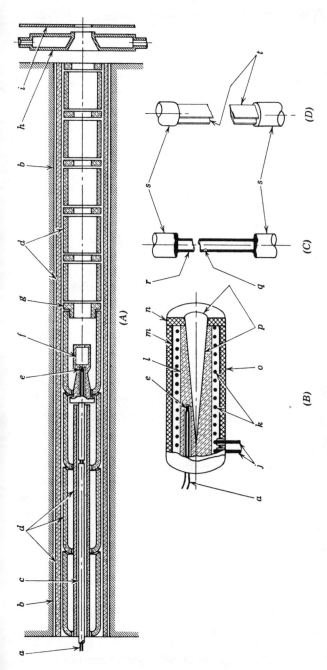

Fig. 3·1. Blackbody designs. (A) Precision furnace-enclosed design; (B) cone; (C) tubular filament; and (D) Mendenhall's open wedge. a, Thermocouple lead wires; b, cylindrical cavity in uniform-temperature furnace; c, two-hole thermocouple insulator tube; d, refractory tubular-section radiation shielding; e, thermocouple junction; f, inner blackbody enclosure; g, disk collimating screens; h, water-jacketed shield; i, shield; j, heater lead wires; k, heater filament; l, metal core; m, reflector; n, refractory end fittings; o, thermal insulation; p, dull smooth conical surface; q, sight hole; r, tubular filament; s, electrodes; and t, Mendenhall open-wedge strip filament. (After E. Brodhun and F. Hoffman, Zeitschrift für Physik, **37**, pp. 140–141, March, 1926; by permission C. E. Mendenhall, Astrophysical Journal, **33**, no. 2, 92, March, 1911; N. Marcus in Instruments, **28**, no. 3, 437, March, 1955.)

tion of the thermocouple-junction temperature to that of the inner blackbody enclosure. The water-jacketed shield serves to protect the elements of the associated optical system from excessive heat and extraneous radiation. Tingewaldt [1,32] and Kunz [32] have replaced the furnace by a bath of gold or silver. The dwell periods on melting and freezing then realize the fixed points for these metals.[1,2,5,8,26–34]

The tubular filament in Fig. 3·1C is a very simple construction wherein the walls of the enclosure are uniformly heated by the passage of an electric current. With a very small sight hole q, blackbody behavior is closely approximated. The tube need not be seamless but can be conveniently rolled from strip material, with an overlapping seam. Sets of readings extrapolated to the point of *disappearance* of the filament by melting serve to realize the fixed points corresponding to the melting temperatures of pure strip materials used for filaments. DeVos [35,36] has provided a detailed analysis of this device.[30,35,36]

A similar arrangement is available in the Mendenhall [37] open-wedge strip filament (see Fig. 3·1D). Here, because of the effect of inter-reflections for a sharp apex and imperfectly reflecting inner surface, the open cavity displays blackbody behavior. The inner surface should be *specular*, i.e., plane and smooth, and of an included angle not exceeding 10 degrees. Then, if the emissivity is not less than 0.3 (reflection coefficient not exceeding 0.7), i.e., approximately that of a smooth surface of platinum, the departure from ideal blackness does not exceed 0.2 per cent. For a mat inner surface, the wedge arrangement is much less effective. Thus for a resultant wedge emissivity of 0.995 (i.e., 0.5 per cent departure from ideal blackness), the diffuse-reflection coefficient of the inner surface must not exceed 0.05 (i.e., the emissivity must be at least 0.95).[2,5,29,37,38]

The open-wedge principle can also be realized in conical form as shown in Fig. 3·1B. Here, the cone is the inner surface of a massive metallic cylinder. As in the straight wedge (Fig. 3·1D), this surface should be specular and truly conical. Then, for an included conical angle of 15 degrees and a surface emissivity of 0.75 (reflection coefficient of 0.25), departure from blackness has been computed to be one per cent (i.e., the emissivity of the cone is 0.99). An oxidized-copper surface may have an emissivity of nearly 0.75. The temperature of a reference blackbody can be known only to within the range of its own uniformity. Making the cone in a massive block of highly conducting metal, such as copper, facilitates equalization of temperature over its surface and with that of the measuring thermocouple junction. The reflector, shown in Fig. 3·1B, surrounding the heater filament also tends to distribute the heat. The outer surface of this reflecting cylinder should be insulated as fully as feasible within the available space. Transite has been found structurally convenient for the end disks. Collimating-disk shields can be used to protect associated instruments. Copper cone material can be used up to 900°F. Gold could be used nearly to its melting point (1945.4°F) but would require a surface plating of lower reflection coefficient. Platinum could be used nearly to its melting point (over 3200°F) but would require a smaller included angle in the cone, i.e., not exceeding 10 degrees, and more thorough thermal insulation. A platinum heating element would then be used.[5, 29, 38–41]

The design of Fig. 3·1B is fortunately available as a package commercial product. Although not intended for the highest precision, it is convenient, for example, when it is desired to expose the radiation-sensitive element alternately to the source-body surface and to that of the reference blackbody. Such a unit can be built compactly into a portable device. It can be calibrated by comparison with a precision blackbody.[1, 2, 39, 41, 42]

3·5   THE RIBBON-FILAMENT LAMP

As a working standard for everyday measurements, the blackbody has several disadvantages. In its most precise forms, it is cumbersome and expensive. Temperature adjustments require time for equilibrating with altered heating currents, and it is difficult to keep the temperature constant during the interval required for an observation. Since a change of 0.1 per cent in the temperature may result in a change of several per cent in the radiant intensity, a high degree of constancy is required.

Thus, as a working standard, the ribbon-filament lamp (see Fig. 3·2) is widely used. It is not a blackbody. However, the direct electric heating permits almost instantaneous as well as accurate adjustments, and high constancy of the radiant intensity is possible. Also, higher temperatures than the maxima ordinarily feasible with blackbodies are conveniently attained.

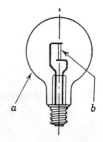

Fig. 3·2.   Ribbon-filament lamp. *a*, Argon-filled glass bulb; and, *b*, tungsten-ribbon filament.

For use as a standard of radiant intensity, calibration of the lamp's filament current against equivalent blackbody temperatures is necessary. Thus, it may be directly compared, such that, when the radiant intensities have been equalized, the currents are measured at a series of temperatures in the blackbody. At high filament temperatures, the intensity of the ribbon-filament lamp can be reduced by a known fraction with a sectored disk (see Eqs. 4·27 and 4·28), thus permitting continued direct comparisons.[10]

Curves are also available for the emissivity of the tungsten ribbon stock used in the filaments. The variation with wavelength is given at a series of temperatures ranging from 1600 to 2900°K (2420 to 4760°F). From such data, the spectral distribution of the radiation is known, and interpolation between calibration points becomes more precise. The relation between the actual temperature and the apparent temperature T_A, corresponding to the observed radiation, is given by Eq. 4·30 with Eqs. 4·2 and 4·4 or approximately by Wiens' law, Eq. 4·51.[1, 2, 6, 16, 25, 35, 43, 44]

3·6 LENS AND WINDOW MATERIALS

The essential design characteristics of materials suitable for lens elements, prisms, and windows in radiation pyrometers are indicated in Table 3·1 and Fig. 3·3, which give short-wave and long-wave cutoff

Table 3·1. Lens and window materials

Material	Chemical Composition	Approximate Reflection Loss per "Glass-Air" Surface r	Approximate Short-Wavelength Cutoff λ, μ
Optical glass	—	.05	.3 to .4
Pyrex 7740	—	.05	.3
Fused silica	SiO_2	.035	.2
Sapphire	Al_2O_3	.05	.2
Fluorite	CaF_2	.035	.15
Servofrax	As_2S_3	.15	.7
Rock salt	NaCl	.05	.2
Silver chloride stibnite coated	AgCl Sb_2S_3	.10	.6
Potassium bromide	KBr	.05	.2
Thallium bromide iodide, KRS-5	42 per cent TlBr 58 per cent TlI	.15	.6

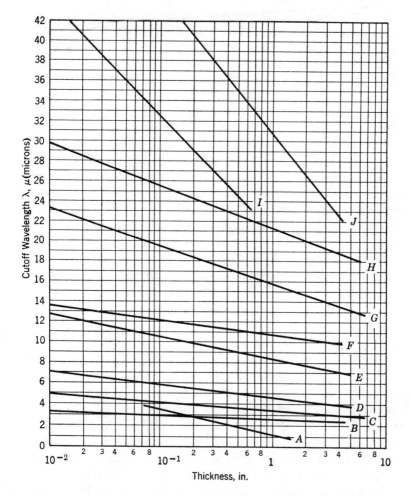

Fig. 3·3. Long-wavelength cutoffs for lens and window materials. Cutoff wave-lengths, i.e., wavelengths for half-maximum transmissions, μ (microns), are plotted vertically against thicknesses of single slabs, in. *A*, Borosilicate crown optical glass; *B*, clear chemical Pyrex-brand glass, Corning Glass Works (Corning, N. Y.), filter 7740; *C*, fused silica or fused quartz, i.e., silicon dioxide (SiO_2); *D*, sapphire, i.e., aluminum trioxide (Al_2O_3), clear, synthetic, crystalline; *E*, fluorite, i.e., calcium fluoride (CaF_2), synthetic, crystalline; *F*, arsenic trisulfide (As_2S_3), available as Servofrax glass from Servo Corporation of America (New Hyde Park, N. Y.); *G*, rock salt, i.e., sodium chloride (NaCl); *H*, silver chloride (AgCl), stibnite-coated, sawn from single, synthetic crystals; *I*, potassium bromide (KBr) clear synthetic crystals; and *J*, KRS-5, i.e., clear, synthetic, crystalline thallium bromide iodide (42 per cent thallium bromide with 58 per cent thallium iodide). These curves represent approximate average values; individual specimens vary.

values. However, other chemical and physical properties may dictate the choice of material under given operating conditions.[5-7]

The various *optical glasses* are used only in the wavelength ranges over which they are transparent. They may not be suitable, however, under certain other conditions, such as those involving exposure to elevated temperatures, chemical reagents, or abrasive materials. *Chemical glasses,* such as Pyrex 7740, available from Corning Glass Works (Corning, N. Y.), are often used when the lens element or window is subjected to chemical reagents, thermal shock, relatively high service temperatures, mechanical stressing, or abrasive action. *Fused silica,* i.e., *fused quartz,* besides transmitting to about 1 μ further into the infrared than glass, can be used at even higher temperatures. In tensile strength 7000 lb/in.^{2}, and hardness (4.9 on Mohs's scale) it resembles other glasses. It is, however, almost immune to thermal shock.[5-7, 45-50]

Sapphire combines the advantages of extending the infrared range nearly 2 μ beyond the limit for fused silica with extraordinary mechanical properties. It is exceedingly hard or abrasion resistant (9 on Mohs's scale) and inert to most reagents at temperatures up to 1800°F. In strength, it is comparable to steel with a high creep limit at 2500°F, but it is brittle, susceptible to thermal stresses and impact. It can, however, be soldered to metals; and, by employing graded seals, it can be joined to glass systems. Furthermore, it can be precision-ground and highly polished by using diamond dust. Although it is a birefringent crystal, it can be used for elements in large-aperture high-resolution lenses.[5, 6, 47, 51-54]

Irtran, available from Eastman Kodak Company (Rochester, N. Y.), transmits around 2 μ further into the infrared than sapphire and is nearly immune to thermal shock. It stays clear up to 800°C (1472°F) and does not melt until 1396°C (2545°F). It is harder than fused quartz (i.e., about 6 on Mohs's scale) and, with a refractive index of about 1.35, effects relatively low surface-reflection losses.

Fluorite transmits to about 2 μ further into the infrared than Irtran, but it is relatively weak, soft (4 on Mohs's scale), brittle, susceptible to thermal shock, and difficult to precision-polish. It, however, withstands moderate temperatures, is not attacked by moisture, and is successfully used for elements in precision optical systems.[5, 7, 48, 51, 55-57]

Arsenic trisulfide, available as Servofrax from Servo Corporation of America (New Hyde Park, N. Y.), transmits about 1.5 μ further into the infrared than fluorite. It resists moisture and many chemical reagents and can be polished for use as elements in precision optical systems. It is however less hard than fluorite, has a large coefficient of thermal expansion, and softens at 383°F.[5, 58]

Rock salt transmits about 6 μ further into the infrared than arsenic trisulfide but has poor mechanical properties. It is soft (2 on Mohs's scale), weak, and brittle, dirties easily, is difficult to precision-polish, is highly susceptible to thermal shock, and must not be exposed to water vapor. It can however be protected from moisture by coating with a nearly transparent, evaporated film of selenium.[5, 7, 48, 51, 55, 59]

Silver chloride, sawn from single crystals, transmits to about 6 μ further into the infrared than rock salt; however, as one of the materials used for photographic emulsions, it is *photochemically* sensitive and becomes opaque with metallic silver deposit if exposed to radiation of wavelengths less than 0.45 μ. It is therefore coated either with antimony trisulfide (Sb_2S_3) by evaporation of *stibnite* crystals or with silver sulfide (Ag_2S). A stibnite coating about 0.5 μ in thickness is entirely opaque below 0.47 μ and furnishes adequate protection, whereas it only slightly affects the transmission beyond about 1 μ. This coating is applied on the side exposed to the source of radiation and can also be controlled in thickness so as to minimize reflection at a given wavelength. Reflection losses which are high, i.e., around 20 per cent, can be further reduced by antireflection-coating the reverse side with hydrogenated polystyrene. The losses can be reduced for a range of only a few microns about some chosen wavelength, whereas absorption occurs at 3.4 to 3.5 μ and at 6.9 to 7.0 μ because of the second coating. Silver sulfide coatings are opaque below 1 μ.[48]

Silver may be plated out from silver chloride through simple contact with many metals and alloys. Such contact, resulting in opacity, must be avoided.

Since silver chloride is extremely soft (1 on Mohs's scale), careful handling is required. It is a ductile material, and rolled multiple-crystal sheet is available but of lower transmission. It can be sealed to most metals and glasses. Silver chloride is insoluble in water, alcohol, benzol, and acid. It can be used for lens elements, but precision-polishing of it is difficult.[5, 55, 60-63]

Potassium bromide transmits about 5 μ further into the infrared than silver chloride. However, its mechanical properties are similar to those of rock salt. It is soft, easily fractured, difficult to precision-polish, and attacked by water vapor.[5, 7, 48, 55, 64-66]

Thallium bromide iodide, i.e., "KRS-5," optical crystals, consisting of 42 per cent thallium bromide (TlBr) and 58 per cent thallium iodide (TlI), transmit about 10 μ further into the infrared than potassium bromide, i.e., are transparent to beyond 42 μ. If the composition is not constant throughout the crystal, regional variation in refractive index occurs. Although soft, it can be ground and polished for use as lens elements. It is highly resistant to water.[5, 48, 55, 60, 67, 68]

Barium fluoride (BaF_2) is not attacked by moisture and is otherwise similar in properties to fluorite (CaF_2) but transmits about 3 μ further into the infrared. Cesium bromide transmits to 38 μ, has lower reflection losses than KRS-5, but is soluble in water. Various two- and three-component silica-base glasses have transmissions about 2 μ further into the infrared than optical glass.[5, 65, 67, 69]

Use of closed systems, evacuated, or limited to transparent gases such as nitrogen, may be necessary to avoid excessive atmospheric absorption in the 2.4-μ and 4.8-μ water-vapor and carbon dioxide bands.[5, 7, 47, 49, 56, 70, 71]

3·7 MIRRORS AND BLACKENED SURFACES

Reflection optics require surfaces with high and constant reflection coefficients in the wavelength range used. In the infrared, materials of high electrical conductivity, such as copper, silver, and gold, are the best reflectors. Gold is particularly useful as also being slow to tarnish. Silver and copper can be protected by infrared-transparent films, providing the films are of sufficient thickness not to function as antireflection coatings. Durable coating materials are available for limited wavelength ranges.[5, 6, 7, 47, 48, 72-75]

High absorption coefficients with minimum attendant loss of radiant input are effected by depositing carbon or finely divided metallic powders on receiver surfaces. Carbon is usually applied as a paint, whereas metallic blacks are deposited by evaporation in partial vacuum.[5, 6, 7, 47, 48, 76-78]

Films and dust deposits accumulating on lens and window surfaces usually tend to reduce transmission. Such transmission loss may be subject to spectral selectivity. Yellowish surface texture, arising with age on optical glass, may increase transmission by reduction of reflection losses. Films of transparent materials of lower refractive indices can be deposited in layers of thickness calculated to eliminate reflection losses at one selected wavelength. For neighboring wavelength ranges, reflection losses are then greatly reduced. Such films may also, at times, serve as protective coatings.[5-7, 47, 48, 50, 71-75, 77]

3·8 THERMOELECTRIC DETECTORS

The first of the radiation-sensitive elements to be described consists essentially of a thermocouple or thermopile. In these devices, both "hot" and "cold" junctions are mounted quite close to one another within some sort of *cell*. It is arranged that only the "hot" junctions are exposed to the incident radiation. They are then warmed by the radiant energy while the "cold" junctions remain at a relatively constant temperature. Usually, this lower temperature is near to that of massive portions of the mounting or case (see Figs. 3·4, 3·5 and 3·6). The heat absorbed from the incident beam is partly transferred directly from the receiver to its surroundings. The remaining portion is conducted along the internal leads to the "cold" junctions. The temperature excess of the "hot" over the "cold" junctions is the product of this thermal current and the thermal resistance of the leads. This temperature difference gives rise to the thermoelectric signal emf. Design variables controlling the responsivity of a given arrangement are, however, numerous and their interrelations too involved for any explanation thereof to be as simple and straightforward as one might desire. In the following paragraphs an attempt is made, at best, to enumerate the various factors and their effects. For full discussions, the reader is advised to consult the references.[6, 7, 79-95]

The thermoelectric emf is proportional: (1) to the temperature difference between the "hot" and the "cold" junctions, (2) to the number of junction pairs in series, and (3) to the thermoelectric power of the combination used. If the circuit is placed in series with a galvanometer, the deflection will be proportional to the electric current in the circuit. This current depends on the ratio of the thermoelectric emf to the circuit resistance.

If the leads between the "hot" and "cold" junctions are of large thermal resistance, the temperature difference and corresponding thermoelectric emf will be proportionately greater. However, the electrical resistance of the leads will tend to increase in the same ratio; therefore, the electric current and galvanometer deflection will not increase in the same proportion as the emf. Similarly, if the number of junction pairs is increased, the thermoelectric emf and the electrical resistance of the lead wires will generally increase in about the same proportion. On the other hand, the thermal resistance between the receivers and the "cold" junctions and thereby the temperature difference will decrease, thus tending to lower the emf.[6, 7, 48, 79-88, 90, 93-98]

The effects of changes in circuit resistance depend on the galvanometer's resistance, which in turn is related to its sensitivity. Similarly, the change in electrical resistance associated with a given change in receiver-to-base thermal resistance depends on the *Wiedemann-Franz* ratio, of electrical to thermal resistivities for the thermocouple materials. When the receiver area is limited, increasing the number of

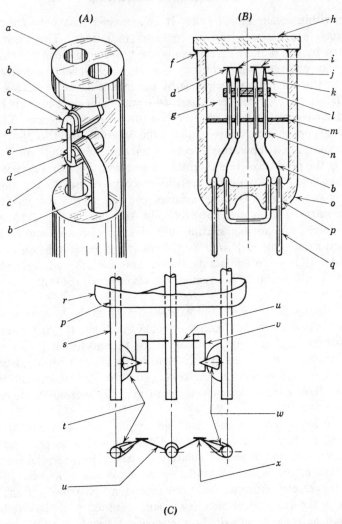

Fig. 3·4. Pin thermoelectric radiation-sensitive elements. (A) Liston single-receiver element; (B) Schwarz compensated element; and (C) Cartwright compensated element. a, Body; b, metallic lead wires; c, 1-mm diameter by 2-mm long semiconducting-alloy pins; d, spot-welded junctions; e, 2-mm by 0.2-mm gold-foil receiver blackened on front side; f, cemented seal; g, evacuated or air-filled space; h, infrared-transparent window; i, 0.4- to 2-mm² area by 0.3-μ thick gold-foil receivers blackened on front side; j, thermoelectric-alloy conical or wedge-tapered pin tips; k, fusion welds; l, silver-mica clamping block; m, mica centering disk; n, silver positive and gold negative pins; o, glass envelope; p, metal-to-glass seals; q, mounting electrodes; r, soft-glass mountings; s, Dumet wires; t, Wood's-metal soldered joint; u, 5-μ diameter by 1-mm long bismuth wires; v, 1-mm² area by 0.1-μ thick gold-foil receivers blackened on front side with evaporated

junctions may require the use of thinner higher-resistance leads.[6,7,79-88, 90,93-96,99,100]

If the thermal resistance of the leads is increased, the time to attain steady state is increased. Evacuation of the space around the receivers and leads may increase the sensitivity twentyfold but also increases the time to attain steady state.[7,47,79-90,93-95,100]

The *thermal-noise* emf, i.e., *Johnson effect*, is proportional to the square root of the circuit resistance but can be decreased by refrigeration. The *thermodynamic limit*, i.e., *temperature-noise emf*, is less for small receiver areas. A full discussion of noise limits is, however, deferred to Sec. 4·7. Drift due to variable radiation exchange with changing ambient temperatures is reduced by smaller receiver areas and by refrigeration.[7,79-82,84,86,88,90,93-96]

For electronic indication, the input impedance of the amplifier is usually large compared to the electric resistance of the thermoelectric circuit. The importance of this circuit resistance is then in its thermal-noise emf. Since the noise in the amplifier can always be made smaller than that in the thermocouple, the ratio of the thermoelectric emf to the square root of the circuit resistance usually determines the least-count or smallest distinguishable radiant input.[6,79,80,82-84,88,90,93-96,101]

Response times of sensitive galvanometers are of the order of several seconds. Hence for galvanometer indication, it is not necessary that the thermocouple response be very fast. Similarly, the most sensitive d-c amplifiers are not of rapid response. With a rapid-response indicator, however, the required response time of the element is determined by the change rate of the temperature being measured. Sensitivity in both the element and the indicator is sacrificed to such extent as is necessary to follow the temperature changes. Elements have thus been built which are usable at frequencies of 5000 cycles/sec, and 300,000 cycles/sec has been predicted as feasible (see Fig. 6·8).[6,7, 81-90,93-98,101-113]

Drift effects, including those in the amplifier, may be reduced or eliminated by *modulation*, i.e., by "*chopping*" with a sectored disk of the incident radiant beam. Modulation provides a pulsating emf which can then be applied to an a-c amplifier. For satisfactory a-c amplification, modulation rates of at least several cycles per second are

---

bismuth; *w*, 1-mm long conical pins of tellurium in its β-allotropic modification; and *x*, flash-welded bismuth tellurium junctions with Picien-wax joints to receivers. (*By permission D. A. H. Brown, R. P. Chasmar, and P. B. Fellgett in J. Sci. Instr.*, **30**, *no. 6, 195, June, 1953; C. H. Cartwright in Rev. Sci. Instr.*, **3**, *no. 2, 74, February, 1952; and M. D. Liston and J. N. White in J. Opt. Soc. Am.*, **40**, *no. 1, 37, January, 1950.*)

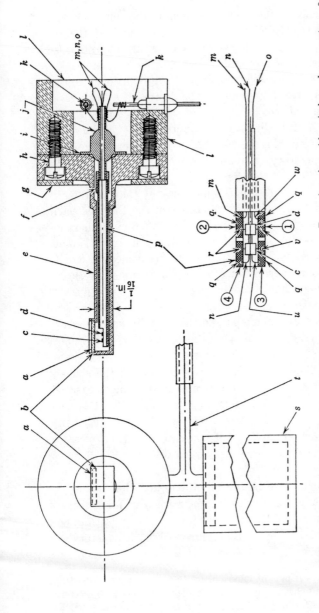

Fig. 3·5. Farrand-Hornig wire-type thermoelectric radiation-sensitive element. a, Potassium bromide window; b, cement; c, 0.1-μ thick 0.75-mm square Aquadag-blackened gold-foil receiver for "active" couple; d, 0.1-μ thick 0.75-mm square Aquadag-blackened gold-foil receiver for compensating couple; e, brass mount; f, coupling cemented to thermocouple tube and hard-soldered to seal; g, washer clamp; h, screws; i, Wood's-metal solder; j, seal; k, three terminal posts; m, No. 34 B & S gage (0.0063 in.) enameled-copper lead wire Wood's-metal-soldered to silver block 2; n, No. 34 B & S gage (0.0063 in.) enameled-copper lead wire Wood's-metal-soldered to silver block 4; o, No. 34 B & S gage (0.0063 in.) enameled-copper lead wire joined to wires from blocks 1 and 3; p, glass thermocouple mount; q, silver junction blocks fired into glass; r, 0.001-in. diameter, bismuth with 5 per cent tin, thermocouple wires welded to gold side of receivers and Wood's-metal-soldered to blocks 2 and 4, 0.3-mm free length; s, charcoal trap; t, exhaust tube for evacuating; u, No. 34 B & S gage (0.0063 in.) enameled-copper lead wire Wood's-metal-soldered to silver block 3; v, 0.0008-in. diameter, bismuth with 3 per cent antimony, thermocouple wires welded to gold side of receivers and Wood's-metal-soldered to blocks 1 and 3, 0.3-mm free length; and w, No. 34 B & S gage (0.0063 in.) enameled-copper lead wire Wood's-metal-soldered to silver block 1.

necessary. Elements of high sensitivity and low thermal noise have been built to this requirement.[6, 7, 80, 82, 84–90, 93–96, 98, 101–103, 111, 112]

In d-c work with galvanometer indication, thermo-relay amplifiers may be used to increase indicator sensitivities to the useful limit imposed by thermal noise.[6, 7, 81, 83, 87, 88, 93, 96, 97, 104–106, 111, 114–120]

It is generally true for both galvanometer and electronic indication, providing the indicator is that best adapted to the given element, that the most precise combination occurs with single-junction thermoelectric receivers. However except for the highest precision, multiple-junction circuits (see Fig. 3·6A and C) have advantages. Thus, the larger emfs permit more rugged indicators and tend to make parasitic emfs less troublesome.[7, 79–85, 88, 90, 93–96, 98, 101, 111, 112, 121–124]

Exhaustive studies have been made to determine the optimum combinations of values for the many variables as related to specific objectives. A large number of designs have resulted, each with its own merits. The principal forms of thermoelectric elements have been classified as: (1) *wire*, (2) *ribbon*, (3) *film*, and (4) *pin*.[47, 79–85, 87, 88, 90, 93–96, 99, 100, 105, 111, 125–128]

In the wire element (see Fig. 3·5) the thermocouple materials are in the form of fine wires with thin blackened sheet-metal receivers at the junctions.[7, 79–84, 86, 90, 91, 93–95, 99, 100, 122, 124, 129–135]

In the ribbon element (see Fig. 3·6A and B) the thermocouple materials are in the form of thin butt-joined ribbons whose greater widths serve for radiation-receiving surfaces.[93, 101, 118, 121, 122, 135, 136]

In the film element (see Fig. 3·7B) the thermocouple materials are evaporated in slightly overlapping films onto thin nonmetallic ribbons. The thus-coated films also serve as receiver areas.[85–89, 91, 93, 98, 101, 103, 110–112, 134, 135]

The pin element (see Fig. 3·4A, B and C) is similar to the wire element but with the wires replaced by conical pieces of thermoelectric materials. These materials may be semiconductors.[93, 134, 135, 137–140]

In the ribbon and film element, the receiving surfaces have usually been made somewhat larger than in the wire and pin element. This tends to make them less suitable for application to measurement of temperature "at a point." Some multiple-junction elements permit loss of radiation through the gaps or less-sensitive areas between the various receivers (see Fig. 3·6A and C). Calibration will be affected by the exact location and pattern in which the image of the source body surface is focused on such an element.[47, 85, 93, 98, 101, 111, 121–123, 126, 127, 141]

Pin elements (see Fig. 3·4) exploit the high thermoelectric powers of certain brittle semiconducting materials. The high electrical and thermal resistivities of such substances permit the thick stubby forms

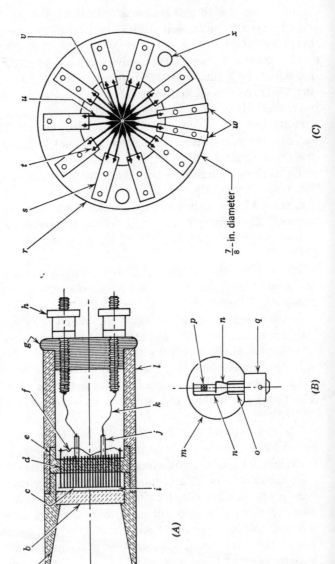

Fig. 3·6. Industrial thermoelectric radiation-sensitive elements. (A) Moll ribbon 90-junction pile; (B) Stack ribbon bayonet-mounting glass-bulb-enclosed element; and (C) Harrison and Wannamaker radial wire 10-junction pile. a, Polished-surface gilded collecting cone; b, rock salt or fluorite window; c, ninety, camphor-black-painted, 0.025-mm thick by 0.5-mm wide ribbon, manganin (84 per cent copper with 12 per cent manganese and 4 per cent nickel) against eureka (60 per cent copper with 40 per cent nickel) silver-soldered junctions in series, soft-soldered to ends of mounting pins; d, ninety-three, No. 22 S.W. gage (0.028 in.) 9.5-mm long enameled-copper-wire mounting pins, Bakelite-varnish-cemented, push-fit holes in brass disk; e, 3-mm thick by 25-mm diameter brass disk; f, four copper interconnecting wires soldered to ends of six longer mounting pins; g, fiber terminal block; h, two brass binding posts; i, air space; j, two, copper terminal pins; k, copper lead wires soldered to terminals; l, brass case; m, evacuated glass bulb; n, two massive, metal, anchor supports; o, glass seal; p, 0.001-mm thick 2-mm wide ribbon welded junction with 2-mm square blackened receiver area; q, single-contact bayonet-mounting automobile-lamp base; r, 0.87-in. outside diameter annular mica mounting disk; s, eleven thin flat metal terminal strips staked to mica mounting disk; t, spot welds; u, thermocouple wires; v, ten flattened V-shaped junctions; w, two terminals; and x, two locating holes. (By permission A. Gridley in Instrument Practice, 3, no. 1, 9, November, 1948; S. S. Stack in Gen. Elec. Rev., 42, no. 8, 365, August, 1939; and T. R. Harrison and W. H. Wannamaker in American Institute of Physics, Temperature, 1219, Reinhold Publishing Corp., New York, 1941.)

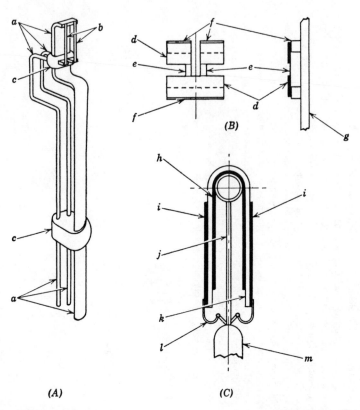

Fig. 3·7.   Film and ribbon bolometers.   (A) Baker-Robb ribbon bolometer; (B) Mönch-Wichert-Böttger film bolometer; (C) Moon-Steinhardt dielectric bolometer. a, Kovar supporting elctrodes; b, two 1-μ thick, 0.3-mm wide, by 5-mm long blackened platinum-foil ribbons soldered to supporting electrodes; c, electric-insulation mounting; d, bismuth electrodes evaporated onto 0.04- to 0.3-mm thick celluloid membrane and brass strips; e, bismuth-film bolometer arms evaporated onto celluloid supporting membrane; f, brass strips cemented to glass mounting plate; g, glass mounting plate; h, common, Aquadag (graphite) condenser plate; i, 32-mm by 12.5-mm receiving area, Aquadag condenser plates in the bridge arms; j, bright-nickel frame shielding balancing condenser arm; k, 22-μ thick Cellophane or 25-μ thick Pliofilm condenser dielectric; l, tinfoil leads Aquadag-cemented to the condenser plates; and m, glass support sealed to nickel frame and evacuated, glass containing bulb.   (By permission, E. B. Baker and C. D. Robb in Rev. Sci. Instr., 14, no. 12, 356, December, 1943; and P. Moon and L. R. Steinhardt in J. Opt. Soc. Am., 28, no. 5, 156, May, 1938.)

required for fabrication, and, with point or line contacts, the cross-sectional areas at the junctions can be made arbitrarily small. Cartwright's [81-83,99,100,140] design (Fig. 3·4C) is intended for galvanometer indication where rapid response is unimportant. With β-tellurium against bismuth, thermoelectric powers of 600 $\mu v/°C$ are available. These powers permit responsivities of up to 45 v/w with resistances of 50 to 60 ohms. A vacuum of 10^{-4} mm of mercury is necessary for full sensitivity; whereas, for air-filled cells, the responsivities are fifteen to thirty times smaller. For junctions of bismuth with 3 per cent antimony against bismuth with 10 per cent tin, responsivities were three times smaller.

Compensation for zero error and drift due to stray and ambient radiation is effected by using two identical junctions connected in opposition. This spurious radiation affects both junctions alike, whereas the signal beam is incident on the receiver alone. Parasitic thermoelectric and voltaic effects, variations in thermoelectric power, changes in compensating-junction and case temperatures, and loss of vacuum will, however, cause drifts which are not compensated by the use of two junctions. These drifts must be taken into account by frequent zero readings and occasional recalibrations.

Figure 3·4A and B are modifications of Cartwright's [81-83,99,100,140] design. These modifications provide sufficiently quick response for sectored-disk modulation of the incident beam at 5 to 15 cycles/sec. The resultant pulsating output emf permits a-c electronic amplification tuned to this frequency. The amplified output depends essentially on the energy in the beam cut by the sectored disk, whereas d-c drift effects and noise in frequencies outside the passband of the amplifier are eliminated. Drifts in the responsivity of the element lumped with those in the gain of the amplifier necessitate occasional recalibrations.[7,140]

Liston's [137] design (Fig. 3·4A) omits the compensating junction. Drift correction is provided by modulation alone. In individual cases, 70 to 90 per cent of full response remains at modulation frequencies up to 5 to 15 cycles/sec. Resistances are 10 to 20 ohms with full responsivities of 5 to 10 v/w. Elements of this type are available from Perkin-Elmer Corporation (Norwalk, Conn.)

The Schwarz [141] design (Fig. 3·4B) has been made to yield over 60 v/w; however, individual units vary. The positive material is 27 per cent copper, 32 per cent silver, 33 per cent tellurium, 7 per cent selenium, and 1 per cent sulfur. For the negative material, silver selenide and silver sulfide are melted together. Depending on final proportions in the negative material, thermoelectric powers of up to

1000 μv/°C are possible. Resistances vary from 30 to 150 ohms; response-time constants are as low as 0.005 sec. Elements of this type are available from Hilger and Watts, Ltd. (London, England).[135, 138,139,141]

A highly developed form of the wire element is shown in Fig. 3·5, as evolved in the studies of Firestone,[94] Cartwright,[81–83, 99, 100, 140] Hornig and O'Keefe,[79] Strong,[80] and others. A similar device is available from Farrand Optical Co., Inc. (New York, N. Y.). The stability is such as to permit galvanometer indication; however, gradual loss of vacuum requires occasional recalibration and periodic re-evacuation. The response time, of around 0.036 sec for 88 per cent of full response at 5-cycles/sec interrupted radiation, is suited to electronic indication, and the drift may be reduced by thus using modulation and a-c amplification. For bismuth with 3 per cent antimony against bismuth with 5 per cent tin, thermoelectric powers of 105 μv/°C are available. These thermoelectric powers permit responsivities of 6.5 v/w at steady state, with resistances of 5 to 10 ohms. A vacuum of 10^{-4} mm of mercury is required for full sensitivity, whereas the sensitivity may drop twentyfold with air leakage into the cell. The potassium bromide window requires protection from moisture. Moisture-etched windows can, however, be repolished with a nearly dry paste of tin oxide and water-free acetone on a cotton swab. The nearly identical junctions are adjusted to effective equality by careful choice of a resistance shunted across the leads from the more sensitive junction, i.e., between leads m and o in Fig. 3·5 if the working couple is the more sensitive or between n and o if the compensating couple is the more sensitive.[7, 79–84, 86, 90, 94, 95, 99, 100, 129, 138, 140]

The Moll [121] element (see Fig. 3·6A) is intended to combine ruggedness and stability with high responsivity and a short time constant. A 90-junction pile of this design with a resistance of 11.32 ohms and a response time of 1 to 2 sec showed a responsivity of 0.225 v/w. A more sensitive design has also been produced having 176 junctions. With thinner ribbons of materials of higher thermoelectric power, higher responsivities could be achieved. Other more rugged infrared-transparent window materials could be used.[121, 122]

The Stack [136] element (see Fig. 3·6B) is a design of great convenience since it mounts in an ordinary automobile lamp socket. These elements are commercially available from General Electric Co. (Schenectady, N. Y.). An element of this type with a resistance of 5 ohms and a response time of around 1 sec showed a responsivity of 1.25 v/w.

The Harrison-Wannamaker [123] element (see Fig. 3·6C), similar to that used in a radiation-pyrometer device available from Brown Instrument Co. (Philadelphia, Pa.), is intended to combine the ruggedness and dependability required in normal industrial service with maximum responsivity.

3·9 BOLOMETER DETECTORS

A *bolometer* is essentially a resistance thermometer arranged for response to radiation. The component resistances are so disposed that only one bridge-arm resistor is exposed to the incident radiation. This resistance, i.e., the element r_e in Eq. 2·1 and Fig. 2·1, is then warmed by the incident radiant-energy beam while the balancing resistor r_b is maintained at a nearly constant temperature. Usually, this temperature is that of massive portions of the mounting or case (see Figs. 3·7 and 3·8). The heat absorbed from the incident beam is partly lost directly from the receiver to its surroundings. The remaining portion is conducted through the resulting temperature difference along the leads to the mounting. Since the noise-limited output is found usually

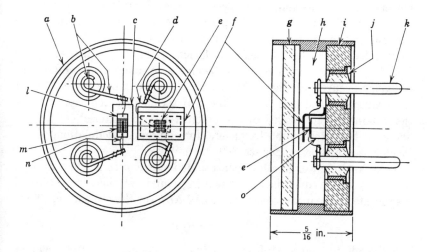

Fig. 3·8. Thermistor bolometer. *a*, Metal case; *b*, electrodes; *c*, backing of glass, quartz, or sapphire for active element; *d*, lead wires to shielded compensating element; *e*, blackened 0.01-mm thick semiconducting flake of compensating element; *f*, shield; *g*, infrared-transparent window of coated silver chloride, arsenic trisulfide, thallium bromide iodide, sodium chloride, potassium bromide, or fluorothene; *h*, evacuated space; *i*, metal plate; *j*, electric-insulation seals; *k*, mounting terminal pins to fit standard miniature socket; *l*, evaporated-gold flake electrodes; *m*, blackened 0.01-mm thick semiconducting flake of "active" element; *n*, lead wires soldered to gold electrodes on "active" element; and *o*, backing for compensating element. (*By permission Barnes Engineering Co., 30 Commerce Road, Stamford, Conn.*)

to be almost independent of the electrical resistance of the element r_e, the leads can without ill effects be made of large electrical resistance and thereby of thermal resistance ample to suppress the lead-conduction loss. The resulting high resistances are convenient for input-stage design in electronic indicators. Although an a-c power supply can be used to permit a-c amplification, the alternative of modulating the incident beam has the advantage of also eliminating many drift effects. For modulation, rapidity of response is essential. The desired short time constant is promoted by low thermal capacity in the element, per unit of receiving area. Since the consequent high electrical resistances are otherwise suitable, very thin strips or films of resistance material are used.[6, 81, 83, 134, 142-145]

Billings, Hyde, and Barr [144] have shown that the responsivity S_t of a bolometer element thus designed is approximately given by

$$S_t = \alpha (\Delta t/UA)^{\frac{1}{2}} [U^2 r_e/(4\pi^2 c^2 d^2 f_m^2 + U^2)]^{\frac{1}{2}} \qquad (3\cdot1)$$

where S_t is the increment in output emf per unit of incident radiant power, v/w; α is the temperature coefficient of resistance of the bolometer element r_e, per °C; Δt is the permissible rise in temperature of the element due to the heating effect of the exciting current, °F; U is the surface-boundary, heat-transfer coefficient referred to area A, w/in.^{2} °F; A is the surface area of the bolometer element over which heat exchange occurs with the ambient, in.^{2}; r_e is the electric resistance of the element, ohms; d is the thickness of the bolometer strip, in.; c is the volume heat capacity of the bolometer-strip material, j/in.^{3} °F; and f_m is the interruption frequency, for sinusoidal modulation, of the incident radiant beam, per sec.[81, 83, 134, 148-149]

The least-count or smallest measurable increment in incident radiant power $\Delta \Phi$, w, occurs when the resulting emf is of the same order of magnitude as the mean-square noise emf ΔE_{tn} for the element, v. Thus

$$\Delta \Phi = \Delta E_{tn}/S_t \qquad (4\cdot19)$$

Although the noise emf in a bolometer element usually includes *current* noise and may, in some designs, be augmented by *microphonic* noise, it cannot be less than the *thermal* or Johnson noise E_{tn}, v. Since the latter is usually greater than the *thermodynamic* or *temperature* noise given by Eq. 4·21, it becomes the condition limiting the minimum-distinguishable radiant-power increment $\Delta \Phi$, w. This noise emf is given by

$$\Delta E_{tn} = 5.54 \times 10^{-12} (rT \Delta f)^{\frac{1}{2}} \qquad (2\cdot11)$$

where r can usually be taken as the bolometer-element resistance r_e, ohms; T is its temperature, °R; and Δf is the passband of the electronic indicator, cycles/sec.[6, 81, 83, 134, 143-145, 150-152]

Substituting Eqs. 2·11 and 4·19 into Eq. 3·1, we have

$$\Delta\Phi = 5.54 \times 10^{-12}(T\,\Delta f)^{1/2}/\{\alpha(\Delta t/UA)^{1/2}[U^2/(4\pi^2c^2d^2f_m{}^2 + U^2)]^{1/2}\}$$
$$(3\cdot2)$$

This form assumes that the four arms of the Wheatstone bridge are alike and that the input resistance is small compared to that of the bolometer r_e.

For zero modulation frequency f_m, this reduces to

$$\Delta\Phi = 5.54 \times 10^{-12}(T\,\Delta f)^{1/2}/[\alpha(\Delta t/UA)^{1/2}] \qquad (3.3)$$

These expressions for $\Delta\Phi$ do not contain the bolometer-element resistance r_e, which can therefore be made as large as desired. When the term $4\pi^2d^2c^2f_m{}^2$ in the denominator of Eq. 3·1 exceeds U^2, the responsivity S_t decreases rapidly with further increase in the modulation frequency f_m. The reciprocal of that frequency which marks the point of decline determines the *time constant* of the bolometer.[81, 83, 134, 143–148, 150]

For all modulation frequencies (Eq. 3·2), $\Delta\Phi$ is minimized at the lowest absolute temperatures T of operation and for the most sharply tuned indicators. But, Δf is limited to the minimum frequency range which does not exclude essential portions of the bolometer-response spectrum. Also, $\Delta\Phi$ is smaller for larger numerical values of the temperature coefficient of resistance α and for larger values of the exciting voltage. The effect of this voltage must not, however, exceed the maximum safe temperature rise Δt in the element. Likewise, small values for the area A and the coefficient U tend to minimize $\Delta\Phi$.[81, 83, 134, 143–148, 150]

The time constant is determined by the modulation frequency f_m at which the term $4\pi^2c^2d^2f_m{}^2$ ceases to be small compared to U^2. This will occur at higher frequencies f_m when the heat capacity cd per unit of area A is smaller. Since the volume heat capacity c does not vary greatly for different materials, the principal effort must be directed toward attaining the minimum feasible thickness d. Czerny, Kofink, and Lippert [143] defined this thickness as that at which only half of the incident radiant energy is absorbed in the layer, the remainder being transmitted or reflected. To increase the total absorption, they arranged mirrors behind the strips to reflect the transmitted fraction back so as to pass through the strip a second time. They thus used values of d in the range 0.01 μ (4×10^{-7} in.) and thinner. An evaporated silver or bismuth film was supported on a 0.04 μ (1.6×10^{-6} in.) thick celluloid membrane, mounted on a 1 mm thick silver frame (see Fig. 3·7B).[81, 83, 134, 143, 144, 146–148, 153–157]

The frequency f_m at which the term $4\pi^2c^2d^2f_m{}^2$ ceases to be small compared to U^2 is also larger for larger values of the surface heat-transfer coefficient U. For maximum zero-frequency responsivity as would be required for galvanometer indication, U is made as small as possible by evacuating the space about the element. This advantage is commonly sacrificed, however, with a-c electronic indication, and U is made as large as possible to minimize the time constant. Thus, thin bolometer elements are built in intimate thermal contact with massive solid backing slabs. These slabs may be electrically insulated metals or nonmetallic materials such as glass. (Glass is of relatively high thermal conductivity.) The rigidity of such backing slabs reduces microphonic noise.[81, 83, 134, 135, 143, 144, 158–160]

At the temperature of transition to the *superconducting* state, the electrical resistance of a pure material drops discontinuously to zero. For available degrees of purity, this change occurs in a narrow range of temperature; as a result, large values of the temperature coefficient of resistance α occur. This principle is employed in the superconducting bolometer. In this type of element, a film of columbium nitride cemented to a massive copper base serves as the resistance r_e (Fig. 2·1). The transition temperature for columbium nitride is relatively high, i.e., $15°K$ ($27°R$), and is thus in the range accessible with liquid hydrogen. Devices provided with such cooling have been built sufficiently rugged for field use and for which one hydrogen filling suffices for many hours of continuous operation. Package hydrogen liquefiers of as little as 50 lb weight serve to replenish the cooling jacket.[48, 135, 161–167]

Operation at this low temperature, i.e., $15°K$, reduces thermal or Johnson noise, current noise, and temperature noise. Microphonic noise is reduced by the rigid backing. Other noise effects, however, occur in the transition zone to the superconducting state. Smaller values of the minimum-distinguishable radiant power $\Delta\Phi$ have, nevertheless, been successfully attained with the superconducting bolometer than with any other rapid-response thermal element. The *Havens*[168] *limit* is surpassed by tenfold, and the room-temperature thermodynamic limit attained.[135, 139, 151, 152, 162–166, 168–171]

In a form built by Andrews,[163, 166, 172, 173] Milton,[166, 171] and DeSorbo,[166] the bolometer resistance r_e consisted of a 0.2-ohm columbium nitride ribbon, 0.006 mm thick by 0.25 mm wide and 5 mm long, cemented to the end of a copper rod with a 0.001 mm thick layer of Bakelite. A 1-l capacity jacket containing liquid hydrogen thermostated the element to within $0.04°F$; this in turn was shielded by a similar jacket filled with liquid nitrogen. Values of 28 per $°F$ were attained for the temperature coefficient of resistance, i.e., values 10,000-fold higher than those for metals and 1000-fold higher than those for available semiconductor materials. Responsivities S_t of 1 to 2 v/w were achieved together with the desired very short time constants. The primary response time was thus about 5×10^{-4} sec, permitting modulation at up to 3000 cycles/sec. A $\Delta\Phi$ of 5×10^{-10} w was equivalent to the noise.[134,135,161–166,169,172]

For a superconducting element with a time constant of 10^{-2} sec, Fuson [164,165] found $\Delta\Phi$ to be 2×10^{-11} w. A tin element due to Hulbert and Jones [162] operating at 3.7°K (6.7°R) with a time constant of 20 sec had a $\Delta\Phi$ of 3×10^{-12} w permitting measurement of the thermal radiation from a body at 10°K (18°R). A solution of sodium in ammonia becomes superconducting at liquid-air temperatures, offering the possibility of higher-temperature, and hence more convenient, cryostating.[134,135,147,162,164–166,169,170,173]

The thermistor bolometer, or Sett element (see Fig. 3.8), is widely used industrially. Here, the relatively high temperature coefficients of resistance of semiconductor materials are exploited. The high electrical and thermal resistivities, also characteristic of nonmetals, permit the use of ribbons of sufficient thickness for opacity and with degrees of ruggedness not possible in similar metallic films. Thus, self-supporting ribbons have been used that also attain maximum zero-frequency responsivity. Solid backing, however, provides the low time constants required for modulation of the incident beam at frequencies high enough for convenient a-c amplification, while also providing ruggedness and reducing microphonic noise. Evacuation of the space surrounding the element reduces the "swish" noise due to air currents set in motion by ambient mechanical vibrations. Current noise usually predominates and appears to arise largely from effects in the junctions to the metallic leads. This source of noise usually does not exceed the Johnson noise by more than 50 to 100 per cent. Element resistances range from 1 to 10 megohms at room temperature; therefore, potential drops across the element of 100 to 150 v can be used. With a 100-v bias, responsivities may range from 50 to 500 v/w at a modulation frequency of 15 cycles/sec. Time constants range from 0.0015 to 0.04 sec, and the surface character suffices to insure not less than 80 per cent absorption of the incident radiant energy. An element with a 0.003-sec time constant, modulated at over 300 cycles/sec, was found to have a least-count $\Delta\Phi$ of 2×10^{-8} w. Modifications of the original product of Western Electric Company (New York, N. Y.) are available from various commercial sources.[135,139,144,151,169,170,174,175]

Thin ribbon elements can be made in several ways. Strips just thick enough to be self-supporting in service are made by peeling off evaporated deposits of the metal. Alternatively instead of peeling off the strips, the supporting bases can be removed by dissolving away chemically. Wollaston- or Taylor-process wire is produced commercially by drawing down strips of the required metal within much thicker sheathings of silver. These annular structures can also be rolled down into thin ribbons. In either case, the silver sheathings finally are dissolved away leaving the inner strips. Thicknesses of less than 0.08 μ (3.2×10^{-6} in.) have been attained in this manner. Figure 3·7A shows a bolometer in which the arms are made of 1-μ (4×10^{-5}-in.) thick ribbons cut from a piece of foil made by rolling out platinum between silver. Then after the ribbon is soldered in position, the silver is removed. This is effected by electrolysis in concentrated potassium cyanide solution. A least-count $\Delta\Phi$ of 6×10^{-8} w was attained with a 0.2-sec time constant.[135,169,170,176-178]

Figure 3·7B illustrates a typical construction used for film elements in both bolometers and thermocouples. By use of two successive shadowing screens, bismuth is evaporated onto 0.04- to 0.3-mm (0.0016- to 0.012-in.) thick celluloid supporting membranes and in the configurations shown. Two strips of very thin film serve as the bolometer arms; much thicker layers, in contact at their outer edges with the brass blocks, serve as electrodes. The unit shown is mounted in a suitable massive housing equipped with an infrared-transparent window. Bolometer-arm resistances ranged from 177 to 439 ohms. When well evacuated, a least-count $\Delta\Phi$ of 1×10^{-8} w was attained. This corresponded to a time constant of 0.1 sec. At atmospheric pressure, the time constant was reduced to 0.035 sec, and $\Delta\Phi$ increased to 3×10^{-8} w.[135,141,154-157,169,170,179]

Figure 3·7C illustrates a bolometer in which electric-capacitative impedances replace the usual resistive impedances in the bridge area. An a-c power supply to the bridge is required. The elements then become pairs of electric-conducting sheets serving as condenser plates separated by very thin dielectric membranes. The high temperature coefficients of the dielectric constants for available materials result in responsivities comparable to those for resistive elements. Since the capacity of a condenser is proportional to its plate area, which in the dielectric bolometer is necessarily also the receiving area, this area is not made small. The advantages usually attributed to small receiving areas, normally made a few square millimeters, are then sacrificed; and, in the case illustrated, an area of 400 mm² (0.62 in.²) is used. Capacitances thus attained were 500 $\mu\mu$f (5×10^{-10} f) in each arm with a 3.5-sec time constant. A least-count $\Delta\Phi$ of 3×10^{-9} w was achieved, although 1000-fold greater sensitivities are considered attainable. In a similar device, Ewles achieved a responsivity of 330 v/w with a time constant of 0.1 sec. This sort of design seems better adapted to the measurement of radiant intensity, w/in.^{2}, where the use of a relatively large image is not objectionable, rather than to the determination of radiant power emanating from a small area at a point on the source-body surface.[180-182]

3·10 PNEUMATIC DETECTORS

In a pneumatic element, radiation absorbed by an opaque film within a small closed vessel serves to heat the contained gas. The gas then expands or undergoes a rise in pressure. Structurally, the end of the cell through which the radiation enters is closed by an infrared-transparent window. Sensitive means are provided for the indication of very small expansions or variations in pressure. Calibration then determines the relationship between incident radiant power and the scale indications.[183-185]

The Golay [186-189] Pneumatic Detector, available commercially from The Eppley Laboratory, Inc. (Newport, R. I.), is an example of what is possible when the ultimate of ingenuity is employed in the refinement of such a design. This "package" device employing a pneumatic element achieves a sensitivity and precision comparable or superior to nearly all other thermal elements. It is so arranged that expansion of the confined gas distorts a flexible mirror, the movement of which alters ray lengths in a critically focused optical system. Resulting "leakage" of *exciting* light, through a precision line screen, varies the output of a photocell. The amplified output of this cell is rectified to eliminate the effect of chopping in the incident radiant-signal beam. For a $\frac{3}{32}$-in.-effective-diameter sensitive area and a time constant of 1.6 sec, the minimum distinguishable radiant power $\Delta\Phi$ is 6×10^{-11} w.[185-190]

3·11 DEPOSITED-FILM PHOTOCONDUCTIVE DETECTORS

Evaporated or chemically deposited multicrystalline films of lead sulfide, cadmium sulfide, lead selenide, lead telluride, and similar compounds become electrically conducting on being exposed to radiation in wavelengths that they absorb. Film thicknesses are just sufficient for opacity in the absorbing wavelength ranges and are usually of about 1 μ (0.00004 in.) depth laid on a glass insulating base. Typical constructions are shown in Fig. 3·9 with electrodes, lead wires, and mounting arrangements.[134, 191-205]

Photoconductivity results from *photon capture*, and the corresponding release of *photoelectrons*, within the microcrystals forming the films. These electrons serve as carriers of electricity and also affect crystal-boundary charge configurations. They thereby reduce the electrical

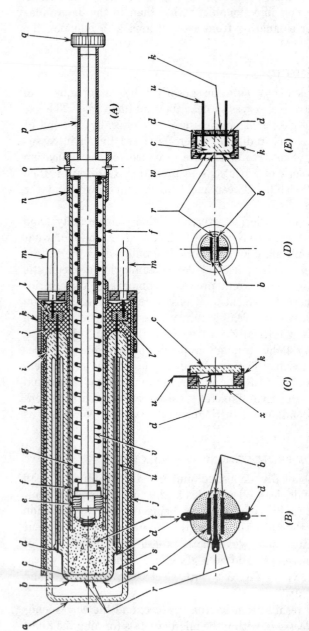

Fig. 3·9. Photoconductive radiation-sensitive elements. (A) Dewar-construction cooled-element cell; (B) front view of sensitive surface of A; (C) enclosed uncooled cell; (D)front view of sensitive surface of E; and (E) rugged compact uncooled cell. a, Infrared-transparent window formed by outer wall of Dewar flask; b, electrodes; c, glass base material; d, junctions of electrodes to lead wires; e, felt-washer piston; f, bonded-paper tube; g, compression spring; h, metal shield tube; i, Dewar flask; j, electric-insulating cement; k, electric-insulating multiple-pin base; l, electric-connector buttons soldered to leads and pins; m, plug-in pins; n, metal ferrule; o, bayonet fitting; p, metal tube; q, knurled knob; r, photoconducting-deposited-film radiation-sensitive surface between electrodes; s, evacuated space; t, powdered solid carbon dioxide; u, lead wires; v, thermally insulating rod; w, infrared-transparent protective coating; and x, infrared-transparent window.

resistances of the films. This effect is independent of, and very much larger than, any change in resistance due to the heating effect of the radiation.[191-193, 197, 199, 201, 202, 206-209]

When not maintained at constant temperature, photoconductors in common with thermistors follow the semiconductor law (see Fig. 1·1 and Eq. 1·1) for decrease in electrical resistance with rise in temperature. Thus, temperature coefficients of resistance of -0.02 per °F may occur. Also at room temperature, the photoconductive responsivity may change with temperature by as much as, or more than, -0.1 per °F. Thus, changes in operating temperature, whether due to the heating effect of the radiation, *exciting* current, or ambient conditions, must be controlled to minimize *drift*.[191, 199, 201-203, 210, 211]

Photoconductive elements, in common with other photo elements, respond nonuniformly with wavelength and over limited wavelength ranges, but they have much larger responsivities in these ranges than good thermal elements. Whereas most photo elements are limited to the visible and ultraviolet regions, for photoconductive elements the response ranges extend far into the infrared. Thus, lead sulfide elements have peak responsivities at around 2 μ of nearly 300 times those for good thermal elements and also have appreciable response to beyond 3 μ. Cooling these cells, with a mixture of solid carbon dioxide and acetone, to -80°C or -112°F increases this margin by nearly 10,000-fold. Lead telluride elements, cooled with liquid nitrogen to 77°K (-321°F), have peak responsivities at around 4.3 μ, capability of detecting 7×10^{-12} w, and response times of 30 μsec. Lead selenide elements, cooled with liquid air to 90°K (-298°F), have responsivities exceeding those of good thermal elements to around 6.5 μ, the responsivities being at least 5 times as great as those for the thermal elements over the range from 2 to 6 μ. Zinc-impurity germanium elements, commercially available from Perkin-Elmer Corp. (Norwalk, Conn.), have peak sensitivities at nearly 40 μ and are said to be effective over the wavelength range from 3.5 to 40 μ.[196, 199-203, 212-216]

The responsivities of photoconductive elements thus increase with decreasing temperatures. Also, whereas the response times for thermal elements are rarely much less than 0.01 sec, photoconductive elements may have response times of less than 2×10^{-5} sec. Unfortunately, the advantages of maximum responsivity cannot be had simultaneously with those of minimum response time. This is because the response time increases with decreasing temperature. However, even at the temperatures for maximum responsivity, the response times are lower than for the fastest thermal elements.[191, 199, 201-203, 209, 214]

Photoconductive elements, deposited on rigid blocks of base material (see Fig. 3·9), are free from *microphonic noise*. Usually, the minimum distinguishable signal is limited by *current noise*. The root-mean-square current-noise emf is approximately proportional to the electric current i through the element. As the responsivity S_t, which is the emf per unit of incident radiant power, also increases approximately linearly with the current i, the ratio of response to the noise emf varies little with the current, once the response has become sufficiently large relative to the Johnson-noise emf. The current-noise emf varies inversely as the sensitive-surface area. Current noise increases with the duration of the exciting current and may double in a few hours or days, the rate of increase being greater for high current densities and small sensitive-surface areas. Since recovery periods are of about the same duration, current-noise growth can be avoided by using a-c exciting currents. Frequencies may range from 10^{-2} to 10^5 cycles/sec.[201, 209, 217]

The effect of current noise is minimized by operation at low temperatures. Figure 3·9A and B shows a commercially available arrangement for maintaining an element at carbon-dioxide-snow temperature. When cooling with liquid air is necessary, as in the case of lead selenide and lead telluride elements, the Dewar flask must stand upright. In this case, mirrors can be used, or the window can be placed in the side. The window may be an infrared-transparent slab (see Fig. 3·3 and Table 3·1) cemented to a neck protruding in the outer wall. However, a 20-μ (0.0008-in.) thick hemispherical blown-glass bubble transmits over 90 per cent in wavelengths up to beyond 6 μ and is sufficiently strong to withstand atmospheric pressure. Sapphire or periclase (MgO) windows can be fused into the wall using intermediate glasses in a range of expansion coefficients. Room-temperature radiation falling on an element affects its response; hence, it may be desirable to cool all surfaces "seen" by the element, limiting the aperture to the path of the signal beam.[191, 193, 201, 215, 218-220]

The sensitive surface usually requires protection. Where it is not located in a sealed-in space (see Fig. 3·9A, B and C), it is coated with an infrared-transparent lacquer such as polystyrene (see Fig. 3·9D and E). Since element resistances are large, i.e., 10^4 to 10^8 ohms, insulation between electrodes and lead wires must be carefully provided.[203]

Photoconductive elements are commercially available with sensitive-surface areas ranging from 0.020 in. square to over a square inch. Although an element intercepts radiant energy from a uniform beam in direct proportion to its area, the response due to the integrated effect increases slowly with area size. Thus, for a given incident radiant power intercepted by the element, the response may vary inversely as at least the square root of the area size. Also, some portions of the element's area may be more sensitive than others. Thus, responsivities for concentrated beams incident on various local portions of the sensitive area may differ by as much as 50 per cent from their mean. Hence, if the sensitive area is larger than the incident beam (see Fig. 4·2A, B, and C), permitting different portions to be used will result in corresponding variations in responsivity. Excessive concentration of the beam may also cause local saturation of the surface.[221]

Although the responses of photoconductive elements are linear with the incident radiant power, the responsivities tend to drift with time. Their short response times, however, permit modulation at frequencies up to 10,000 cycles/sec. Then, by alternately presenting the element with radiation from the source body and from a variable known-temperature source, these elements need merely to serve as null indicators (see Fig. 3·1B).[201, 209, 216]

Circuit arrangements can be similar to those used with other resistance elements discussed in Chs. 1 and 2. An equal series "load" resistance is, however, often used to protect a photoconductive element.[6, 48, 71, 202, 203, 222, 223]

3·12 SINGLE-CRYSTAL PHOTOCONDUCTIVE AND PHOTORESISTIVE DETECTORS

Devices similar to the transistors employed in radio circuits can be used as radiation-sensitive elements. Single crystals of pure 4-valence nonmetals, such as germanium, copper oxide, selenium, and silicon, may be insulators or intrinsic semiconductors. However, with added impurities of even less than one part in 100,000,000 of 5-valence elements, such as arsenic, phosphorous, and antimony, or of 3-valence elements, such as boron, aluminum, gallium, and indium, these crystals become semiconducting. The 5-valence atoms each tend to liberate their fifth valence electron in taking their places in the 4-valence lattice, whereas the 3-valence atoms each tend to acquire a fourth valence electron, leaving a positive deficiency or *hole* in some other atom. The holes and liberated electrons are, in effect, mobile positive and negative electric charges, respectively. Thus, an electric field applied to the crystal will cause these charges to move through the crystal as an electric current. If the mobile charges are negative, i.e., electrons, the crystal is described as *n-type;* if the mobile charges are positive, i.e., holes, it is said to be *p-type*. Single crystals can be grown in successive n- and p-layers.[48, 201, 224–227]

Junctions between metals and either n-type or p-type crystals, or between n- and p-layers, are characterized by *contact differences in potential*. They thus act as rectifiers; i.e., current tends to flow across them with smaller applied potential difference in the one direction than in the other. Metal contacts are often sharply pointed as *whiskers* (see Fig. 3·10) to effect higher local electric-field intensities for any given applied potential differences. The first crystal layer may then be in the form of a small island (see Fig. 3·10C) such that the first n-p junction is also within this region of high field intensity.[48, 201, 224, 225, 228–230]

When radiation is absorbed by a crystal, the energies of the captured photons may separate additional electrons from their parent atoms leaving holes. The resultant pairs of mobile positive and

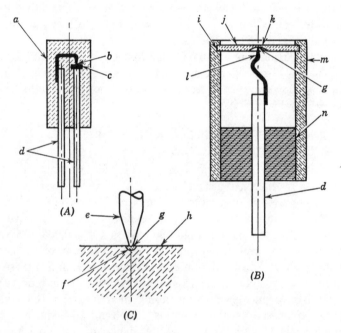

Fig. 3·10. Germanium photocells. (*A*) Molded-in-plastic photocell; (*B*) mounted-in-cylinder photocell; and (*C*) whisker in contact with small "island" of p-type germanium embedded in the surface of a n-type body. In each case radiation enters from the top. *a*, Molded-plastic cylinder; *b*, whisker contact; *c*, germanium wafer; *d*, electrode; *e*, whisker point; *f*, island of p-type germanium; *g*, contact; *h*, wafer of n-type germanium; *i*, peripheral electrode; *j*, germanium wafer; *k*, area opposite contact, through which radiation passes, thinned to few thousandths of an inch; *l*, collector whisker; *m*, metal cylinder; and *n*, electric-insulation seal. (*By permission G. D. O'Neill in Germanium Photocells, 1, 8, Sylvania Electric Products Inc., Bayside, N. Y., 1950.*)

negative charges add to the local electric conductivity. This increase is most effective when such charge pairs are generated near a junction in an intense electric field. However, crystal layers essentially devoid of the sort of irregularities called *deathnium*, which tend to "catalyse" recombination of such pairs, also provide effective radiation-absorption areas. The increased conductivity through the crystal, between a pair of electrodes, is proportional to the intensity of the incident radiation in the absorption wavelength range and depends on the potential difference applied between the two electrodes and on the potential at which any third electrode may be maintained. The electric current flow between electrodes, thus proportional in magnitude to the absorbed radiation, may be either in the *forward* direction of "easy flow," i.e., as assisted by the contact difference in potential, or in the *reverse* direction. Elements in which the forward current is varied are called *photoconductive* elements, and those in which the reverse current is varied are called *photoresistive* elements. Two-electrode elements are called *photodiodes*, and three-electrode elements are called *phototransistors*.[48, 201, 224, 225, 228–230]

Phototransistors are very similar in construction and principle to the *transistors* used in electronic circuits for amplification. The reader is advised to consult the extensive literature in *transistor physics* to acquire an understanding of the functional principles of single-crystal photoconductive and photoresistive elements.[48, 201, 224, 225, 228–230]

Single-crystal elements, as rigid blocks of material (see Fig. 3·10A and *B*), are free from *microphonic noise*. Usually the minimum distinguishable signal is limited by *current noise*. The radiation-sensitive area, at a point-contact electrode (whisker) or at an n-p junction, is usually less than 0.04 in. in diameter. Germanium-crystal elements are sensitive in the wavelength range from 0.4 μ to 1.7 μ. Cells may be used with direct or modulated radiation. Limiting modulation frequencies depend on the recombination times for electron-hole pairs. The recombination times and consequently the limiting frequencies are subject to production control by varying the deathnium concentration in the crystals. Frequencies up to 20,000 cycles/sec are used.[48, 71, 151, 201, 212, 224, 225, 228–230]

3·13 PHOTOEMISSIVE DETECTORS

When radiation is absorbed by a metallic surface, electrons tend to be emitted from the surface. By arranging such a surface as a negative electrode (see Fig. 3·11A) in an evacuated glass bulb, the *photoelectrons* can be drawn over to a positively charged surface. Thus, an electron current flows from the negative to the positive electrode, i.e.,

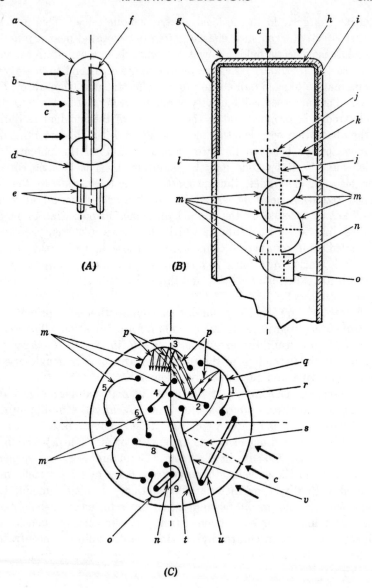

(A)   (B)

(C)

Fig. 3·11. Photoemissive cells. (A) Evacuated or gas-filled diode; (B) box-dynode photomultiplier; and (C) squirrel-cage photomultiplier. a, Evacuated or gas-filled glass envelope; b, metallic-rod anode; c, incident radiation; d, plastic-seal insulating base; e, plug-in pins; f, alkali-metal-coated cathode; g, evacuated glass envelope; h, end-window semitransparent photoemissive-surface cathode, i.e., photocathode; i, electron-focusing aluminum-coating radiation shield; j, electron-focusing grids; k, electron-focusing shield; l, first dynode; m, intermediate dy-

from the *cathode* to the *anode*. It is necessary that the energy per photon of the incident radiation be sufficient to perform the work of removing the individual electrons from the metallic structure. The required energy per electron, i.e., the *work function*, is dependent on the character of the cathode surface layer. The energy of the individual radiant-energy "packets," or *photons*, depends on the wavelength of the radiant energy. It is least for long wavelengths. Thus, surfaces with low work functions have the longest threshold-wavelength limits. However, the *sensitivity* S of a surface, amp/w, in the effective wavelength range depends on the *efficiency* of the photon-absorption electron-emission process. Thus, it depends on the number of incident photons required, on the average, for the emission of one *photoelectron*. The variation of this efficiency with wavelength results in the response curves characteristic of various cathode surfaces.[6, 231–235]

If instead of being *evacuated* the bulb or *cell* is filled with an inert gas at a suitable low pressure, the gas tends to be ionized by collisions with the photoelectrons as they are accelerated in passing to the *collecting* anode. Such ionization multiplies the number of charged particles available to carry the electric current and thus effects internal amplification.[6, 232, 235–237]

If in an evacuated cell the photoelectrons are reflected from or transmitted through intermediate *dynodes, secondary* electrons emitted at each stage add to or *multiply* the electron current. This process effects internal amplification with gain factors of 3 to 6 at each stage. The gain factors depend on the dynode surface materials and on the interdynode voltages.[237–244]

Evacuated diodes (see Fig. 3·11A) tend to the highest degrees of stability, linearity, and response speed. The sensitive surface should be backed by a metallic plate and not deposited on the inner surface of the glass bulb. The single voltage supply is not critical and is usually only about 100 v. However, some cells require as much as 500 v. Their high output impedances tend to facilitate amplification and other circuit incorporation. Ultimate sensitivity is, however, usually limited by the thermal or Johnson noise in the coupling resistor, or tube noise in the first stage of amplification. Thus, when the highest sensitivity is not required, as for measuring radiation from nearby

---

nodes; *n*, collecting anode; *o*, last dynode; *p*, secondary-electron trajectories; *q*, first dynode; *r*, primary-photoelectron trajectory; *s*, incident-photon trajectory; *t*, mica shield; *u*, focusing grill; and *v*, photocathode. (*By permission Du Mont Multiplier Phototubes, 7, Allen B. Du Mont Laboratories, Clifton, N. J., 1955; and R. W. Engstrom in J. Opt. Soc. Am., 37, no. 6, 421, June, 1947.*)

bodies which are at elevated temperatures, evacuated diodes may be chosen.[47, 233, 235]

Gas-filled diodes (see Fig. 3·11A) tend to lower degrees of stability, linearity, and response speed than evacuated cells. Internal amplification factors up to 10 may be useful, but the cell current depends on the potential difference maintained between the electrodes. Thus, a constant-voltage supply is necessary, whereas the low output impedance limits the choice of indicators.[47, 235, 236, 240]

Figure 3·11B and C indicates the electrode arrangements of two typical *photomultiplier cells*, or *multiplier photocells*, in which electrostatic-focusing shells direct the successive beams of electrons. These beams consist of the original photoelectrons plus the accumulated secondary-electron additions. Internal amplification factors may range from 10^3 or 10^4 to 10^7 as the potential differences between successive dynodes increase from 50 to 175 v. Thus, for stability, i.e., sensitivity which does not change with time, precise interdynode voltage control is required. Gains of 10^6 are feasible with frequency responses of up to 10^8 cycles/sec. Resolutions to within a few micromicroseconds are also attainable.[47, 232, 234–236, 239–249]

Photomultipliers or multiplier photocells (see Fig. 3·11B and C) with internal-amplification factors of 10^6 require less amplification of their outputs than is needed for diodes. This permits simpler output circuits of more rapid response. The least-count or smallest distinguishable signal is limited by the dark-current thermionic-emission noise at the cathode. This noise in turn can be greatly decreased by refrigeration and by using small cathodes with focused incident radiation. *Fatigue* is negligible for photocurrents not exceeding 10^{-6} amp. Linearity is to within 3 per cent for anode currents over the entire range from 10^{-13} to 10^{-3} amp.[239]

The dynodes must be maintained with exact constancy at potentials successively higher in steps of usually around 100 v. Ordinarily 9 or 10 dynodes are used; however, there may be as many as 16. Over-all voltage supply is usually around 1000 v but may be as high as 2500 v.[234, 244–246, 249]

Fortunately, the anode current can be made essentially independent of the potential difference in the final stage, i.e., from the last dynode to the anode, providing this potential difference always exceeds a certain minimum of perhaps 50 v; then a coupling resistor can be used to convert the output signal from a current to a potential variation. In d-c operation, batteries can be used with galvanometer indication or d-c amplification. The ohmic-leakage component can be "balanced out" but may drift, requiring annoying readjustments. A-c amplification, lessening drift effects, can be used with modulated radiation while retaining battery supply voltage. A-c supply can also be used but with lessened sensitivity. Thus the peaks must not exceed the highest permissible interdynode potential difference. Photomultiplier cells should always be operated surrounded by shielding of suitable magnetic conductors, such as Mumetal, maintained at cathode potential.[233, 234, 236, 241, 242, 244, 246]

Threshold wavelengths of 0.6 to 1.3 μ characteristic of photoemissive elements tend to limit response to wavelength ranges beyond those for which thermal radiation is appreciable in magnitude, except when the source body is at a relatively high temperature. Response to very low radiant intensities tends, however, to extend the low-temperature limit for temperature-measurement applications. High linearity and sensitivity, low noise limits, high stability and speed of response, and convenient adaptability to indicating devices characterize photoemissive elements. These advantages all tend to indicate the serious consideration of photoemissive vacuum diodes whenever the temperatures to be measured are not too low.[6, 71, 234, 236, 240, 245, 250-254]

Circuit arrangements used with photoemissive elements are too numerous and varied for detailed description here. The reader is advised to consult the references for circuit diagrams adapted to his requirements.[234-236, 242, 244, 253, 255]

3·14 PHOTOVOLTAIC DETECTORS

Photovoltaic elements resemble the photoconductive and photoresistive elements in their functioning, and occur as both film and single-crystal types. The principal advantages of the photovoltaic elements lie: (1) in their having simplicity and mechanical ruggedness, (2) in their not requiring any external power supply, and (3) in their often furnishing, without amplification, sufficient output current for simple rugged indicators. They thus tend to find a place in portable shop instruments where high accuracy is not required.

In the film elements, radiation transmitted by the molecular-thickness layers b and c (see Fig. 3·12) is absorbed releasing photoelectrons in the surface regions of the semiconducting selenium layer d. Some of the photoelectrons upon crossing the *barrier layer* of selenium oxide c are prevented, by its *rectifying* properties, from returning and remain "trapped" in the metallic front electrode b, tending to build up a negative charge. The conducting iron base e supplies electrons which pass through the semiconducting-selenium layer to replace those going to the cathode. A potential difference, proportional to the intensity of the incident radiation, is thus maintained.

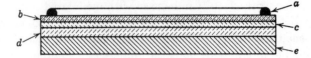

Fig. 3·12. Selenium photovoltaic cell. *a*, Sprayed-metal collector ring; *b*, radiation-transparent molecular-thickness front electrode, i.e., cathode, of platinum, gold, cadmium, or tin-cadmium alloy applied by sputtering; *c*, radiation-transparent molecular-thickness *rectifying* or "barrier" layer of selenium oxide applied by evaporation; *d*, semiconducting 0.001- to 0.003-in. thick selenium layer applied by evaporation and tempered in air below the melting point; and, *e*, iron base plate underlying the selenium, i.e., the anode, which may be coated by evaporation with a 0.5-μ thick layer of bismuth or nickel. The entire assembly is coated with a protective lacquer.

The film photovoltaic elements (Fig. 3·12) are somewhat similar in construction and appearance to film photoconductive elements (Fig. 3·9). They are solid and rugged but have sensitive areas extending to hundreds of square millimeters; therefore, they are not well adapted to local-temperature measurements. The extended infrared responses of the photoconductive films are, also, largely absent. This limits application to bodies at relatively high temperatures. Circuitry must be such as to provide the effect of low or "zero" load resistance. Response is slower, and stability and linearity are not comparable to those for evacuated photoemissive cells.

Protection against heating must be furnished to prevent damage as well as calibration drifts. Temperature coefficients of 0.1 per cent per °F may occur.[48, 71, 134, 151, 256-269]

The indium antimonide single-crystal photovoltaic detector is commercially available with a noise-equivalent power of 7×10^{-10} w for a 1-mm² receiver area at 6.6 μ and 1 cycle/sec bandwidth with a response time of only 0.4 μsec.[270]

3·15 APPLICATIONS

The general scope of radiation detectors has been surveyed. However, it might be asked what are the respective uses of these devices—to what ranges of temperature are they individually adapted and to what accuracies can they be expected to attain. In Tables 3·2 and 3·3 the essential characteristics are collected for a number of thermal detectors. Response times are given in seconds, and minimum distinguishable incident radiant powers are given in watts. These thermal detectors respond to all wavelengths. Hence, they can be used at any temperatures for which the aggregate power focused on the sensitive

Table 3·2.   Data for 33 detectors assumed to have a noise output equal to the calculated Johnson noise

Identification	Time Constant, milli-seconds	Zero-Frequency Responsivity, volts/watt	Sensitive Area, mm^2	Resistance, ohms	Minimum-Distinguishable Incident Radiant Power, 10^{-10} watt
The Weyrich Vacuum Thermocouple					
in air	68	0.29	2.0	20	26.7
evacuated	1000	4.35	2.0	20	0.465
The Eppley (Farrand) Thermocouple	90	0.375	1.0	5.8	13.7
The Schwarz Thermopiles					
#B4772/9	20	0.41	4.0	23.3	26.7
#B4772/11	20	0.55	4.0	51.0	29.3
#B4772/12	20	0.66	4.0	20.7	15.6
The Harris Evaporated Thermopiles					
#1	13.3	0.280	11.0	100	59.7
#2	13.3	0.334	11.0	100	50.0
The Eppley (Emerson) Thermopile	250	0.1	80	18	5.76
The Harris Thermocouples					
Bi–Te	212	34.2	1.2	150,000	14.4
Bi–Sb	90	3.96	1.2	25,000	77.7
The Harris and Scholp Thermocouples					
#3	177	50	1.2	1480	1.07
#5	110	47.5	1.2	1430	1.40
#7	134	60.2	4.8	4900	0.928
#8	345	406	1.2	183,000	1.05
#2	175	400	1.2	90,000	1.05
The Hornig and O'Keefe Thermopiles	36	6.5	0.5	5	1.64
	36	6.5	1.0	10	1.64
	41	3.8	4.0	12.5	1.47
The Perkin-Elmer Thermocouples					
J. Opt. Soc. Am.	58	5	0.4	10	2.66
Rev. Sci. Inst.	45	10	0.4	20	2.13
letter	17	10	0.4	20	3.47
The Strong Bolometer	5.3	0.61	5.7	4.2	12.4
The Felix Bolometers					
2A	20.2	1.09	17.2	16	3.99
15	21.2	1.41	17.2	16	3.01
11A	21.5	1.14	17.2	16	3.69
19	21.2	2.26	17.2	16	1.88
The Polaroid Bolometers					
Ni324	4.7	1.46	4.5	64	24.1
Ni347	7.2	1.60	4.5	44	14.7
Ni350	3.6	1.61	4.5	128	35.3
The Thermistor Bolometers					
S-19	5.9	730	0.60	3×10^6	25.5
S-20	1.27	378	0.62	3×10^6	105.0
XB-108	135	3460	0.58	3×10^6	1.14

*By permission R. C. Jones in J. Opt. Soc. Am., **39**, no. 5, p. 350 (May, 1949).*

Table 3·3. Data for 15 detectors whose noise level was directly measured.

Identification	Time Constant, milliseconds	Noise Equivalent Power, 10^{-10} watt	Sensitive Area, mm^2	Band Width, c.p.s.	Minimum-Distinguishable Incident Radiant Power, 10^{-10} watt
The Superconducting Bolometers					
22-k-¼	10.0	3.67	1.8	4000	0.216
25-k-¼	1.2	14.5	1.2	4000	3.02
8-f-1	0.9	18.5	0.7	4000	5.83
11-f-1	1.7	14.6	0.4	4000	4.43
24-k-¼	0.7	35.3	0.7	4000	12.6
10-f-1	1.5	20.6	0.4	4000	6.65
5-d-1	0.8	90.0	1.6	4000	19.9
13-g-1	4.2	115.00	6.4	4000	5.54
The Baird Bolometers					
slow	50	60	3.6	5000	1.00
fast	4.1	64.8	0.2	5000	16.0
The Thermistor Bolometer					
A	3.0	100	0.6	30	215
The Polaroid Bolometer					
A	4.0	263	6.0	100	85
The Aiken Bolometers					
G 165	3.8	185	27.5	1.85	210
G 22	6.9	232	27.5	1.85	196
The Golay Pneumatic Heat Detector	5.0	0.48	7.0	1.0	1.28

*By permission R. C. Jones in J. Opt. Soc. Am., **30**, no. 5, p. 351 (May, 1949).*

surface suffices for the required response. Photo detectors, such as the human eye and the various photoelectric cells, however, respond only in limited wavelength ranges. Hence, they can be used only where the temperatures are such as to yield sufficient radiant powers in the respective ranges.

Short response times are necessary for rapidly changing temperatures and when the signal is chopped for a-c amplification.

It can readily be seen from the curves of Figs. 4·1, 4·5 and 4·7 that, for detectors sensitive only in the visible or near-infrared regions of the spectrum, source bodies must be at elevated temperatures to emit appreciable radiation at these wavelengths. It is also evident from

Eq. 4·1 that the total amount of radiation varies markedly with the temperature. Thus, at high temperatures, energy is abundant and high detector sensitivities are not necessary unless extreme precision is required. On the other hand, if the temperatures to be measured are low, a detector must be chosen for which the least-count radiant power is very small. Of course, one is actually interested not in the total amount but rather in the change in radiant power corresponding to a given increment in *source-body* temperature. This power increment is proportional to the magnitude of temperature increment, and the minimum measurable value of the temperature increment becomes the error. Thus, precision in measurement of low temperatures is dependent on the use of very sensitive detectors.

Complex interrelations exist among the variables of the problem. These variables are the factors representing the required time precision, location precision, and magnitude precision of the intended temperature measurement, the characteristics of the prospective detector, the expected optical-system performance, and the various installation arrangements. The simple categorization that one might seek gives way necessarily to a set of algebraic relations. The result is that choosing a detector for a job takes the form of a design calculation.

3·16 SUMMARY

Within the space limitations of this chapter, it has been possible to provide, at best, a sketch of the salient features of the principal types of apparatus available. It is hoped that this information may serve to introduce the reader to the respective alternatives pertinent for comparative consideration in design. The reader is advised, however, to consult the extensive list of references for full information regarding any device of which he contemplates the actual use.[205, 270-291]

REFERENCES *

1. F. Hoffmann and C. Tingwaldt, *Optische Pyrometrie* (Optical Pyrometry), 134 pp., Friedr. Vieweg & Sohn, Braunschweig, Germany, 1938; J. W. Edwards, Ann Arbor, 1944.
2. W. E. Forsythe, *Measurement of Radiant Energy*, 452 pp., McGraw-Hill Book Co., New York, 1937.
3. W. E. Forsythe, "Optical Pyrometry," American Institute of Physics, *Temperature*, pp. 1115–1131, Reinhold Publishing Corp., New York, 1941.
4. A. Rose, "A Unified Approach to the Performance of Photographic Film, Television Pickup Tubes, and the Human Eye," *J. Soc. Motion Picture Engineers*, **47**, no. 4, pp. 273–294 (October, 1946).

* See footnote on page 26.

5. W. E. Forsythe, *Smithsonian Miscellaneous Collections*, **120**, Smithsonian Physical Tables, 9th ed., 827 pp., Smithsonian Institution, Washington, D. C., 1954.

6. H. J. J. Braddick, *The Physics of Experimental Method*, 404 pp., John Wiley & Sons, New York, 1954.

7. J. Strong, H. V. Neher, A. E. Whitford, and C. H. Cartwright, *Procedures in Experimental Physics*, 642 pp., Prentice-Hall, New York, 1941.

8. J. Krönert, "Temperatur-Messung durch Messung der Strahlung" (Temperature Measurement by Radiation), *ATM Archiv für technisches Messen*, V214-1, T8–T9 (1931).

9. M. M. Benarie, "Optical Pyrometry below Red Heat," *J. Opt. Soc. Am.*, **47**, no. 11, pp. 1005–1009 (November, 1957).

10. D. R. Lovejoy, "Photometry of the Optical Pyrometer and Its Use Below 800°C," *J. Opt. Soc. Am.*, **49**, no. 3, pp. 249–253 (March, 1959).

11. E. Griffeths, *Methods of Measuring Temperature*, 223 pp., Charles Griffen, London, 1947.

12. R. G. Giovanelli and W. R. G. Kemp, "The Use of a Polarizer in the Disappearing Filament Optical Pyrometer," *J. Sci. Instr.*, **27**, no. 3, pp. 69–71 (March, 1950).

13. F. Hoffmann, "Die optische Temperaturskala und die Strahlungskonstanten" (The Optical Temperature Scale and the Radiation Constants), *Zeitschrift für angewandte Physik*, **2**, no. 2, pp. 88–95 (February, 1950).

14. N. A. Blum, "Recording Optical Pyrometer," *Rev. Sci. Instr.*, **30**, no. 4, pp. 251–253 (April, 1959).

15. G. K. Burgess, "A Micropyrometer," *Bulletin of the Bureau of Standards*, **9**, no. 198, pp. 475–478 (December, 1913).

16. American Institute of Mining and Metallurgical Engineers, *Pyrometry*, 701 pp., American Institute Mining and Metallurgical Engineers, New York, 1920.

17. J. Euler and W. Schneider, "Über die Messgenauigkeit bei Fadenpyrometern" (The Accuracy of the Disappearing Filament Pyrometer), *Zeitschrift für angewandte Physik*, **3**, no. 12, pp. 459–467 (December, 1951).

18. J. Euler, "Über die Messgenauigkeit von Teilstrahlungspyrometern in der Mired Skala" (On the Accuracy of Optical Pyrometers in the Mired Scale), *Zeitschrift für angewandte Physik*, **7**, no. 2, pp. 86–90 (February, 1955).

19. J. Euler, "Fortschritte auf dem Gebiet der optischen Pyrometrie in den Jahren 1940 bis 1950" (Progress in the Field of Optical Pyrometry 1940–1950), *Zeitschrift für angewandte Physik*, **2**, no. 12, pp. 505–509 (December, 1950).

20. M. Jakob, "Balance of Radiation in Employing Optical Pyrometry," *Combustion*, **16**, no. 2, pp. 49–50 (August, 1944).

21. G. Urbain, "Influence de la temperature ambiante sur les lectures de différents pyromètres optiques à disparition de filament" (Influence of the Ambient Temperature on the Readings of Different Disappearing-Filament Optical Pyrometers), *Revue d'optique*, **34**, no. 4, pp. 193–203 (April, 1955).

22. G. Urbain, "Essai sur la dispersion des mesures en pyromètrie optique" (Test on the Scatter of Measurements in Optical Pyrometry), *Revue d'optique*, **30**, no. 1, pp. 32–45 (January, 1951).

23. G. A. W. Rutgers, "The Second Radiation Constant in Planck's Radiation Formula II," *Physica*, **17**, no. 11, pp. 137–148 (November, 1951).

24. J. Euler, "Höhere Einstellgenauigkeit bei Fadenpyrometern durch Kontrastplatten" (More Accurate Adjustment of Filament Pyrometers by Means of Contrasting Plates), *Optik*, **15**, no. 6, pp. 373–381 (June, 1958).

25. D. R. Lovejoy, "Accuracy of Optical Pyrometry in the Range 800°C to 4000°C," *Can. J. Phys.*, **36**, no. 10, pp. 1397–1408 (October, 1958).

26. C. W. Waidner and G. K. Burgess, "The Radiation from the Melting Points of Palladium and Platinum," *Bulletin of the Bureau of Standards*, **3**, no. 2, pp. 163–208 (May, 1907).

27. E. Brodhun and F. Hoffmann, "Die Gesamthelligkeit des schwarzen Strahlers beim Palladium- und Platinschmelzpunkt und ihre Verwendbarkeit für eine Lichteinheit" (The Brightnesses of the Blackbody Radiator at the Palladium- and Platinum Melting Points and their Applicability for a unit of Light), *Zeitschrift für Physik*, **37**, pp. 138–145 (March, 1926).

28. E. P. Hyde and W. E. Forsythe, "The Gold-Point Palladium-Point Brightness Ratio," *Astrophysical Journal*, **51**, no. 4, pp. 244–251 (May, 1920).

29. M. C. Féry, "Sur l'approximation des corps noirs employés comme récepteurs" (On the Approximation of Blackbodies Employed as Receivers), *Compt. rend.*, pp. 777–780 (March, 1909).

30. H. Moser, J. Otto, and W. Thomas, "Gasthermometrische Messungen bei hohen Temperaturen. I—Neue gasthermometrische Methode; II—Bestimmung des Goldpunktes" (High Temperature Measurements with a Gas Thermometer. I—A New Gas Thermometer Method. II—Determination of the Gold Point), *Zeitschrift für Physik*, **147**, no. 1, pp. 59–91 (1957).

31. H. Satone, "Researches on the Establishment of Standards for Measuring Thermal Radiation," *Researches Electrotech. Lab. (Tokyo)*, **565**, 81 pp. (February, 1958) (in Japanese); *Sci. Abstr. Sect. A*, **62**, no. 733, p. 23 (January, 1959).

32. C. Tingwaldt and H. Kunz, "Über die Verwirklichung des schwarzen Körpers am Gold- und am Silberpunkt bei pyrometrischen Temperaturmessungen" (The Realization of a Blackbody at the Gold and at the Silver Point for Pyrometric Temperature Measurements), *Optik*, **15**, no. 6, pp. 333–342 (June, 1958).

33. C. W. Waidner and G. K. Burgess, "Optical Pyrometry," *Bulletin of the Bureau of Standards*, **1**, no. 2, pp. 189–254 (February, 1905).

34. G. T. Lalos, R. J. Corruccini, and H. P. Broida, "Design and Construction of a Blackbody and Its Use in the Calibration of a Grating Spectroradiometer," *Rev. Sci. Instr.*, **29**, no. 6, pp. 505–509 (June, 1958).

35. J. C. DeVos, "A New Determination of the Emissivity of Tungsten Ribbon," *Physica*, **20**, no. 10, pp. 690–714 (October, 1954).

36. J. C. DeVos, "Evaluation of the Quality of a Blackbody," *Physica*, **20**, no. 10, pp. 669–689 (October, 1954).

37. C. E. Mendenhall, "On the Emissive Power of Wedge-Shaped Cavities and Their Use in Temperature Measurements," *Astrophysical Journal*, **33**, no. 2, pp. 91–97 (March, 1911).

38. A. Gouffé, "Corrections d'ouverture des corps-noirs artificiels compte tenu des diffusions multiple internes" (Aperture Corrections for Artificial Blackbodies Calculated for Dissipation in Multiple Reflections), *Revue d'optique*, **24**, nos. 1–3, pp. 1–10 (January–March, 1945).

39. R. H. McFee, "Blackbody Source Unit with Electronic Temperature Control," *Rev. Sci. Instr.*, **23**, no. 1, pp. 52–53 (January, 1952).

40. A. J. Cussen, W. L. Eisenman, "A Comparative Study of Several Black Bodies," *Navord Report* 4582, pp. 39–44, U. S. Naval Ordnance Laboratory, Corona, California (July, 1956).

41. "Adjustable Blackbody Radiation Standard," *Instruments*, **29**, no. 2, p. 316 (February, 1956).

42. A. LaRocca and G. Zissis, "Field Sources of Blackbody Radiation," *Rev. Sci. Instr.*, **30**, no. 3, pp. 200–201 (March, 1959).

43. C. R. Barber, "Factors Affecting the Reproducibility of Brightness of Tungsten Strip Lamps for Pyrometer Standardization," *J. Sci. Instr.*, **23**, no. 10, pp. 238–243 (October, 1946).

44. D. R. Lovejoy, "Absorbing Filters and High-Temperature Optical Pyrometry," *J. Opt. Soc. Am.*, **50**, no. 7, pp. 698–706 (July, 1960).

45. Corning, *Glass Color Filters*, pp. 4, 8–9, Corning Glass Works, Corning, N. Y. (1948).

46. W. W. Coblentz, "Radiometric Investigation of Water of Crystallization, Light Filters, and Standard Absorption Bands," *Bulletin of the Bureau of Standards*, **7**, no. 4, p. 638 (December, 1911).

47. C. H. Bachman, *Techniques in Experimental Electronics*, 252 pp., John Wiley & Sons, New York, 1948.

48. G. Joos, "Physik der festen Körper" (Physics of Solid Bodies), *Naturforschung und Medizin in Deutschland*, **9**, Part 2, 235 pp., Dieterich'sche Verlagsbuchhandlung inh. W. Klemm, Wiesbaden, 1948.

49. R. M. Scott, "Optics for Infrared Systems," *Proceedings of the IRE*, The Institute of Radio Engineers, New York, **47**, no. 9, pp. 1530–1536 (September, 1959).

50. W. L. Wolfe and S. S. Ballard, "Optical Materials Films and Filters for Infrared Instrumentation," *Proceedings of the IRE*, The Institute of Radio Engineers, New York, **47**, no. 9, pp. 1540–1546 (September, 1959).

51. G. Calingaert, S. D. Heron, and R. Stair, "Sapphire and Other New Combustion-Chamber Window Materials," *S.A.E. Trans.*, Society of Automotive Engineers, **39**, no. 5, pp. 448–450 (November, 1936).

52. R. W. Kebler, *Optical Properties of Synthetic Sapphire*, 20 pp., Linde Air Products Co., New York (1954).

53. H. Rawson, "A Method of Sealing Sapphire to Glass," *J. Sci. Instr.*, **28**, no. 7, pp. 208–209 (July, 1951).

54. R. P. Chasmar, J. L. Craston, G. Isaacs, and A. S. Young, "A Method of Sealing Sapphire to Glass and Its Application to Infrared Photocells," *J. Sci. Instr.*, **28**, no. 7, pp. 206–207 (July, 1951).

55. The Harshaw Chemical Co., *Synthetic Optical Crystals*, 32 pp., The Harshaw Chemical Co., Cleveland, O. (1951).

56. R. T. Corry, *A Method for Detecting Chemiluminescent Heat Loss in an Internal-Combustion Engine, and Test Results for Iso-Octane*, 177 pp., Doctoral Dissertation, Columbia University, New York, 1957.

57. D. C. Stockbarger, "Artificial Fluorite," *J. Opt. Soc. Am.*, **39**, no. 9, pp. 731–740 (September, 1949).

58. F. W. Glaze, D. H. Blackburn, J. S. Osmalov, D. Hubbard, and M. H. Black, "Properties of Arsenic Sulfide Glass," RP 2774, *J. Research Natl. Bur. Standards*, **59**, no. 2, pp. 83–92 (August, 1957).

59. S. Anderson, W. J. Anderson, and M. Krakowski, "Water-Proofing Rocksalt for Infra-Red Absorption Cells," *Rev. Sci. Instr.*, **21**, no. 6, pp. 574–575 (June, 1950).

60. E. K. Plyler, "Infrared Prism Spectrometry from 24 to 40 Microns," RP 1911. *J. Research Natl. Bur. Standards*, **41**, no. 2, pp. 125–128 (August, 1948).

61. M. Hyman, Jr. and B. Billings, "High Transmission Windows for Radiation of 3 to 14 Microns Wave-Length," *J. Opt. Soc. Am.,* **37,** no. 2, pp. 113–118 (February, 1947).

62. H. C. Kremers, "Optical Silver Chloride," *J. Opt. Soc. Am.,* **37,** no. 5, pp. 337–341 (May, 1947).

63. D. H. Anderson and O. E. Miller, "Silver Chloride Beam Condensing Lens System for Micro Infrared Measurements," *J. Opt. Soc. Am.,* **43,** no. 9, pp. 777–779 (September, 1953).

64. A. Mentzel, "Untersuchung des Absorptionsverlaufes von KCl und KBr auf der kurzewelligen Seite ihrer ultraroten Eigenschwingen" (Investigation of the Absorption Curves for KCl and KBr on the Short-Wavelength Side of their Infrared Resonance Bands), *Zeitschrift für Physik,* **88,** nos. 3 and 4, pp. 178–196 (March, 1934).

65. H. W. Hohls, "Über Dispersion und Absorption von Lithiumfluoride und Natriumfluoride im Ultraroten" (On the Dispersion and Absorption of Lithium Fluoride and Sodium Fluoride in the Infrared), *Annalen der Physik,* **29,** Series 5, no. 5, pp. 433–448 (May, 1937).

66. J. W. Forrest, "Refractive Index Values for Potassium Bromide," *J. Opt. Soc. Am.,* **32,** no. 7, p. 382 (July, 1942).

67. "New Transmitting Crystal Materials for the Infrared," *Perkin-Elmer Inst. News,* **6,** no. 4, p. 6 (Summer, 1951).

68. L. W. Tilton, E. K. Plyler, and R. E. Stephens, "Refractive Indices of Thallium Bromide-Iodide Crystals for Visible and Infrared Energy," *RP* 2008, *J. Research Natl. Bur. Standards,* **43,** no. 1, pp. 81–86 (July, 1949).

69. J. M. Florence, F. W. Glaze, and M. H. Black, "Transmission of Near-Infrared Energy by Some Two- and Three-Component Glasses," *RP* 2408, *J. Research Natl. Bur. Standards,* **50,** no. 4, pp. 187–196 (April, 1953).

70. H. A. Gebbie, W. R. Harding, C. Hilsum, A. W. Pryce, and V. Roberts, "Atmospheric Transmission in the 1 to 14μ Region," *Proc. Roy. Soc. London A,* **206,** no. 1084, pp. 87–107 (March, 1951).

71. G. R. Harrison, R. C. Lord, J. R. Loofbourow, *Practical Spectroscopy,* 605 pp., Prentice-Hall, New York, 1954.

72. Bausch & Lomb Optical Company, "Coated Safety Lenses," *Rev. Sci. Instr.,* **21,** no. 8, p. 778 (August, 1950).

73. J. L. Rood, "Some Properties of Thin Evaporated Films on Glass," *J. Opt. Soc. Am.,* **39,** no. 10, pp. 854–859 (October, 1949).

74. O. S. Heavens, *Optical Properties of Thin Solid Films,* 272 pp., Academic Press, New York, 1955.

75. A. Rothen and M. Hanson, "Optical Properties of Surface Films. Parts I and II," *Rev. Sci. Instr.,* **19,** no. 12, pp. 839–841 (December, 1948); **20,** no. 1, pp. 66–72 (January, 1949).

76. A. H. Pfund, "The Optical Properties of Metallic and Crystalline Powders," *J. Opt. Soc. Am.,* **23,** no. 10, pp. 375–378 (October, 1933).

77. R. L. Henry, "The Transmission of Powder Films in the Infra-Red," *J. Opt Soc. Am.,* **38,** no. 9, pp. 775–789 (September, 1948).

78. L. Harris and R. T. McGinnies and B. M. Siegel, "The Preparation and Optical Properties of Gold Blacks," *J. Opt. Soc. Am.,* **38,** no. 7, pp. 582–589 (July, 1948).

79. D. F. Hornig and J. O'Keefe, "The Design of Fast Thermopiles and Ultimate Sensitivity of Thermal Detectors," *Rev. Sci. Instr.,* **18,** no. 7, pp. 474–482 (July, 1947).

80. J. Strong, "Notes on Radiation Thermopiles," *Rev. Sci. Instr.*, **3**, no. 2, pp. 65–70 (February, 1932).

81. C. H. Cartwright, "Über die Empfindlichkeit von Thermosäulen, Mikroradiometern und Bolometern" (On the Sensitivity of Thermopiles, Microradiometers, and Bolometers), *Zeitschrift für Physik*, **92**, nos. 3 and 4, pp. 153–171 (November, 1934).

82. C. H. Cartwright, "General Theory, Design and Construction of Sensitive Vacuum Thermopiles," *Rev. Sci. Instr.*, **1**, no. 10, pp. 592–604 (October, 1930).

83. C. H. Cartwright, "Natural Observation Limit of Radiometric Measurements," *Physics*, **1**, no. 4, pp. 211–229 (October, 1931).

84. H. Schlitt, "Empfindlichkeit und Einstellzeit gasgefüllter thermoelecktrischer Strahlungsempfänger" (Sensitivity and Response Time of Gas-filled Thermoelectric Radiation Detectors), *Zeitschrift für angewandte Physik*, **7**, no. 3, pp. 113–118 (March, 1955).

85. L. Harris and E. A. Johnson, "The Technique of Sputtering Sensitive Thermocouples," *Rev. Sci. Instr.*, **5**, no. 4, pp. 153–158 (April, 1934).

86. R. V. Jones, "The Design and Construction of Thermoelectric Cells," *J. Sci Instr.*, **11**, no. 8, pp. 247–257 (August, 1934).

87. L. Harris and A. C. Scholp, "The Response of Sputtered Thermocouples to Interrupted Radiation," *J. Opt. Soc. Am.*, **30**, no. 11, pp. 519–522 (November, 1940); **31**, no. 1, p. 25 (January, 1941).

88. L. C. Roess and E. N. Dacus, "The Design and Construction of Rapid-Response Thermocouples for Use as Radiation Detectors in Infra-Red Spectrographs," *Rev. Sci. Instr.*, **16**, no. 7, pp. 164–172 (July, 1945).

89. L. Harris and E. A. Johnson, "The Production of Strong, Cellulose Acetate Films," *Rev. Sci. Instr.*, **4**, no. 8, pp. 454–455 (August, 1933).

90. I. Ambur and N. L. Brown, "Effect of Temperature on the Steady-State Sensitivity of Vacuum Radiation Detectors," *Rev. Sci. Instr.*, **20**, no. 6, pp. 435–441 (June, 1949).

91. E. J. Gillham, "A Method for Measuring the Spectral Reflectivity of a Thermopile," *Brit. J. Appl. Phys.*, **4**, no. 5, pp. 151–155 (May, 1953).

92. E. K. Plyler and J. J. Ball, "Infra-Red Absorption of Deposited Blacks," *J. Opt. Soc. Am.*, **38**, no. 11, p. 988 (November, 1948).

93. L. Geiling, "Das Thermoelement als Strahlungsmesser" (The Thermoelectric Element as a Measuring Instrument for Radiation), *Zeitschrift für angewandte Physik*, **3**, no. 12, pp. 467–477 (1951).

94. F. A. Firestone, "Radiation Thermopile Design," *Rev. Sci. Instr.*, **1**, no. 11, pp. 630–649 (November, 1930).

95. W. G. Fastie, "Ambient Temperature Independent Thermopiles for Radiation Pyrometry," *J. Opt. Soc. Am.*, **41**, no. 11, pp. 823–829 (November, 1951).

96. L. Geiling, "Sur le problem de l'adaptation d'un thermocouplo à un galvanomètre" (On the Problem of the Adaptation of a Thermocouple to a Galvanometer), *Annales des telecommunications*, **8**, no. 3, pp. 103–112 (March, 1953).

97. A. C. Downing, "The Construction of Micro-Galvanometer Systems," *J. Sci. Instr.*, **25**, no. 7, pp. 230–231 (July, 1948).

98. L. Harris, "Rapid Response Thermopiles," *J. Opt. Soc. Am.*, **36**, no. 10, pp. 597–603 (October, 1946).

99. C. H. Cartwright, "Wiedemann-Franzsche Zahl, Wärmeleitfähigkeit und thermo-elektrische Kraft von Tellur" (Wiedmann-Franz Ratio, Thermal

Conductivity, and Thermoelectric Power of Tellurium), *Annalen der Physik,* **18,** Series 5, no. 6 (1933).

100. C. H. Cartwright, "Radiation Thermopiles for Use at Liquid Air Temperatures," *Rev. Sci. Instr.,* **4,** no. **7,** pp. 382–384 (July, 1933).

101. R. V. Jones, "Radiation Thermopiles of Quick Response," *J. Sci. Instr.,* **14,** no. 3, pp. 83–89 (March, 1937).

102. A. V. Hill, "The Speed of Response of a Thermopile-Galvanometer System," *J. Sci. Instr.,* **11,** no. 8, pp. 246–247 (August, 1934).

103. L. Harris, "The Evaporation of Antimony," *J. Appl. Phys.,* **17,** no. 9, p. 757 (September, 1946).

104. A. V. Hill, "A Method of Increasing the Speed of Response of Radiation Thermopiles," *J. Sci. Instr.,* **26,** no. 8, p. 277 (August, 1949).

105. J. D. Hardy, "A Theoretical and Experimental Study of the Resonance Radiometer," *Rev. Sci. Instr.,* **1,** no. 8, pp. 429–448 (August, 1930).

106. A. V. Hill, "Moving-Coil Galvanometers of Short Period and Their Amplification," *J. Sci. Instr.,* **25,** no. 7, pp. 225–229 (July, 1948); no. 8 (August, 1948).

107. A. V. Hill, "The Time-Lag in Recording Current with a Galvanometer," *J. Sci. Instr.,* **25,** no. 10, p. 351 (October, 1948).

108. A. V. Hill, "The Brownian Fluctuations of a Coupled Galvanometer System," *J. Sci. Instr.,* **30,** no. 2, pp. 44–45 (February, 1953).

109. K. Copeland, A. C. Downing, and A. V. Hill, "A Moving Coil Galvanometer of Extreme Sensitivity," *J. Sci. Instr.,* **30,** no. 2, pp. 40–45 (February, 1953).

110. E. A. Johnson, "The Measurement of Temperature of Sound Fields," *Phys. Rev.,* **45,** no. 9, pp. 641–645 (May, 1934).

111. L. Harris, "Thermocouples for the Measurement of Small Intensities of Radiation," *Phys. Rev.,* **45,** no. 9, pp. 635–640 (May, 1934).

112. H. C. Burger and P. H. van Cittert, "Die Herstellung von Wismut-Antimon-Vacuumthermoelementen durch Verdampfung" (The Production of Bismuth-Antimony Vacuum Thermoelectric Elements through Evaporation), *Zeitschrift für Physik,* **66,** nos. 3 and 4, pp. 210–217 (November, 1930).

113. P. B. Fellgett, "Dynamic Impedance and Sensitivity of Radiation Thermocouples," *Proc. Phys. Soc. London B,* **62,** no. 354B, Part 6, pp. 351–359 (June, 1949).

114. L. Recart, "Amplificateur pour piles thermoélectriques" (Amplifier for Thermopiles), *Revue d'optique,* **33,** no. 10, pp. 504–507 (October, 1954).

115. C. H. Cartwright, "Construction of Thermo-Relay Amplifiers," *Rev. Sci. Instr.,* **3,** no. 5, pp. 221–224 (May, 1932).

116. R. K. Brinton and C. T. O'Konski, "A Phototube Measuring Circuit for Thermopiles," *Rev. Sci. Instr.,* **24,** no. 12, pp. 1102–1104 (December, 1953).

117. W. Leo and W. Hübner, "Zur Strahlungsmessung mittels Thermoelementen und hochempfindlicher Photozellenkompensation" (Measurement of Radiation by Means of Thermocouples and High-Sensitivity Photocell Compensation), *Zeitschrift für angewandte Physik,* **2,** no. 11, pp. 454–461 (November, 1950).

118. F. Hoffmann and U. Schley, "Zur Messung sehr geringer Strahlungsleistungen mit Thermoelementen" (On the Measurement of Very Faint Radiation with Thermocouples), *Zeitschrift für angewandte Physik,* **7,** no. 3, pp. 109–113 (1955).

119. R. K. Brinton and C. T. O'Konski, "A Phototube Measuring Circuit for Thermopiles," *Rev. Sci. Instr.,* **24,** no. 12, pp. 1102–1104 (December, 1953).

120. J. R. Beattie and G. K. T. Conn, "A Tuned Galvanometer Amplifier," *Rev. Sci., Instr.*, **25**, no. 9, pp. 888–891 (September, 1954).

121. W. J. H. Moll, "A Thermopile for Measuring Radiation," *Proc. Phys. Soc. London*, **35**, no. 5, pp. 257–260 (December, 1922 to August, 1923).

122. A. Gridley, "Construction of a Moll Type of Thermopile," *Instrum. Prac.*, **3**, no. 1, pp. 9–10 (November, 1948).

123. T. R. Harrison and W. H. Wannamaker, "An Improved Radiation Pyrometer," American Institute of Physics, *Temperature*, pp. 1206–1224, Reinhold Publishing Corp., New York, 1941.

124. W. W. Coblentz, "A Portable Vacuum Thermopile," *Scientific Paper* **413**, pp. 187–192, U. S. Bur. Standards, Washington (July, 1921).

125. L. M. K. Boelter, E. R. Dempster, R. Bromberg, and J. T. Gier, "An Investigation of Aircraft Heaters XXVI—Development of a Sensitive Plated-Type Thermopile for Measuring Radiation," *Technical Note* **1450**, pp. 1–66, U. S. National Advisory Committee for Aeronautics, Washington (July, 1948).

126. T. Benzinger and C. Kitzinger, "A 4π-Radiometer," *Rev. Sci. Instr.*, **21**, no. 7, pp. 599–604 (July, 1950).

127. R. Gardon, "An Instrument for the Direct Measurement of Intense Radiation," *Rev. Sci. Instr.*, **24**, no. 5, pp. 366–370 (May, 1953).

128. A. B. Willoughby, "Absolute Water Flow Calorimeter for the Measurement of Intense Beams of Radiant Energy," *Rev. Sci. Instr.*, **25**, no. 7, pp. 667–670 (July, 1954).

129. G. Rosenthal, "Über den Bau eines hochempfindlichen Thermoelementes für Strahlungsmessung" (On the Construction of High-Sensitivity Thermocouple for Radiation Measurement), *Zeitschrift für Instrumentenkunde*, **59**, no. 11, pp. 432–439 (November, 1939); **59**, no. 12, pp. 457–463 (December, 1939).

130. H. Wilson and T. D. Epps, "The Construction of Thermo-Couples by Electro-Deposition," *Proc. Phys. Soc. London*, **32**, no. 29, Part 5, pp. 326–340 (August, 1920).

131. R. A. Crane and F. E. Blacet, "A Series Parallel Linear Thermopile with Interchangeable Receiving Units," *Rev. Sci. Instr.*, **21**, no. 3, p. 259 (March, 1958).

132. D. M. Packer and C. Lock, "Thermocouple Measurements of Spectral Intensities in the Vacuum Ultraviolet," *J. Opt. Soc. Am.*, **41**, no. 10, pp. 699–701 (October, 1951).

133. F. T. Rogers, "On the Construction of Very Sensitive Vacuum Thermoelectric Cells," *Rev. Sci. Instr.*, **11**, no. 9, pp. 281–282 (September, 1940).

134. G. B. B. M. Sutherland and E. Lee, "Development in the Infra-Red Region of the Spectrum," *Reports Phys. Soc. Progress Physics*, **11**, pp. 145–167 (1946–1947).

135. V. Z. Williams, "Infra-Red Instrumentation and Techniques," *Rev. Sci. Instr.*, **19**, no. 3, pp. 135–178 (March, 1948).

136. S. S. Stack, "Vacuum Thermocouples of the Radiation Type," *Gen. Elec. Rev.*, **42**, no. 8, pp. 365–366 (August, 1939).

137. M. D. Liston, "Amplification and Electrical Systems for a Double Beam Recording Infra-Red Spectrometer," *J. Opt. Soc. Am.*, **40**, no. 1, pp. 36–41 (January, 1950).

138. D. A. H. Brown, R. P. Chasmar, and P. B. Fellgett, "The Construction of Radiation Thermocouples Using Semi-Conducting Thermoelectric Materials," *J. Sci. Instr.,* **30,** no. 6, pp. 195–199 (June, 1953).

139. G. B. B. M. Sutherland, "The Application of New Infra-Red Detectors to Problems in Infra-Red Spectroscopy and Molecular Structure," *Revue d'optique,* **28,** no. 7, pp. 423–428 (July, 1949).

140. C. H. Cartwright, "Tellurium-Bismuth Vacuum Radiation Thermocouple," *Rev. Sci. Instr.,* **3,** no. 2, pp. 73–79 (February, 1932).

141. E. Schwarz, "Sensitivity of Schwarz-Hilger Thermopiles," *Rev. Sci. Instr.,* **20,** no. 12, p. 962 (December, 1949).

142. P. Moon and W. R. Mills, "Construction and Test of an Alternating-Current Bolometer," *Rev. Sci. Instr.,* **6,** no. 1, pp. 8–15 (January, 1935).

143. M. Czerny, W. Kofink, and W. Lippert, "Bolometer geringer Trägheit" (Bolometer of Low Inertia), *Annalen der Physik,* **8,** series 6, nos. 1–2, pp. 65–86 (1950).

144. B. H. Billings, W. L. Hyde, and E. F urr, "An Investigation of the Properties of Evaporated Metal Bolometers," *J. Opt. Soc. Am.,* **37,** no. 3, pp. 123–132 (March, 1947).

145. J. M. W. Milatz and H. A. Van der Velden, "Natural Limit of Measuring Radiation with a Bolometer," *Physica,* **10,** no. 6, pp. 369–380 (June, 1943).

146. R. Novak, "The Theory of Metallic Bolometers," *Czechoslav. J. Phys.,* **7,** no. 3, pp. 284–292 (1957); *Sci. Abstr. Sect. A,* **62,** no. 737, p. 420 (May, 1959).

147. R. Novak, "Metallic Bolometers with Temperature Dependent Thermal Impedance," *Czechoslav. J. Phys.,* **7,** no. 4, pp. 432–443 (1957); *Sci. Abstr. Sect. A,* **62,** no. 740, p. 768 (August, 1959).

148. R. Novak, "Metallic Bolometers in Periodically Interrupted Radiation," *Czechoslav. J. Phys.,* **8,** no. 2, pp. 196–207 (1958); *Sci. Abstr. Sect. A,* **62,** no 737, p. 420 (May, 1959).

149. G. Barth, "Bolometer für Strahlungsmessungen" (Bolometers for Radiation Measurement), *A.T.M. Archiv. für technisches Messen,* **260,** Ref. J23-3, pp 201–204 (September, 1957).

150. G. Barth, "Die natürliche Nachweisgrenze beim Metallbolometer" (The Natural Limits of Sensitivity of Metal Bolometers), *Optik,* **15,** no. 11, pp. 694–709 (November, 1958).

151. J. I. Pantchechnikoff, "On the Nature of a Soldered Contact on a Semiconductor," *Phys. Rev.,* **79,** no. 6, pp. 1027–1028 (September, 1950).

152. R. C. Jones, "Factors of Merit for Radiation Detectors," *J. Opt. Soc. of Am.,* **39,** no. 5, pp. 344–356 (May, 1949).

153. E. Archibold, "An Evaporated Gold Bolometer," *J. Sci. Instr.,* **34,** no. 6, pp. 240–242 (June, 1957).

154. H. Dewhurst, "A Rapid Bolometer Made by Sputtering on Thin Films," *Proc. Phys. Soc. London,* **39,** Part 1, pp. 39–78 (December, 1926).

155. C. B. Aiken, W. H. Carter, Jr., and F. S. Phillips, "The Production of Film-Type Bolometers with Rapid Response," *Rev. Sci. Instr.,* **17,** no. 10, pp. 377–385 (October, 1946).

156. H. Riemann, "Temperungseinfluss auf das Widerstandsverhalten von aufgedämpften Wismutbolometern" (The Effect of Tempering on the Resistance of Evaporated Bismuth Bolometers), *Annalen der Physik,* **16,** Series 6, nos. 1–2, pp. 52–58 (1955).

157. H. Reimann, "Untersuchungen am Wismutbolometer bei rechteckig und sinusformig modulierter Bestrahlung" (Experiments with the Bismuth Bolometer and Radiation Modulated to Have a Rectangular or Sine-Wave Form), *Annalen der Physik*, **16**, Series 6, nos. 1–2, pp. 59–67 (1955).

158. Von K. Bischoff, E. Justi, M. Kohler, and G. Lautz, "Metall-Widerstandsbolometer bei tiefen Temperaturen" (Metal Resistance Bolometer at Low Temperatures), *Zeitschrift für Naturforschung* **10a**, no. 5, pp. 401–412 (May, 1955).

159. J. N. Shive, "Heating and Cooling of Bolometer Elements," *J. Appl. Phys.*, **18**, no. 4, pp. 398–405 (April, 1947).

160. K. M. Laing and J. V. Fitzgerald, "Glass Film Bolometers," *Rev. Sci. Instr.*, **22**, no. 7, pp. 540–541 (July, 1951).

161. P. Morrison, "Physics in 1946," *J. Appl. Phys.*, **18**, no. 2, pp. 134–135 (February, 1947).

162. J. A. Hulbert and G. O. Jones, "The Superconducting Bolometer as a Detector of Thermal Radiation from Low-Temperature Sources," *Proc. Phys. Soc. London B*, **68**, no. 431B, Part 11, pp. 801–804 (November, 1955).

163. J. V. Lebacqz, C. W. Clark, M. C. Williams, and D. H. Andrews, "Detection at Radio Frequencies by Superconductivity," *Proceedings of the IRE*, The Institute of Radio Engineers, New York, **37**, no. 10, pp. 1147–1152 (October, 1949).

164. N. Fuson, "The Effect of Current Magnitude upon the Behavior of a Superconducting Bolometer in Its Transition Region," *J. Appl. Phys.*, **20**, no. 1, pp. 59–66 (January, 1949).

165. N. Fuson, "The Infra-Red Sensitivity of Superconducting Bolometers," *J. Opt. Soc. Am.*, **38**, no. 10, pp. 845–853 (October, 1948).

166. D. H. Andrews, R. M. Milton, and W. DeSorbo, "A Fast Superconducting Bolometer," *J. Opt. Soc. Am.*, **36**, no. 9, pp. 518–524 (September, 1946).

167. A. Goetz, "The Possible Use of Superconductivity for Radiometric Purposes," *Phys. Rev.*, **55**, no. 12, pp. 1270–1271 (June, 1939).

168. R. Havens, "Theoretical Comparison of Heat Detectors," *J. Opt. Soc. Am.*, **36**, no. 6, pp. 351–356 (June, 1946).

169. O. S. Duffendack, "Wartime Developments in the Detection and Measurement of Thermal Radiation," *The Engineers' Digest, N. Y.*, **3**, no. 10, pp. 483, 530, 531 (October, 1946).

170. "Thermal Detectors," *Electronic Industries*, **5**, no. 9, pp. 87, 116, 118 (September, 1946).

171. R. M. Milton, "A Superconducting Bolometer for Infrared Measurements," *Chemical Reviews*, **39**, no. 3, pp. 419–433 (December, 1946).

172. J. V. Lebacqz and D. H. Andrews, "Properties of CbN at Radio Frequencies," *Proc. Natl. Electronics Conf.*, **4**, pp. 11–23 (1948).

173. D. H. Andrews, W. F. Brucksch, Jr., W. T. Ziegler, and E. R. Blanchard, "Attenuated Superconductors—I. For Measuring Infra-Red Radiation," *Rev. Sci. Instr.*, **13**, no. 7, pp. 281–292 (July, 1942).

174. E. F. Daly and G. B. B. M. Sutherland, "An Infra-Red Spectroscope with Cathode-Ray Presentation," *Proc. Phys. Soc. London*, **59**, pp. 77–87 (1947); *Nature*, **157**, no. 3991, p. 547 (April, 1946).

175. M. Varicak, "Sensitive Semiconductor-Detector for Infrared Radiation," *Am. J. Phys.*, **26**, no. 8, pp. 561–562 (November, 1958).

176. F. G. Brockman, "Production and Properties of Nickel Bolometers," *J. Opt. Soc. Am.*, **36**, no. 1, pp. 32–35 (January, 1946).

177. R. C. L. Bosworth, "New Types of Linear Bolometers," *Trans. Faraday Soc.*, **30**, Part 7, no. 158, pp. 554–569 (July, 1934).

178. E. B. Baker and C. D. Robb, "A Fast and Sensitive Bolometer and Galvanometer System for an Infra-Red Spectrometer," *Rev. Sci. Instr.*, **14**, no. 12, pp. 356–359 (December, 1943).

179. G. C. Mönch, G. Wichert, and O. Böttger, "Experimentelle Untersuchungen am Wismut und theoretische Auslegungen der Ergebnisse" (Experimental Investigations of Bismuth Bolometers and Theoretical Interpretation of Results), *Annalen der Physik*, **12**, Series 6, nos. 4–6, pp. 183–221 (1953).

180. P. Moon and L. R. Steinhardt, "The Dielectric Bolometer," *J. Opt. Soc. Am.*, **28**, no. 5, pp. 148–162 (May, 1938).

181. J. Ewles, "A Fast and Sensitive Dielectric Bolometer of New Material and Construction," *J. Sci. Instr.*, **24**, no. 3, pp. 57–61 (March, 1947).

182. M. L. Harbold and J. L. Bohn, "Capacitor Microphone as a Radiation Detector," *Rev. Sci. Instr.*, **29**, no. 3, pp. 229–232 (March, 1958).

183. H. V. Hayes, "A New Receiver of Radiant Energy," *Rev. Sci. Instr.*, **7**, no. 5, pp. 202–204 (May, 1936).

184. A. Bayle, "Récepteur pour la mesure de la temperature des nuages" (Receiver for Measuring the Temperature of Clouds), *Revue d'optique*, **33**, no. 10, pp. 507–513 (October, 1954).

185. W. M. Hall, "A New Method of Measurement of Radiant Energy," *Rev. Sci. Instr.*, **7**, no. 5, pp. 205–206 (May, 1936).

186. M. J. E. Golay, "A Pneumatic Infra-Red Detector," *Rev. Sci. Instr.*, **18**, no. 5, pp. 357–362 (May, 1947).

187. M. J. E. Golay, "The Theoretical and Practical Sensitivity of the Pneumatic Infra-Red Detector," *Rev. Sci. Instr.*, **20**, no. 11, pp. 816–820 (November, 1949).

188. M. J. E. Golay, "Static Multislit Spectrometry and Its Application to the Panoramic Display of Infrared Spectra," *J. Opt. Soc. Am.*, **41**, no. 7, pp. 468–472 (July, 1951).

189. M. J. E. Golay, "The Theoretical and Practical Sensitivity of the Pneumatic Infra-Red Detector," *Rev. Sci. Instr.*, **20**, no. 11, pp. 816–820 (November, 1949).

190. J. T. Agnew, "Combustion Studies Using the Golay Photothermal Detector with an Infrared Monochromator," *Paper* 48-SA-16, 12 pp., American Society of Mechanical Engineers, New York (1950).

191. A. F. Gibson, "The Sensitivity and Response Time of Lead Sulphide Photoconductive Cells," *Proc. Phys. Soc. London B*, **64**, no. 379B, Part 7, pp. 603–615 (July, 1951).

192. G. K. Teal, J. R. Fisher, and A. W. Treptow, "A New Bridge Photo-Cell Employing a Photo-Conductive Effect in Silicon. Some Properties of High Purity Silicon," *J. Appl. Phys.*, **17**, no. 11, pp. 879–886 (November, 1946).

193. T. S. Moss, "Lead Telluride and Lead Selenide Infra-Red Detectors," *Research*, **6**, pp. 258–264 (July, 1953).

194. C. J. Milner and B. N. Watts, "Lead Selenide Photoconductive Cells," *Nature*, **163**, no. 4139, p. 322 (February, 1949).

195. L. Sosnowski, J. Starkiewicz, and O. Simpson, "Lead Sulphide Photoconductive Cells," *Nature*, **159**, no. 4050, pp. 818–819 (June, 1947).

196. A. F. Gibson, W. D. Lawson, and T. S. Moss, "The Long-Wave Limit of Infra-Red Photoconductivity in PbSe," *Proc. Phys. Soc. London A*, **64**, no. 383A, Part 11, pp. 1054–1055 (November, 1951).

197. M. Smollett and R. G. Pratt, "The Effect of Adsorbed Air on Photoconductive Layers of Lead Sulphide," *Proc. Phys. Soc. London B*, **68**, Part 6, pp. 390–391 (June, 1955).

198. J. C. S. Richards, "Portable Radiation Detectors Employing Photoconductive Cells," *J. Sci. Instr.*, **32**, no. 9, pp. 340–343 (September, 1955).

199. R. H. Bube, "Photoconductivity of the Sulfide, Selenide, and Telluride of Zinc or Cadmium," *Proceedings of the IRE*, The Institute of Radio Engineers, New York, **43**, no. 12, pp. 1836–1850 (December, 1955).

200. T. S. Moss, "Spectral Sensitivity of Lead Telluride Layers," *Nature*, **161**, no 4098, pp. 766–767 (May, 1948).

201. R. G. Breckenridge, B. R. Russell, and E. E. Hahn, *Photoconductivity Conference*, 653 pp., John Wiley & Sons, New York, 1956.

202. B. J. Kolomiets, "Characteristics and Properties of Lead-Sulphide Photoresistances" (In Russian), *J. Tech. Phys.*, *U.S.S.R.*, **21**, pp. 1–11 (January, 1951).

203. O. Simpson, "Conductivity of Evaporated Films of Lead Selenide," *Nature*, **160**, no. 4075, pp. 791–792 (December, 1947).

204. R. J. Cashman, "Film-Type Infrared Photoconductors," *Proceedings of the IRE*, The Institute of Radio Engineers, New York, **47**, no. 9, pp. 1471–1475 (September, 1959).

205. R. F. Potter, J. M. Pernett, and A. B. Naugle, "The Measurement and Interpretation of Photodetector Parameters," *Proceedings of the IRE*, The Institute of Radio Engineers, New York, **47**, no. 9, pp. 1503–1507 (September, 1959).

206. R. L. Petritz, "Theory of Photoconductivity in Semiconductor Films," *Phys. Rev.*, **104**, no. 6, pp. 1508–1516 (December, 1956).

207. F. H. Nicoll and B. Kazan, "Large Area High-Current Photoconductive Cells Using Cadmium Sulfide Powder," *J. Opt. Soc. Am.*, **45**, no. 8, pp. 647–650 (August, 1955).

208. R. H. Bube, "Infrared Quenching and a Unified Description of Photoconductivity Phenomena in Cadmium Sulfide and Selenide," *Phys. Rev.*, **99**, no. 4, pp. 1105–1116 (August, 1955).

209. R. P. Chasmar, "High-Frequency Characteristics of Lead Sulphide and Lead Selenide Layers," *Nature*, **161**, no. 4086, pp. 281–282 (February, 1948).

210. S. S. Carlisle and G. Alderton, "Temperature Coefficient of Sensitivity of Lead Sulphide Photo-conductive Cells at Room Temperature," *Nature*, **163**, p. 529 (April, 1949).

211. J. D. Harmer, "An Infrared Radiation Pyrometer," *J. Sci. Instr.*, **32**, no. 5, pp. 167–170 (May, 1955).

212. "New Eyes for Infrared," *R & D Letter*, **2**, no. 3, 4 pp., Westinghouse Electric Corp., Pittsburgh (December, 1958).

213. T. S. Moss, "Spectral Sensitivity of Lead Sulphide Layers," *Nature*, **159**, no. 4040, pp. 476–477 (April, 1947).

214. V. Roberts and A. S. Young, "The Application of Lead Selenide Photoconductive Cells to Infra-Red Spectroscopy," *J. Sci. Instr.*, **30**, no. 6, pp. 199–200 (June, 1953).

215. O. Simpson, G. B. B. M. Sutherland, and D. E. Blackwell, "Lead Telluride Cells for Infra-Red Spectroscopy," *Nature,* **161,** no. 4086, pp. 281–282 (February, 1948).

216. C. R. Barber and E. C. Pyatt, "Low-Temperature Radiation Pyrometry Using a Lead Sulphide Photoconductive Cell," *Nature,* **165,** no. 4200, pp. 691–692 (April, 1950).

217. Eastman Kodak Co., *Kodak Ektron Detector,* 24 pp., Eastman Kodak Co., Rochester, N. Y., 1955.

218. O. Simpson, "The Effect of Room Temperature Radiation on the Infra-Red Response of Lead Telluride Photoconductors," *Proc. Phys. Soc. London,* **61,** no. 347, Part 5, pp. 486–487 (November, 1948).

219. T. S. Moss and R. P. Chasmar, "Spectral Response of Lead Selenide," *Nature,* **161,** no. 4085, p. 244 (February, 1948).

220. E. C. Pyatt, "A Brightness Temperature Pyrometer Using a Photoconductive Cell," *J. Sci. Instr.,* **29,** no. 4, pp. 125–127 (April, 1952).

221. "Miniature Cadmium Sulfide and Lead Sulfide Photocells," *Elec. Mfg.,* **54,** no. 4, pp. 108–113 (April, 1955).

222. P. R. Marshall, "A Portable Radiation Pyrometer," *J. Sci. Instr.,* **27,** no. 2, pp. 33–36 (February, 1950).

223. G. B. B. M. Sutherland, "The Application of New Infra-Red Detectors to Problems in Infra-Red Spectroscopy and Molecular Structure," *Revue d'optique,* **28,** no. 7, pp. 423–428 (July, 1949).

224. T. R. Lawson, Jr., "Semiconductors—Their Characteristics and Principles," *Westinghouse Engineer,* **14,** no. 5, pp. 178–182 (September, 1954).

225. J. N. Shive, "A New Germanium Photo-Resistance Cell," *Phys. Rev.,* **76,** no. 4, p. 575 (August, 1949).

226. "A Survey of the Transistor," *General Motors Engineering Journal,* **2,** no. 1, pp. 40–47 (January–February, 1955).

227. F. F. Rieke, L. H. DeVaux and A. J. Tuzzalino, "Single-Crystal Infrared Detectors Based on Intrinsic Absorption," *Proceedings of the IRE,* The Institute of Radio Engineers, New York, **47,** no. 9, pp. 1475–1478 (September, 1959).

228. W. Shockley, "Transistor Physics," *Bell Telephone System Technical Publications, Monograph No. 2217; American Scientist,* **42,** pp. 41–72 (January, 1954).

229. Members of the Technical Staff of the Bell Telephone Laboratories, Inc., "Some Contributions to Transistor Electronics," *Bell Telephone System Technical Publications, Monograph No. 1726; Bell System Technical Journal,* **28,** pp. 335–489 (July, 1949).

230. G. D. O'Neill, *Germanium Photocells,* 13 pp., Sylvania Electric Products, Inc., Bayside, N. Y., 1950.

231. G. A. Morton, "Infrared Photoemission," *Proceedings of the IRE,* The Institute of Radio Engineers, New York, **47,** no. 9, pp. 1467–1469 (September, 1959).

232. F. K. Richtmyer, E. H. Kennard, and T. Lauritsen, *Introduction to Modern Physics,* 666 pp., McGraw-Hill Book Co., New York, 1955.

233. J. S. Preston, "Photoelectric Cells: A Review of Progress with Special Reference to Use in Photometry and Radiometry," *Revue d'optique,* **27,** nos. 8 and 9, pp. 513–537 (August–September, 1948).

234. Allen B. Du Mont Laboratories, *Du Mont Multiplier Photo-Tubes,* 57 pp., Allen B. Du Mont Laboratories, Clifton, N. J., 1955.

235. A. Sommer, *Photoelectric Tubes,* 118 pp., Methuen & Co., London, 1951.

236. E. O. Johnson, "Increased Light Sensitivity from Standard Gas Phototubes," *Rev. Sci. Instr.,* **25,** no. 8, pp. 839–840 (August, 1954).

237. C. H. Vincent, "The Gas-Multiplier: A New Type of Electron Multiplier," *Nature,* **177,** no. 4504, pp. 391–392 (February, 1956).

238. "Transmission-Type Photomultiplier," *Science,* **123,** no. 3199, p. 663 (April, 1956).

239. H. J. Marrinan, "The Use of Photomultipliers in Raman Spectroscopy," *J. Opt. Soc. Am.,* **43,** no. 12, pp. 1211–1215 (December, 1953).

240. Farnsworth Electronics Co., "Photomultiplier," *Rev. Sci. Instr.,* **26,** no. 10, p. 1002 (October, 1955).

241. D. Glansholm and B. Kleman, "The Use of Photomultipliers in Spectroscopy," *Arkiv for Fysik,* **2,** no. 29, pp. 305–308 (1950).

242. R. W. Hendrick, "Precision Photomultiplier Gain Stabilization," *Rev. Sci. Instr.,* **27,** no. 4, pp. 240–241 (April, 1956).

243. E. M. Baker and B. M. Tolbert, " 'Cosmic-Ray' Effect in Photomultiplier Tubes," *Rev. Sci. Instr.,* **25,** no. 12, p. 1218 (December, 1954).

244. "Multiplier Phototubes," *Du Mont Oscillographer,* **14,** no. 4, pp. 3–15 (April–June, 1954).

245. R. W. Engstrom, "Multiplier Phototube Characteristics; Application to Low Light Levels," *J. Opt. Soc. Am.,* **37,** no. 6, pp. 420–431 (June, 1947).

246. B. R. Linden, "Five New Photomultipliers for Scintillation Counting," *Nucleonics,* **11,** no. 9, pp. 30–33 (September, 1953).

247. J. E. Draper, "Millimicrosecond Photomultiplier Tests with Oscilloscope Light Pulses," *Rev. Sci. Instr.,* **29,** no. 2, pp. 179–180 (February, 1958).

248. G. A. Morton, R. M. Matheson, and M. H. Greenblatt, "Design of Photomultipliers for the Submillimicrosecond Region," *I.R.E. Trans. on Nuclear Sci.,* **NS-5,** no. 3, pp. 98–104, Institute of Radio Engineers (December, 1958).

249. P. L. Tea, Jr. and H. D. Baker, "New Detector Unit for Irradiance Measurement, Utilizing an Integrating Sphere and a Photomultiplier Tube," *J. Opt. Soc. Am.,* **46,** no. 10, pp. 875–878 (October, 1956).

250. H. W. Russell and C. F. Lucks, "A New Two-color Optical Pyrometer," American Institute of Physics, *Temperature,* pp. 1159–1163, Reinhold Publishing Corp., New York, 1941.

251. A. Peuteman, "Un nouveau pyromètre à cellule photoélectrique" (A New Photoelectric Pyrometer), *Compt. rend.,* **237,** no. 17, pp. 975–977 (October, 1953).

252. H. J. Zetzmann, "Temperaturmessung mit Photozellen" (Temperature Measurement with Photo Cells), *ATM Archiv für technisches Messen,* V214-3, T116–T117 (September, 1934).

253. R. W. Engstrom, "Refrigerator for a Multiplier Phototube," *Rev. Sci. Instr.,* **18,** no. 8, pp. 587–588 (August, 1947).

254. A. H. Canada, "Infrared: Its Military and Peacetime Uses," *Data Folder* 87516, 65 pp., General Electric, Schenectady, N. Y., 1954.

255. B. D. E. Flagge and O. R. Harris, "Individual Dynode Voltage Regulator for Photomultiplier Tubes," *Rev. Sci. Instr.,* **26,** no. 6, p. 619 (June, 1955).

256. J. Starkiewicz, L. Sosnowski, and O. Simpson, "Photovoltaic Effects Exhibited in High-resistance Semi-conducting Films," *Nature,* **158,** no. 4001, p. 28 (July, 1946).

257. N. R. Campbell, "Compensating Circuits for Rectifier Cells," *J. Sci. Instr.*, **11**, no. 4, pp. 125–126 (April, 1934).

258. "Special Load Circuits for Use with the Weston Photoelectric Cell," *Weston Engineering Notes*, **2**, no. 2, pp. 4–7 (April, 1947).

259. R. W. Gilbert, "Photocell Range Network," *Weston Engineering Notes*, **6**, no. 2, pp. 7–8 (December, 1951).

260. T. Land and H. Lund, "A Photo-Electric Pyrometer for a Small High-Frequency Induction Furnace," *J. Iron Steel Inst. London*, **156**, Part 1, pp. 75–77 (May, 1947).

261. T. Land, "Barrier-Layer Photo-Electric Cells for Temperature Measurement," *J. Iron Steel Inst. London*, **149**, no. 1, 481P–511P (1944).

262. T. Land, "A Photo-Electric Roof Pyrometer for Open-Hearth Furnaces," *J. Iron Steel Inst. London*, **155**, Part 4, pp. 568–576 (April, 1947).

263. B. M. Larsen and W. E. Shenk, "Temperature Measurement with Blocking-layer Photocells," American Institute of Physics, *Temperature*, pp. 1150–1158, Reinhold Publishing Corp., New York, 1941.

264. E. Virasoro and G. Berraz, "Novel Photoelectric Pyrometer," *The Engineers' Digest, N. Y.*, **2**, no. 7, pp. 327–330 (July, 1945).

265. R. A. Houstoun, "The Efficiency of the Barrier Layer Photo-cell," *Phil. Mag.*, Series 7, **39**, no. 298, pp. 902–910 (November, 1948).

266. M. E. Fogle, "Temperature Measurement and Control with Solid Photoelectric Cells," *Trans. Electrochem. Soc.*, **83**, pp. 77–86 (April, 1943).

267. "25th Anniversary Summary on the Weston Photronic Cell," *Weston Engineering Notes*, **11**, no. 3, pp. 1–8 (September, 1956).

268. J. A. Hall, "The Drift of Selenium Photo-Electric Cells in Relation to Their Use in Temperature Measurement," *J. Iron Steel Inst. London*, **149**, no. 1, pp. 547P–557P (1944).

269. H. T. Wrobel and H. H. Chamberlain, "Photometric Equipment for Blocking-Layer Light-Sensitive Cells," *Gen. Elec. Rev.*, **49**, pp. 25–29 (April, 1946).

270. G. R. Pruett and R. L. Petritz, "Detectivity and Preamplifier Considerations for Indium Antimonide Photovoltaic Detectors," *Proceedings of the IRE*, The Institute of Radio Engineers, New York, **47**, no. 9, pp. 1524–1529 (September, 1959).

271. J. Vollmer, J. Duke, and C. Wysocki, "High-Speed Radiation Pyrometer," *J. Opt. Soc. Am.*, **46**, no. 3, pp. 215–217 (March, 1956).

272. W. Derganc and S. N. Howell, "Two New Total Radiation Pyrometers," *Paper* 56-98, 8 pp., American Institute of Electrical Engineers, New York (1955).

273. R. Chion, "Les pyromètres à rayonnement pour la mesure des températures en regime transitoire" (Radiation Pyrometers for the Measurement of Transient Temperatures), *Métaux Corrosion Industries*, **31**, no. 365, pp. 22–37 (January, 1956).

274. "Instruments and Control Systems—1960 Buyers' Guide," *Instruments*, **32**, no. 10, Part 2, 220 pp. (October, 1959).

275. W. L. Wolfe, "A Selected Bibliography on Infrared Techniques and Applications," *Proceedings of the IRE*, The Institute of Radio Engineers, New York, **47**, no. 9, pp. 1647–1649 (September, 1959).

276. R. L. Petritz, "Fundamentals of Infrared Detectors," *Proceedings of the IRE*, The Institute of Radio Engineers, New York, **47**, no. 9, pp. 1458–1467 (September, 1959).

277. R. C. Jones, "Noise in Radiation Detectors," *Proceedings of the IRE,* The Institute of Radio Engineers, New York, **47,** no. 9, pp. 1481–1486 (September, 1959).

278. L. Larmore, "Infrared Photography," *Proceedings of the IRE,* The Institute of Radio Engineers, New York, **47,** no. 9, pp. 1487–1488 (September, 1959).

279. T. Land, "Practical Aspects of Radiation Pyrometry," *Trans. Soc. Instrum. Tech.,* **11,** no. 1, pp. 10–18 (March, 1959).

280. A. M. Stoll, "A Wide-Range Thermistor Radiometer for the Measurement of Skin Temperature and Environmental Radiant Temperature," *Rev. Sci. Instr.,* **25,** no. 2, pp. 184–187 (February, 1954).

281. "A Blackbody Standard," *Instruments,* **28,** no. 3, pp. 436–438 (March, 1955).

282. J. J. Brophy, "Current Noise in Thermistor Bolometer Flakes," *J. Appl. Phys.,* **25,** no. 2, pp. 222–224 (February, 1954).

283. T. S. Moss, "Photoconductivity in the Elements," *Proc. Roy. Soc. London A,* **64,** pp. 590–591 (June, 1951).

284. J. A. Becker, W. H. Brattain, H. Christiansen, and N. G. Wade, "Final Report on Development and Operating Characteristics of Thermistor Bolometers," *Office of Scientific Research and Development, OSRD 5991, PB* 27361, 139 pp. (October, 1945).

285. R. Cutting, "Film-Type Bolometers," *U. S. Office of Technical Services, Report PB* 85405, 87 pp. (August, 1945).

286. R. B. Belser, "A Technique of Soldering to Thin Metal Films," *Rev. Sci. Instr.,* **25,** no. 2 (February, 1954).

287. D. L. Birx and N. Fuschillo, "The Theory of Low-Temperature Bolometer Detectors Applied to the Measurement of Low-Level RF Power," *IRE Trans. Instrum.,* I-7, nos. 3–4, pp. 310–315 (December, 1958), Institute of Radio Engineers, New York.

288. H. J. Bomelburg, "Handling of Extremely Thin Wollaston Wires," *Rev. Sci. Instr.,* **30,** no. 12, pp. 1114–1115 (December, 1959).

289. H. König, "Les récepteurs physiques de radiation. Informations bibliographiques: Periode 1939–1949" (Physical Radiation Detectors. Bibliographical Information: Period 1939–1949), *U.N.E.S.C.O. Document* C104, 39 pp., June, 1950; *Revue d'optique,* **29,** nos. 8–9, pp. 439–478 (August–September, 1950).

290. R. M. Huey and B. J. Lancaster, "Tunable Galvanometer Amplifier," *J. Sci. Instr.,* **37,** no. 4, pp. 136–138 (April, 1960).

291. R. V. Jones, "The Detection of Thermal Radiation Using Linear Expansion," *Proc. Roy. Soc. London A,* **249,** no. 1256, pp. 100–113 (January, 1959).

4

RADIATION PYROMETRY—
DESIGN-CALCULATION TECHNIQUES

4·1 INTRODUCTION

In the present chapter, a systematic procedure is outlined for arriving at an engineering design. The objective in design is obviously to evolve a device for measuring temperature in accord with the requirements of the case at hand. Methods here are limited, however, to those cases where it appears expedient to consider using the radiation sensitive element.

Formulas and charts used in sequence permit quantitative determination of the correct structural features. This is all without recourse to lengthy calculations. However, by thus employing a comparatively exact design technique, it is hoped that applications can be made with confidence to problems which might not otherwise be attempted. After the essentials of a design are arrived at by this procedure, any desired degree of refinement in study can be added in the development of a perfected result.

4·2 DESIGN CONSIDERATIONS

A pyrometer-design problem is usually presented in terms of: (1), a range of source-body surface temperatures to be measured; (2), a desired precision in the temperature measurements to be made; (3), a desired precision in the locations on the source-body surface to which these measurements apply; and, (4), a desired precision in the determination of the time at which this temperature has occurred.

If the source-body surface is on a rapidly moving body or if its temperature is rapidly changing, determinations will be affected by the *lag time*, i.e., *response time*, of the pyrometer. The time for transit of the radiation itself is negligible so that, with suitable indicating instrumentation, the effective response time is that of the radiation-sensitive element itself. The element must be selected, if possible, to conform to the requirements. If temperature gradients occur on the source-body surface, determination of local temperatures will require that the source area A be sufficiently restricted that temperature variations within this area are not excessive.

A pyrometer design must provide means to indicate the increment in absolute or relative radiant-power emission from the source area A corresponding to the increment Δt in local source-body temperature. The limit on Δt is determined by the precision requirements. The radiant-power increment will vary: (1), with the magnitude of the increment Δt; (2), with the required restriction of the source area A; and, (3), with the source-body local surface temperature. The increment in radiant power absorbed by the radiation-sensitive element will depend on the transfer factor F_t or F_i. A sensitive element must be selected to yield an output signal to which suitable indicating instruments will respond, within stability and noise limitations.

The responsivities S_i or S_t and the response times τ attainable in radiation-sensitive elements depend on the short-wavelength content of the radiant power. The short-wavelength content in turn depends on the source-body surface temperature and is less for lower temperatures.

Any margin available will be utilized to increase the convenience and ruggedness of the equipment or to reduce its cost. If a design cannot be found that meets the requirements initially set, the requirements must be liberalized by: (1), increasing the permissible temperature error Δt; (2), increasing the permissible source area A; (3), increasing the permissible response time τ; or, (4), raising the lower limit of source-body surface temperature at which the pyrometer will be expected to meet the requirement on Δt.

4·3 RADIATION LAWS

The rate of thermal emission of radiant energy from a solid surface is greatest in a direction normal to this surface. For other directions, it declines in magnitude in proportion to the cosine of the angle with this normal, reaching the value of zero along the tangent to the surface. The intensity of such emission is measured in terms of the total energy emitted by unit area in unit time in all directions. Thus, the *total hemispherical emission* is the radiant power per unit area, w/in.[2] This is greatest for an ideal *blackbody* surface, i.e., a surface which absorbs all incident radiation and reflects none.[1]

For a blackbody, the Stefan-Boltzmann law is

$$W_{0-\infty} = \sigma T^4 \qquad (4 \cdot 1)$$

where $W_{0-\infty}$ is the total hemispherical emission in all wavelengths from 0 to ∞, w/in.[2]; T is the absolute temperature of the source-body surface, °R; and σ is the Stefan-Boltzmann constant, whose value is given as 3.49×10^{-12} w/in.^{2} (°R)^4. For $W_{0-\infty}$ in w/cm^2 and T in °K, $\sigma = 5.67 \times 10^{-12}$ w/cm^2 (°K)^4; or, for $W_{0-\infty}$ in ergs/cm^2 sec and T in °K, $\sigma = 5.67 \times 10^{-5}$ erg/cm^2 sec (°K)^4. Also, $\sigma = 0.172 \times 10^{-8}$ Btu/hr ft^2 (°R)^4 for that system of units.

For an actual, i.e., a nonblackbody surface, the radiant emission is less and in proportion to the emissivity of the surface. The emissivity of a surface is a dimensionless factor and is always equal to the *absorption coefficient*. This factor ϵ is defined as the fraction of an incident beam of radiant power absorbed by the surface. The fraction absorbed is unity minus the fraction reflected. The absorption coefficient, i.e., the *emittance* or *emissivity*, generally depends on the direction of the incident or emitted radiation and tends to be greatest in the direction normal to the surface.

Radiation is characterized not merely as a space flow of power which is propagated in straight lines in vacuo or within a homogeneous medium but also by wavelength. Within the narrow range discernible to the human eye, wavelength is recognized as *color*.

A blackbody emits radiation in all wavelengths. However the distribution among the various wavelengths, of the radiant power emitted, depends on the source-body surface temperature. Thus, for a blackbody, Planck's law is

$$W_\lambda = c_1/\lambda^5(e^{c_2/\lambda T} - 1) \tag{4·2}$$

where $W_\lambda \, \Delta\lambda$ is the total hemispherical emission in the wavelength range from λ to $\lambda + \Delta\lambda$, ergs/cm^2 sec; λ is the wavelength of the radiation, cm; T is the absolute temperature, °K; $c_1 = 3.740 \times 10^{-5}$ erg cm^2/sec; and $c_2 = 1.438$ cm °K. Then

$$W_{0-\infty} = \int_0^\infty W_\lambda \, d\lambda = \sigma T^4 \tag{4·3}$$

and

$$W_{\lambda_1-\lambda_2} = \int_{\lambda_1}^{\lambda_2} W_\lambda \, d\lambda \tag{4·4}$$

where $W_{\lambda_1-\lambda_2}$ is the total hemispherical radiant power emitted in the wavelength range from λ_1 to λ_2.

Also

$$W_{\lambda_1-\lambda_2} = W_{0-\lambda_2} - W_{0-\lambda_1} \tag{4·5}$$

and

$$W_{\lambda_1-\lambda_2} = (W_{0-\lambda_2}/W_{0-\infty} - W_{0-\lambda_1}/W_{0-\infty})W_{0-\infty} \tag{4·6}$$

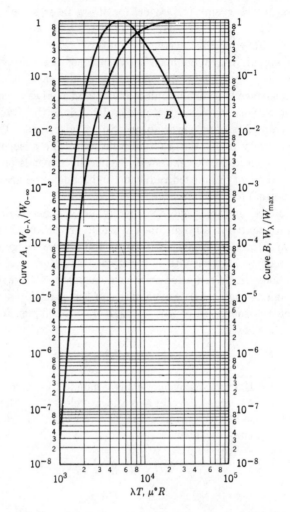

Fig. 4·1. Planck's radiation function. Curves are: A, fraction of the total hemispherical blackbody radiant power per unit area in the wavelength range 0 to λ, μ (microns); and B, ratio of the total hemispherical blackbody radiant power per unit area per unit wavelength increment at wavelength λ, μ, to its maximum value, $W_\lambda/W_{\lambda_{max}}$; plotted against the product of the wavelength and the absolute temperature T, $\mu°R$.

The integration of Planck's function Eq. 4·2, indicated in Eqs. 4·3 and 4·4, is laborious. However, tables are available from which the curves on Fig. 4·1 have been plotted.[2-4]

4·4 OPTICAL SYSTEMS

A light-gathering and focusing device is used to direct the maximum portion of the radiant power emitted by the source-body surface onto the sensitive surface of the radiation-sensitive element. This device may be a system of lenses, as indicated in Fig. 4·2A and D; mirrors, as indicated in Fig. 4·2B, C, E, and F; or a combination of lenses and mirrors. The image of the source-body surface area may be smaller than, so as to be entirely contained within, the area of maximum sensitivity on the surface of the radiation-sensitive element (see Fig. 4·2A, B, and C. Or, the image may be larger than, so as to entirely contain, the sensitive area on the surface of the radiation-sensitive element (see Fig. 4·2D, E, and F).

For the single-lens system of Fig. 4·2A and D, the required image distance is approximately * given by

$$D_e = D_s(A_e'/A)^{1/2} \qquad (4·7)$$

where D_e is the distance from the objective lens to the surface of the detector, in.; D_s is the distance from the objective lens to the source-body surface, in.; A is the area, in.^{2}, on the source-body surface whose temperature it is desired to measure, projected onto a plane normal to D_s; and A_e' is the area, in.^{2}, of the image formed on the detector surface, projected onto a plane normal to D_e. For Fig. 4·2A, the image diameter A_e' is smaller than the detector area A_e; whereas, for Fig. 4·2D, it is larger.

The required focal length of the objective lens is given by

$$f = D_e D_s/(D_e + D_s) \qquad (4·8)$$

where f is the *focal length*, i.e., the distance at which radiation from an infinitely distant source would be focused, in.

In Fig. 4·2B and E, the auxiliary plane mirror serves merely to reflect the image out to one side. For this simple mirror system, the magnification ratio is given by Eq. 4·7, and the required focal length of the mirror is given by Eq. 4·8. The focal length is half the radius of curvature of the mirror, so that

$$D_c = 2D_e D_s/(D_e + D_s) \qquad (4·9)$$

---

* For thick or multiple-element lenses D_e and D_s are measured, respectively, to the principal points of the lens combination.[5]

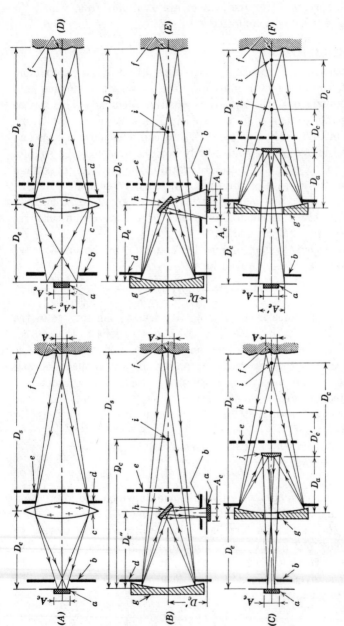

Fig. 4·2. Schematic optical-system diagrams. (A) Lens system for total transfer factor; (B) simple mirror system for total transfer factor; (C) coaxial mirror system for total transfer factor; (D) lens system for intensity transfer factor; (E) simple mirror system for intensity transfer factor; and (F) coaxial mirror system for intensity transfer factor. a, Sensitive element; b, screen; c, objective lens; d, stop; e, plane of the sectored rotating chopper disk; f, source-body surface; g, objective concave mirror; h, auxiliary plane mirror; i, center of curvature of concave mirror; j, convex mirror; and k, center of curvature of convex mirror.

where D_c is the radius of curvature of the reflecting surface of the mirror, in.; and $D_e = D_e' + D_e''$ (see Fig. 4·2B and E), in.

For the axially symmetric multiple-mirror system of Fig. 4·2C and F, the magnification ratio is given by

$$A_e'/A = (D_1 D_3 / D_s D_2)^2 \tag{4·10}$$

where

$$D_1 = D_c D_s / (2D_s - D_c) \tag{4·11}$$

$$D_2 = D_c D_s / (2D_s - D_c) - D_a \tag{4·12}$$

$$D_3 = D_c' D_2 / (D_c' - 2D_2) \tag{4·13}$$

and where A is the area, in.², on the source-body surface whose temperature it is desired to measure, projected onto a plane normal to D_s; A_e' is the area, in.², of the image of A formed on the plane of the sensitive-element surface, projected onto a plane normal to D_e; D_c is the radius of curvature of the concave reflecting surface of the objective mirror, i.e., twice its focal length; D_c' is the radius of curvature of the convex reflecting surface of the auxiliary mirror, i.e., minus twice its focal length (which is negative for a convex mirror), in.; D_s is the distance from the objective lens or mirror to the source-body surface, in.; D_a is the distance from the concave objective mirror to the convex auxiliary mirror in Fig. 4·2C and F; the distances D_1 and D_2, in., are from the surfaces of the concave and convex mirrors, respectively, to the virtual image, not shown on Fig. 4·2C and F; and D_3, also not shown, is the distance from the convex mirror to the sensitive element.

The auxiliary mirrors should be just large enough to intercept all of the radiation, i.e., all of the rays reflected from the concave objective mirror. The transfer factors F_t and F_i (see Sec. 4·9) will then be reduced only in the ratio of the area of the shadow cast by the auxiliary mirror on the objective-mirror surface to the area of the objective-mirror surface. For suitable design this ratio is usually small.

A lens system, such as in Fig. 4·2A and D, is compact. The materials for the lens elements and any windows must be transparent throughout the wavelength range λ_1 to λ_2 in which radiation is being measured. Thus, in Fig. 4·3 the permissible long-wavelength cutoff is plotted as a function of the source body's temperature. In Fig. 3·3, the long-wavelength cutoffs for single lens or window elements are plotted as functions of the thicknesses of these elements. Similarly, the short-wavelength cutoffs for various materials are listed in Table 3·1. There is of course no advantage in designing an optical

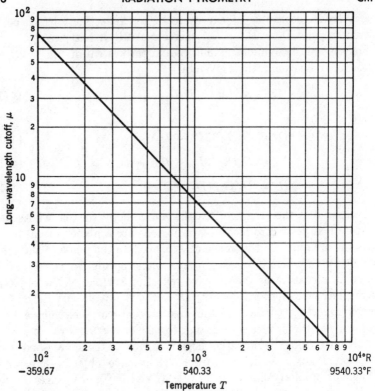

Fig. 4·3. Infrared transmission required of lenses and windows for measurements at various source-body temperatures. Minimum permissible value of the long-wavelength cutoff λ, μ, is plotted vertically against the body temperature, °R.

system to transmit wavelengths to which the intended radiation detector has no response. Thus, photo detectors have limited passbands. For thermal detectors, however, the optical system should be designed whenever possible to transmit the available radiant energy in accord with Fig. 4·3.

A window or lens, which is opaque outside a given range, may be used as a *filter* to limit the radiation reaching the sensitive element to that within a selected range λ_1 to λ_2. If precision image formation is necessary, the aberrations of a single-element lens may not be permissible; therefore, a corrected lens of two or more elements of different materials may be required. Making corrected lenses of materials satisfying the transparency requirements in the long wavelengths of the far infrared is difficult, and such materials may not be durable.

A mirror system, such as in Fig. 4·2B and E or C and F, involves the use of transparent materials only for such partitions as may be required to protect the detector. Thus, an evacuated cell requires a transparent window. Mirror systems are not subject to the chromatic aberrations so difficult to correct in lens systems and can be made with high definition even in the simplest forms. This is achieved by grinding the reflecting surfaces slightly aspherical, i.e., ellipsoidal or paraboloidal, and to such extent as indicated necessary in successive resolution tests. The system of Fig. 4·2B or E is bulky; however, that of Fig. 4·2C or F is competitive in convenience with lens systems such as Fig. 4·2A or D. Mirror surfaces tend to tarnish and require re-plating. For the infrared, gold is desirable as being highly reflecting and slow to tarnish.

4·5 CIRCUITS

The electric-circuit problems for radiation thermocouples and thermopiles are, in general, the same as those for thermoelectric thermometers. These problems are discussed in Ch. 5 of Volume I. Usually the "cold" junction is close to the "hot" junction and is exposed to the same ambient-temperature field but is shielded from the signal beam. Much of the circuit is thus determined in the design of the sensitive element. The radiation may be *modulated* by a *chopper* yielding an intermittent electric-output emf, thereby being susceptible to low-frequency a-c amplification. If no chopper is used, indication must be by means of a sensitive galvanometer, or with d-c preamplification.

The electric-circuit problems for radiation bolometers are likewise, in general, the same as those for resistance thermometers. These problems are discussed in Ch. 2. Usually the balancing arm r_b (Fig. 2·1) is close to, and identical in construction with, the sensitive element r_e. It is exposed to the same ambient-temperature field but remains shielded from the signal beam. Much of the circuit is thus determined, here also, in the design of the sensitive element. The radiation may be modulated by a chopper, or a-c power may be used. A-c power can be of relatively high frequency, permitting more rapid response and stable amplification. D-c response can also be employed.[6,7]

Photoconductive and photoresistive diodes, as variable-resistance elements, can be used with circuit arrangements similar to those used in resistance thermometry. The heat-transfer calculations described in Secs. 2·11 and 2·12 for resistance thermometry are, however, largely irrelevant for these photo elements. Also, random noise effects are usually of different origin (see Sec. 4·7).

Nonelectric radiation detectors, such as pneumatic and bimetallic elements, can be arranged for electrical indication by suitable auxiliary devices. Similarly, photoemissive-, photovoltaic-, phototransistor-, and photomultiplier-cell elements employ specially adapted circuits. These circuits are too numerous and varied for detailed description here. The reader is advised to consult the references, listed in Ch. 3 at the points the elements themselves are discussed, for circuit diagrams adapted to his requirements.

4·6 RESPONSIVITY OF THE ELEMENT

The *responsivity* of a radiation-sensitive element may be specified in terms of either the intensity of the radiation or the total radiant power incident upon and absorbed by the element.

In the first case, the image formed of the source-body surface area is larger than the exposed area of sensitive-element surface (see Fig. 4·2D, E, and F). The entire sensitive surface is thus subjected to an intensity of radiation proportional to the *brightness* of the source-body surface. The total radiant power absorbed by the element then depends on the area of its sensitive surface. The element receives radiation from only that portion of the source-body surface imaged on the element. This effective source-body area is thus limited by the element's area. The actual size of the effective source-body area is determined by the magnification ratio of the optical system. The sensitivity is usually not uniform over the surface of a detector. This factor has no effect if the *brightness* of the source-body surface is uniform, i.e., if the radiation is of uniform intensity over the image area. However, if substantial temperature differences occur on the source-body surface within the patch imaged on the sensitive element, an ambiguously weighted average will often result.

In the second case (see Fig. 4·2A, B, and C), the area on the source-body surface imaged on the sensitive element is limited by a *stop* or screen. This area can be made arbitrarily small, within the scope of other design variables; as a result, local temperatures can be measured on the source-body surface. The responsivity of the sensitive element may depend on the location of this source-body image on the element surface. In such cases, constancy of calibration will depend on maintaining the element in a fixed position with respect to the optical system.

The *responsivity* is defined as the ratio of the increment in emf in the sensitive-element circuit to the corresponding increment in radiant power, total or per unit area.

Thus

$$\Delta E_s = S_t \, \Delta \Phi \qquad (4 \cdot 14)$$

where S_t is the responsivity of the sensitive element for the case of total radiant power, v/w; ΔE_s is the output-emf increment, v; and $\Delta\Phi$ is the increment in total radiant power absorbed by the sensitive-element surface, w.

Similarly

$$\Delta E_s = S_i \, \Delta H \qquad (4\cdot15)$$

where S_i is the responsivity of the sensitive element for the case of radiant-power intensity, v in.^{2}/w; ΔE_s is the output-emf increment, v; and ΔH is the increment in uniform radiant intensity absorbed by the entire sensitive-element surface, w/in.^{2}

If the effective area of the sensitive-element surface is known, an approximate conversion can be estimated. Thus

$$\Phi = A_e H \qquad (4\cdot16)$$

where A_e is the effective area of the sensitive-element surface, in.^{2}; Φ is the total radiant power assumed to be spread uniformly over this area, w; and H is the corresponding radiant intensity, w/in.^{2} Then

$$S_i = A_e S_t \qquad (4\cdot17)$$

The responsivity of a sensitive element may depend on the magnitude of the radiation Φ, or H, such that E_s is not linear in Φ or H. In such cases, values for S_i and S_t, specified for a total magnitude Φ or H, will differ from those for specific intervals Φ_1 to Φ_2, or H_1 to H_2. A knowledge of the range of values expected for Φ or H is thus necessary to the determination of values for S_i, or S_t. In design it is correspondingly suitable to limit Φ or H to a range for which S_i or S_t is a maximum or most nearly constant.

4·7 NOISE LIMITS FOR RADIATION-SENSITIVE ELEMENTS

In Secs. 2·5 and 2·7 there was a discussion of noise as a limitation to the sensitivity of indicators. It was noted that a signal is measurable only when it can be distinguished from random effects. By sufficient elaboration in technique, such random effects in the indicators can be reduced to below those inherent in the sensitive element. The thermal-noise emf, i.e., Johnson noise, in an electric resistor is one form of such limitation. The root-mean-square Johnson-noise emf ΔE_{tn} is given by Eqs. 2·10 and 2·11 for galvanometer and electronic indicators, respectively.[8-22]

Thermistor bolometers (see Fig. 3·8) are subject to *semiconductor noise,* which may be much larger than the Johnson noise. Thermocouple and bolometer elements, in the form of metallic films deposited on thin membranes (see Fig. 3·7B), may be limited by *microphonic noise*. These effects differ for individual specimens and are reduced by selection from among elements produced by the same procedure. Manufacturers' tolerances are sometimes expressed in multiples of the Johnson noise ΔE_{tn}, thus used as a unit of measure.[16, 19, 20, 22–25]

Under the conditions most suitable for their operation, photoconductive photoelectric cells (see Fig. 3·9) are limited by *current noise*. The root-mean-square current-noise emf is approximately proportional to i, the electric current in amperes through the element. The distribution of this noise in its own frequency spectrum is such that the amplitude is almost inversely proportional to the square root of the frequency. Individual cells of the same type differ.[8, 12, 19, 20, 22, 25–29]

Photoemissive photoelectric cells (see Fig. 3·10) are subject to fluctuations in *thermionic emission* of electrons from the radiation-sensitive surface of the cathode, i.e., *dark current*. The root mean square of the random fluctuations in this dark electron current Δi_{te} constitutes the noise limit. Smaller values of currents due to photoemission cannot be distinguished. This and other imperfectly understood sources of noise are minimized by operation at low temperatures. The corresponding noise emf is given by

$$\Delta E_{te} = r \, \Delta i_{te} \qquad (4·18)$$

where ΔE_{te} is the root-mean-square thermionic-emission noise emf, v; Δi_{te} is the root mean square of the random variations in the current amps; and r is the resistance of the coupling to the amplifier, ohms.[9, 10, 12, 19, 20, 22, 30–32]

Pneumatic, radiometer, photographic, and solid-expansion elements are subject to analogous noise effects.[9–11, 13–16, 33]

The various types of noise described in the preceding paragraphs all pertain to a limiting distinguishable magnitude of signal, where the signal is of the sort produced by the given type of radiation-sensitive element in response to incident radiation. They do not always suffice to determine the minimum magnitude of radiant energy that can be measured by the element. This minimum energy depends also on the *responsivity* S_t of the radiation-sensitive element (see Eq. 4·14).

The limiting condition occurs when the increment in signal emf is equal to the noise emf ΔE_{tn} or ΔE_{te}. Then

$$\Delta \Phi = \Delta E_{tn}/S_t \qquad (4·19)$$

or

$$\Delta \Phi = \Delta E_{te}/S_t \qquad (4·20)$$

Thus as affected by the above-mentioned forms of noise, the value to which $\Delta\Phi$ can be reduced is dependent only on the magnitude to which S_t can be raised with available materials.

Temperature noise results from random fluctuations in heat transfer to the detector. The minimum distinguishable increment $\Delta\Phi$ in the incident beam of radiation is then the root-mean-square $\Delta\Phi_m$ of the random fluctuations in power absorbed by the detector from the ambient. This *thermodynamic limit* is the same for all types of radiation detectors that depend on the heating effect of the radiation, and it can be computed from

$$\Delta\Phi_m = 1.5 \times 10^{-12} \times T(1/R\tau)^{1/2}/\epsilon \qquad (4\cdot21)$$

where $\Delta\Phi_m$ is the root-mean-square temperature-noise radiant power, w; T is the mean temperature of the receiving surface, °R; ϵ is the absorption coefficient of the blackened receiving surface; R is the thermal resistance of the heat-flow path from the detector to the ambient, hr °F/Btu; and τ is the time constant of the detector, sec.[8–14, 16, 17, 20, 26, 34, 35]

The *time constant* τ is given by

$$\tau = [(1 - \eta^2)/(\eta^2 f_1^2 - f_2^2)]^{1/2}/2\pi \qquad (4\cdot22)$$

where η is the ratio of the responsivity of the detector, when the incident beam of radiation is *modulated*, i.e., *chopped* at a frequency f_1 to that when the modulation frequency is f_2, sec^{-1}. Thus, τ is a readily determined performance characteristic, which may be listed by the manufacturer. It can also be estimated by

$$\tau = 3600VcR \qquad (4\cdot23)$$

where τ is the time constant, sec; V is the volume of sensitive-element material heated by the successive pulses of incident radiation, ft³; c is the mean volume heat capacity of this material, Btu/ft³°F; and R is the thermal resistance of the heat-flow path from the sensitive element to the ambient, hr °F/Btu.

R can be estimated either from Eq. 4·23, if τ is known, or from

$$R = 1/[(U_r + U_f)A_1 + kA_2/D] \qquad (4\cdot24)$$

where A_1 is the exposed area of sensitive-element surface, ft²; U_r is the mean radiation boundary conductance over this area, Btu/hr ft² °F; U_f is the mean fluid boundary conductance over this area, Btu/hr ft² °F; k is the mean thermal conductivity of the leads or portions of the element serving as heat-flow paths to the ambient, Btu/hr ft °F;

A_2 is the mean total cross-sectional area of this path, ft^2; and D is the path length to the ambient, ft.

4·8 PASSBAND OF A RADIATION-SENSITIVE ELEMENT

Thermal elements, such as bolometers, radiation thermopiles, bimetallic strips, and pneumatic cells, respond to radiant power in all wavelengths. The response depends only on the total radiant power absorbed by the element.

Photo elements, such as photoelectric cells and photographic emulsions, respond appreciably only to radiant power within limited wavelength ranges characteristic of the individual detectors. Curves in which responsivity is plotted against wavelength can be obtained by calibration. Standard curves, applying approximately to elements of a given type, are usually available from the manufacturer. Such curves are varied in shape and may have more than one peak.

In radiation-pyrometer design it is convenient to use the simplified concept of a passband (see Fig. 4·4). Here, the actual response curve has been replaced by a square-wave curve. The ordinate is that of the peak of the actual curve. The limits λ_1 and λ_2 are set at the wavelengths at which the response is half the maximum value. The passband corresponding to this response curve is then defined as the wavelength range λ_1 to λ_2. The output emf of the radiation-sensitive element can be estimated by multiplying the peak responsivity by the quantity of radiant power absorbed by the element in the wavelength range λ_1 to λ_2. Radiant power outside the passband, which is thus

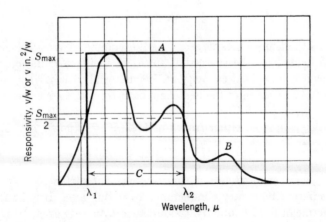

Fig. 4·4. Passband of an element. *A*, Square wave; *B*, actual response curve for the element; and *C*, passband λ_1 to λ_2, μ.

neglected, is intended to be approximately compensated for by using the value given for the responsivity S_t or S_i at the peak of the curve, i.e., the value at the wavelength of radiation for which it is a maximum.

4·9 TRANSFER FACTOR

The *transfer factor* is defined as the ratio of the radiant power absorbed by the sensitive area of the detector to the total hemispherical emission of the source-body area whose temperature it is desired to measure. Thus

$$F_t = \Phi/\epsilon W_{\lambda_1-\lambda_2,T} \tag{4·25}$$

and

$$F_i = H/\epsilon W_{\lambda_1-\lambda_2,T} \tag{4·26}$$

where F_t is the *total transfer factor* for total radiant power absorbed by the detector, in.²; F_i is the *intensity transfer factor* for radiant power absorbed by the element per unit area of detector surface, dimensionless; Φ is the total radiant power absorbed by the sensitive detector, w; H is the radiant power absorbed per unit area of detector surface, w/in.²; ϵ is the emissivity of the source-body surface; $W_{\lambda_1-\lambda_2,T}$ is the total hemispherical blackbody radiant power in the wavelength range λ_1 to λ_2 emitted per unit area of source-body surface at temperature T, w/in.².

Materials for lenses and windows in the optical systems can usually be selected to have transparent wavelength ranges greater than those set by the passband of the sensitive element or by Planck's law for the source-body surface temperature. Within the transparent range, transmission is limited principally by surface-reflection losses. Then

$$F_t = A_oA\epsilon_ef_m(1 - \rho)^N/\pi D_s^2 \tag{4·27}$$

$$F_i = A_oA\epsilon_ef_m(1 - \rho)^N/\pi D_s^2A_e' \tag{4·28}$$

where (see Fig. 4.2) D_s is the distance from the center of the objective lens or mirror to the point on the source-body surface at which it is desired to measure temperature, in.; A_o is the area of the objective-lens or objective-mirror aperture projected on a plane normal to the direction of D_e, in.²; A is the area, projected on this same plane, on the source-body surface surrounding the point from which radiation is accepted, as limited by the aperture in the optical system, in.²; ϵ_e is the absorption coefficient for the detector surface; f_m is the ratio of *open time* to total time cycle provided by any chopper used in modulation; ρ is the average value of the reflection coefficients at the *free* (i.e., uncemented or "air-glass") surfaces of transmission components, including lenses, prisms, and windows, and of the absorption coefficients (i.e., one minus the reflection coefficient) at surfaces of reflection components such as mirrors; N is the total number of such surfaces at which *loss* occurs in the path of the radiant beam through the optical system; A_e' is the area projected on a plane normal to the direction of D_e (see Fig. 4·2) of the image of A (see Eqs. 4·7 and 4·10) formed on the detector surface, in.^{2}.

When the rays are bent by intervening plane mirrors, as in Fig. 4·2B and E, the distances D_s and D_e are measured along the path of the central ray. If A_o, A, and A_e' are not small in comparison to D_e^2 and D_s^2, i.e., for a *large-aperture* or *wide-angle* system, a correction may be required to be computed from formulas for *angle factors* in radiation exchange, as given in textbooks on heat transfer and optics.[5-7, 36]

The receiving area A_e for thermal detectors is usually well blackened such that the absorption coefficient ϵ_e is 0.9 or greater. For photo elements, the effective value of ϵ_e is usually included in the value given for responsivity S_i or S_t, and ϵ_e can then be taken as unity in computing the transfer factor F_t or F_i.

4·10 EMISSIVITY

The observed radiant power emanating from an area of source-body surface is proportional to the product $\epsilon W_{0-\infty,T}$ or $\epsilon W_{\lambda_1-\lambda_2,T}$ of the blackbody emission and the emittance or emissivity of the source-body surface over this area. The temperature T of the source-body surface, which it is desired to measure, is related by Planck's law to $W_{0-\infty,T}$ or $W_{\lambda_1-\lambda_2,T}$. The emissivity ϵ, in a given wavelength range, is dependent on the material, the condition, and the geometry of the source-body surface as well as on its temperature. If values for ϵ are available for the source-body surface, $W_{0-\infty,T}$ or $W_{\lambda_1-\lambda_2,T}$ can be obtained from the observed product $\epsilon W_{0-\infty,T}$ or $\epsilon W_{\lambda_1-\lambda_2,T}$, and T is then determined from Planck's law.[37-50]

Temperatures obtained directly from $\epsilon W_{0-\infty,T}$ or $\epsilon W_{\lambda_1-\lambda_2,T}$, as though this were the radiation from a blackbody, are called *apparent temperatures*. The apparent temperature T_A can thus be defined as the temperature a blackbody would be required to have were its emission to equal that of the actual source-body surface, i.e.,

$$\epsilon W_{0-\infty,T} = W_{0-\infty,T_A} \qquad (4·29)$$

or

$$\epsilon W_{\lambda_1-\lambda_2,T} = W_{\lambda_1-\lambda_2,T_A} \qquad (4·30)$$

where $W_{0-\infty}$ and $W_{\lambda_1-\lambda_2}$ are the total hemispherical emissions in the respective wavelength ranges 0 to ∞ and λ_1 to λ_2, w/in.^{2}; ϵ is the average emissivity of the source-body surface in this wavelength range at the temperature T; T is the temperature of the source-body surface, °R; and T_A is the apparent temperature of the source-body surface, °R. A radiation-pyrometer assembly may be calibrated by taking readings on an artificial blackbody surface whose temperature is independently indicated, as, for example, by means of an embedded thermocouple. When used for actual surfaces, the calibration will then yield apparent temperatures.[51]

If the calibration can be made by thus taking readings on a surface of known temperature and of the same material, surface condition, and surface geometry as on the ultimate source-body surface, the calibration will yield actual temperatures.

4·11 TWO-COLOR OR RATIO PYROMETRY

The *two-color* or *ratio pyrometer* is based on the assumption that the ratio of the emissivities in two wavelength bands can be more accurately known than the absolute values of either emissivity.

The ratio of the emissions $\epsilon_{\lambda_1-\lambda_2,T} W_{\lambda_1-\lambda_2,T}/\epsilon_{\lambda_1'-\lambda_2',T} W_{\lambda_1'-\lambda_2',T}$ may be determined either directly or by taking separate readings and dividing. $W_{\lambda_1-\lambda_2,T}/W_{\lambda_1'-\lambda_2',T}$ is then related by Planck's law to the actual source-body surface temperature. For an ideal *gray body*, $\epsilon_{\lambda_1-\lambda_2,T}/\epsilon_{\lambda_1'-\lambda_2',T}$ has the value of unity. For actual bodies, depending on the spectral locations of the wavelength ranges λ_1 to λ_2 and λ_1' to λ_2', $\epsilon_{\lambda_1-\lambda_2,T}/\epsilon_{\lambda_1'-\lambda_2',T}$ may have values subject to less uncertainty than $\epsilon_{\lambda_1-\lambda_2,T}$ or $\epsilon_{\lambda_1'-\lambda_2',T}$ individually. This is the assumed advantage of the *two-color* or *ratio* pyrometer.[46, 52-60]

4·12 RESPONSIVITIES FOR RATIO PYROMETRY

In *two-color* or *ratio* pyrometry, two passbands or wavelength ranges λ_1 to λ_2 and λ_1' to λ_2' are used, and the ratio of the respective responses to radiation, from the same source-body surface area, is measured. Two separate radiation-sensitive elements may be employed, or one element with two interchanged filters may suffice. Similarly, the output emfs E_s and E_s' may be read separately on the same or different indicators, or an indicator designed to respond to emf ratios can be used.[61, 62]

In case two separate indicators are used with individual least-count emfs ΔE_s and $\Delta E_s'$, the resultant least count for the ratio is given by

$$\Delta(E_s/E_s') = \Delta E_s/E_s' - E_s \, \Delta E_s'/(E_s')^2 \tag{4·31}$$

where $\Delta(E_s/E_s')$ is the least-count or minimum increment in the ratio E_s/E_s' that can be measured with this combination of instruments; ΔE_s and $\Delta E_s'$ are the least-count emfs for the two indicators, respectively, v; E_s and $E_s{}'$ are the emf outputs corresponding to the two wavelength ranges, respectively, v. In case the same indicator is used for both wavelength ranges, $\Delta E_s = \Delta E_s{}'$.

The emf outputs E_s and $E_s{}'$ in the two wavelength ranges, respectively, are given by

$$E_s = S_t\Phi \qquad (4\cdot32)$$

and

$$E_s{}' = S_t{}'\Phi' \qquad (4\cdot33)$$

or

$$E_s = S_iH \qquad (4\cdot34)$$

and

$$E_s{}' = S_i{}'H' \qquad (4\cdot35)$$

where E_s and $E_s{}'$ are the output emfs in the two wavelength ranges, v; S_t and $S_t{}'$ are the average values of the detector responsivities for total radiant power over the ranges from zero to Φ and Φ', respectively, for the two wavelength ranges λ_1 to λ_2 and $\lambda_1{}'$ to $\lambda_2{}'$, v/w; S_i and $S_i{}'$ are the average values of the responsivities for radiant intensity over the ranges from zero to H and H', respectively, for the two wavelength ranges, v in.^{2}/w; Φ and Φ' are the radiant powers incident upon and absorbed by the sensitive surfaces of the two detectors in the wavelength ranges λ_1 to λ_2 and $\lambda_1{}'$ and $\lambda_2{}'$, respectively, w; and H and H' are radiant powers per unit area incident upon and absorbed by the entire sensitive surfaces of the two detectors in the wavelength ranges λ_1 to λ_2 and $\lambda_1{}'$ to $\lambda_2{}'$, respectively, w/in.^{2}.

The responsivity for a ratio pyrometer is the ratio of the increment in output-emf ratio to the increment in the ratio of radiant powers. The responsivity $S_t/S_t{}'$ or $S_i/S_i{}'$ is the ratio of the responsivities for the two wavelength ranges, respectively. Thus

$$\Delta(E_s/E_s{}') = (S_t/S_t{}')\,\Delta(\Phi/\Phi') \qquad (4\cdot36)$$

$$\Delta(E_s/E_s{}') = (S_i/S_i{}')\,\Delta(H/H') \qquad (4\cdot37)$$

where $\Delta(E_s/E_s{}')$ is the increment in output-emf ratio; S_t and $S_t{}'$ are the responsivities for total radiant power for the two wavelength ranges λ_1 to λ_2 and $\lambda_1{}'$ to $\lambda_2{}'$, respectively, v/w; S_i and $S_i{}'$ are the responsivities for radiant intensity for the two wavelength ranges λ_1 to λ_2 and $\lambda_1{}'$ to $\lambda_2{}'$ respectively, v in.^{2}/w; $\Delta(\Phi/\Phi')$ is the increment in the ratio of the radiant powers incident upon and absorbed by the sensitive surfaces of the radiation-sensitive elements in the wavelength ranges λ_1 to λ_2 and λ_1' to λ_2' respectively; and $\Delta(H/H')$ is the increment in the ratio of the radiant powers per unit area incident upon and absorbed by the entire sensitive surfaces of the two detectors in the wavelength ranges λ_1 to λ_2 and λ_1' to λ_2', respectively.

4·13   CALCULATION OF RADIANT POWER

The responsivities of radiation-sensitive elements may depend on the radiant power Φ or H absorbed. Thus, it may be necessary to compute

$$\Phi = \epsilon F_t W_{0-\infty}(W_{\lambda_1-\lambda_2}/W_{0-\infty}) \qquad (4\cdot38)$$

and

$$H = \epsilon F_i W_{0-\infty}(W_{\lambda_1-\lambda_2}/W_{0-\infty}) \qquad (4\cdot39)$$

where Φ is the radiant power incident upon and absorbed by the sensitive surface of the detector, w; H is the radiant power per unit area incident upon and absorbed by the entire sensitive surface of the detector, w/in.^{2}; $W_{0-\infty}$ is the total hemispherical blackbody radiant-power emission per unit area of source-body surface, w/in.^{2}; $W_{\lambda_1-\lambda_2}/W_{0-\infty}$ is the fraction of $W_{0-\infty}$ in the passband λ_1 to λ_2 for the given detector; ϵ is the emissivity of the source-body surface; F_t is the total transfer factor, in.^{2}; and F_i is the intensity transfer factor.[2-4]

In pyrometer design, data found in the various tabulations can be used to estimate probable values for ϵ. For any given design of optical system under consideration (see Fig. 4·2), F_t or F_i can be computed using Eq. 4·27 or 4·28 in Sec. 4·9. $W_{0-\infty}$ can be calculated by the Stefan-Boltzmann law (Eq. 4·1 in Sec. 4·3) for the given source-body surface temperature T, °R. Values of $W_{\lambda_1-\lambda_2}/W_{0-\infty}$ for passbands characteristic of typical photo elements are plotted against source-body surface temperature T in Fig. 4·5. The curve most nearly approximating the response of the element under consideration should be used. It is conservative to use a curve giving a lower, rather than a higher, value for $W_{\lambda_1-\lambda_2}/W_{0-\infty}$. For convenience, in Fig. 4·6 values of the product $F_t W_{0-\infty}$ or $F_i W_{0-\infty}$ are plotted against source-body surface temperature T for various values of F_t or F_i.[2-4, 37-39, 43-47]

The total radiant power Φ and its intensity H are related, for the cases D, E, and F in Fig. 4·2, by

$$\Phi = A_e H \qquad (4\cdot16)$$

where A_e is the sensitive area (entirely irradiated) on the surface of the sensitive element projected on a plane normal to D_e in Fig. 4·2, in.^{2}

The increment in output signal ΔE_s (see Eqs. 4·14 and 4·15) depends

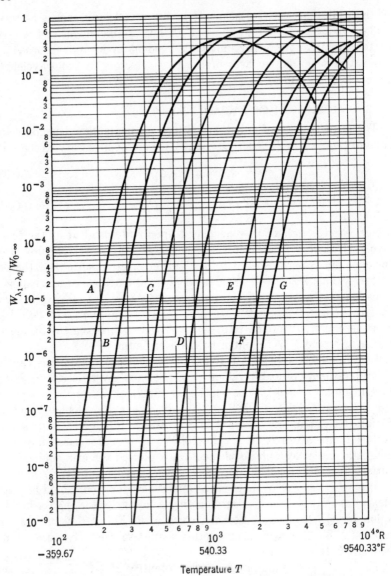

Fig. 4·5. Fractions of the total hemispherical blackbody radiant power per unit area in the passbands of photo elements $W_{\lambda_1-\lambda_2}/W_{0-\infty}$ for source temperatures T, °R. Curves are for: A, photoconductive cells of passband 7 to 4 μ; B, photoconductive cells of passband 5 to 2 μ; C, photoconductive cells of passband 2.85 to 0.85 μ; D, phototransistor cells of passband 1.7 to 0.39 μ; E, infrared photoemissive cells of passband 0.91 to 0.58 μ; F, photovoltaic cells of passband 0.69 to 0.34 μ; and G, photomultiplier cells of passband 0.57 to 0.31 μ.

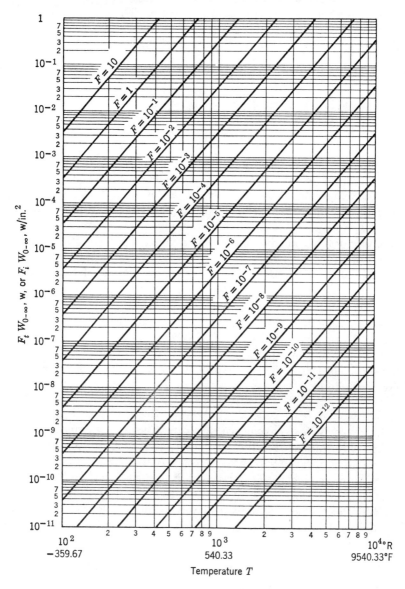

Fig. 4·6. Total hemispherical blackbody radiant power per unit area of source multiplied by the transfer factor $F_t W_{0-\infty}$, w, or $F_i W_{0-\infty}$, w/in.^{2}, for source temperatures T, °R.

on the increment $\Delta\Phi$ or ΔH in radiant power corresponding to an increment ΔT in source-body surface temperature. Thus

$$\Delta\Phi = \epsilon F_t(dW_{\lambda_1-\lambda_2}/dT)\,\Delta T \qquad (4\cdot40)$$

and

$$\Delta H = \epsilon F_i(dW_{\lambda_1-\lambda_2}/dT)\,\Delta T \qquad (4\cdot41)$$

also, for the cases of Fig. $4\cdot2D$, E, and F,

$$\Delta\Phi = A_e\,\Delta H \qquad (4\cdot42)$$

where $\Delta\Phi$ is the increment in radiant power, w; ΔH is the increment in radiant power per unit area, w/in.^{2}, for an increment ΔT in source-body surface temperature, °R; and $dW_{\lambda_1-\lambda_2}/dT$ is the rate of change with source-body surface temperature of the portion, lying within the passband λ_1 to λ_2 for the given radiation-sensitive element, of the total hemispherical blackbody radiant-power emission per unit area of source-body surface, w/in.^{2} °R.

Values for $dW_{\lambda_1-\lambda_2}/dT$ for passbands characteristic of typical photo elements are plotted against source-body surface temperature T in Fig. $4\cdot7$. The curve most nearly approximating the response of the element under consideration should be used. It is conservative to use a lower, rather than a higher, value for $dW_{\lambda_1-\lambda_2}/dT$.

For thermal elements the passband λ_1 to λ_2 is the entire range from 0 to ∞, and $dW_{0-\infty}/dT$ can be calculated from the Stefan-Boltzmann law in the form

$$dW_{0-\infty}/dT = 4\sigma T^3 \qquad (4\cdot43)$$

In Fig. $4\cdot8$, for convenience in computations on thermal elements, values of the product $F_t(dW_{0-\infty}/dT)$ or $F_i(dW_{0-\infty}/dT)$ are plotted against source-body surface temperature T for various values of F_t or F_i.

In ratio pyrometry the increment in output signal $\Delta(E_s/E_s')$ (see Eqs. $4\cdot36$ and $4\cdot37$ in Sec. $4\cdot12$) depends on the increment $\Delta(\Phi/\Phi')$ or $\Delta(H/H')$ in the ratio of radiant powers in the wavelength ranges λ_1 to λ_2 and λ_1' to λ_2', respectively, corresponding to an increment ΔT in source-body surface temperature. Thus

$$\Delta(\Phi/\Phi') = \Delta T[(\epsilon F_t)/(\epsilon' F_t')](d/dT)(W_{\lambda_1-\lambda_2}/W_{\lambda_1'-\lambda_2'}) \qquad (4\cdot44)$$

$$\Delta(H/H') = \Delta T[(\epsilon F_i)/(\epsilon' F_i')](d/dT)(W_{\lambda_1-\lambda_2}/W_{\lambda_1'-\lambda_2'}) \qquad (4\cdot45)$$

for

$$(d/dT)(W_{\lambda_1-\lambda_2}/W_{\lambda_1'-\lambda_2'}) = [(d/dT)(W_{\lambda_1-\lambda_2}/W_{0-\infty})]/(W_{\lambda_1'-\lambda_2'}/W_{0-\infty})$$

$$- [(d/dT)(W_{\lambda_1'-\lambda_2'}/W_{0-\infty})][(W_{\lambda_1-\lambda_2}/W_{0-\infty})/(W_{\lambda_1'-\lambda_2'}/W_{0-\infty})^2] \qquad (4\cdot46)$$

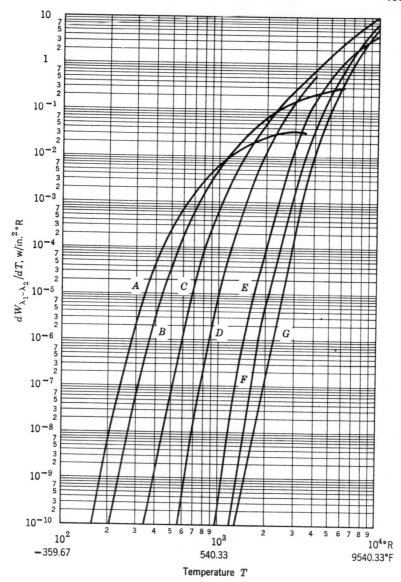

Fig. 4·7. Temperature rate of change of the total hemispherical blackbody radiant power per unit area of source in the response ranges of photo elements $dW_{\lambda^1-\lambda_2}$/dT, w/in.²°F, for source temperatures T, °R. Curves are for; A, photoconductive cells of passband 7 to 4 μ; B, photoconductive cells of passband 5 to 2 μ; C, photoconductive cells of passband 2.85 to 0.85 μ; D, phototransistor cells of passband 1.7 to 0.39 μ; E, infrared photoemissive cells of passband 0.91 to 0.58 μ; F, photovoltaic cells of passband 0.69 to 0.34 μ; and G, photomultiplier cells of passband 0.57 to 0.31 μ.

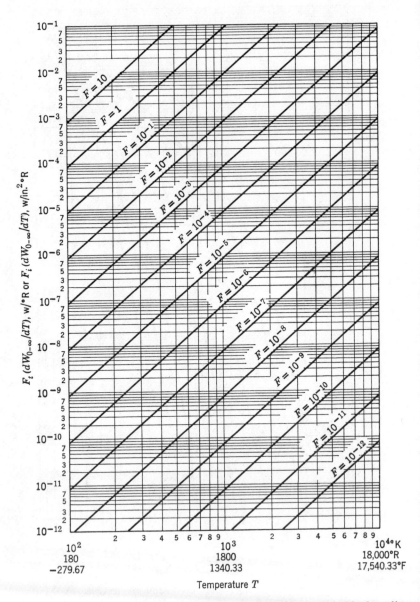

Fig. 4·8. Temperature rate of change of the total hemispherical blackbody radiant power per unit area of source multiplied by the transfer factor $F_t(dW_{0-\infty}/dT)$, w/°R, or $F_i(dW_{0-\infty}/dT)$, w/in.² °R, for source temperatures T, °R.

where $\Delta(\Phi/\Phi')$ is the increment in the ratio of the radiant powers incident upon and absorbed by the sensitive surfaces of the detectors in the wavelength ranges λ_1 to λ_2 and λ_1' to λ_2' respectively; $\Delta(H/H')$ is the increment in the ratio of the radiant powers per unit area incident upon and absorbed by the entire sensitive surfaces of the detectors in the wavelength ranges λ_1 to λ_2 and λ_1' to λ_2', respectively; ϵ and ϵ' are the average values for the emissivity of the source-body surface over the wavelength ranges λ_1 to λ_2 and λ_1' to λ_2' and the temperature range ΔT, respectively; F_t and F_t' are the total transfer factors for the optical systems used in the wavelength ranges λ_1 to λ_2 and λ_1' to λ_2', respectively, in.^{2}; F_i and F_i' are the intensity transfer factors for the optical systems used in the wavelength ranges λ_1 to λ_2 and λ_1' to λ_2', respectively; $d(W_{\lambda_1-\lambda_2}/W_{\lambda_1'-\lambda_2'})/dT$ is the rate of change, with source-body surface temperature, in the ratio $W_{\lambda_1-\lambda_2}/W_{\lambda_1'-\lambda_2'}$ of the total hemispherical blackbody radiant-power emission for the source-body surface in the wavelength ranges λ_1 to λ_2 and λ_1' to λ_2', per °R; ΔT is the increment in source-body surface temperature, °R; $d(W_{\lambda_1-\lambda_2}/W_{0-\infty})/dT$ and $d(W_{\lambda_1'-\lambda_2'}/W_{0-\infty})/dT$ are the rates of change, with source-body surface temperature, in the ratios $W_{\lambda_1-\lambda_2}/W_{0-\infty}$ and $W_{\lambda_1'-\lambda_2'}/W_{0-\infty}$ of total hemispherical blackbody radiant-power emission for the wavelength ranges λ_1 to λ_2 and λ_1' to λ_2', respectively, to that for the entire range from 0 to ∞, per °R; and $W_{\lambda_1-\lambda_2}/W_{0-\infty}$ and $W_{\lambda_1'-\lambda_2'}/W_{0-\infty}$ are ratios of total hemispherical blackbody radiant-power emission for the wavelength ranges λ_1 to λ_2 and λ_1' to λ_2', respectively, to that for the entire range from 0 to ∞.[63, 64]

Values for $W_{\lambda_1-\lambda_2}/W_{0-\infty}$ and $d(W_{\lambda_1-\lambda_2}/W_{0-\infty})/dT$ for passbands characteristic of typical photo elements are plotted against source-body surface temperature T in Figs. 4·5 and 4·9, respectively. The curve most nearly approximating the element under consideration should be used. It is conservative to use a lower, rather than a higher, value for $d(W_{\lambda_1-\lambda_2}/W_{0-\infty})/dT$.[2-4, 57]

4·14   CALIBRATION

Pyrometer-design calculations suffice for the selection of components and structural features to provide means for performing the required temperature measurements. Such calculations are not intended to predict the scale markings by which readings can be taken. Calibration is usually required.

An artificial approximation to an ideal blackbody can be used as a reference standard. It may be in the form of a heated enclosure with a small aperture through which the interior surface can be viewed; or a correctly proportioned cone or wedge design can be used (see Fig.

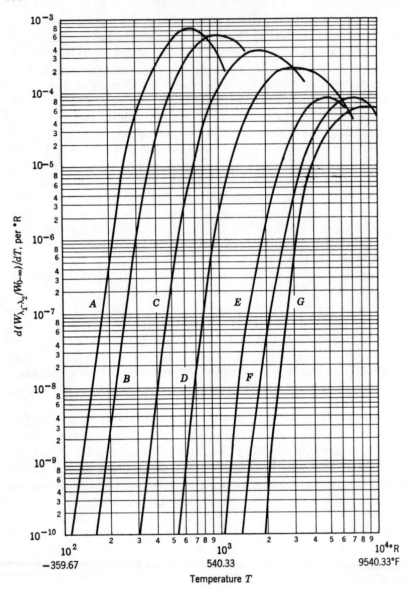

Fig. 4·9. Temperature rate of change of the fraction of the total hemispherical blackbody radiant power per unit area in the passbands of photo elements $d(W_{\lambda_{1-2}\lambda}/W_{0-\infty})/dT$, per °R, for source temperatures T, °R. Curves are for: A, photoconductive cells of passband 7 to 4 μ; B, photoconductive cells of passband 5 to 2 μ; C, photoconductive cells of passband 2.85 to 0.85 μ; D, phototransistor cells of passband 1.7 to 0.39 μ; E, infrared photoemissive cells of passband 0.91 to 0.58 μ; F, photovoltaic cells of passband 0.69 to 0.34 μ; and G, photomultiplier cells of passband 0.57 to 0.31 μ.

$3 \cdot 1A, B, C,$ and $D.$ The temperature of the blackbody can be measured by the instrument prescribed in the International Temperature Scale for the given temperature range. Calibrated ribbon-filament incandescent lamps are also available for use as surfaces of equivalent blackbody temperatures, indicated directly by the corresponding filament currents (see Fig. 3·2).[51]

A pyrometer calibrated by taking readings on a reference blackbody will read in apparent temperatures (see Eqs. 4·29 and 4·30). Actual temperatures must then be deduced by correction of the apparent-temperature indications for the emissivity of the source-body surface area.

For thermal elements without filters, i.e., elements uniformly sensitive in all wavelengths, this correction is given by

$$T = (1/\epsilon)^{\frac{1}{4}} T_A \qquad (4 \cdot 47)$$

where T_A is the apparent temperature, °R; ϵ is the average value of the emissivity of the source-body surface area, over the wavelength range in which radiation is important at the source-body temperature (see Fig. 4·1); and T is the corrected value for the temperature determination, °R. Since ϵ occurs as the fourth root, the per cent error in T is roughly only one-fourth of that in ϵ. Hence, approximate data for ϵ may yield useful degrees of precision in values for T and for changes in T.

For photo elements and thermal elements with filters such that the effective wavelength range is limited to a passband λ_1 to λ_2, the relation between the apparent and the corrected temperatures is given by

$$T^4(W_{0-\lambda_1,T}/W_{0-\infty,T} - W_{0-\lambda_2,T}/W_{0-\infty,T})$$
$$= T_A{}^4(W_{0-\lambda_1,T_A}/W_{0-\infty,T_A} - W_{0-\lambda_2,T_A}/W_{0-\infty,T_A})/\epsilon \qquad (4 \cdot 48)$$

where T is the corrected value for the temperature determination, °R; T_A is the apparent temperature, °R; ϵ is the average value of the emissivity of the source-body surface area over the wavelength range λ_1 to λ_2 at temperature T; $W_{0-\lambda_1,T}/W_{0-\infty,T}$ is the fraction of the total hemispherical blackbody radiant-power emission in the wavelength range 0 to λ_1 at temperature T; $W_{0-\lambda_2,T}/W_{0-\infty,T}$ is this fraction for the range 0 to λ_2 at temperature T; $W_{0-\lambda_1,T_A}/W_{0-\infty,T_A}$ is this fraction for the range 0 to λ_1 at temperature T_A; and $W_{0-\lambda_2,T_A}/W_{0-\infty,T_A}$ is this fraction for the range 0 to λ_2 at temperature T_A.

The function $\Psi(T)$ is given by

$$\Psi(T) = T^4(W_{0-\lambda_1,T}/W_{0-\infty,T} - W_{0-\lambda_2,T}/W_{0-\infty,T}) \qquad (4 \cdot 49)$$

Figure 4·1 gives values of the fraction $W_{0-\lambda,T}/W_{0-\infty,T}$ for corresponding values of the product λT, $\mu°R$. Using this chart for the values of λ_1 and λ_2 characteristic of the detector and optical system, a curve can be plotted for $\Psi(T)$ as ordinate against T as abscissa.

To find the corrected temperature determination T, the value of $\Psi(T)$ is first found from the curve for $T = T_A$. This value for $\Psi(T_A)$ is then divided by the value to be used for the emissivity ϵ. The resulting quotient is then the value for $\Psi(T)$; thus

$$\Psi(T) = \Psi(T_A)/\epsilon \qquad (4\cdot50)$$

The corrected value for the temperature determination T, °R, can then be read from the curve corresponding to the value found for $\Psi(T)$.

If the wavelength range λ_1 to λ_2 is narrow so that a mean value λ_m can be used, an approximate value for the corrected temperature can be computed from a relation based on Wien's law

$$T = 1/(1/T_A + 8.896 \times 10^{-5}\lambda_m \log_{10} \epsilon) \qquad (4\cdot51)$$

where T is the corrected value for the temperature determination, °R; T_A is the apparent temperature, °R; λ_m is the mean value for the wavelength range, μ; and ϵ is the emissivity of the source-body surface at wavelength λ_m and temperature T.[65]

Wien's law, on which Eq. 4·51 depends, is accurate to within one per cent provided that the product λT does not exceed 5400 $\mu°R$.[66]

Calibration against a blackbody reference standard may not be a separate operation. Means of calibration may be incorporated into the device such that the sensitive element is exposed alternately, by means of a chopper, to the source-body surface and to the reference blackbody. The temperature of the blackbody is then adjusted to the null point, at which the amplified difference signal vanishes. The temperature of the reference body is then the indicated value of apparent temperature T_A of the source-body surface. This arrangement, providing effectively continuous recalibration, largely eliminates errors due to drift. It thereby renders feasible the use of types of radiation-sensitive elements of inconstant responsivities S_i and S_t and amplifiers of varying *gain*.

If instead of an artificial blackbody a reference surface is used which is of the same material, surface condition, surface geometry, and ambient geometry as the source-body surface, actual rather than apparent temperatures will be indicated.

For ratio pyrometers utilizing two passbands of wavelength ranges λ_1 to λ_2 and λ_1' to λ_2', respectively, the relation between the corrected and the apparent indicated temperatures is given by

$$\frac{(\epsilon_{\lambda_1-\lambda_2,T}/\epsilon_{\lambda'_1-\lambda'_2,T})(W_{0-\lambda_1,T}/W_{0-\infty,T} - W_{0-\lambda_2,T}/W_{0-\infty,T})}{(W_{0-\lambda_1',T}/W_{0-\infty,T} - W_{0-\lambda_2',T}/W_{0-\infty,T})}$$

$$= \frac{(W_{0-\lambda_1,T_A}/W_{0-\infty,T_A} - W_{0-\lambda_2,T_A}/W_{0-\infty,T_A})}{(W_{0-\lambda_1',T_A}/W_{0-\infty,T_A} - W_{0-\lambda_2',T_A}/W_{0-\infty,T_A})} \quad (4.52)$$

where T is the corrected value for the temperature determination, °R; T_A is the apparent temperature, °R; $\epsilon_{\lambda_1-\lambda_2,T}/\epsilon_{\lambda_1'-\lambda_2',T}$ is the ratio of the average values of the emissivity of the source-body surface area over the wavelength ranges λ_1 to λ_2 and λ_1' to λ_2', respectively, at temperature T; $W_{0-\lambda_1,T}/W_{0-\infty,T}$ is the fraction of the total hemispherical blackbody radiant-power emission in the wavelength range 0 to λ_1 at temperature T; $W_{0-\lambda_2,T}/W_{0-\infty,T}$ is this fraction for the range 0 to λ_2 at temperature T; $W_{0-\lambda_1',T}/W_{0-\infty,T}$ is this fraction for the range 0 to λ_1' at temperature T; $W_{0-\lambda_2',T}/W_{0-\infty,T}$ is this fraction for the range 0 to λ_2' at temperature T; $W_{0-\lambda_1,T_A}/W_{0-\infty,T_A}$ is this fraction for the range 0 to λ_1 at temperature T_A; $W_{0-\lambda_2,T_A}/W_{0-\infty,T_A}$ is this fraction for the range 0 to λ_2 at temperature T_A; $W_{0-\lambda_1',T_A}/W_{0-\infty,T_A}$ is this fraction for the range 0 to λ_1' at temperature T_A; and $W_{0-\lambda_2',T_A}/W_{0-\infty,T_A}$ is this fraction for the range 0 to λ_2' at temperature T_A.

The function $\Phi(T)$ is given by

$$\Phi(T) = \frac{(W_{0-\lambda_1,T}/W_{0-\infty,T} - W_{0-\lambda_2,T}/W_{0-\infty,T})}{(W_{0-\lambda_1',T}/W_{0-\infty,T} - W_{0-\lambda_2',T}/W_{0-\infty,T})} \quad (4.53)$$

Using Fig. 4·1 with the values of λ_1, λ_2, λ_1', and λ_2' at the limits of the two passbands, a curve can be plotted for $\Phi(T)$ as ordinate against T as abscissa.

To find the corrected temperature determination T, the value of $\Phi(T)$ is first found from the curve for $T = T_A$. This value for $\Phi(T_A)$ is then divided by the value to be used for the emissivity ratio $\epsilon_{\lambda_1-\lambda_2,T}/\epsilon_{\lambda_1'-\lambda_2',T}$. The resulting quotient is the value for $\Phi(T)$. Thus

$$\Phi(T) = \Phi(T_A)/(\epsilon_{\lambda_1-\lambda_2,T}/\epsilon_{\lambda_1'-\lambda_2',T}) \quad (4.54)$$

The corrected value for the temperature determination T, °R, can then be read from the curve at the point corresponding to the value found for $\Phi(T)$.

If the wavelength ranges λ_1 to λ_2 and λ_1' to λ_2' are narrow so that mean values λ_m and λ_m' can be used, an approximate value for the corrected temperature can be computed from a relation based on Wien's law

$$T = 1/\{1/T_A - 8.896 \times 10^{-5}[\lambda_m\lambda_m'/(\lambda_m - \lambda_m')]\log_{10}(\epsilon_{\lambda,T}/\epsilon_{\lambda',T})\}$$

$$(4.55)$$

where T is the corrected value for the temperature determination, °R; T_A is the apparent temperature, °R; λ_m and λ_m' are the mean values of the wavelength in the two ranges, respectively, μ; and $\epsilon_{\lambda,T}/\epsilon_{\lambda',T}$ is the ratio of the values of the emissivity of the source-body surface area at the wavelengths λ_m and λ_m', respectively, at temperature T. Wien's law, on which Eq. 4·56 depends, is accurate to within one per cent provided that neither product $\lambda_m T$ nor product $\lambda_m'T$ exceeds 5400 μ °R.[57, 58, 63, 65-67]

4·15 ERRORS

The equations, charts, and methods of the preceding sections provide means for computing the minimum temperature change on the source-body surface, which will be observable under the given conditions. Similarly, the minimum feasible area on the source-body surface, over which the indicated temperature will be an average, is calculated. The lag time, or error in knowledge of the instant in time to which the temperature indication applies, is the response time of the system, where the system includes the radiation-sensitive element and the indicating instrumentation.[68-71]

Calibration errors will affect the precision of absolute temperature indications in amounts depending: (1) on the means employed to perform the calibration, (2) on the frequency of recalibrations, and (3) on the drift rate of the system. The precision can be no greater than that of the means used to determine the temperatures of the reference blackbody at the instants the calibration readings are taken. Similarly, departures from ideal blackness in the reference standards will introduce emissivity errors in the calibration. Drift errors can be made small by the effectively continuous recalibration that is provided by the modulation of the detector so as to be alternately presented with the beams from the reference standard and from the source-body surface, respectively.[68-71]

Apparent temperatures must be corrected by a factor that depends on the emissivity of the source-body surface. This factor is a fairly slow function, i.e., one of the order of the fourth root or the logarithm, of the emissivity or emissivity ratio. However, precise knowledge of the emissivity of the source-body surface is usually unavailable. Hence, corrected temperature determinations are subject to the uncertainty in the knowledge of the value to be used for the emissivity or emissivity ratio. If it is possible to use in calibration the actual source-body surface area or one of the same material, surface condition, and geometry, this error can be made small. It seems possible that the ratio of the emissivity in two wavelength ranges, as used in ratio pyrometry, may not depend as much on transient effects in surface conditions as the emissivities themselves. That these wavelength ranges can be made close together and overlapping might tend to lessen the differences between the emissivities.[68-72]

When temperature measurements are made on an ideally black source-body surface of uniform temperature, emissivity errors do not appear. Likewise errors due to averaging over a finite source area are absent; this condition can be realized to an approximation in the case of the interiors of furnaces viewed through "peep" holes. If the temperatures are high enough to permit use of the visual optical pyrometer and if calibration is performed in accord with the provisions of the International Temperature Scale, precision measurements are possible. Euler has shown that the precision can be as great as that to which the constants c_1 and c_2 in Planck's law (Eq. 4·2) have been determined.[73-75]

When the source-body surface area is exposed to the radiation from bodies at higher temperatures and unless it is ideally black, very large errors may occur. Thus, reflected radiation from the other bodies may be large in amount. Added to the thermal radiation emitted by the source-body surface, it is included in the indicated value of Φ or H. The increment in indicated temperature corresponding to the additional reflected radiation may be large. If the geometrical configuration of the adjacent bodies and the approximate values of their surface temperatures and emissivities are known, the amount of the reflected radiation may be estimated. Model methods, i.e., analogue computers, are available for its determination. Similarly, computation can be performed on electronic computing machines. Thus, corrections can be applied; however, the error may remain large. Calibration against an embedded thermometer directly on the source-body surface in the presence of the adjacent sources of radiation may suffice to render such errors small. Shielding the source-body surface area from such extraneous radiation may also serve to render its effects small.[11, 16, 57, 69-71, 76-82]

REFERENCES *

1. M. A. Melvin, "Blackbody Radiation and Lambert's Law," *Am. J. Phys.*, **23**, no. 8, pp. 508–510 (November, 1955).
2. C. D. Reid, "Nomographic-Type Slide Rule for Obtaining Spectral Blackbody Radiation Directly," *Rev. Sci. Instr.*, **31**, no. 8, pp. 886–890 (August, 1960).
3. A. N. Lowan and G. Blanch, "Tables of Planck's Radiation and Photon Functions," *J. Opt. Soc. Am.*, **30**, no. 2, pp. 70–81 (February, 1940).

---

* See footnote on page 26.

4. M. Czerny, "Zur Integration des Planckschen Strahlungsgesetze" (On Integrating Planck's Law of Radiation), *Zeitschrift für Physik,* **139**, no. 3, pp. 302–308 (1954).
5. A. R. Greenleaf, *Photographic Optics,* 214 pp., The Macmillan Co., New York, 1950.
6. G. C. Mönch, "Lichtmodulation durch Öffnungen in rotierenden Scheiben" (Light Modulation by Openings in Rotating Shutters), *Optik,* **10**, no. 8, pp. 365–374 (1953).
7. G. Kivenson, R. T. Steinback, and M. Rider, "An Infra-Red Chopped-Radiation Analyser," *J. Opt. Soc. Am.,* **38**, no. 12, pp. 1086–1091 (December, 1948).
8. R. C. Jones, "A Method of Describing the Detectivity of Photoconductive Cells," *Rev. Sci. Instr.,* **24**, no. 11, pp. 1035–1040 (November, 1953).
9. R. C. Jones, "The Ultimate Sensitivity of Radiation Detectors," *J. Opt. Soc. Am.,* **37**, no. 11, pp. 879–890 (November, 1947).
10. R. C. Jones, "A New Classification System for Radiation Detectors," *J. Opt. Soc. Am.,* **39**, no. 5, pp. 327–343 (May, 1949).
11. R. C. Jones, "Factors of Merit for Radiation Detectors," *J. Opt. Soc. Am.,* **39**, no. 5, pp. 344–356 (May, 1949).
12. P. B. Fellgett, "On the Ultimate Sensitivity and Practical Performance of Radiation Detectors," *J. Opt. Soc. Am.,* **39**, no. 11, pp. 970–976 (November, 1949).
13. M. J. E. Golay, "Theoretical Consideration in Heat and Infra-Red Detection, with Particular Reference to the Pneumatic Detector," *Rev. Sci. Instr.,* **18**, no. 5, pp. 347–356 (May, 1947).
14. M. J. E. Golay, "The Theoretical and Practical Sensitivity of the Pneumatic Infra-Red Detector," *Rev. Sci. Instr.,* **20**, no. 11, pp. 816–820 (November, 1949).
15. C. H. Cartwright, "Natural Observation Limit of Radiometric Measurements," *Physics,* **1**, no. 4, pp. 211–229 (October, 1931).
16. J. L. Doob, S. O. Rice, M. Kac, S. Chandrasekhar, G. E. Uhlenbeck, L. S. Ornstein, and N. Wax, *Selected Papers on Noise and Stochastic Processes,* 337 pp., Dover Publications, New York, 1954.
17. J. M. W. Milatz and H. A. Van der Velden, "Natural Limit of Measuring Radiation with a Bolometer," *Physica,* **10**, no. 6, pp. 369–380 (June, 1943).
18. J. B. Johnson and F. B. Llewellyn, "Limits to Amplification," *Bell System Technical Journal,* **14**, no. 1, pp. 85–96 (January, 1935).
19. H. Dänzer, "Zur Theorie des Schrot- und Johnson-Effektes" (On the Theory of the Shot and Johnson Effects), *Annalen der Physik,* **8**, Series 6, nos. 3–4, pp. 176–188 (1950).
20. S. M. Rytov, "Electric Fluctuations and Thermal Radiation" (in Russian), *Uspekhi Fizicheskikh Nauk SSSR,* **55**, no. 3, pp. 299–314 (March, 1955).
21. J. M. Richardson, "Linear Theory of Fluctuations Arising from Diffusional Mechanisms—An Attempt at a Theory of Contact Noise," *Bell System Technical Journal,* **29**, pp. 117–141 (January, 1950); Bell Telephone System Tech. Publ. Monograph No. 1739.
22. R. C. Jones, "Noise in Radiation Detectors," *Proceedings of the IRE,* The Institute of Radio Engineers, New York, **47**, no. 9, pp. 1481–1486 (September, 1959).
23. G. G. Macfarlane, "A Theory of Contact Noise in Semiconductors," *Proc. Phys. Soc. London B,* **63**, no. 370B, Part 10, pp. 807–814 (October, 1950).

24. C. J. Christensen and G. L. Pearson, "Resistance Fluctuations in Carbon Microphones and Other Granular Resistances," *Bell System Tech. J.*, **15**, no. 2, pp. 197–223 (April, 1936).

25. M. Surdin, "Une théorie des fluctuations électriques dans les semi-conducteurs" (A Theory of Electrical Fluctuations in Semiconductors), *Journal de physique et le radium*, **12**, no. 10, pp. 777–783 (October, 1951).

26. O. Simpson and G. B. B. M. Sutherland, "Photoconductivity in the Infra-Red Region of the Spectrum. Part I. The Preparation and Properties of Photoconductive Films of Lead Telluride. Part II. The Mechanism of Photoconductivity in Lead Telluride," *Phil. Trans. Roy. Soc. London, Ser. A*, **243**, no. 872, pp. 547–584 (August, 1951).

27. H. Müser, "Leistungsgrenzen von Photowiderständen (Limits of Performance of Photoconductors), *Zeitschrift für Physik*, **129**, no. 5, pp. 504–516 (1951).

28. T. R. Williams and J. B. Thomas, "Current Noise and Nonlinearity in Pyrolytic Carbon Films," *Rev. Sci. Instr.*, **30**, no. 7, pp. 586–590 (July, 1959).

29. D. Barber, "Measurements of Current Noise in Lead Sulphide at Audio Frequencies," *Proc. Phys. Soc. London B*, **68**, no. 431B, Part 11, pp. 898–907 (November, 1955).

30. R. W. Engstrom, "Multiplier Phototube Characteristics; Application to Low Light Levels," *J. Opt. Soc. Am.*, **37**, no. 6, pp. 420–421 (June, 1947).

31. R. W. Engstrom, "Refrigerator for a Multiplier Phototube," *Rev. Sci. Instr.*, **18**, no. 8, pp. 587–588 (August, 1947).

32. C. J. Bronco, R. M. St. John, and R. G. Fowler, "Pyrex Demountable Photomultiplier Refrigerator," *Rev. Sci. Instr.*, **29**, no. 12, pp. 1145–1146 (December, 1958).

33. L. A. Jones and G. C. Higgins, "Photographic Granularity and Graininess," *J. Opt. Soc. Am.*, **36**, no. 4, pp. 203–227 (April, 1946).

34. W. L. Hyde, "Detectors of Radiation," *Spectrochimica Acta*, **6**, pp. 9–18 (1953).

35. W. B. Lewis, "Fluctuations in Streams of Thermal Radiation," *Proc. Phys. Soc. London*, **59**, Part 1, no. 331, pp. 34–40 (January, 1947).

36. M. Jakob, *Heat Transfer*, Vol. I, 758 pp., 1949; M. Jakob and S. P. Kezios, Vol. II, 652 pp., 1957, John Wiley & Sons, New York.

37. H. Moser, U. Stille, and C. Tingwaldt, "Strahlungskonstanten, Strahlungäquivalent und optische Temperaturskala" (Radiation Constants, the Radiation Equivalent of Light and the Optical Scale of Temperature), *Optik*, **14**, nos. 7–8, pp. 291–302 (July–August, 1957); *Sci. Abstr. Sect. A*, **62**, no. 736, p. 298 (April, 1959).

38. D. J. Price, "Infra-Red Emissivity of Metals at High Temperatures," *Nature*, **157**, pp. 765–766 (June, 1946).

39. H. W. Knop, Jr., "The Emissivity of Iron-Tungsten and Iron-Cobalt Alloys," *Phys. Rev.*, **74**, no. 10, pp. 1413–1416 (November, 1948).

40. R. M. Leedy, "Controlling Radiant Heat," *Prod. Eng.*, **25**, pp. 174–180 (October, 1954).

41. N. W. Snyder, "A Review of Thermal Radiation Constants," *Paper 53-A-176*, pp. 1–7, American Society of Mechanical Engineers, New York (1953).

42. N. W. Snyder, J. T. Gier, and R. V. Dunkle, "Total Normal Emissivity Measurements on Aircraft Materials between 100 and 800°F," *Paper 54-A-139*, pp. 1–11, American Society of Mechanical Engineers, New York (1954).

43. D. J. Price and H. Lowery, "The Emissivity Characteristics of Hot Metals, with Special Reference to the Infra-Red," *J. Iron Steel Inst. London,* **149,** no. 1, Section I, pp. 523P–546P (1944).

44. L. M. K. Boelter, R. Bromberg, and J. T. Gier, "An Investigation of Aircraft Heaters—XV. The Emissivity of Several Materials," *Wartime Report* 4A21, U. S. National Advisory Committee for Aeronautics, Washington (January, 1944).

45. H. B. Wahlin and H. W. Knop, Jr., "The Spectral Emissivity of Iron and Cobalt," *Phys. Rev.,* **74,** no. 6, pp. 687–689 (September, 1948).

46. A. G. Worthing, "Temperature Radiation Emissivities and Emittances," American Institute of Physics, *Temperature,* pp. 1164–1187, Reinhold Publishing Corp., New York, 1941.

47. S. M. DeCorso and R. L. Coit, "Measurement of Total Emissivities of Gas-Turbine Combustor Materials," *Paper* 54-SA-26, 12 pp., American Society of Mechanical Engineers, New York (1954).

48. R. Weil, "A Note on Optical Pyrometry," *J. Iron Steel Inst. London,* **157,** Part 3, pp. 415–416 (November, 1947).

49. M. Michaud, "Influence de l'ètat de surface d'un materiau rayonnant sur la valeur de son facteur d'émission à haute température" (Influence of the State of the Surface of a Radiating Material on its Emissivity at High Temperatures), *Compt. rend.,* **226,** pp. 568–569 (February, 1948).

50. D. J. Price, "The Emissivity of Hot Metals in the Infra-Red," *Proc. Phys. Soc. London,* **59,** pp. 118–131 (July, 1946).

51. R. H. McFee, "Blackbody Source Unit with Electronic Temperature Control," *Rev. Sci. Instr.,* **23,** no. 1, pp. 52–53 (January, 1952).

52. G. A. W. Rutgers and J. C. DeVos, "Relation between Brightness Temperature, True Temperature and Colour Temperature of Tungsten. Luminance of Tungsten," *Physica,* **20,** no. 10, pp. 715–720 (October, 1954).

53. J. C. DeVos, "A New Determination of the Emissivity of Tungsten Ribbon," *Physica,* **20,** no. 10, pp. 690–714 (October, 1954).

54. D. L. Burk, "The Ratio Pyrometer," *Instruments,* **33,** no. 1, pp. 64–67 (January, 1960).

55. A. G. Worthing, "Temperature Radiation Emissivities and Emittances," American Institute of Physics, *Temperature,* pp. 1164–1187, Reinhold Publishing Corp., New York, 1941.

56. R. V. Dunkle, "Thermal Radiation Tables and Applications," *Paper* 53-A-220, pp. 1–7, American Society of Mechanical Engineers, New York (1953).

57. P. H. Dike, *Temperature Measurements with Rayotubes,* 48 pp., Leeds & Northrup Co., Philadelphia (1953).

58. F. P. Bowden and P. H. Thomas, "The Surface Temperature of Sliding Solids," *Proc. Roy. Soc. London A,* **223,** no. 1152, pp. 35–36 (April, 1954).

59. T. P. Gill, "Some Problems in Low-Temperature Pyrometry," *J. Opt. Soc. Am.,* **47,** no. 11, pp. 1000–1005 (November, 1957).

60. D. J. Price, "The Temperature Variation of the Emissivity of Metals in the Near Infra-Red," *Proc. Phys. Soc. London,* **59,** pp. 131–138 (1947).

61. G. Hasse, "Farb-Pyrometrie" (Color Pyrometry), *ATM Archiv für technisches Messen,* V214-2, T133–134 (October, 1933).

62. K. Guthmann, "Ein neues Farbpyrometer I and II" (A New Color Pyrometer), *ATM Archiv für technisches Messen,* V214-7 and 8, T57–59 (May, 1937).

63. A. F. Gibson, "A Two-Color Infra-Red Radiation Pyrometer," *J. Sci. Inst.,* **28,** no. 5, pp. 153–155 (May, 1951).

64. J. T. M. Malpica, "Blocking Layer Cell Color Temperature Pyrometer," *Gen. Elec. Rev.*, **44**, no. 8, pp. 439–443 (August, 1941).

65. E. C. Pyatt, "Some Consideration of the Errors of Brightness and Two-Colour Types of Spectral Radiation Pyrometer," *Brit. J. Appl. Phys.*, **5**, no. 7, pp. 264–268 (July, 1954).

66. W. E. Forsythe, *Measurement of Radiant Energy*, 452 pp., McGraw-Hill Book Co., New York, 1937.

67. H. Schmidt, "Über die Grundzüge der Farbpyrometrie" (On the Foundations of Color Pyrometry), *Mitteilungen aus dem Kaiser-Wilhelm-Institut für Eisenforschung zu Düsseldorf*, **6**, pp. 7-15 (1924–1925).

68. A. E. Martin, "The Accuracy of Infra-Red Intensity Measurements," *Trans. Faraday Soc.*, **47**, no. 347, part II, pp. 1182–1191 (November, 1951).

69. J. C. Boonshaft, "Measurement Errors:—Classification and Interpretation," *Paper* 53-A-219, pp. 1–5, American Society of Mechanical Engineers, New York (1953).

70. E. T. Benedikt, "Errors in Second-Order Measuring Instruments," *Rev. Sci. Instr.*, **20**, no. 4, pp. 229–233 (April, 1949).

71. F. D. Weaver, "Scale and Reading Errors of Electrical Indicators," *Instruments*, **27**, no. 11, pp. 1812–1814 (November, 1954).

72. H. Herne, "The Theoretical Characteristics of Bichromatic Pyrometers," *Brit. J. Appl. Phys.*, **4**, no. 12, pp. 374–377 (December, 1953).

73. J. Euler, "Fortschritte auf dem Gebiet der optischen Pyrometrie in den Jahren 1940 bis 1950" (Advances in the Field of Optical Pyrometry in the Years 1940 to 1950), *Zeitschrift für angewandte Physik*, **2**, no. 12, pp. 505–509 (December, 1950).

74. A. Jagersberger, "Messgenauigkeit der technischen Teilstrahlungspyrometer" (Accuracy of Measurement of Technical Optical Pyrometers), *Bull. assoc. suisse électriciens*, **40**, no. 7, pp. 179–186 (April, 1949).

75. J. Euler and W. Schneider, "Über die Messgenauigkeit bei Fadenpyrometern" (On the Precision of Optical Pyrometers), *Zeitschrift für angewandte Physik*, **3**, no. 12, pp. 459–467 (1951).

76. P. L. Tea, Jr., and H. D. Baker, "A Model Method for Determining Geometric Factors in Solid-to-Solid Radiation Heat Transfer," *Paper* 57-SA-10, pp. 1–9 (1957); *Trans. ASME*, **80**, no. 2, pp. 367–372 (February, 1958), American Society of Mechanical Engineers, New York.

77. P. L. Tea, *Determination of Configuration Factors for Solid-to-Solid Radiation by Use of Model Chambers*, Doctoral Dissertation, Columbia University, New York, 1955.

78. B. T. Chao, "On a Generalized Procedure for the Calculation of Thermal Radiation Transfer," *Paper* 55-SA-61, pp. 1–11, American Society of Mechanical Engineers, New York (1955).

79. B. Gebhart, "Unified Treatment for Thermal Radiation Transfer Processes— Gray, Diffuse Radiators and Absorbers," *Paper* 57-A-34, 14 pp., American Society of Mechanical Engineers, New York (1957).

80. W. W. Coblentz, "Present Status of the Constants and Verification of the Laws of Thermal Radiation of a Uniformly Heated Inclosure," *Scientific Papers U. S. Bur. Standards*, **17**, no. 406, pp. 7–48 (December, 1920).

81. T. R. Harrison, *Radiation Pyrometry and Its Underlying Principles of Radiant Heat Transfer*, 234 pp., John Wiley & Sons, New York, 1960.

82. H. Lund, "The Design of Barrier-Layer Photocell Pyrometers," *J. Sci. Instr.*, **24**, no. 4, pp. 95–97 (April, 1947).

part **II**

APPLICATIONS

5

SURFACE TEMPERATURES

5·1 INTRODUCTION

In Volume I the principles and procedures of *thermoelectric thermometry* were discussed. Methods for applying thermoelectric techniques to the measurement of internal temperatures in solids were then carefully elaborated. In Ch. 2 of that volume, a number of additional principles were also listed. They tended, however, to be somewhat specialized in character and, as such, were considered to be more closely related to their applications in the circumstances of particular problems. Part I of the present volume has been devoted to two others of the primary methods, i.e., to *electric-resistance thermometry* and *radiation pyrometry*. In Chs. 1 and 3 the assortment of available components of useful apparatus has been described; in Chs. 2 and 4 the ensemble of helpful design-calculation procedure has been outlined. Methodical quantitative application of these techniques, in accord with the philosophy and customary practices in engineering design, will yield satisfactory equipment for coping with large scopes of temperature-measurement problems. Space has, unfortunately, been unavailable for the working-out of more than a very few sample cases, sufficient only to illustrate how such calculation can be done. Difficulties that arise in solving design problems, however, tend to be peculiar to the particular conditions; and, in the growth of the art in the laboratory and in industry, many forms of application have been developed. The specialized devices that have arisen in specific circumstances have been adapted to the needs of the local conditions.

Part II of this volume will be devoted to analyses of actual measurement problems, i.e., the measurement of temperature under various classes of *characteristic conditions*.

The classification *surface temperatures* is in nature necessarily a somewhat arbitrary choice. On the one hand the surface of a body is a special case in the more general subject of its interior. Problems of the interior were dealt with in Volume I. The techniques therein described for temperature measurement at an interior point can be applied to the measurement of surface temperature by choosing that point sufficiently close to the surface. "Sufficiently close" means closer than the uncertainty or error accepted for the location of the point that actually has the temperature shown on the indicator. This requirement may be reasonable if the temperature gradients normal to the surface are not too steep and are without such discontinuities as would result from changes in material in the surface layers. Unreliability may result for a measurement on a living organism. There the surgical insertion of an element may, by inciting local fever conditions, change the temperature to be measured. Unfortunately, the procedure of measuring temperatures at interior points and extrapolating to the surface is almost the only unequivocal method for the measurement of surface temperatures, and it is not always possible to apply this method. The existence of this method is a reason why, however, the techniques for the measurement of internal temperatures, at defined positions, are to be regarded as of fundamental importance.

The geometric surface of a body can be thought of as an ideal entity, subject only to the thermal agitation of the atoms in the surface layer. This concept acquires practical significance for surface films of poorly conducting material. Radiation methods deal precisely with this "ideal" surface. The fact that the intended locations are on the surface makes them particularly accessible. Thus, the use of radiation techniques is thereby rendered possible. Also, although it is usually desirable to avoid doing so, bulky attachments to the surface can be used, thereby taking advantage of the freedom of space external to the body. Radiation techniques are without practical limitations to their adaptability to high temperatures, rapidly changing temperatures, motion of the surface observed, and distance from the surface to the detector. In general, the topic "surface temperatures" tends to overlap and include other subjects, to two of which separate, subsequent chapters are devoted, i.e., "Rapidly Changing Temperatures" and "Temperatures of Moving Bodies."

When the accessibility inherent in the surface location is exploited in the use of methods other than those given in Volume I, difficulties are universal, but they are accepted together with the corresponding opportunities. The difficulties arise in two categories.

Any apparatus brought near to, or in contact with, the source-body surface changes the heat-transfer rates between the surface area and its environment. The rates of surface chemical reactions, evaporation, and condensation may be similarly affected. The result of this *blanketing* or *thermal damming* is that the temperature to be measured is altered by the means of measurement. Similar effects occur if part of the surface itself is replaced by other materials to form an integral surface temperature-sensitive element.

On the other hand, if with radiation technique all apparatus is moved to a distance, emissivity and reflection errors result; then the *apparent* and not the actual temperature is *indicated*. Similarly, reflected radiation originating in ambient "hot" bodies may tend to make the measurement that of the temperatures of the other "hot" surfaces. Only when the source-body surface is ideally black do these errors vanish. This rarely occurs except for areas on the inner surfaces of uniform-temperature enclosures.

5·2 INTERIOR THERMOCOUPLES

As a primary-standard measurement of surface temperature, Stoll [1] and Hardy [1,2] extrapolated the readings of interior thermocouples. They wished to test the accuracy with which various conventional devices measured the temperature of the human skin, and they simulated the situation with leather. Since leather is of low thermal conductivity, its surface temperature is sensitive to convective and radiant exchanges with the ambient. Their model consisted essentially of four layers of oak-tanned leather bound tightly to the cylindrical cop-

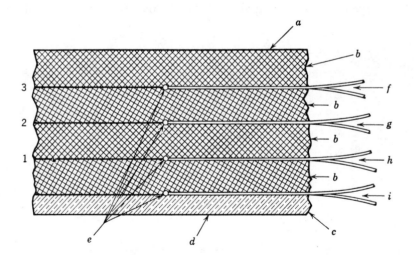

Fig. 5·1. Interior-gradient junctions. *a*, Outer leather surface; *b*, 0.125-in. thick layer of leather; *c*, copper wall of thermostated bath; *d*, inner copper surface swept by circulating water; *e*, thermoelectric junctions of No. 40 B & S gage (0.003 in.) copper and constantan wires pressed between the layers of leather; *f*, leads at interface No. 3; *g*, leads at interface No. 2; *h*, leads at interface No. 1; and *i*, leads at outer cylinder surface.

per surface of a thermostated bath. Junctions embedded in the isothermal surfaces between these layers indicated the successive interface temperatures (see Fig. 5·1). Extrapolation of the curve drawn through the experimental points yielded the surface temperature (see Fig. 5·2). Despite changes, due to arbitrarily varied ambient conditions, the determination was considered uniformly reliable to within 0.05°C (0.09°F).[1-3]

Weills and Ryder [4] performed a similar extrapolation to the end surface of a 3-in. diameter aluminum-alloy bar. Radial thermocouple installations, performed according to Sec. 11·2 of Volume I, at ½-inch longitudinal intervals, supplied the internal-temperature data from which the metal-surface temperatures were determined. By these means, the temperature drop was measured across a dry or oil-filled interface between two closely pressed precision surfaces.[4,5]

Rall and Giedt [6] welded 0.010-in. diameter oxidized nickel wires to the bottoms of 0.0135-in. diameter parallel-drilled holes spaced at ³⁄₆₄-in. successive intervals from the edge of a metal-cutting tool. By extrapolation of the curves plotted from the indications for these nickel-to-toolmetal junctions, they determined the temperatures of the cutting edge.[6,7]

In each of the cases the media were homogeneous; the ambient fluctuations were not rapid, and the temperature fields permitted

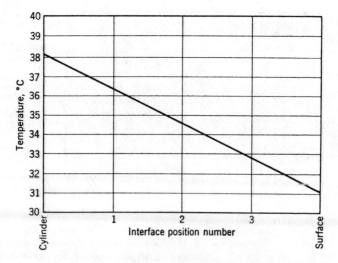

Fig. 5·2. Extrapolation of interior-temperature data to determine surface temperature. (*By permission A. M. Stoll and J. D. Hardy in Rev. Sci. Instr.,* **20,** *no. 9, 681, September, 1949.*)

straight-line or nearly straight-line extrapolations. If, however, the material is inhomogeneous or subjected to local surface heat exchanges or to rapidly fluctuating ambient conditions, the temperature plot corresponding to that in Fig. 5·2 may be sharply curved. Satisfactory extrapolation to the surface then requires points closer to the surface, and these points must be more precisely located with respect to the surface. Although the installations required by Stoll [1] and Hardy [1,2] and by Weills and Ryder [4] were relatively easy to perform, complex patterns may make severe demands on technique. Thus, it may then be necessary to thread fine-wire elements through small-diameter holes drilled parallel to and close to the surface. Figure 8·14 of Volume I indicates the sort of installation then needed. However, it may be necessary to work to a much smaller scale.[1,2,4,8-10]

Hollander's [11,12] problem was an extreme case. It was desired to plot the local transient-temperature pattern under the surface of the workpiece at the operating edge of a metal-cutting tool. Preliminary analogue-computer studies by Paschkis [11] had indicated that the temperature rise would be appreciable to a depth of only about 0.020 in. and for a duration of less than 10^{-4} sec. These predictions indicated that means closely discriminating in space and time would be required. Further studies showed that, under the highly transient conditions, the temperature pattern on an open face of the material, normal to the working surface and direction of cut, would be essentially the same as that on a parallel internal plane. Similarly, emergent thermocouple leads would not transmit sufficient heat to affect junction temperatures because of the relatively long times required for heat-condition effects. However, it would be necessary for the junctions to be thermally integral, i.e., in "wetted" contact with the parent metal.[11-13]

For sufficient resolution of the space pattern in temperature but within feasible limits, 0.0005-in. diameter thermocouple wire was chosen. For this size of wire, 0.001-in. diameter drilled holes provided space for insertion and soldering (see Fig. 5·3A). Hole-cleaning problems were reduced by introducing the flux during drilling, thus using it as the cutting lubricant. Letting the workpiece serve as the second thermoelectric metal limited space requirements to those for one wire.[11-13]

Adequate resolution of the temperature pattern in time was attained by use of electronic indication. A microvolt preamplifier of 10^{-5}-sec response time preceded a cathode-ray oscilloscope of 10^{-2}-sec sweep time. A Ronchi ruling, mounted on the vertical-lathe table, intercepted a narrow light beam focused on a photo element. The

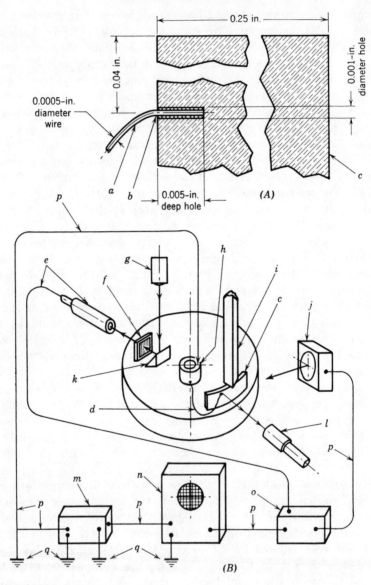

Fig. 5·3. Hollander's thermocouple apparatus. (A) Junction installation; and (B) vertical-lathe table, specimen, and instruments. a, 0.0005-in. diameter constantan thermocouple wire soft-soldered in hole; b, mouth of 0.001-in. diameter drilled hole (no solder is permitted to run up the wire or spread out over the brass surface); c, brass workpiece; d, single-lead constantan thermocouple wire; e, photodiode and its lead wire; f, Ronchi ruling; g, light source; h, mercury-slip-ring moving contact; i, lathe cutting tool; j, strobe-light source; k, reflecting prism; l, telescope; m, preamplifier and calibrator; n, cathode-ray oscilloscope; o, amplifier, differentiator, and clipper; p, shielded lead wires; and q, ground.

first-pulse ray was accurately located in relation to the straight cutting edge of the lathe tool to provide, after amplification, an a-c signal emf to trigger the sweep of the oscilloscope. Thus, the sweep was started at positions of the thermocouple junction precisely measured from the cutting edge. The single oscilloscope trace was recorded on fast photographic film by a 35-mm camera mounted before the screen. These arrangements are shown on Fig. 5·3B.[11–13]

A set of data, obtained on brass for a cutting speed of 95 ft/min and 0.0025 in. depth of cut, is given in Fig. 5·4.[11]

Successive cuts brought an installed junction closer to the surface where it was ultimately removed by the cutting tool. For more continuous operation, the radiation pyrometer, described in Fig. 5·11A and Sec. 7·7, was built.[11–14]

If the medium is one of low thermal conductivity, fine wires may be required to avoid excessive disturbance of local temperatures by heat conducted along the leads. Design calculations should be made according to the methods described in Ch. 7 of Volume I to determine the wire-diameter requirements.

If there is a discontinuity in thermal conductivity of the medium

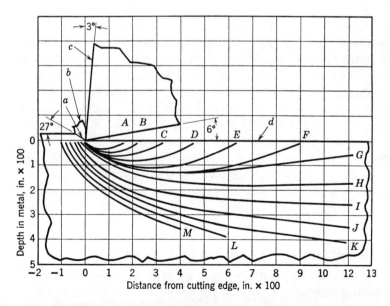

Fig. 5·4. Hollander's thermocouple data. Isothermals in metal, temperature rise above body of workpiece: *A*, 53.5°F; *B*, 41.0°F; *C*, 34.0°F; *D*, 28.5°F; *E*, 23.0°F; *F*, 19.5°F; *G*, 17.5°F; *H*, 11.0°F; *I*, 7.5°F; *J*, 4.0°F; *K*, 2.3°F; *L*, 1.15°F; and *M*, 0.7°F. *a*, Shear plane; *b*, chip; *c*, cutting tool; and *d*, brass workpiece.

so close to the surface that temperature-gradient measurements cannot be made within the surface layer, the methods of this section will fail. Thus, the determination will be that of the temperature which would have prevailed at the surface if this difference in conductivity did not occur. For a thin coating, it will approximate the temperature at the surface of the parent material carrying the coating.

5·3   SURFACE-INSTALLED ELEMENTS

Single-wire or beaded thermoelectric junctions can be soldered or welded to a metal surface, peened into a ductile material at the surface, or pierced into a soft material from the surface. Similarly, fittings in which the wires have been thus installed, or the beads themselves, can be pressed against or screwed into the surface. Many such arrangements are illustrated in Ch. 8 of Volume I. Obviously, the approximation in location relatively to the surface cannot be known more closely than to within the depth of penetration of the installation. Errors due to the *fin effect,* i.e., to heat transfer along the leads, are best determined by calculations according to the methods of Ch. 7 in Volume I. For most of these methods, thermistors can be substituted, retaining the same calculation techniques.

We note two illustrations of this sort of technique. Thus (see Fig. 5·5A), Monroe and Bristow [15] cold-soldered 0.002-in. diameter silk-insulated platinum electric-resistance wire in an 0.008-in. wide helical groove to measure the surface temperature of copper tubes. Similarly, Hübner [16] (see Fig. 5·5B) stretched butt-welded 0.020-in. diameter silver-against-constantan and 0.012-in. diameter iron-against-constantan thermocouple wires across the glass surfaces of operating electric-lamp bulbs. Thermal contact at the junction was effected with films of glycerin, silicone oil, waterglass, and a brown cement at successively higher temperatures, respectively. The transparent contact materials were intended not to absorb the lamp's radiation sufficiently to alter the glass-surface temperature at the point of measurement. Comparison with precision radiation measurements (see Sec. 5·15) convinced Hübner that the thermoelectric measurements were sufficiently accurate for practical purposes.[1, 2, 15–23]

5·4   PORTABLE SURFACE-CONTACT THERMOCOUPLES

Portable devices intended for quick and convenient measurement of surface temperatures have been built in various forms, and many of them have been made available commercially. For example, a handle containing the indicating instrument may be arranged with an assortment of interchangeable sensitive tips for pressing against the surface.

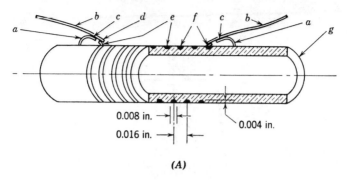

(A)

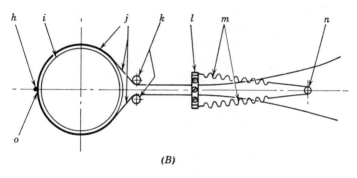

(B)

Fig. 5·5. Surface-installed elements. (*A*) Monroe and Bristow's electric-resistance design; and (*B*) Hübner's thermocouple design. *a*, Anchoring lug; *b*, copper leads; *c*, anchoring to lug; *d*, soldered joint close to surface; *e*, 0.002-in. diameter 23-in. long platinum-wire electric-resistance element; *f*, helical groove in which silk-winding-insulated platinum resistance wire is embedded in cold solder flush with tube surface; *g*, copper tubing; *h*, thermoelectric junction [fused silver-against-constantan bead is 2 to 2.5 mm (0.08 to 0.10 in.) diameter, but iron-against-constantan bead is hard-butt-soldered without enlargement]; *i*, lamp bulb; *j*, 0.5-mm (0.020-in.) diameter silver-against-constantan thermocouple wire or 0.3-mm (0.012-in.) diameter iron-against-constantan thermocouple wire; *k*, guide pins; *l*, insulating clamp; *m*, tension springs; *n*, anchor post; and *o*, thermal-contact film of glycerin or silicone oil, or an 8- by 15-mm (0.315- by 0.592-in.) sodium-waterglass or brown-socket-cement patch. (*By permission A. G. Monroe and H. A. S. Bristow in J. Sci. Instr.,* **30**, *no. 10, 385, October, 1953; and after H. J. Hübner in Zeitschrift für angewardte Physik,* **7,** *no. 6, 277, 1955.*)

Or, there may be an indicating device in a box with a flexible cable leading to the handle carrying the sensitive tips.[24-26]

The sensitive tips are in the following forms: (1), a button to be pressed against the surface; (2), a point or pair of points to be forced into the surface; (3), a ribbon arranged in a yoke for stretching it

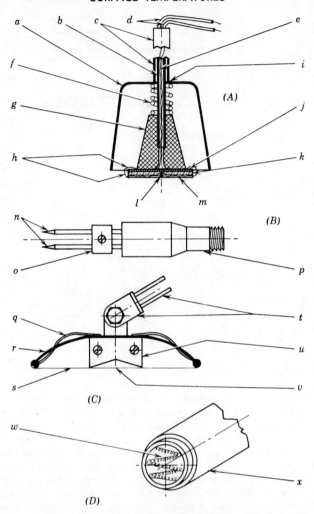

Fig. 5·6. Tip forms for portable surface-temperature instruments. (*A*) King and Blackie's pressure-button design; (*B*) point-contact tip unit; (*C*) stretched-band ribbon junction with spring yoke; and (*D*) Dermalor resistance-wire skin thermometer. *a*, 3-cm (1.18-in.) diameter polished nickel radiation shield; *b*, silica tube, easy sliding fit in stem; *c*, 20-cm (7.9-in.) long brass-tube stem; *d*, insulated thermocouple lead wires; *e*, thermocouple wires firmly packed in asbestos; *f*, helical steel pressure spring; *g*, cork block; *h*, thermocouple wires coated with black insulating varnish; *i*, hard-soldered joint; *j*, asbestos insulating washer; *k*, 1.5-mm (0.06-in.) thick 1.8-cm (0.71-in.) diameter copper disk coated with black insulating varnish; *l*, insulating-varnish-coated thermoelectric junction in indentation; *m*, varnished thermocouple wires lashed in groove; *n*, thermocouple wires sharpened to points; *o*, insulating block; *p*, mounting fitting; *q*, flexible insulated thermocouple lead wires; *r*, spring-tension yoke; *s*, thin ribbon-stock thermo-

across the surface; and, (4), means for stretching meshes of wires across and against the surface (see Fig. 5·6).[1, 2, 24-28]

Devices of this sort are intended rather for convenience than for any high degree of precision. The thermal contact between the surface and sensitive element, with the element merely pressed against the surface, is disposed to be dubious, furthermore through the leads and the massive handle structure, the element is in fair thermal communication with the ambient. If the surface consists of a coating of poorly conducting oxide or is covered with loose dust, a substantial temperature drop may occur in this layer. Tests have been made, however, for various designs and circumstances. They indicate that under favorable conditions surface temperatures are measured correctly to within a few per cent of the elevation above ambient. However, for poorly conducting surface materials, errors may be much larger (see Fig. 8·5 in Volume I).[1, 2, 24, 25, 27]

When the surface is smooth and of uniform temperature such as that of a rotating roll, a sliding element can be in constant motion over new areas during the making of a measurement. This results in an advantage not available with fixed installations in that the instantaneously opposed surface is thus less affected by heat transfer through the instrument to the ambient.[24]

When the two thermoelectric materials are provided as points to be forced into a metallic surface, completing their electric circuit through the parent material, advantages also occur. The temperature indicated will be the average of those at the points of actual contact. With only these needlelike points to be heated, a reading can be taken very quickly. There is thus the possibility of obtaining a measurement before the presence of the instrument has substantially altered the temperature to be measured. This method is, of course, only applicable to clean metallic surfaces and will be subject to a location error equal to the depth of penetration of the points and also to their separation (see Fig. 5·6B).

When a needle element (see Fig. 8·6 in Volume I) is pierced into a soft material, the location error corresponds to the depth of insertion. Thermal contact may be good and readings quickly taken. However, in poorly conducting materials, errors may be substantial.[3]

A portable device that has been found to be precise is the compen-

---

electric leads; t, universal swiveling mount; u, insulating pressure block; v, butt-welded line junction; w, electric-resistance stretched thermometer-element helices; and x, insulating and mounting tube. (*By permission J. G. King and A. Blackie in J. Sci. Instr.*, **2**, *no. 8, 262, May, 1925; and A. M. Stoll and J. D. Hardy in J. Sci. Instr.*, **20**, *no. 9, 679, September, 1949.*)

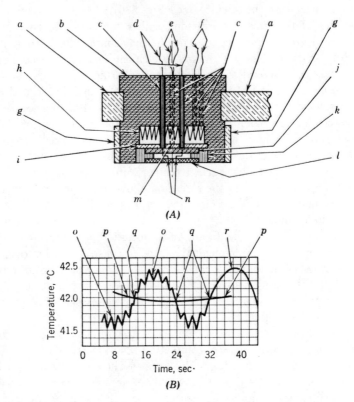

Fig. 5·7. Compensated surface elements. (A) Roeser's null-balance design; and
(B) Sasaki and Kamada's intermittent-contact method. a, Mounting-bracket
clamp; b, Bakelite block; c, porcelain insulating tubes; d, No. 22 B & S gage
(0.025 in.) chromel-against-alumel thermocouple wires for measuring junctions;
e, No. 22 B & S gage (0.025 in.) chromel-against-alumel lead wires for compensator-disk junctions; f, lead wires to heater coil; g, brass ring; h, heater coil
embedded in Alundum cement; i, copper compensator disk; j, mica insulator disk;
k, Bakelite ring; l, Sumet bearing-metal contact disk; m, compensator-disk silver-
soldered junctions; n, measuring junctions silver-soldered in holes drilled into
contact disk; o, maximum junction-temperature modulations in portion of heating cycle when junction temperature differs most from surface temperature; p,
surface-temperature curve; q, zones of zero junction-temperature modulation at
points in heating cycle when junction temperature is the same as the surface
temperature; and r, unmodulated heating-cycle junction-temperature curve, occurring while thermoelectric measuring junction is out of contact with surface.
(By permission W. F. Roeser and E. F. Mueller in RP 231, J. Research Natl. Bur.
Standards, 5, no. 4, 796, October, 1930; and N. Sasaki and A. Kamada in Rev.
Sci., Instr., 23, no. 6, 262, June, 1952.)

sated element (see Fig. 5·7A). Here, an electrically heated shield or compensator disk, near to the element in the heat-transfer path to the ambient, can be adjusted to the same temperature as that of the element. The heat loss to the ambient can thereby be made arbitrarily small and this source of error eliminated. Another error, however, arises in that the surface area affected by the element is now shielded from its normal rate of loss to the ambient and may thereby rise in temperature. If circumstances are such that the element can be continuously moved over fresh uniform-temperature areas, very high precision is possible. If the surface is below ambient temperature, such a device, then requiring a "cooler," would be inconvenient to construct.[24, 25, 29]

Sasaki [30, 31] and Kamada [30] (see Fig. 5·7B) avoided both *blanketing* and *fin-effect* errors by arranging a thermoelectric junction in periodic motion contacting the surface only momentarily at 2-sec intervals. A heating coil varied the junction temperature with a much longer period and over a range adjusted to *bracket* that of the surface. The recorded emf output, corresponding to the sinusoidal heating cycle, showed *pips* as the junction temperature was altered by contact with the surface. For the contacts occurring at points in the junction-heating cycle at which the junction and surface were at the same temperature, the pips vanished. These points were determined with a sensitivity of to within a few hundredths of a degree. For measurements by these means on the glass-bulb surface of an operating 40-w electric lamp, precision to within $\pm 0.3°C$ (0.54°F) was estimated.[30, 31]

5·5   PATCH SURFACE-CONTACT ELEMENTS

These elements usually differ from portable elements essentially in fixity and permanence of installation. Figures 8·21 and 8·22 of Volume I show variations of a form in which a clamp is provided to press the bead or a button against the surface. Figure 1·8B shows a resistance-element patch to be cemented to the surface. Often a thermocouple or thermistor bead is merely pressed under a strip of adhesive plaster. Various convenient clamping devices are available commercially.[1, 2, 17, 18, 27, 32, 33]

These devices tend to be bulky with correspondingly substantial shielding and fin effects. They cannot be moved around over fresh areas as can the portable devices. Their character is more that of *control-point pick-ups* than of measuring devices.

5·6   EXTENDED-SURFACE THERMOELECTRIC JUNCTIONS

When a surface occurs as the interface between two different metals in electric contact, it can be regarded as a thermoelectric junction and

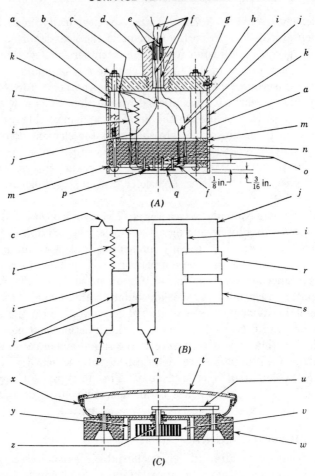

Fig. 5·8. Thermal-equilibrium noncontact elements. (A) Field and Gehman's compensated thermoelectric device; (B) diagram for Field and Gehman's compensating circuit, and (C) bimetallic-element direct-indicating device. a, Six metal spacer studs; b, six hexagonal nuts; c, compensating junction in contact with metal housing; d, metal mounting stem; e, insulating tubes; f, No. 40 B & S gage (0.003 in.) iron-against-constantan thermocouple lead wires; g, metal base disk; h, machine screw; i, iron thermocouple wire; j, constantan thermocouple wire; k, cylindrical metal shell; l, 10-ohm constantan resistor adjusted during calibration; m, metal clamping rings; n, Celotex disk; o, four light wooden supporting pegs; p, compensating junction on 0.001-in. thick copper-foil receiver blackened on front surface and brightly plated on rear surface; q, measuring junction soldered to identical copper-foil receiver; r, amplifier; s, indicator, recorder, or controller; t, transparent window; u, pointer needle; v, spiral bimetallic temperature-sensitive element anchored to base and keyed to shaft; w, nonmetallic base block; x, metal base frame; y, copper shield cup; and z, shaft. (*By permission J. E. Field and S. D. Gehman in J. Appl. Phys.*, **22**, no. 1, 106, *January, 1951.*)

its temperature accordingly indicated. Such a surface may be internal or external when two different bodies are in contact, or it may be separated by only a thin film from an external surface. If the temperature is uniform over both surfaces in contact, this is the temperature indicated. If nonuniform, the indicated resultant is an intermediate, but not in general the arithmetic mean, temperature.

This topic will be discussed in its applications in Secs. 5·9 and 7·6, particularly with regard to problems in moving bodies.

5·7   NONCONTACT ELEMENTS

Figure 5·8 indicates two varieties of element intended to approximate thermal equilibrium with the corresponding surface area, but without mechanical contact. Radiation, convection, and gaseous conduction are the modes of heat transfer. Communication with the ambient, through the body structure and its lateral surface, is relatively substantial.

Field and Gehman [34] (see Fig. 5·8A) thus found an element temperature of 175°F for a surface temperature of 165°F when the instrument housing was at 250°F. By use of a compensating thermocouple (see Fig. 5·8B), this error due to conduction to the ambient was automatically corrected. The compensating resistance r, however, had to be adjusted in calibration for given ambient heat-transfer conditions. Since mechanical contact is unnecessary, these methods are suitable for moving surfaces. Field and Gehman thus measured the temperature of a moving belt, over the range 140 to 180°F, to within ±2°F, at a 250°F ambient.

A commercially available device intended for measuring rotating-roll surface temperatures depends on aspirating air from close to the roll. A noncontact, but closely fitting, cup collects the roll-surface air, which is then passed over a shielded thermoelectric junction. Figure 5·8C illustrates another package device of wide application. [35]

Waugh and Yphantis [36] employed an ingenious noncontact principle depending entirely on radiant heat transfer. Their problem was to measure to within ±0.03°C (±0.054°F) the temperatures of ultracentrifuge rotors while the rotors were spinning at rates up to 60,000 rpm. Since the theory of their method is specialized and exacting, the reader is referred to the very complete discussion given in the original paper.

5·8   BLACKBODY PYROMETER

Figure 5·9 indicates a commercially available design of radiation pyrometer intended to reduce emissivity and reflection errors. A

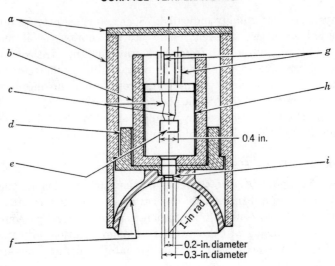

Fig. 5·9. Land blackbody element. a, Outer metal case with swivel mounting to handle; b, metal inner case for radiation-sensitive element; c, lead wires; d, Sindanyo insulating mounting; e, receiver area on radiation-sensitive element; f, polished gold- or platinum-plated hemispherical steel reflector; g, terminals; h, Kipp-thermoelectric (Moll-type), Schwartz-Hilger-thermoelectric, bolometer, or photo radiation-sensitive-element assembly; and i, fluorite or other suitable infra-red-transparent window. (*By permission Instruments*, **28**, *no. 9, 1444, September, 1955*.)

brightly polished hemispherical shield surrounding the source-body surface collects the emitted radiation. This shield also intercepts all radiation from ambient sources thus preventing its reaching the sensitive element. Except for the fraction passing out through the aperture for indication and that absorbed by the reflector, all emitted radiation is returned to the source area. If the source area is nonblack, the reflected fraction is returned to the *hollow space* or *hohlraum* within the shield and the process repeated. An approximation to the black-body *radiation density*, corresponding to the temperature of the source-body surface, is thus established. The sensitive element sampling the radiation density through an aperture then tends to indicate the *actual* rather than the *apparent* temperature. Furthermore, the indication is unaffected by ambient radiant sources.[37-40]

The temperature thus indicated is not always that which would have prevailed on the surface had the instrument been absent. Shielding effected by the device prevents customary heat-transfer exchange with the ambient. The surface temperature of a cooling hot body may thus

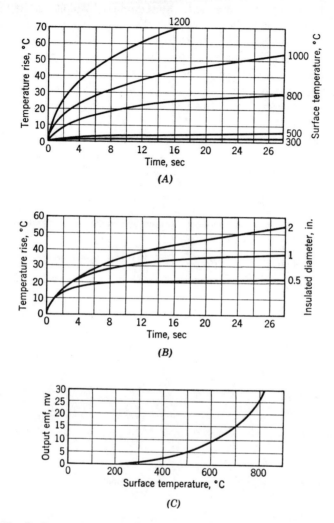

Fig. 5·10. Performance curves for Land's blackbody elements. (*A*) Calculated variation of surface-temperature rise at center of a perfectly insulated 2-in. diameter area for different surface temperatures. Mild-steel emissivity is assumed to be 0.7, and thermal conductivity 0.06 cal/sec cm °C (14.5 Btu/hr ft °F); (*B*) this calculated variation of surface-temperature rise when the initial surface temperature is 1000°C but for different diameters of the insulated area; and (*C*) relative actual temperature indications for different surface temperatures, where this curve represents the data for oxidized mild steel, brass, lightly oxidized mild steel, and unoxidized cast iron equally well and to within less than 0.5 mv. (*By permission E. J. Burton, in Instruments, 26, no. 10, 1524, 1525, October, 1953.*)

rise at the point of measurement. For complete blanketing, the rise has been found to be of such amount that the surface temperature becomes about that prevailing at a depth equal to the radius of the reflector. However, a certain time must first elapse. Tending to balance this effect is the departure from true *hohlraum* behavior due to imperfect reflectance on the shield surface and to radiation loss through the aperture. Thereby, also, the actual emissivity of the surface tends to assert itself.[38]

Computed values for the performance characteristics of pyrometers of this type are indicated in Fig. 5·10A and B and Table 5·1. Actual test results are given in Fig. 5·10C and Table 5·2.[37, 38]

Table 5·1. Errors of surface pyrometer caused by variations from standard emissivity

Actual Surface Emissivity	Effective Emissivity	Error at true temperatures, °C			
		400	600	800	1000
0.4	0.81	−15	−19	−23	−27
0.5	0.91	−7	−9	−12	−14
0.6	0.94	−2	−2	−3	−3
0.7	0.95	2	2	3	3
0.8	0.98	5	7	8	10
0.9	0.99	7	9	11	13

By permission, Burton in Instruments, **26**, *no. 10, 1525 (October, 1953).*

Table 5·2. Rise in temperature of surface after application of pyrometer

	Temperature rise, °C		
	After	After	After
Temperature before	5	10	15
Application of Pyrometer, °C	sec.	sec.	sec.
300	1	1	2
500	2	2	3
800	8	9	14

By permission, Burton in Instruments, **26**, *no. 10, 1525 (October, 1953).*

By taking the reading quickly, the blanketing error can be minimized. With a rapid-response element and electronic indication, instrument lag can be made negligible. The device requires then merely to be suddenly moved into position over the desired area. The effects of varied or unknown surface emissivities, as well as of ambient radiant sources, are minimized by the design. Thereby, calibration of this instrument provides a means for precision measurement of surface temperatures. Burton [38] suggests an accuracy of to within $\pm\frac{1}{2}$ per cent; however, this does not seem to be the limit.

Measurements for the actual surfaces are unaltered by any installation procedures. The minimum surface area over which an average value is obtained cannot, however, be made arbitrarily small. It is required that this area be much larger than the aperture to the sensitive element. The surface can be in rapid motion and of nonuniform temperature. Rapid-response recording instrumentation will yield surface-temperature mapping data. It is not feasible, however, to measure surface temperatures from a distance, under corrosive conditions, or within opaque liquid media.

5·9   TEMPERATURE OF MODIFIED SURFACE

The inconvenience of temperature measurement on the surface of the actual body has often led to the substitution, for a portion of this body, of another body whose surface temperature is more readily determined. Usually the new surface occupies the same position as the original and is exposed to the same ambient conditions. For it to assume the same temperature, however, it must also have the same surface heat-transfer coefficient and the same subsurface thermal-diffusivity pattern. These conditions are not, in general, satisfied.[41]

For example a gold-foil-strip electric-resistance element separated from a metallic body by a layer of electrical insulation will usually also be to a degree thermally insulated thereby from the parent body. It will thus tend to assume different temperatures than those of the unmodified surface at the same location. Similarly, a plug of different material and construction, penetrating through the thickness of a body, will usually provide a different heat-flow path to its surface than the unmodified body would have. Thus, under the same ambient or heat-flow conditions, its surface will tend to assume a different temperature.[42, 43]

It is often feasible with suitable coatings to restore the surface heat-transfer coefficient to its original value. Very careful estimation must, however, be made of the corresponding effects of such changes in the solid structure. Thus, if the substituted surface layers are very thin, one may argue that they will assume sufficiently close approximations to the unmodified surface temperatures. This will be considered more likely if the thermal current is sufficiently small and the period of its changes sufficiently long.

Hyman and Bonilla [44] applied these means, in the form of an extended-surface thermocouple, to measure the average surface temperature of a 0.5-in. diameter quartz rod. The cleaned quartz was first conditioned with fired silver paste, then plated with a 0.0005-in. thickness of copper, followed by a 0.0025-in. thickness of nickel, the two layers overlapping through the middle inch of rod length. Copper and nickel leads were soldered to the two ends, respectively. Presumably, the silver layer was too thin to have appreciable effects, and, in steady-state heat flow, the temperature difference was small across the 0.003-in. thickness of the composite metallic layer. The ambient media were liquids, opaque to thermal radiation, and it was shown that, here, the surface heat transfer depended little on the surface material. When temperatures are nonuniform, the averaging effect of such an extended thermoelectric junction is, however, only approximate. [44–46]

Extended-interface junctions have also been used to measure the temperatures of sliding surfaces. However, this topic will be deferred to Sec. 7·6 as a technique for moving bodies.

5·10　TEMPERATURE-INDICATING PAINTS

Coatings which visibly change at known temperatures are widely used when, with a minimum of apparatus, comprehensive mapping of surface-temperature changes is required. High precision is usually not attempted with these coatings, and no time-temperature records at points are produced. A pattern of isotherms over an entire surface at a given time or a series of such plots at successive times is a common result. Visual warnings of excess temperature can also be provided. [47–56]

The coatings are in two classes: those that melt and those that change color. The first class includes a commercially available graded assortment of materials, which melt sharply at a corresponding series of temperatures. They can be brushed or sprayed on or rubbed on from crayons. Pellets are also available. When the pellets melt, they assume a "wet" appearance, readily observed. On cooling, an altered texture effects a permanent visible change. The other class consists of a limited group of pigments which partly decompose at definite temperatures with striking changes in color. Materials are commercially available for which such changes are permanent and for which recovery occurs after cooling. Compounds not only may change color at one temperature but also may undergo several changes at a series of temperatures. Thus, a material originally blue changes to bright green, yellow, and finally to brown as it is heated. These pigments are usually complex inorganic or inorganic-organic compounds, or mixtures thereof, ground to fine powders and mixed with a colorless synthetic resin dissolved in alcohol. They can thus be brushed or sprayed on to dry quickly or are rubbed on from crayons. Color photographs provide records of successive temperature patterns. Spotting or striping with several pigments yields a more complete gradation of transition temperatures over the surface. Suitably weather- and wear-resistant paints are available at prices permitting danger-signal use in normal operation of equipment.[47–55]

Melting coatings are rated as dependable to within ± 1 per cent, independently of other circumstances, and occur in close gradations. The results are not, however, so conveniently portrayed photographically. Color changes, on the other hand, occur through transition ranges of temperature as functions of time. Thus, effects occur in 1 or 2 sec, but progressive further changes continue for hours. Ten minutes is an example of a standard *exposure time*. Color changes result from liberation of water, sulfur, ammonia, and carbon dioxide from the decomposing pigments. Concentrations of these constituents in the ambient atmospheres thus affect decomposition rates and also recovery rates in the case of reversible reactions. High humidity may have an important effect. Although, as affected by time and other factors, transition ranges may extend to hundreds of degrees, careful work is said to permit color determinations to within 10 or 15°C (18 or 27°F).[47–56]

Whether by melting or color change, the indication (for nonreversible coatings) refers only to the highest temperature reached. If photographs are to be taken after cooling, it is necessary to avoid having local temperatures temporarily raised above those at operation by redistribution of heat after shutdown.[47–56]

A coating, as a temperature-sensitive element, indicates its own temperature. This may or may not sufficiently approximate that which the surface would have attained in its absence. Thus, on metallic bodies, the coating behaves as an outer layer of thermal insulation. It can, however, be made as thin as the grain size of the powdered pigment. Coatings 0.001 in. thick are feasible. Whereas rapidly changing temperatures are scarcely accessible by these means anyhow, thermal transients in the coating depth cannot be significant. Fluid-boundary resistances are usually little affected by such coatings. Because of the colors and textures attained, radiation-boundary resistances may, however, be substantially altered. Hence, when radiation exchange is important, errors due to changed absorptances may be serious.[47-56]

It is to be emphasized that these methods are of great practical utility because of the broad scope of information yielded by the barest minimum of effort. They are of particular value when the temperature distribution, rather than actual temperature, is the primary concern. If the actual temperature is also required, one check point by other means may suffice.[16, 47-56]

5·11 THERMOGRAPHY

Thermography depends upon the phenomenon whereby certain substances called *phosphors* or *Lenard* [57] *phosphors* radiate in the visible range, e.g., perhaps yellow, upon being simultaneously or previously irradiated with ultraviolet light. Such light may be that from a mercury arc. A phosphor is not ordinarily a compound of phosphorus but may be the sulfide of a metal activated by trace percentages of other metals. The intensity of the reradiation is proportional to that of the *exciting* irradiation and can be made readily visible to the naked eye. Within limited temperature ranges characteristic of certain individual phosphors, the *efficiency* of the reradiation process decreases rapidly with increase in the temperature of the phosphor. Thus, with constant intensity of ultraviolet exciting radiation, the phosphorescent reradiation may change by as much as 10 per cent per °F and lies in the spectral region conveniently accessible to photography.[56-64]

The application of this phenomenon in temperature measurement has taken two forms: *contact thermography* and *projection thermography*. In contact thermography the phosphor is coated onto the surface as a paint or cemented on in precalibrated coated films. The phosphor thus assumes an approximation to thermal equilibrium with the parent surface. In projection thermography, the image of the source-body surface is focused by an optical system (see Fig. 4·2D, E, and F) upon a precalibrated phosphor-coated *screen*. The temperature rise of the phosphor coating is then proportional to the intensity of the radiation at the respective points in the image. The actual temperature of the phosphor is not necessarily at all similar to that of the source body, and the screen may be removed to a considerable distance therefrom. In contact thermography, the body itself is irradiated with ultraviolet exciting light, and it is essential that the incident intensity be uniform over the surface being investigated. In projection thermography, only the screen requires to be thus uniformly irradiated; however, only the apparent temperature is measured.[56, 58-64]

Contact thermography suffers from the same error sources that occur with temperature-indicating paints; therefore, the temperature of the coating may differ from that of the surface in its absence. The minimum possible grain size tends to be larger, limiting thinness in coatings as well as resolution of small areas. The primary advantage is the same, i.e., that of mapping temperatures for an entire surface simultaneously. Temperatures are indicated on a continuous brightness scale, including their time variations. Response may occur in a small fraction of a second; however, investigation of continued and cyclic changes tends to be complicated by hysteresis aftereffects in the phosphors. Painted-on coatings generally require calibration, and providing a constant and uniform ultraviolet exciting radiation over a geometrically complex surface will require equipment and preparation. Quantitative measurements depend on photographic recording and *densiometric* determinations. Elimination of stray-light effects usually requires working in partial darkness. Available temperature ranges are lower than for indicating paints, reaching but a few hundred degrees up from the ice point.[56, 58-66]

In projection thermography, the screen is in effect an extended-surface thermal radiation-sensitive element, adapted to indicating fine definition in image formation. A large-aperture objective mirror or lens system is required because of the low responsivities of phosphors, thus complicating attainment of sharp definition. Lateral heat conduction in the image tends also to cause blurring. The setup includes a camera and an ultraviolet source, with filters to exclude ambient and exciting radiations from the photographic emulsion. Determinations are of apparent temperature, and the difficulties are those of radiation pyrometry aggravated by the hysteresis-type aftereffects in the phosphors. The advantage is that of recording an entire temperature pattern at each exposure.[56, 58-66]

5·12 INFRARED PHOTOGRAPHY

Photographic emulsions of spectral sensitivity extending to 1.2 μ permit photography of "hot" objects. For bodies at temperatures below 1000°F, the long exposure times, extending into minutes—or even hours, below 600°F—and the required extreme precautions to exclude stray light are difficulties greatly reduced in thermography. There, radiant intensities are amplified and translated into the spectral regions of greatest photographic responsivity.[65-73]

However, at temperatures above 2000°F (see Fig. 4·5), radiant energy in the wavelength range for the infrared emulsions is adequate for brief exposures, and stray light may cease to be a problem. Hase[70] was thus able to plot the cooling curve for a silicon carbide rod in the range of from 2250 to 2600°F, with exposures at 0.1-sec intervals and temperature-measurement precision to within $\pm 6°F$.[65-73]

Apparent temperature is indicated. Also, calibration is required as for other photo radiation-sensitive elements. The necessary equipment consists only of a suitable camera. Mapping of temperature distribution is the principal objective as with thermography and temperature-indicating paints. However, only a limited temperature range (see Fig. 4·5) can be included in any one exposure because of the narrow *latitude* of available emulsions. Quantitative data result from densiometric determinations of the silver-deposit distribution over the processed photographic plates. Check targets of independently measured temperature are included in each *shot* or film to provide a density-temperature scale for the corresponding silver deposit.[65-73]

At sufficiently high temperatures, exposure times can be so short as to provide exceptional adaptation to the measurement of rapidly changing temperatures and the temperatures of moving bodies.[65-73]

5·13   FLYING-SPOT SCANNERS

By means of an electronic scanning system, the temperature distribution over an extended surface can be measured continuously using a single detector. The short time constants available in thermal and photo detectors permit almost simultaneous indications over the entire surface. Furthermore, the high stability and many thousandfold higher responsivities available in these detectors are distinct advantages with respect to infrared photography, thermography, and paints.[66,74-82]

5·14   OPTICAL AND RADIATION PYROMETRY

Radiation emanates from the *surface* of a body. In consequence, radiation methods always relate to surface temperatures and are hence peculiarly adapted to the measurement thereof. The flexibility and power of the radiation approach to surface-temperature measurement were discussed in Part I where a systematized procedure was described which is applicable to almost any situation. Chapters 3 and 4 were devoted to a survey of available materials and equipment and to an outline of the calculation techniques required to prepare the design of an instrument adapted to the requirements of a specific problem.[27,83]

5·15   SPECTRALLY DISCRIMINATIVE METHODS

Two designs illustrate the possibility of ingeniously exploiting variations occurring with wavelength.

Bayle,[84] wishing to measure the temperatures of clouds which he would have to observe through the intervening atmosphere, took note of the following facts. Even a great depth of normally humid air is virtually transparent in the wavelength range from 8.5 to 13 μ, although such a depth is generally opaque elsewhere in the infrared. In the opaque wavelength range, the air radiates nearly as a blackbody. The air temperature might differ substantially from that of the cloud, and the radiation received therefrom might be much greater. A cloud consists of a vast number of suspended droplets of water. At 9 μ, Bayle noted that the reflection coefficient for water is only 2 per cent, whereas it absorbs 99.9 per cent in a depth of 1 mm. Thereby, at this wavelength, a cloud would have virtually blackbody behavior and, although irradiated by sun and sky light, would transmit little thereof.

He therefore arranged a pyrometer to operate in the wavelength range 8 to 12 μ, in which the cloud would appear as an isolated blackbody. A fluorite window excluded radiation beyond about 12 μ, and a mica receiver did not absorb wavelengths shorter than about 8 μ. He built instruments with both pneumatic and thermoelectric elements, stationary and for use on board ships and in airplanes. Measurements were found to be accurate to within ½ and 2°C (± 0.09 and ± 3.6°F), respectively, for the two designs.[84]

Hübner [16] used a radiation measurement to verify the precision with which the glass-bulb-surface temperature of an electric incandescent lamp can be determined by means of indicating paints and surface-contact thermoelectric junctions, respectively. His method rests on careful demonstration that, at the wavelength 7.76 μ, the reflection coefficient for the glass-bulb surface was less than 1 per cent. He also noted that at this wavelength air is transparent and glass opaque. He could thus regard a bulb-surface patch as an isolated blackbody source and measure its temperature by comparison of its radiation with that from a standard blackbody. Thus, the bulb could be alternated in the optical system with the blackbody source, and the thermoelectric-indicated temperature of the latter adjusted to give the same galvanometer reading for the radiation-thermopile output emf. His optical system consisted of front-surface aluminized mirrors, a slit, and a sodium chloride window to the spectrometer case containing a sodium chloride prism. Stray-light effects from the lamp-filament emission were evaluated by the successive use of suitable filters. After making all corrections, Hübner concluded that his determinations were precise to within ± 0.4 to ± 0.7°C (± 0.72 to ± 1.26°F).[16,85]

Whereas readings with the surface-contact thermoelectric junctions described in Sec. 5·3 and with temperature-indicating paints were spread over ranges of up to 10 or 15°C (18 or 27°F), Hübner [16] felt that careful study of such data would afford determinations of sufficient precision for practical purposes.[1, 2, 16–18, 32, 33, 47–56, 85]

5·16 SHIELDING

Radiation pyrometers may indicate apparent temperature. The temperature indicated, however, usually differs from the actual source-body surface temperature, not only by the amount whereby the emission is less than that for a blackbody but also by the reflected radiation received from ambient bodies.

Various attempts have been made (see Fig. 5·11) to restrict the radiation received by the sensitive element to that emitted by the source-body surface area. Ideally this implies limiting the beam to a solid angle, subtended by the objective mirror or lens (see Fig. 4·2) at the source-body surface area. Hollander [11–13] (see Fig. 5·11A and Sec. 7·7) used a blackened conical shield coincident with this angle. The surface surrounding the source area being thus blackened, little of the emitted radiation is returned to the source area. The inner surface of the cone, however, radiates thermally at a rate corresponding to its own temperature. Part of this radiation is directed to the source area, but the sensitive element cannot "see" the conical surface and does not receive radiation directly from it. The portion of the shield radiation received by the source area and reflected from it to the sensitive element effects a contribution to the indication dependent on the shield temperature. This temperature must hence be maintained constant, preferably at the temperature of the housing for the optical system and the mean for the receiving surface of the element. As thus independent of source-body surface and ambient temperatures, the shield-radiation contribution will be canceled out in calibration of the pyrometer. Hollander calibrated his pyrometer against thermoelectric junctions installed in a uniform-temperature body of the source-body surface emissivity. His indications are thereby those of actual surface temperatures.[11–13, 86–95]

The surface temperature measured by a Hollander [11–13] device may not be that which would prevail in its absence, since the presence of the instrument tends to obstruct normal radiation exchange with the ambient. Percy,[86, 87] Johnston,[87] and Sosman [87] (see Fig. 5·11B) sought to lessen this effect by arranging a reflecting thermally insulated undersurface facing the source body. Hollander's conical structure affects a minimum area on the source body. With an insulated reflecting outer surface, this shield would least alter ambient radiant-exchange conditions. By means of a rapid-response indicator and sweeping motion

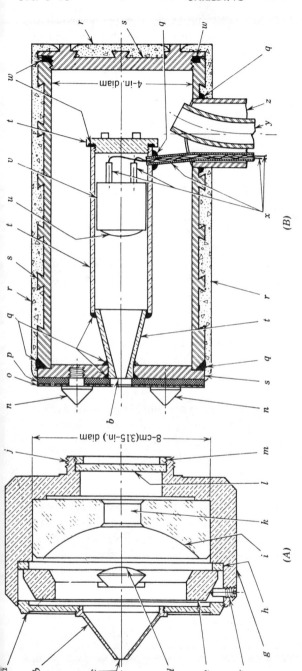

Fig. 5·11. Shielding (A) Hollander's conical shield with reflection optical system; and (B) Percy, Johnston, and Sosman's pyrometer with water-cooled shield and long handle. a, Metal plate; b, conical copper, brass, or aluminum shield, polished outside with blackened inner surface; c, aperture; d, convex mirror; e, metal plate; f, adjusting screw; g, metal case; h, spacer ring; i, concave objective mirror; j, mounting threads; k, hole for radiation to pass out to bolometer receiving surface; l, infrared-transparent window; m, metal retaining ring; n, three conical feet; o, polished stainless-steel reflecting surface; p, asbestos-board thermal insulation; q, refractory-cement thermal insulation; r, silver-soldered joints; r, infrared-transparent objective lens; s, steel housing; t, brass conical shield and casing for radiation-sensitive element; u, infrared-transparent objective lens; v, radiation-sensitive element in case; w, lead gaskets; x, electric terminals and lead wires passing out through 0.25-in. diameter copper tube; y, inner pipe for circulating-water inlet passage; and z, 1.5-in.-steel outlet pipe, also serving as a long handle for insertion of pyrometer unit into furnaces. (By permission

Industrial Heating, **14**, no. 5, 786, May, 1947.)

over the surface, it may be arranged that the source-body surface area is not blanketed long enough to change appreciably in temperature.[11-13, 86-95]

The designs of Percy,[86, 87] Johnston,[87] and Sosman,[87] and also of Larsen and Shenk,[90, 91] provide water-jacketing to protect the pyrometer parts from furnace conditions, when "reaching in" to measure interior surface temperatures. Thus, attaining proximity to the source-body surface may be required when intervening media, such as smoke and flames, absorb and emit as ambient bodies of different temperature.[86-91]

5·17 MOLECULAR-BEAM METHOD

McFee, Marcus, and Estermann [96-97] have proposed measuring surface temperatures by directing a potassium or rubidium beam on the solid surface. The scattered, or reflected, atoms will then emerge with a *velocity distribution* corresponding to their kinetic temperature, see Eq. 13·1. This temperature will approximate that of the solid surface if the *temperature jump* to that surface is small, see Sec. 10·5. The necessary method has been described for accurately measuring the velocity distribution in the reflected beam. Measurements made by this technique at about 2000°K (3600°R) have been shown to be precise effectively to within ±25°K (±45°F). An accuracy of to within 1 per cent in the range 500 to 3000°K (900 to 5400°R) is said to be possible.

This method, although perhaps somewhat cumbersome, has the advantage of providing a means of measuring surface temperatures without the necessity making an emissivity correction and without the disturbing effect of an inserted thermometer element.[96-98]

5·18 CONCLUSION

Whereas the attempt in this chapter has been to deal with questions peculiar to surface-temperature measurement, much has been said that is applicable to problems in rapidly changing temperatures and temperatures of moving bodies. Similarly, Chs. 6 and 7 will be found to contain further material applicable to the study of surface temperatures.[99-105]

REFERENCES *

1. A. M. Stoll and J. D. Hardy, "Direct Experimental Comparison of Several Surface Temperature Measuring Devices," *Rev. Sci. Instr.*, **20**, no. 9, pp. 678–686 (September, 1949).

---

* See footnote on page 26.

2. J. D. Hardy and G. F. Soderstrom, "An Improved Apparatus for Measuring Surface and Body Temperature," *Rev. Sci. Instr.*, **8**, no. 11, pp. 419–422 (November, 1937).

3. J. Krog, "Improved Needle Thermocouple for Subcutaneous and Intramuscular Temperature Measurements in Animals and Man," *Rev. Sci. Instr.*, **25**, no. 8, pp. 799–800 (August, 1954).

4. N. D. Weills and E. A. Ryder, "Thermal Resistance Measurements of Joints Formed Between Stationary Metal Surfaces," *Paper* 48-SA-43, 35 pp. (1943), *Trans. ASME*, **71**, no. 3, pp. 259–267 (April, 1949), American Society of Mechanical Engineers, New York.

5. M. E. Barzelay, K. N. Tong, and G. F. Holloway, "Effect of Pressure on Thermal Conductance of Contact Joints," *Technical Note* 3295, p. 29, U. S. National Advisory Committee for Aeronautics, Washington (May, 1955).

6. D. L. Rall and W. H. Giedt, "Heat Transfer to, and Temperature Distribution in, a Metal-Cutting Tool," *Paper* 55-A-217, *Trans. ASME*, **78**, no. 7, pp. 1507–1515 (October, 1956), American Society of Mechanical Engineers, New York.

7. R. J. Grosh and R. A. Hawkins, "Experimental Study of the Temperature Distribution in Plates During Arc Welding," *Paper* 55-A-26, 9 pp., American Society of Mechanical Engineers, New York (1955).

8. A. R. Thomas, B. Schurin, and J. C. Morris, "Temperature Error Associated with Imbedded Thermocouples," *Rev. Sci. Instr.*, **29**, no. 11, pp. 1045–1046 (November, 1958).

9. A. C. Simon and D. A. Gildner, "Microscope Attachment for Accurate Micro-drilling and the Removal of Analytical Samples from Small Areas," *Rev. Sci. Instr.*, **29**, no. 12, pp. 1125–1128 (December, 1958).

10. R. K. Gould and W. L. Nyborg, "Imbedded Thermistor for Boundary Layer Measurements," *J. Acoust. Soc. Am.*, **31**, no. 2, pp. 249–250 (February, 1959).

11. M. Hollander, *An Experimental Measurement of the Temperature Distribution in the Workpiece during Metal-Cutting*, 243 pp., Doctoral Dissertation, Columbia University, New York, 1959.

12. M. B. Hollander and J. E. Englund, "Thermocouple-Technique Investigation of Temperature Distribution in the Workpiece during Metal Cutting," *Research Report* 7, 18 pp., American Society of Tool Engineers, Detroit (July, 1957).

13. A. E. Bowen, Jr., "Thin Thermocouple Technique for Measurement of Friction Temperatures in the Contact Area," *Lubrication Newsletter*, **2**, no. 1, pp. 2–8 (1957).

14. G. S. Reichenbach, "Experimental Measurement of Metal-Cutting Temperature Distributions," *Paper* 57-SA-53, pp. 1–15 (1957); *Trans. ASME*, **80**, no. 3, pp. 525–539 (April, 1958), American Society of Mechanical Engineers, New York.

15. A. G. Monroe and H. A. S. Bristow, "A Method of Measuring the Temperature at the Surface of a Metal Tube," *J. Sci. Instr.*, **30**, no. 10, p. 385 (October, 1953).

16. H. J. Hübner, "Messung der Oberflächentemperatur von Gläsern, die durch Strahlung erhitzt werden" (Measurement of the Surface Temperature of Glass Heated by Radiation), *Zeitschrift für angewandte Physik*, **7**, no. 6, pp. 273–279 (1955).

17. M. H. Hunt, C. A. Heller, and A. S. Gordon, "The Surface Temperature of a Burning Double-Base Propellant," U. S. Naval Ordnance Test Station, *Technical Memorandum*, NOTS TM 971 (January, 1953).

18. F. D. Dodge, "Measuring Boiler Tube Temperatures," *Industry and Power*, p. 82 (May, 1953); *Instrumentation*, **7**, no. 4, p. 31 (Third Quarter, 1954).

19. C. H. W. Slater, "Improvements in Fine Wire Thermocouples," *J. Sci. Instr.*, **30**, no. 8, pp. 293–294 (August, 1953).

20. R. M. Atkins, "Temperature Measurement with Thermistors," *Instruments*, **33**, no. 1, pp. 86–88 (January, 1960).

21. C. E. Moeller, "Welding a Thermocouple Junction," *Instruments*, **32**, no. 6, p. 895 (June, 1959).

22. C. E. Moeller, "Resistance Welding of Platinum-10 per cent Rhodium Wire to Platinum Sheet," *Paper* 57-A-118, American Society of Mechanical Engineers (December, 1957).

23. R. F. Chaiken and D. K. Van de Mark, "Thermocouple Junction for a Hot-Plate Linear Pyrolysis Apparatus," *Rev. Sci. Instr.*, **30**, no. 5, pp. 376–377 (May, 1959).

24. W. F. Roeser and E. F. Mueller, "Measurement of Surface Temperatures," *RP* 231, *J. Research Natl. Bur. Standards*, **5**, no. 4, pp. 793–802 (October, 1930).

25. J. G. King and A. Blackie, "Design of a Thermocouple for Measuring Surface Temperatures," *J. Sci. Instr.*, **2**, no. 8, pp. 260–264 (May, 1925).

26. Pyrometer Instrument Co. (Bergenfield, N. J.), *Mech. Eng.*, **74**, no. 8, pp. 46–47 (August, 1952).

27. R. B. Sosman, *The Pyrometry of Solids and Surfaces*, 98 pp., American Society for Metals, Cleveland, 1940.

28. W. G. Rauch, "Design and Construction of Needle Thermocouples," *Metal Progress*, **65**, no. 3, pp. 71–74 (March, 1954).

29. M. W. Boyer and J. Buss, "Measurement of Surface Temperature—I. A Portable Thermocouple Device Compensated for Heat Losses," *Ind. Eng. Chem.*, **18**, no. 7, pp. 728–729 (July, 1926).

30. N. Sasaki and A. Kamada, "A Recording Device for Surface Temperature Measurements," *Rev. Sci. Instr.*, **23**, no. 6, pp. 261–263 (June, 1952).

31. N. Sasaki, "A New Method for Surface-Temperature Measurement," *Rev. Sci. Instr.*, **21**, no. 1, pp. 1–3 (January, 1950).

32. Trans-sonics, Inc., "Temperature Transducer," *Rev. Sci. Instr.*, **28**, no. 3, p. 218 (March, 1957).

33. Charles Engelhard, Inc., "Surface-Temperature Platinum-Grid Element," *Instruments*, **30**, no. 5, pp. 934–935 (May, 1957).

34. J. E. Field and S. D. Gehman, "A Noncontact Temperature Measuring Device," *J. Appl. Phys.*, **22**, no. 1, pp. 106–107 (January, 1951).

35. Leeds & Northrup Co., *New L&N Roll Surface Temperature Equipment for Industrial Rolls and Other Moving Surfaces*, Leeds & Northrup Co., Philadelphia, 1951.

36. D. F. Waugh and D. A. Yphantis, "Rotor Temperature Measurement and Control in the Ultracentrifuge," *Rev. Sci. Instr.*, **23**, no. 11, pp. 609–614 (November, 1952).

37. M. D. Drury, K. P. Perry, and T. Land, "Pyrometers for Surface-Temperature Measurement," *J. Iron Steel Inst. London*, **169**, pp. 245–250 (November, 1951).

38. E. J. Burton, "Recent Advances in Radiation and Immersion Pyrometry," *Instruments*, **26**, no. 10, pp. 1524–1525 (October, 1953).

39. Fielden Instrument Division, Robertshaw-Fulton Controls Company, "Pyrometer," *Rev. Sci. Instr.*, **26**, no. 9, p. 904 (September, 1955); "Surface Pyrometer," *Instruments*, **28**, no. 9, pp. 1444–1445 (September, 1955).

40. Atlantic Pyrometers, Inc., "Atlantic Type SP Portable Surface Pyrometer," *Bulletin* 0051, 4 pp., Atlantic Pyrometers, Inc., Hawthorne, N. J. (May, 1959).
41. A. J. Chabai and R. J. Emrich, "Measurement of Wall Temperature and Heat Flow in the Shock Tube," *J. Appl. Phys.*, **26**, no. 6, pp. 779–780 (June, 1955).
42. D. Bendersky, "A Special Thermocouple for Measuring Transient Temperatures," *Paper* 52-A-57, *Mech. Eng.*, **75**, no. 2, pp. 117–122 (February, 1953), American Society of Mechanical Engineers, New York.
43. A. Meier, "Messungschnellveränderlicher Zylinderwandtemperaturen" (Measurement of Rapidly Changing Cylinder-Wall Temperatures), *Forschung*, **10**, no. 1, pp. 41–54 (January-February, 1939); translation, "Recording Rapidly Changing Cylinder-Wall Temperatures," *Technical Memorandum* 1013, 27 pp., U. S. National Advisory Committee for Aeronautics, Washington (1942).
44. S. C. Hyman and C. F. Bonilla, "Heat Transfer by Natural Convection from Horizontal Cylinder to Liquid Metals; Final Report for July 1, 1949 to June 30, 1950." U. S. Atomic Energy Commission *NYO-560*, pp. 22–37 (June, 1950).
45. D. F. Othmer and H. B. Coats, "Measurement of Surface Temperature," *Ind. Eng. Chem.*, **20**, no. 2, pp. 124–128 (February, 1928).
46. P. W. Kilpatrick, "Accuracy of Thermocouples in Parallel," *Instruments*, **30**, no. 9, pp. 1706–1709 (September, 1957).
47. L. C. Tyte, "Temperature-Indicating Paints," *Inst. Mech. Engrs. London, J. & Proc.*, **152**, no. 2, pp. 226–231 (September, 1945).
48. Bryson Oil Co., "Thermocolor, Temperature Indicating Pigments—Thermochrom, Temperature Indicating Crayons," *Bulletin* R-3, Harriman, Tenn. (1953).
49. Tempil ° Corp., "Tempilsticks—The Amazing Crayons That Tell Temperatures," *Catalog No.* 501, Tempil ° Corp., New York, N. Y.
50. K. Guthmann, "Temperaturmessfarben und Messfarbstifte" (Temperature Measuring Colors and Pencils), *ATM Archiv für technisches Messen*, no. 152, Ref. V215-4, T4–5 (July, 1947).
51. K. Guthmann, "Erfahrungen mit Temperaturmessfarben" (Experiences with Temperature Measuring Colors), *Stahl und Eisen*, **70**, no. 3, pp. 116–118 (1950); translation, Bryson Oil Co., *Bulletin* T-2, Harriman, Tenn.
52. Tempil ° Corp., "Temperature Control," *Automobile Engineer*, **35**, no. 462, pp. 183–189 (May, 1945).
53. R. Berthold, "A New Method of Non-Destructive Testing of Materials" (in German), *Metallwirtschaft*, **20**, no. 17, pp. 425–426 (1941); translation, Bryson Oil Co., *Bulletin* T-3, Harriman, Tenn.
54. A. Matting, "The Use of Indicating Paints to Measure the Diffusion of Heat in Welding" (in German), *Schweissen und Schneiden*, **2**, no. 4, pp. 68–73 (1950); translation, Bryson Oil Co., *Bulletin* T-1, Harriman, Tenn.
55. H. Schallbroch and M. Lang, "Messung der Schnitttemperatur mittels temperaturanzeigender Farbenstriche" (Measurement of the Cutting Temperature by Means of Temperature Indicating Paints), *VDI Zeitschrift des Vereines Deutscher Ingenieure*, **87**, nos. 1–2, pp. 15–19 (January, 1943); translation, Bryson Oil Co., *Bulletin* T-2a, Harriman, Tenn.
56. R. B. Sims and J. A. Place, "A Surface-Scanning Pyrometer," *J. Sci. Instr.*, **31**, no. 8, pp. 293–294 (August, 1954).

57. P. Neubert, "Die direkte Sichtbarmachung von Temperaturfeldern durch Lenard-Phosphore (Temperatursehen)" (The Making Visible of Temperature Fields by Means of Lenard Phosphors), *ATM Archiv für technisches Messen*, V214-6, T3 (January, 1937).

58. F. Urbach, N. R. Nail, and D. Pearlman, "The Observation of Temperature Distributions and of Thermal Radiation by Means of Non-Linear Phosphors," *J. Opt. Soc. Am.*, **39**, no. 12, pp. 1011–1019 (December, 1949).

59. L. C. Bradley, "A Temperature-Sensitive Phosphor Used to Measure Surface Temperatures in Aerodynamics," *Rev. Sci. Instr.*, **24**, no. 3, pp. 219–220 (March, 1953).

60. F. Urbach, "Thermography," *Photographic Journal, Sect. B*, **90**, pp. 109–114 (July-August, 1950).

61. B. O'Brien, "Development of Infra-Red Sensitive Phosphors," *J. Opt. Soc. Am.*, **36**, no. 7, pp. 369–371 (July, 1946).

62. F. R. Scott, R. H. Thompson, and R. T. Ellickson, "Inertia Effects in Infra-Red Sensitive Phosphors," *J. Opt. Soc. Am.*, **39**, no. 1, pp. 64–67 (January, 1949).

63. F. Urbach, D. Pearlman, and H. Hemmendinger, "On Infra-Red Sensitive Phosphors," *J. Opt. Soc. Am.*, **36**, no. 7, pp. 372–381 (July, 1946).

64. G. F. Fonda, "Preparation and Characteristics of Zinc Sulfide Phosphors Sensitive to Infra-Red," *J. Opt. Soc. Am.*, **36**, no. 7, pp. 382–389 (July, 1946).

65. A. Rose, "A Unified Approach to the Performance of Photographic Film, Television Pickup Tubes, and the Human Eye," *J. Soc. Motion Picture Engrs.*, **47**, no. 4, pp. 273–294 (October, 1946).

66. D. E. Billings, R. H. Cooper, J. W. Evans, and R. H. Lee, "Microphotometer Scans Spectrum Photographs," *Electronics*, **27**, no. 12, pp. 174–178 (December, 1954).

67. W. Clark, *Photography by Infrared: Its Principles and Applications*, pp. 325–327, John Wiley & Sons, New York, 1946.

68. J. W. Londeree, Jr., "Photographic Pyrometry," *J. Am. Ceram. Soc.*, **37**, no. 8, pp. 354–360 (August, 1954).

69. D. W. Male, "A Photographic Pyrometer," *Rev. Sci. Instr.*, **22**, no. 10, pp. 769–772 (October, 1951).

70. R. Hase, "Untersuchung der Abkühlung glühender Silitstabe mittels photographische Pyrometrie" (Investigation of the Cooling of Incandescent Silicon Carbide Rods by Means of Photographic Pyrometry), *Zeitschrift für technische Physik*, **13**, no. 9, pp. 410–415 (August, 1932).

71. P. Neubert, "Anwendung der Photo-Thermometrie" (Application of Photographic Thermometry), *ATM Archiv für technisches Messen*, V214-5, T114–115 (September, 1936).

72. K, Hencky and P. Neubert, "Die Photo-Thermometrie" (Photographic Thermometry), *ATM Archiv für technisches Messen*, V214-4, T100–T101 (August, 1936).

73. L. Larmore, "Infrared Photography," *Proceedings of the IRE*, The Institute of Radio Engineers, New York, **47**, no. 9, pp. 1487–1488 (September, 1959).

74. Ven F. Eckart, "Zur Entwicklung von Bildwandlern und Bildverstärkern" (On the Development of Image Converters and Image Amplifiers), *Ann. Physik*, **14**, Series 6, nos. 1–2, pp. 1–13 (1954).

75. R. H. Dehn, "A New Method for the Measurement of Rapid Fluctuations of Temperature," *Brit. J. Appl. Phys.*, **7**, no. 4, pp. 144–148 (April, 1956).

76. "Thermal Photography," *Techniques,* pp. 3–10, Fall, 1957.

77. C. D. Papaliolios, "Results of ERDL Thermograph Measurements," *Techniques,* pp. 18–21, Fall, 1957.

78. "Thermal Photography," *Mech. Eng.,* **80,** no. 1, p. 67 (January, 1958).

79. J. I. Pantchechnikoff, S. Lasof, J. Kurshan, and A. R. Moore, "Use of the Flying-Spot Scanner to Study Photosensitive Surfaces," *Rev. Sci. Instr.,* **23,** no. 9, pp. 465–466 (September, 1952).

80. R. W. Bullock and S. Silverman, "Rapid Scanning Spectrometer for Oscillographic Recording," *J. Opt. Soc. Am.,* **39,** no. 2, pp. 200–201 (February, 1949).

81. H. P. Mansberg, "Flying Spot Techniques and Application—Part II," *Du Mont Instrument Journal,* Issue 4, pp. 8–15 (February, 1958).

82. M. R. Halter and W. L. Wolfe, "Optical Mechanical Scanning Techniques," *Proceedings of the IRE,* The Institute of Radio Engineers, New York, **47,** no. 9, pp. 1546–1550 (September, 1959).

83. F. Lieneweg, "Oberflächen-Temperatur" (Surface Temperature), *ATM Archiv für technisches Messen,* V2162-1, T99–T100 (August, 1937).

84. A. Bayle, "Récepteur pour la mesure de la température des nuages" (Receiver for Measuring the Temperature of Clouds), *Revue d'optique,* **33,** no. 10, pp. 507–513 (October, 1954).

85. H. O. McMahon, "Thermal Radiation from Partially Transparent Reflecting Bodies," *J. Opt. Soc. Am.,* **40,** no. 6, pp. 376–380 (June, 1950).

86. J. W. Percy, "Measurement of Heating Rates in Reheating Furnaces," *Iron and Steel Engineer,* **24,** no. 7, pp. 65–75 (July, 1947).

87. J. W. Percy, J. Johnston, and R. B. Sosman, "Surface Temperature Pyrometer," *U. S. Patent Office* 2366285, 1 p., Government Printing Office, Washington (1945).

88. "Steel-Surface Pyrometer Developed by U. S. Steel Research Laboratory," *Industrial Heating,* **14,** no. 5, pp. 786–788 (May, 1947).

89. B. M. Larsen and W. E. Shenk, "Radiation Pyrometer Device," *U. S. Patent Office* 2054382, 4 pp., Government Printing Office, Washington (1936).

90. B. M. Larsen and W. E. Shenk, "Temperature Measurement with Blocking-Layer Photocells," American Institute of Physics, *Temperature,* pp. 1150–1158, Reinhold Publishing Corp., New York, 1941.

91. B. M. Larsen and W. E. Shenk, "Temperature Measurement with Blocking-Layer Photocells," *J. Appl. Phys.,* **11,** no. 8, pp. 555–560 (August, 1940).

92. W. Koch, "Measurement of Wall Temperatures," *J. Sci. Instr.,* **28,** no. 10, pp. 319–320 (October, 1951).

93. J. C. Mouzon and C. A. Dyer, "Low Temperature Radiation Pyrometry in Industry," *J. Opt. Soc. Am.,* **39,** no. 3, pp. 203–210 (March, 1949).

94. T. R. Harrison, "Industrial Use of Radiation Pyrometers under Non-Blackbody Conditions," *Instrumentation,* **1,** no. 5, pp. 7–15 (July and August, 1945); *J. Opt. Soc. Am.,* **35,** no. 11, pp. 706–723 (November, 1945).

95. T. R. Harrison, "The Significance of Emittance in Radiation Pyrometry," *J. Opt. Soc. Am.,* **35,** no. 11, pp. 706–723 (November, 1945).

96. J. H. McFee, P. M. Marcus, and I. Estermann, "Possible Application of Molecular Beam Techniques to the Measurement of Surface Temperatures, *Rev. Sci. Instr.,* **31,** no. 9, pp. 1013–1014 (September, 1960).

97. P. M. Marcus and J. H. McFee, "Velocity Distributions in Molecular Beams" in I. Estermann *Recent Researches in Molecular Beams,* pp. 43–63, Academic Press, New York, 1959.

98. A. G. Emslie and H. H. Blau, Jr., "On the Measurement of the Temperatures of Unenclosed Objects by Radiation Methods," *Journal of the Electrochemical Society,* **106,** no. 10, pp. 877–880 (October, 1959).

99. F. C. Houghten and H. T. Olson, "Measurement of Surface Temperatures," American Institute of Physics, *Temperature,* pp. 855–861, Reinhold Publishing Corp., New York, 1941.

100. F. W. Adams and R. H. Kean, "The Measurement of Surface Temperatures. II—Comparison of Various Methods," *Ind. Eng. Chem.,* **18,** no. 8, pp. 856–857 (August, 1926).

101. W. K. Moen, "Surface Temperature Measurement," *Instruments,* **33,** no. 1, pp. 70–73 (January, 1960).

102. R. E. Thun and G. F. Caudle, "Rugged Film Resistor Thermometer for the Measurement of Surface Temperatures," *Rev. Sci. Instr.,* **31,** no. 4, pp. 446–449 (April, 1960).

103. C. M. Stover, "Method of Butt Welding Small Thermocouples 0.001 to 0.010 Inch in Diameter," *Rev. Sci. Instr.,* **31,** no. 6, pp. 605–608 (June, 1960).

104. A. I. Morgan, Jr. and R. A. Carlson, "Wall Temperature and Heat Flux Measurements in a Round Tube," *Paper* 60-HT-1, American Society of Mechanical Engineers, New York (1960).

105. D. Robertson, "A New Sensitive Temperature Detector for Use in High Pressure Fluid Piping," *Paper* 59-A-201, American Society of Mechanical Engineers, New York (1959).

6

RAPIDLY CHANGING
TEMPERATURES

6·1 INTRODUCTION

Various situations arise in which the point temperatures in a body change rapidly with time. Some sudden intense source of heat in the vicinity, as from a combustion or nuclear explosion, may cause a large thermal current to enter the body, setting up steep temperature gradients and rapid rise of surface temperature. Similarly, dissipation of an electric discharge in a conductor may cause rapid heating. When a hot body is plunged into a relatively cool liquid, as in *quenching* to *harden* steel, there is rapid removal of heat, causing a sudden drop in the surface temperature of the body. Changes in temperature of the surface, or of some internal region, resulting from local influx or removal of heat are followed by similar but smaller changes emanating by heat transfer to other parts of the body.

Specification of the temperature at a point in a body, under these circumstances, implies the requirement of stating it as a function of time, as well as of location in the body. In order to achieve this result with any temperature-measuring device, it is essential that the sensitive element "follow," i.e., keep accurately in accord with, the body-point temperature of interest. This consideration sets the basic objective in design for the measurement of *rapidly changing* temperatures. It is for the *time lag* of the measuring system, *coupled* to the source body, to be so small that the temperature change in the interval is either acceptable as an *error* or adequately calculable as a correction.

The time lag here is, in effect, the sum of the time-lag increments accumulated as the signal pulse proceeds step-by-step from the original source-body-point temperature rise to the final swing of the indicating pointer. In any such summation of different-sized quantities, the order of magnitude of the largest contribution usually determines that of the result. It is convenient to group these contributions into two categories or subtotals: (1), the time lag for the coupled sensitive element; and, (2), the time lag for the indicating system. The two are obviously of equal importance, but they are grouped thus to segregate two entirely different sorts of design problems.

When the source body is of nonuniform temperature and moving relatively to the measuring device, the problem is often very similar to that for a rapidly changing temperature. Thus, the temperature of the materials successively presented in this flow process to the sensitive element is a function of time. Here, however, an error in the indication of the time for the occurrence of a given temperature magnitude is to be interpreted as an error in location for the point on the nonuniform-temperature moving body. If the moving body is not only nonuniform but also changing in temperature, the indication corresponds to the previous temperature at a displaced point. This displacement is given approximately by the product of the velocity of the body and the *lag time* τ.

6·2 LAG

Lag or *response time* τ is the time required for a degree of approach to equilibrium after a sudden imposed change. The name *lag* may have arisen through the quantity τ being also a measure of the time interval since the instant at which the indicated temperature has occurred in the source body. This is only the case, however, when the source-body temperature is *uniformly* changing. The degree of approximation to equilibrium is arbitrarily defined. Thus, the lag τ usually measures the time for the element to come to within $1/e$ of equilibrium, i.e., to within $1 - 1/e$ or 63.2 per cent of full response. Here $e = 2.71828$ as the base for natural logarithms.

For the residual discrepancy to become small, a longer time is required. Thus, the necessary time is 2.3 τ for 90 per cent response, 4.6 τ for 99 per cent response, 6.9 τ for 99.9 per cent response, 9.2 τ for 99.99 per cent response, etc.[1]

When the sensitive element is a thermoelectric junction or a thermometer bulb attaining thermal equilibrium with the source body, the lag concept is readily analyzed. Thus, a flow q of heat into the sensitive element results in a rate of mean-temperature rise according to the relation

$$q = Vc \, dT/dt \qquad (6·1)$$

where q is heat flow, Btu/hr; V is the volume of the sensitive element, ft³; c is the mean volume heat capacity of the sensitive-element material, Btu/ft³°F; and dT/dt is the rate of mean-temperature rise in the sensitive element, °F/hr.[2]

Substituting $q = (T' - T)/R$ according to Newton's heat-transfer law into Eq. 6·1 gives

$$T' - T = VcR\, dT/dt \tag{6·2}$$

where T is the mean temperature of the sensitive element, °F; T' is the mean temperature of the opposing source-body material, °F; and R is the thermal resistance of the heat-flow path from the source body to the sensitive element, hr °F/Btu.[1]

A sensitive element may be suddenly applied, as when a thermometer bulb is inserted into a large body of stationary liquid where the body temperature T' can be regarded as essentially constant. The lag time τ is then the time for an approach to equilibrium. The solution to the differential equation Eq. 6·2 for this case of *step change* can be written as

$$(T - T_o)/(T' - T_o) = 1 - e^{-t/\tau} \tag{6·3}$$

$$= 1 - e^{-t'/\tau'}$$

where $$\tau = VcR \tag{6·4}$$

and τ is the lag time, hr; $\tau' = 3600\, VcR$ is the lag time, sec; t is the elapsed time, hr; t' is the elapsed time, sec; T' is the source-body temperature, °F; T is the mean instantaneous sensitive-element temperature, °F; and T_o is the initial sensitive-element temperature, °F.[3]

Thus, when the elapsed time t is equal to the lag time τ, the approach to equilibrium is $(T - T_o)/(T' - T_o) = 1 - 1/e$, or 63.2 per cent.[1]

When the source-body temperature T' is rapidly changing, the result depends somewhat on how it changes. Thus, the change may merely be a steady increase, such that T' can be approximated by

$$T' = T_o' + mt \tag{6·5}$$

with m a constant rate, °F/hr; and T_o' the initial source-body temperature, °F.

For this case of *ramp change*, the solution to Eq. 6·2 is

$$T' - T = m\tau + (T_o' - T_o - m\tau)e^{-t/\tau} \tag{6·6}$$

After a lapse of time such that t greatly exceeds τ, the second term, i.e., the *transient effect*, becomes negligible, and the residual discrepancy $T' - T$ between the sensitive-element temperature and that of the source-body is given by

$$T' - T = m\tau \tag{6·7}$$

The quantity $m\tau$ is the amount that the source-body temperature changes in the lag time τ. Thus, the sensitive-element temperature is that which the source body had attained τ sec previously. The quantity τ is here, in this sense, the time lag.[1]

The exact time displacement for the indication of the temperature-time pattern of the source body occurs only for the ramp case, i.e., when it is a simple linear rate of change. When the fluctuations in the source-body temperature are of more intricate character, the temperature-time pattern in the sensitive element is but an approximation to that in the source body. Although the various phases continue to be delayed by about the same lag time τ, the "corners" are somewhat rounded off. The curves may be warped and the amplitude is decreased.[1]

That this must, in general, be true can be seen quite readily by writing Eq. 6·7 as though it were intended as a Taylor's-series representation of the time function T for the sensitive-element temperature. Thus, replacing m in Eq. 6·7 by dT'/dt, obtained by differentiating Eq. 6·5, yields

$$T = T' + (-\tau)\,dT'/dt \qquad (6\cdot 8)$$

whereas a full Taylor's series, as given in the handbooks and calculus textbooks, has the form

$$T = T' + \tau\,dT'/dt + (\tfrac{1}{2})\tau^2\,d^2T'/dt^2 + (\tfrac{1}{6})\tau^3\,d^3T'/dt^3 + \cdots \qquad (6\cdot 9)$$

It is evident that Eq. 6·8, and consequently the solution Eq. 6·6, does not describe the response to those aspects of the source-body-temperature fluctuations corresponding to the higher order terms in Eq. 6·9, i.e., the terms $(\tfrac{1}{2})\tau^2\,d^2T'/d^2t$, $(\tfrac{1}{6})\tau^3\,d^3T'/dt^3$, etc. This is apparent by the absence of all such terms in Eq. 6·8.[4]

The higher derivatives vanish only for the linear rate of change given by Eq. 6·5. The higher order terms in Eq. 6·9 are, however, also proportional to the higher powers τ^2, τ^3, etc., of the lag time τ. Such terms can then also be made negligible by designing the sensitive element with a sufficiently brief lag time τ.[4]

It is only when the higher order terms in Eq. 6·9 are zero or negligible that the sensitive element can be made to read correctly by the simple expedient of introducing a "time-delay" circuit component in the indicating instrument. Such a circuit element is then set to advance all readings by an independently determined value for the lag time τ.[5-7]

An illustration of a more complex pattern of temperature change is that of periodic oscillations. Here the source-body temperature is assumed to be a sinusoidal function of time about an average value T_o'; thus

$$T' = T_o' + \Delta T' \sin 2\pi ft \qquad (6\cdot10)$$

The steady-state response for this case is given by Hornfeck [8] as

$$T = T_o' + [\Delta T'/(1 + 4\pi^2 f^2 \tau'^2)^{1/2}] \sin (2\pi ft - \tan^{-1} 2\pi f\tau') \qquad (6\cdot11)$$

where T is the sensitive-element temperature, °F; T_o' is the average source-body temperature, °F; $\Delta T'$ is the amplitude of source-body-temperature oscillations, °F; f is the oscillation frequency, sec^{-1}; τ' is the lag time, sec; and t is time, sec.[1, 3, 8–15]

Here the response amplitude is decreased in the ratio $1/(1 + 4\pi^2 f^2 \tau'^2)^{1/2}$; whereas $\tan^{-1} 2\pi f\tau'$ is the *angular lag* or *phase shift*. As the product $f\tau'$ of the frequency and lag time becomes large, the amplitude factor in Eq. 6·11 becomes small, and the sensitive element tends to indicate the average, rather than the instantaneous, temperature of the source body.[1, 3, 8–16]

A disturbance occurring but once may be thought of roughly as one "loop" of an oscillation and thereby *damped* approximately in accord with Eq. 6·11. If of much less duration than the lag time τ', it will not be indicated at all.[1, 3, 8–14, 16]

When the sensitive element is of composite construction such that one mean element temperature becomes an unduly rough approximation, more complex response must be considered. Thus, in a liquid-in-glass thermometer with a long stem, the *stem lag* may constitute a second and much longer time constant. Similarly, an element may have several lag or response times measuring the individual times for its various parts to attain equilibrium.[1, 3, 8–14, 16, 17]

For thermal radiation detectors, the reasoning and conclusions are similar to those for *thermal-contact* elements (see Eqs. 4·22 to 4·24). In fact, the concepts of lag or response time have similar meanings for sensitive elements generally. They apply, therefore, with somewhat altered language, to the characteristics of indicating instruments.[10, 13, 14, 16, 18–28]

6·3 RESPONSE TIMES FOR INDICATORS

With millimicrosecond oscilloscopy a reality, the rapidity of change in temperature that can be measured is evidently not limited by the response times of available indicating instruments. Thus, one can always select components, such as galvanometers, recorders, amplifiers, dial indicators, and oscilloscopes, of response times that are as fast or faster than that of a previously chosen sensitive element. The devices are commercially available, as amply described in the manufacturers' bulletins, and are advertised in the various directories and instrument journals. As such, little needs to be said about them here.[10, 13, 14, 16, 18–40]

One should, however, be prepared to find that, in instruments designed for faster response, other desirable features may have been sacrificed. Thus, in both galvanometers and cathode-ray oscilloscopes, the sensitivities tend to be lower when the responses are faster. This implies that more robust signals will be required, with the effect of lower over-all responsivity and decreased precision in temperature measurement or with the requirement of additional preamplification.[10, 13, 14, 16, 18–26, 28]

When electronic preamplification is used, the input stage can be so designed (see Secs. 2·7 and 4·7) that the noise due to the sensitive element is no greater than that in the first stage of amplification. However, Eq. 2·11 indicates that the thermal-noise emf ΔE_{tn} due to the sensitive element will be proportional to the square root of the width of the response curve for the indicator, i.e., to $(\Delta f)^{1/2}$ where Δf here is the passband of the amplifier-and-oscilloscope circuit, $\sec^{-1}$. Therefore, *wide-band* amplification, which may occur in rapid-response circuits, tends to *pass* more noise (see Eq. 2·11).[10, 13, 14, 16, 18–26, 28]

The most desirable combination of responsivity, noise limit, and speed may be at times attained only by sacrificing reliability or ruggedness or by increasing the cost and thereby limiting application.[10, 13, 14, 16, 18–26, 28]

6·4 INDUSTRIAL THERMOMETERS

The temperature indicators used in industrial-process control are necessarily of such rugged design as to perform the required function with a minimum of attention and breakdown hazard. Figures 1·9, 6·1, and 9·1 illustrate examples of the resistance, liquid-in-glass, and thermoelectric designs, respectively. The liquid-in-glass design has probably had the broadest use, but the resistance design is considered the most accurate. Other common types are the gas-, vapor-, and liquid-filled pressure thermometers mentioned in Secs. 2·5 to 2·7 of Volume I. For protection against mechanical injury and the corrosive effects of flames, steam, and chemicals, metal casings, protection tubes, and thermowells are used, even though construction tends to be massive. Such designs are not adapted to the most rapid response.[1, 3, 8, 12, 18, 27, 41–54]

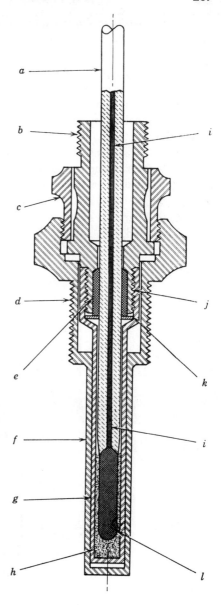

Fig. 6·1. Industrial mercury-in-glass thermometer. *a*, Glass thermometer stem; *b*, thread for mounting scale; *c*, threaded bushing to hold unit in separable socket; *d*, thread for mounting to apparatus; *e*, asbestos packing; *f*, separable socket; *g*, stainless-steel bulb chamber, taper fit in socket; *h*, mercury, carbon- or copper-granule, thermally conducting packing; *i*, mercury-filled thermometer capillary; *j*, left-hand thread; *k*, metal washer; and, *l*, mercury-filled thermometer bulb. (*By permission R. Beck in Trans. ASME,* **63,** *533, American Society of Mechanical Engineers, August, 1941.*)

Industrial thermometers are usually permanent installations; however, they may also be manually inserted into the "batch." In the latter case the operator needs to know how long to wait before taking a reading. For permanent installations, it is necessary to know whether the selected thermometer will yield the required precision. Although rates of temperature change may not seem rapid in ordinary industrial processes, the relatively slow-response thermometers that are used yield lag effects that may cause excessive errors.[1, 3, 8, 12, 27, 42-51, 55]

For example, suppose that the source-body temperature is changing at a uniform rate m' of 2°F/sec and the thermometer has a lag time τ' of 20 sec. Equation 6·7 gives $T' - T = m'\tau' = 2 \times 20 = 40°F$. Or, consider the case of a batch of candy 200°F above room temperature. Suppose a manually inserted liquid-in-glass thermometer to have a bulb lag of 20 sec and a stem lag of 300 sec. A 99 per cent response would then correspond to a measurement error of $0.01 \times 200 = 2°F$ for the candy. The operator must wait $4.6 \ \tau' = 4.6 \times 20 = 92$ sec for 99 per cent bulb response alone. However, since the stem response may amount to 2 per cent of the total, a wait of at least 300 sec (i.e., 5 min) will be required. The actual time to come to within 1°F is found to be 7 min.[1, 3, 8, 12, 27, 42-46, 49-51]

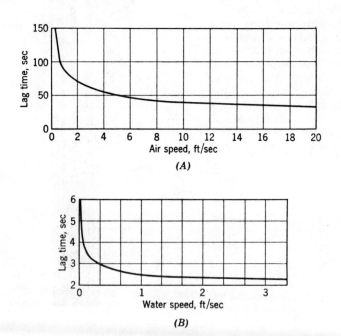

Fig. 6·2. Effect of stirring speeds on lag time for mercury-in-glass thermometers. (A) Change of lag time in air for various speeds of air past the bulb; and (B) change of lag time in water for various speeds of water past the bulb. (By permission R. Beck in Trans. ASME, **63**, 535, 536, American Society of Mechanical Engineers, August, 1941.)

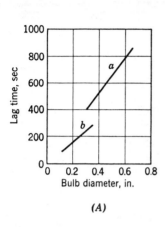

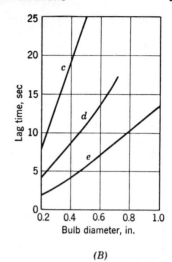

Fig. 6·3. Effect of bulb diameter on lag time. (A) Lag times in quiet air; and (B) lag times for mercury-in-steel, vapor-pressure, and gas-pressure-actuated thermometers with bare bulbs. a, Mercury-in-glass thermometer; b, mercury-in-steel thermometer; c, in oil; d, in lavite; and e, in water. (By permission R. Beck in Trans. ASME, **63**, 535, 536, American Society of Mechanical Engineers, August, 1941.)

Lag characteristics of typical industrial thermometers are illustrated in Figs. 6·2 to 6·4 and Table 6·1. Ordinarily, the manufacturer will supply such data, describing the equipment he proposes to furnish. Inspection can be performed by insertion in a constant-temperature bath and recording the time-temperature response. The time for 63.2 per cent of the ultimate change is the principal lag-time constant τ'; however, there may be a secondary lag or response time. Thus, on the *semilog* plots of Fig. 6·4, the slope is inversely proportional to the lag time. The slope is seen to decrease abruptly for the last few per cent during which equilibrium penetrates to the stems of the liquid-in-glass thermometers. On initial insertion, the bulb glass may heat and expand before the mercury temperature is affected, causing a transient drop in indication. In resistance thermometers, there is a thermal resistance from the source body to the casing and another from the casing to the resistance coil. There may also be an external thermowell, thus effecting three thermal capacitances coupled by intermediate thermal resistances. A similar situation occurs for thermocouples and also when liquid-in-glass thermometers are in loose contact with casings or wells.

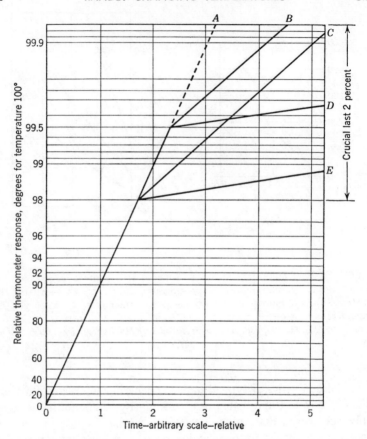

Fig. 6·4. Response of liquid-in-glass thermometers for Newton-Harper-law bulb lag, and secondary stem lags. *A*, Ideal behavior, i.e., bulb lag only; *B*, stem relatively "fast" and short—a "good" thermometer; *C*, frequent case: stem relatively "fast" but long; *D*, frequent case: stem is of slow construction but short; and *E*, "worst" kind of case: long "slow" stem. (*By permission R. Beck in Trans. ASME*, **63**, *540, American Society of Mechanical Engineers, August, 1941.*)

In these cases, the number of lag- or response-time constants for the thermometer will equal that of the respective thermal capacitances. Their relative magnitudes will depend on those of the capacitances and of the corresponding coupling resistances.[1, 3, 8, 10–12, 16, 27, 42–51, 56–58]

In gas and vapor-pressure thermometers, tubes perhaps hundreds of feet in length may run to pressure indicators such as Bourdon gages. Here, because of the appreciable quantities of compressible gas that must flow through the long small-diameter tubes, the lag time in such

Table 6·1. Equivalent time constants for resistance thermometers and thermocouples in air and water.* A, experimental and commercial resistance thermometers; and B, thermocouples

A

	Lag Time τ, sec			
Description	In Air, fpm			Water at 60 fpm (Approx)
	350	950	5300	
Bare flat element	5.6	4.1	2.6 at 1800	Less than 1 sec
Bare flat element with guard springs	34.5	24	15 at 1800	Less than 1 sec
Element in high-pressure, flat socket		136		23
Low-pressure high-speed unit, in socket	49	33.5	15.5	1.3
Silver springs, in round, stainless (18-8) socket, 0.6-in. OD, 0.596-in. ID.	55.5	40	16.5	7.5
Same with Inconel springs	81.0	65.0	42	31.8
Silver springs, in brass socket, 0.593-in. OD, 0.568-in. ID.	38.5	29.0	13.3	6.0
Same with Inconel springs	67.5	55.0	38.0	30.5
Silver springs, in aluminum socket, 0.6-in. OD, 0.563-in. ID.	30.5	25	12	5.0
Low-pressure, round unit in round stainless-steel socket	32.5	24	13.3	5.1
Integral unit, socket not separable, stainless-steel socket	68	47	18	1.6
Integral unit for low pressure and temperature applications	43	28	10	0.9
Same in 0.75-in.-OD separable brass socket			48.3	5.7

Average temperatures are: air, 130°F; water, 100°F. Range of temperature change: air, 100°F; water, 40°F. Pressure: atmospheric 29.6 in. Hg (approx).

Table 6·1. Equivalent time constants for resistance thermometers and thermocouples in air and water * (Continued)

B

Unit No.	Description	Lag Time τ, sec					
		In Air, fpm					In Water, fpm
		50	350	1150	3350	5300	60
1	Bare No. 14 B & S gage (0.064 in.) wire, iron-constantan	20	13	8	7.4	5.3	Less than 1
2	Bare No. 19 B & S gage (0.036 in.) wire, chromel-alumel	12.5	7.7	3			Less than 1
3	Same as No. 1 in round brass socket, 0.88-in. OD, 0.56-in. ID	750	325	198	135	103	Erratic
4	Same as No. 2 in round brass socket, 0.63-in. OD, 0.44-in. ID	332	150	109	59	39	Erratic
5	No. 20 B & S gage (0.032 in.) wire, iron-constantan, in 0.63-in.-OD, 0.44-in.-ID brass socket. Wire not touching wall	362	283	171	111	78	76.5
6	Same as No. 5 but thermocouple silver-soldered to socket wall	282	144	77	38	30.5	2.7
7	No. 20 B & S gage (0.032 in.) wire, iron-constantan couple, soldered into 0.25-in. brass cube	56	36	22.0	12	8	Less than 1
8	Same as No. 7 but couple soldered to 0.25-in. aluminum cube	35	19	14	6	4.5	Less than 1
9	Commercial thermocouple and socket assembly. No. 12 B & S gage (0.081 in.) wire in steel socket, 0.56-in. OD, 0.44-in. ID		220	136	79	73	57

Average temperatures are: air, 130°F; water, 100°F; range of temperature: air, 100°F; water, 40°F.

By permission A. J. Hornfeck in Trans. ASME, 71, 126–127 (October, 1948).

leads may become the dominant time constant. In heating for the vapor-pressure thermometer only the liquid's surface and the vapor need be warm; whereas, in cooling, the entire mass of liquid must be also cooled. Thus, vapor-pressure thermometers have shorter lags or response-times for rising than for falling temperatures.[3, 14, 16, 42-44]

As indicated in Fig. 6·2 the lag time depends on the properties and flow rates when the source body is a fluid. Hornfeck,[8] Clark,[47] Beck,[48] Bailey,[56] Goodwin,[3] Looney,[11] and others have described procedures for calculating response times from the values of fluid-boundary heat-transfer coefficients as given in the various textbooks. Such calculations may be very reliable if used only to estimate the change in lag for a medium other than that specified in the manufacturer's rating. Techniques are also given for determining lag-error corrections in operation.[2, 3, 8, 11, 43, 44, 46-48, 56, 59]

6·5 DESIGN-CALCULATION TECHNIQUE

The lag time τ given by Eq. 6·4 as

$$\tau = VcR \tag{6·4}$$

usually describes to a fair approximation the rapidity of response for a sensitive element. The time is the product of: (1), the thermal capacitance Vc of the sensitive element; and, (2), the thermal resistance R of the heat-flow path from the sensitive element to the local source-body material.

Since the volume heat capacity c does not vary widely among materials otherwise suitable, the thermal capacitance Vc depends principally on the volume of the sensitive element. Thus, when rapid response or small lag time τ is essential, elements of very small volume are used.

Unless the thickness is very great or a nonmetallic wall is used, the thermal conductivity of the casing material is usually not a controlling variable and may often be unimportant.

Although volume heat capacities do not vary widely among materials, Clark [47] has noted that titanium, zirconium, tin, and lead have values of c around half those for iron, nickel, and copper, together with excellent corrosion resistance. He suggests titanium or zirconium for high-temperature service and tin or lead for low-temperature service.[48, 47]

When an element is in thermal contact with a solid or viscous material such that heat flow is largely by conduction, the thermal resistances of the heat-flow paths for various geometries are given by the Eqs. 7·2,

7·3, 7·5, 7·12, 7·13, and 7·14 of Volume I. In particular, if the element is made in an elongated and bare cylindrical form

$$R = \frac{1}{A U_{c,e}} \tag{6·12}$$

where A is the surface area, ft^2, and

$$U_{c,e} = 3k/[d \sinh^{-1}(2L/d)] \tag{6·13}$$

as Eq. 7·14 of Volume I, where $U_{c,e}$ ($= U_b$ in Volume I) is the thermal conductance (referred to the lateral-surface area of the sensitive ele-

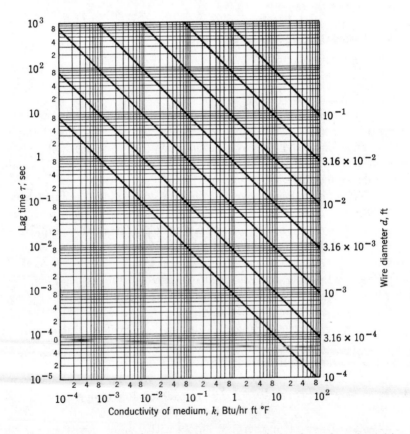

Fig. 6·5. Lag times τ' for wires immersed in still media for thermal conductivities k of the media and different wire diameters d. The L/d ratio is assumed large (i.e., 37.1) for immersed length L and c has an average value (i.e., 50 Btu/ft^3 °F).

ment) to portions of the body sufficiently distant not to be affected by the flow of heat to and from the element, Btu/hr ft² °F; k is the thermal conductivity of the source-body material, Btu/hr ft °F; L is the length of the sensitive element, ft, and d is its diameter, ft.[60]

The volume V and area A are given by

$$V = \pi d^2 L/4 \qquad (6·14)$$

and

$$A = \pi d L \qquad (6·15)$$

respectively.

Substituting Eqs. 6·12, 6·13, 6·14, and 6·15 into Eq. 6·4, we have the lag time τ given by

$$\tau = [cd^2 \sinh^{-1}(2L/d)]/12k \qquad (6·16)$$

For large length–diameter ratios L/d, the inverse hyperbolic-sine function $\sinh^{-1}(2L/d)$ increases but slowly as d decreases so that, for small values of d, τ is approximated by

$$\tau = cd^2/k \qquad (6·17)$$

Thus, the lag time τ tends to be longer for poorly conducting materials, but it can always be almost indefinitely decreased by using a sufficiently small diameter of wire d. For convenience in computations, the relationship of Eq. 6·16 is also plotted graphically in Fig. 6·5.[61]

When the element is immersed in a mobile or rapidly moving fluid, the fluid-boundary conductance U_f replaces $U_{c,e}$ in Eq. 6·12, and Eqs. 6·12, 6·14, and 6·15, substituted into Eq. 6·4, yield the lag time as

$$\tau = cd/4U_f \qquad (6·18)$$

where τ is the lag time, hr; $\tau' = 3600\ \tau$ is the lag time, sec; c is the volume heat capacity for the element material, Btu/ft³ °F; d is the diameter of the fluid-swept surface of the sensitive element, ft; and U_f is the fluid-boundary conductance referred to this surface, Btu/hr ft² °F.[62, 63]

The fluid-boundary conductance depends on the properties of the fluid and its manner and velocity of flow. This topic is discussed in the heat-transfer textbooks. The conductance is greater for high flow velocities and small diameters d. Thus, although it depends on several factors, the lag time can always be almost indefinitely decreased by using a sufficiently small diameter of wire d. Curves plotted in Fig. 6·2 to 6·6 indicate the dependence of lag time τ on various factors.[44, 46, 57, 58, 61–64]

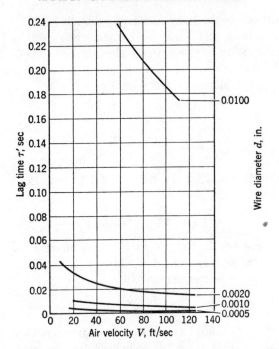

Fig. 6·6. Lag times for butt-welded thermoelectric junctions in transverse air flow at atmospheric pressure. Platinum against platinum with 10 per cent rhodium wire was used, and at temperatures ranging from 70 to 950°F. Conduction and radiation effects were small. (*By permission M. W. Carbon, H. J. Kutsch, and G. A. Hawkins in Trans. ASME, **72**, 657, American Society of Mechanical Engineers, July, 1950.*)

6·6 GAS-CONTACT RESISTANCE ELEMENTS

Schultz [4] wished to measure the fluctuating local air temperatures within the cylinder space of a hot-air engine operating at 3000 rpm. The expansion-stroke time for this engine was about 0.01 sec, and he wished to measure the time-temperature function during expansion. For indication, he used a cathode-ray oscilloscope synchronized to one sweep per revolution. For measurement, he chose the resistance-thermometer method in preference to the thermoelectric because he believed wire could be drawn to smaller diameters than junctions could be welded. His sensitive element was thus a 4-mm long bare platinum resistance wire, reduced by the Wollaston or Taylor process to 1.5 or 2 μ (0.00006 to 0.00008 in.) diameter. This element, of around 2000 to 1 length–diameter ratio, was mounted between more massive electrodes, as indicated in Fig. 6·7A.[4, 8, 26, 47, 61]

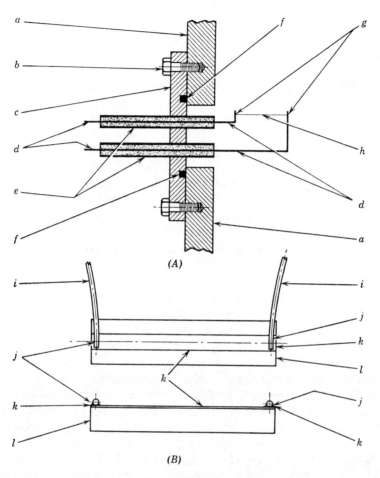

Fig. 6·7. Rapid-response electric-resistance gas-temperature elements. (A)
Schultz's air-engine thermometer; and (B) Rabinowicz, Jessey, and Bartsch's
shock-tube thermometer. a, Cylinder wall; b, cap screw; c, flange plate; d, 1-mm
(0.040-in.) diameter wire electrodes; e, 1.6-mm (0.063-in.) inside diameter metal
tubes filled with magnesium oxide electric insulation; f, air-tight gasket; g, soft-
or silver-solder joint; h, 1.5- to 2-μ (6×10^{-5}- to 8×10^{-5}-in.) diameter platinum-wire thermometer element; i, wire leads; j, soft-soldered joint to thickened
film; k, 10^{-6}-cm (0.4×10^{-6}-in.) thick sputtered-platinum film baked 1.5 hr at
1100°F; and l, Pyrex-glass insulator backing plate. (After B. H. Schultz, Philips
Tech. Rev., **13**, no. 4, 108, October, 1951.)

For such element dimensions, the second time constant, i.e., that corresponding to the internal-temperature equilibrating process, was computed to be less than 10^{-8} sec. With a rapid-response Wheatstone-bridge circuit too, instrument time lags were negligible, and the static bridge-element calibration performed was assumed to remain valid under operating conditions. The cathode-ray-oscilloscope y-axis deflections were then calibrated in operation, in terms of the known bridge-element calibration. A mechanical interrupter in the bridge circuit provided for zero-input indication, i.e., for determining the zero mark on the oscilloscope y-axis. The degrees crankangle, at which this interruption occurred, corresponded to the dip points on the oscilloscope trace. Thus, the phases at which the deflections dropped abruptly to zero were read off the interrupter-mechanism scale. In this manner the oscilloscope x-axis was calibrated in degrees crankangle. Correctly synchronized with the engine in steady operation, a stationary trace appeared on the oscilloscope screen.[4, 24]

Schultz[4] estimated his measurements to be accurate to within about $1°C$ ($1.8°F$) with phase shifts of 1.5 to 2.5 degrees of crankangle, i.e., lag times of 1 to 1.5×10^{-4} sec. He made time-temperature studies at four points within the cylinder spaces. Despite the apparent fragility of his bare Wollaston-wire sensitive element, he also successfully mounted it on the crown of the moving piston to measure the fluctuating temperatures of the thin surface layer of air. Simply connected to the external bridge coils with flexible coiled leads, the installation lasted for several millions of cycles of the engine.[4, 24]

Rabinowicz, Jessey, and Bartsch[65] have used a deposited-film electric-resistance element to measure air temperatures in a shock tube. With intervals limited to around 10^{-4} sec for flow of sufficient uniformity to permit measurement work, a rapid-response element was regarded as indispensable. As a suitable design (see Fig. 6·7B), they sputtered a 0.01-μ thick (4×10^{-7}-in.) platinum-film strip on a narrow glass plate. This resulted in 50 ohms resistance with 800- to 1400-μv/°F element sensitivity at a constant 0.01-amp exciting current. The response time τ' was less than 1 μsec. Wire leads were soft-soldered to the film ends, and the entire assembly shock-mounted with the film oriented along the *stagnation line* of a shield tube. The air stream impinged on the element, entering through an opposing slot in the shield tube.

Static bridge calibration conducted to within an accuracy of 0.5 per cent revealed a nearly linear temperature-potential relationship. Outputs of 0.01 to 0.1 v were indicated on the screen of a cathode-ray oscilloscope, using sweep speeds of 10 and 20 μsec/scale division. Thus, local shock-tube air temperatures were measured as time functions over the 200-μsec uniform-flow intervals available.

A flush-mounting wall-surface-plug design was also provided. In fact, it appears that the shape and size of such elements can usually be made to suit the circumstances.[65]

6·7   GAS-CONTACT THERMOELECTRIC ELEMENTS

Johnson's [66] sound-field thermocouple (see Fig. 6·8A and B), although fragile, is adapted to transient-gas-temperature measurements generally. Unfortunately, definite wave-propagation directions must be assumed in devising installation orientations. His design has the advantage of having been tested in dynamic-calibration against independently determined oscillatory-temperature amplitudes, and his refined, and thus verified, analysis may well find application in designs evolved by other workers.

The deposited-film construction he used is described as it applies to radiation-sensitive elements in Secs. 3·8 and 3·9 and Fig. 3·7B. With the thin-film plane oriented in the direction of particle motion, i.e., that of sound-wave propagation, its ruggedness sufficed to sustain pressure amplitudes of 100 bars (1450 lb/in.²) at frequencies as low as 200 and up to 5000 cycles/sec. Theoretical studies had indicated that diffraction errors would not exceed around 2 per cent unless the wave-splitting thickness exceeded one tenth of a wavelength. The 0.1-mm element thickness he thereby regarded as usable, without diffraction corrections, down to the 1.2-mm wavelengths occurring at frequencies of 300,000 cycles/sec.[66]

Since a sensitive element responds to the average over its own width of the adjacent-gas temperature, for it to correctly record peak values the width should not exceed around $\frac{1}{10}$ wavelength. Thus, although a 1-mm width sufficed for 5000 cycles/sec, a 0.1-mm width would be required for 300,000 cycles/sec.[66]

Prior heat-flow calculations had indicated that the attenuation factor η, measuring the dynamic-response amplitude of the element as a fraction of that of the oscillatory air temperatures, would depend on fd^2. Here, f is the sound-wave frequency, sec^{-1}, and d is the element film thickness, cm. Thus, for bismuth-film elements, η was found to range from 0.68 at $fd^2 = 4 \times 10^{-8}$ cm²/sec to 0.018 at $fd^2 = 4 \times 10^{-4}$ cm²/sec. The composite cellulose-and-metal film construction achieved was estimated to have an equivalent bismuth thickness of 3.5×10^{-5} cm. For this thickness, η is slightly less than 0.16 at 5000 cycles/sec and a little over 0.018 at 300,000 cycles/sec.[66]

Calculated response was based on the known thermoelectric power

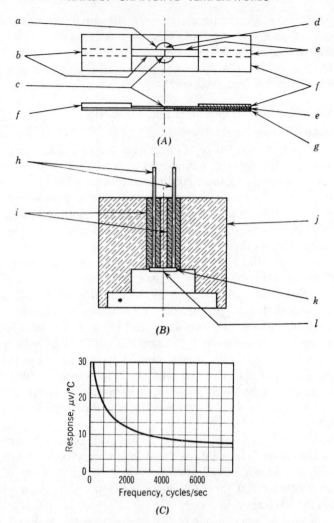

Fig. 6·8. Johnson's sound-field thermocouple. (A) Film sensitive element; (B) head assembly; and (C) experimentally verified frequency-response curve. a, 5-mm diameter hole in mica frame; b, 1-mm wide 1.2×10^{-5}-cm thick sputtered bismuth film; c, bismuth antimony thermoelectric junction with 0.12- to 0.5-mm film overlap; d, 0.5×10^{-5}-cm thick cellulose acetate film spread over mica frame; e, 1-mm wide 0.6×10^{-5}-cm thick antimony film sputtered onto cellulose acetate film; f, heavy gold contacts sputtered over the bismuth and antimony strips; g, 0.1-mm thick 1-cm wide 3-cm long mica frame; h, 0.125-in. diameter brass leads; i, 0.375-in. diameter paraffin electric insulators; j, brass head; k, thermocouple frame shown in A; and l, thermoelectric junction. (By permission E. A. Johnson in Phys. Rev., **45**, no. 9, 643–645, May, 1934.)

$e = 60 \ \mu v/°C$ for bismuth against antimony and on the attenuation factor η for the given frequency. The theoretical-response curve (Fig. 6·8C) was checked over the 200 to 500 sec^{-1} range by comparison with the actual response. Temperatures for comparison were computed from the amplitudes of oscillatory sound pressure measured with a calibrated condenser microphone.[66]

The calculated attenuated sensitivity of the element is only tenfold less at 300,000 cycles/sec than at the last verified point. Hence, Johnson [66] believed that the lowered sensitivity would still suffice for precision if lower-noise-limit amplifiers were used. The input transformer, subsequently developed, effected a fully 100-fold improvement over what Johnson anticipated so that one might expect precision at even higher frequencies.[67]

For quantitative measurements, it is evidently necessary to use carefully determined η values, i.e., attenuation-factor values.[66]

To study respiratory air temperatures in the human nasal airway, Webb [68] used a thermoelectric *probe*. It consisted of a shielded 0.0005-in. thick by 0.020-in. wide flattened-strip butt-silver-soldered copper-against-constantan element. The bare junction, after being soldered, hammered flat, and assembled in its aluminum shield, was mounted on the end of a No. 4 *urethral catheter*. The leads were then brought back through the *lumen* of the catheter. Amplified outputs, recorded on a pen oscillograph, yielded measurements to $\pm 0.1°C$ with 50 per cent response in 0.2 sec.

In studies of survival after ultrarapid freezing of plant and animal tissues, Luyet and Gonzales [69] measured cooling rates with thermocouples. Bare soldered copper-against-constantan junctions of 0.001-, 0.002-, and 0.003-in. wire were embedded in the tissue. Solid wads of tissue 0.06 in. in diameter, or liquids wetted between 0.001- to 0.002-in. thick mica sheets spaced 0.004 in. apart, were plunged into $-238°F$ liquid isopentane. Cooling rates of 150,000 to 300,000°F/sec were recorded. The sweep on a cathode-ray oscilloscope was triggered by a metal-blade electric contacter during fall in the "guillotine"-type immersing device. Electronic-square-wave 2000-cycle/sec and also 60-cycle timing dots were included in the photographed traces. Lag times, apparently, did not exceed a few milliseconds.

6·8 INTERIORS OF METALS

The measurement of internal temperatures in solids was discussed in Volume I. There are transient conditions, however, when the cemented installations therein described are not the best. This may be the case for installations in highly conducting materials if extremely steep temperature gradients occur. The error represented by the second term in Eq. 7·9 of Volume I, plotted in Fig. 7·6 of that volume, may then be excessive. Similarly, the lag time may be too long. Thus, $\tau = VcR$ is proportional to the thermal resistance R through the cement between the sensitive element and the opposing source-body material. In fact, this heat-flow path includes not only a layer of cement but also an adjacent length of the leads, whose thermal capacity is thus, in effect, added to that of the element.

The sort of circumstances referred to are best illustrated by Hollander's [70] problem, described in Sec. 5·2 and Figs. 5·3 and 5·4, where nearly the entire temperature field was included in a space of a few thousandths of an inch and in around 10^{-4} sec of time.

The only satisfactory installation design for these conditions is one in which a metallic sensitive element of minimum size is in direct wetted metallic contact with the source body. The conditions are satisfied when a small thermoelectric junction is soldered or welded to the parent material at the point of measurement. The one-wire installation used by Hollander [70] reduces junction size to a minimum when, as he did, 0.0005-in. diameter thermocouple wire is used.

Producing satisfactory installations of this sort at the bottoms of holes leading to internal points is difficult, and results may lack ruggedness. These objections are faced however when necessitated by the steepness of gradients and rapidity of temperature changes. The various procedures available are described in Chs. 5 and 8 of Volume I.[71-73]

Paschkis et al.[74] fused the ends of 0.020-in. diameter alundum-tubing-insulated nickel wires to the bottoms of 0.042-in. diameter 1.2-in. deep holes drilled in silver spheres. The spheres, heated to 1600°F, were dropped into liquid quenching baths. The purpose was to study quenching fluid-boundary conductances, as dependent on the interface temperature differences between the silver surface and the fluid. Output emfs were photographically recorded from string-galvanometer deflections to within lag times of about 0.01 sec. Paschkis believed the location accuracy to be to within 0.005 in. with absolute temperature readings to within 2 or 3°F. Surface temperatures were determined by computer extrapolation from measurements of time-temperature patterns at several internal points. Hole-bottom welds were made by the condenser-discharge method discussed in Sec. 5·8 of Volume I. Difficulties due to fragile welds and contamination were surmounted to achieve usable weld service lifetimes.

Bendersky has proposed using his element (shown in Fig. 7·6), bottomed in a hole against a crushed gold-leaf pellet, for measuring rapidly changing interior temperatures. Adequate thermal contact through the crushed gold and a heat-flow pattern not excessively disturbed by the inserted body of the device are assumed.

6·9   VELOCITY-OF-SOUND METHOD

The velocity-of-sound method offers the possibility of very brief lag times.

In Suits'[75] form, the sound wave is emitted by the electric discharge at one spark gap and its arrival time recorded at a second spark gap (see Fig. 6·9A). The *sender spark* is devised to produce a sharp strong mechanical pulse, whose electrical counterpart is photographed as a narrow peak or *pip* on a cathode-ray-oscilloscope screen. The potential drop across the second steady-arcing gap changes as the pressure front of the wave pulse passes, resulting in another pip on the screen. The distance between the two spark gaps divided by the time interval between the two pips, measured on the time-calibrated x-axis of the oscilloscope, gives the mean velocity of the sound wave over this distance. Since the initial *shock front* travels faster than sound, two readings are taken at different gap separations, so that the initial portion can be eliminated by subtraction. The mean gas temperature is then given by

$$T = Ma^2/\gamma R_m \tag{6·19}$$

where T is the absolute temperature, °K; γ is the ratio of the specific heat at constant pressure to that at constant volume for the gas; a is the measured value for the velocity of sound in the gas, cm/sec; R_m is the universal gas constant, 8.3136×10^7 ergs/gram molecule °C; and M is the molecular weight for the gas, or its mean value for a gaseous mixture.[75-85]

Where static calibration of the T-versus-a relationship is not performed, it is necessary to have specific-heat data for the particular gas in the temperature range of measurement and also to know the mean molecular weight M. When the gas consists of a mixture of different-molecular-weight molecules, M is given approximately by

$$M = 1/(c_1/M_1 + c_2/M_2 + c_3/M_3 + \cdots) \tag{6·20}$$

or

$$M = (M_1 n_1 + M_2 n_2 + M_3 n_3 + \cdots)/n \tag{6·21}$$

where M_1 is the molecular weight for gaseous constituent 1, and c_1 is the number of mass units of constituent 1 per unit mass of gas; M_2

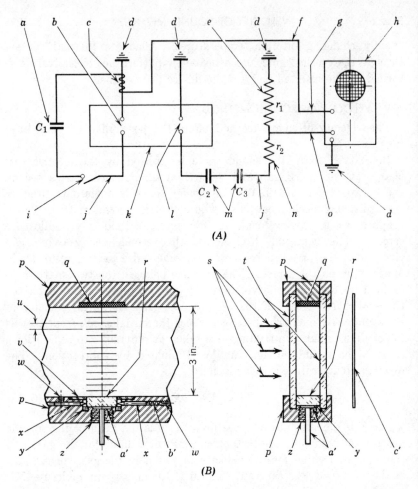

Fig. 6·9. Velocity-of-sound apparatus. (A) Agosta's Suits-type circuit; and (B) Marlow, Nisewanger, and Cady's shock-tube device. a, 1.5-μf 14,000-v capacitor; b, sound-generator spark gap; c, oscilloscope-synchronizer-input transducer; d, common ground; e, nichrome-wire resistor; f, coaxial transmission wire; g, synchronizer input; h, cathode-ray oscilloscope; i, high-voltage switch; j, automotive ignition wire; k, vessel wall; l, sound-transducer spark gap; m, 0.1-μf 10,000-v capacitor; n, carbon resistors; o, Y-deflection input; p, steel wall of shock tube; q, felt sound-absorber pad; r, X-cut 344-kc quartz-crystal sound generator; s, collimated light from synchronized high-intensity spark of 1-μsec (or less) duration; t, 0.5-in. thick water-white plate-glass windows in shock tube; u, wavelength in ultrasonic sound beam; v, closely fitting inlaid steel cover plate; w, set screw; x, steel rods providing lateral constraint to quartz crystal and making electric contact with silver-plated strips extending down sides from plated upper surface; y, lucite plate supporting the rectangular quartz crystal at its four corners; z, bakelite plug screwed in or out to tune the air cavity coupled to quartz crystal; a', driving electrode plate with stem, capacitatively coupled to the quartz crystal; b', spring; and c', photographic film. (By permission D. G. Marlow, C. R. Nisewanger, and W. M. Cady, in J. Appl. Phys., **20**, no. 8, 772, August, 1949.)

is the molecular weight for gaseous constituent 2, and c_2 is the number of mass units of constituent 2 per unit mass of gas, etc. And n_1 is the number of molecules of constituent 1, n_2 is the number of molecules of constituent 2, etc., where n is the total number of molecules.[86]

The lag time τ in this measurement can be regarded as the sound-wave transit time between spark gaps. To achieve precision in temperature measurement, short time constants in the electric-circuit components are required. For this, together with a sufficiently strong pulse, electric potentials exceeding 10,000 v with *lethal* charge magnitudes are used.[75, 82-84]

Temperature measurements to within a few per cent were attained by Agosta [82-84] and Baker [83, 84] while measuring the time for a sound wave to traverse the distance between electric-spark gaps spaced by as little as 3 in. This corresponded to a time interval of around 10^{-4} sec.

In the form described by Marlow, Nisewanger, and Cady [87] (see Fig. 6·9B), a beam of ultrasonic sound waves is projected through the body of gas from an oscillating-quartz-crystal source. To avoid confusion from reflected waves, the opposing wall is "deadened" with felt surfacing. A schlieren shadow picture of the sound-wave train, produced by the transverse light from an electric-spark pulse, permits measurement of the wavelength. The sound-wave velocity is then computed from

$$a = f\lambda \qquad\qquad (6·22)$$

where a is the sound velocity, cm/sec; f is the oscillator frequency, sec^{-1}; and λ is the measured value of the sound wavelength, cm. The temperature is then determined from Eq. 6·19 using this measured value for the sound velocity a, cm/sec.[87-89]

The lag time τ in this measurement can be regarded as the time constant of the photographic spark-discharge circuit. For sufficient light to expose fast film, high voltages and lethal charge magnitudes are required. At 10,000 v, the time can be reduced to a few microseconds. Marlow et al.[87] achieved times of less than 1 μsec. The application of the velocity-of-sound method is limited to gases. It can be applied in any gas at any temperature and at any known flow velocity. In the Suits' [75] form, although the time constant is longer, the method is also adapted to measurements in opaque, corrosive, and luminous gases. Agosta [82-84] and Baker [83, 84] have achieved quantitative determinations of *kinetic temperatures* in the *afterburning* stage for flames, and Suits performed measurements in a copper arc.[75, 82-84, 87, 90]

6·10   RADIATION METHODS

Application of radiation pyrometry is usually limited to the measurement of surface temperatures. Interior temperatures can, however, be measured with radiation technique if a hole is made permitting the radiation to pass from an internal region out to the radiation-sensitive element. Such holes introduce some of the errors which arise when holes are drilled for the installation of thermal-contact elements. The source-body surface area is limited to the cross section at the bottom. Unless mirrors are inserted, the holes must also be straight. Errors from conduction along leads do not occur, whereas other conduction errors are usually small. Although radiation methods yield apparent temperatures unless shields or emissivity corrections are applied, sighting on the bottom of a hole tends to effect black-cavity behavior. If the hole is of adequate depth–diameter ratio and the temperature sufficiently uniform in the vicinity of the bottom, a close approximation to actual blackbody temperature will be measured.

A hole in a liquid body can be maintained by inserting a tube. The end of the tube can be open, exposing the bare liquid, if gas pressure is provided equal to the fluid pressure at the bottom.

Subject to these limitations and to the errors due to ambient reflections and emissivities, radiation pyrometry is ideally adapted to the measurement of rapidly changing temperatures. To recognize this fact, one needs merely to note: (1) that the transmission time for radiation is always negligible, except for astronomical distances; (2) that the response time of the indicating instrumentation can always be made less than that for the radiation-sensitive element; and (3) that radiation-sensitive elements of very short response times are available.[30, 91]

General design-calculation techniques are elaborated in Ch. 4; and necessary information concerning available types of radiation-sensitive elements and window, lens, and mirror materials is outlined in Ch. 3. If this technology is utilized, it is possible in a systematic procedure to design a radiation pyrometer suited to the requirements of the problem at hand.

6·11   CONCLUSION

Some of the techniques outlined in this chapter are applicable to the measurement of surface temperatures and the temperatures of moving bodies. Similarly, methods described in Chs. 5 and 7 may apply to the measurement of rapidly changing temperatures.[92–97]

REFERENCES *

1. D. R. Harper, 3d, "Thermometric Lag," *Bulletin of the Bureau of Standards*, **8**, no. 4, *Sci. Paper* 185, pp. 659–714 (March, 1912).
2. M. Jakob, *Heat Transfer*, Vol. I, 758 pp., 1949; M. Jakob and S. P. Kezios, Vol. II, 652 pp., 1957, John Wiley & Sons, New York.
3. W. N. Goodwin, Jr., "Response Time and Lag of a Thermometer Element Mounted in a Protecting Case," *Trans. AIEE*, **64**, pp. 665–670 (September, 1945).
4. B. H. Schultz, "Measuring Rapidly Fluctuating Gas Temperatures," *Philips Tech. Rev.*, **13**, no. 4, pp. 104–108 (October, 1951).
5. C. E. Shepard and I. Warshawsky, "Electrical Techniques for Time Lag Compensation of Thermocouples Used in Jet Engine Gas Temperature Measurement," *Instruments*, **26**, no. 11, pp. 1725–1730 (November, 1953).
6. R. L. Garwin, "A Servomechanism for the Elimination of Time Lag," *Rev. Sci. Instr.*, **23**, no. 12, pp. 681–683 (December, 1952).
7. C. E. Shepard and I. Warshawsky, "Electrical Techniques for Compensation of Thermal Time Lag of Thermocouples and Resistance Thermometer Elements," *Technical Note* 2703, 85 pp., U. S. National Advisory Committee for Aeronautics, Washington (May, 1952).
8. A. J. Hornfeck, "Response Characteristics of Thermometer Elements," *Paper* 48-IIRD-2, pp. 1–12 (1948); *Trans. ASME*, **71**, pp. 121–133 (February, 1949), American Society of Mechanical Engineers, New York.
9. S. P. Higgins and J. R. Keim, "A Thermal Sine-Wave Apparatus for Testing Industrial Thermometers," *Paper* 54-SA-20, pp. 1–9, American Society of Mechanical Engineers, New York (1954).
10. G. A. Coon, "Responses of Temperature-Sensing-Element Analogs," *Paper* 56-A-101, pp. 1–9, American Society of Mechanical Engineers, New York (1956).
11. R. Looney, "Method for Presenting the Response of Temperature-Measuring Systems," *Paper* 56-A-102, pp. 1–5, American Society of Mechanical Engineers, New York (1956).
12. A. J. Young, "Control of Chemical Processes," *Instruments*, **26**, no. 2, pp. 254, 255, 292–294 (February, 1953).
13. C. S. Draper, W. McKay, and S. Lees, *Instrument Engineering*, Vol. I, 269 pp., 1952; Vol. II, 827 pp., 1953; Vol. III, 879 pp., 1955, McGraw-Hill Book Co., New York.
14. A. S. Iberall, "Attenuation of Oscillatory Pressures in Instrument Lines," *RP* 2115, *J. Research Natl. Bur. Standards*, **45**, no. 1, pp. 85–108 (July, 1950).
15. F. Lieneweg, "Anzeigedämpfung von Thermometern bei zeitlichen Temperaturänderungen" (Indication Damping of Thermometers with Periodic Temperature Changes), *ATM Archiv für technisches Messen*, V21-2, T143 (November, 1938).
16. O. Muller-Girard, "The Dynamics of Filled Temperature-Measuring Systems," *Paper* 54-SA-29, pp. 1–9, American Society of Mechanical Engineers, New York (1954).

---

* See footnote on page 26.

17. F. Lieneweg, "Bestimmung der Anzeigeverzögerung von Thermometern" (Determination of Indication Lag in Thermometers), *ATM Archiv für technisches Messen*, V21-1, T16–T17 (February, 1938); and V21-3, T79 (July, 1941).

18. G. A. Hawkins, "The Measurement of Rapidly Changing Temperatures," *Heat Transfer Lectures*, 1, pp. 47–58, AECV-116, NEPA-804, Atomic Energy Commission, Washington (December, 1948).

19. V. L. Parsegian and C. O. Fairchild, "Performance Characteristics of Recording Potentiometers," American Institute of Physics, *Temperature*, pp. 639–645, Reinhold Publishing Corp., New York, 1941.

20. F. A. Brooks, C. E. Barbee, R. A. Kepner, and C. Lorenzen, Jr., "Fast Single-Curve Recording of Multiple Thermocouple Measurements of Soil and Air Temperatures," American Institute of Physics, *Temperature*, pp. 629–633, Reinhold Publishing Corp., New York, 1941.

21. A. R. Champion and G. K. Brokaw, "A High-Speed Multiple-Temperature Recorder," American Institute of Physics, *Temperature*, pp. 624–625, Reinhold Publishing Corp., New York, 1941.

22. C. A. Vogelsang, "A New Era in Pyrometry," *Instrumentation*, 2, no. 1, pp. 3–7 (January-February, 1946).

23. N. Rohats, "High Speed Oscillograph," *Electronics*, 19, no. 4, pp. 135–137 (April, 1946).

24. A. Miller, "Factors Affecting Accuracy of Oscillographic Records," *Right Angle*, 1, no. 2, pp. 3–5 (November, 1953).

25. N. L. Davis, *Millimicrosecond Oscilloscopy*, Navy-DPPO Princ, 22 pp., Naval Research Laboratory, Radio Division III, Washington (1951).

26. V. C. Westcott, "Some Design Considerations in Connection with the Use of High Speed Thermometry for Telemetering," *Instruments*, 23, no. 12, pp. 1298–1299 (December, 1950).

27. L. Gess, "Response Speeds of Pressure Type Indicators," *Instrumentation*, 1, no. 2, pp. 10–12 (May-June, 1944).

28. H. Chestnut and R. W. Mayer, *Servomechanisms and Regulating System Design*, Vol. I, 2nd ed., 680 pp., John Wiley & Sons, New York, 1959.

29. H. Pfriem, "Messung schnell veränderlicher Wandtemperaturen im Motorenbau" (Measurement of Rapidly Changing Temperatures in Motors), *ATM Archiv für technisches Messen*, V2167-1, T73–T74 (July, 1940).

30. W. Göing, "Über ein neues Zeitlupenverfahren zur Untersuchung von Stossenladungen" (On a New Microtime Technique for Investigation of Spark Discharges), *Naturwissenschaften*, 37, no. 24, pp. 1–3 (1950).

31. C. A. Heiland, "Recording Oscillographs," *Instrumentation*, 7, no. 6, pp. 35–39 (First Quarter, 1955).

32. W. I. J. Price and J. J. Trott, "Multi-channel Apparatus for Recording Temperatures," *J. Sci. Instr.*, 28, no. 1, pp. 15–17 (January, 1951).

33. "Dynamic Temperature and Strain Recorder," *Rev. Sci. Instr.*, 23, no. 7, p. 386 (July, 1952).

34. M. E. Moore, "Automatic Temperature-Recording Control System," *Trans. ASME*, 65, pp. 809–815 (November, 1943).

35. M. E. Moore, "Automatic Temperature," *Automotive and Aviation Industries*, 91, pp. 32–35, 70, 72, 74 (December, 1944).

36. I. M. Stein, A. J. Williams, Jr., and W. R. Clark, "High-Speed Multiple-Point Potentiometer Recorder for Measuring Thermocouple Temperatures During Test-Plane Flights," *Trans. ASME*, 66, pp. 271–275 (May, 1944).

37. C. B. Stegner, "Calibrating and Standardizing Procedures," *Weston Engineering Notes,* **13,** no. 2, pp. 1–8 (December, 1959).

38. J. Dobrin, "Use and Maintenance of Oscilloscopes," *Instruments,* **27,** no. 3, pp. 449–451 (March, 1954).

39. H. B. Phillips, "Photoelectric Comparator for Measuring Oscillograms," *Rev. Sci. Instr.,* **25,** no. 10, pp. 971–976 (October, 1954).

40. R. C. Fletcher, "Production and Measurement of Ultra-High Speed Impulses," *Rev. Sci. Instr.,* **20,** no. 12, pp. 861–869 (December, 1949).

41. W. Wuest, "Temperaturmessung mit Federthermometern" (Temperature Measurement with Spring Thermometers), *ATM Archiv für technisches Messen,* V211-1, T77–T78 (July, 1943).

42. H. Sontag and W. G. Brombacher, "Aircraft Power-Plant Instruments," *Report* 466, pp. 35–40, U. S. National Advisory Committee for Aeronautics, Washington (December, 1933).

43. H. J. Hoge, "Temperature Measurement in Engineering," American Institute of Physics, *Temperature,* Vol. II, pp. 287–325, Reinhold Publishing Corp., New York, 1955.

44. J. S. Alford and C. R. Heising, "Fast Thermocouples as Control System Elements Sensing Exhaust Gas Temperature in Aircraft Gas Turbines," *Paper* 52-SA-35, American Society of Mechanical Engineers, New York (1952).

45. A. I. Dahl and E. F. Fiock, "Response Characteristics of Temperature-Sensing Elements for Use in the Control of Jet Engines," *RP* 2136, *J. Research Natl. Bur. Standards,* **45,** no. 4, pp. 292–298 (October, 1950).

46. A. F. Wormser, "Experimental Determination of Thermocouple Time Constants with Use of a Variable Turbulence, Variable Density Wind Tunnel, and the Analytic Evaluation of Conduction, Radiation, and Other Secondary Effects," *S.A.E. Annual Meeting Paper,* 158D, 21 pp., Society of Automotive Engineers, April, 1960.

47. J. A. Clark, "Response of Measuring Elements to Thermal Transients," *Paper* 55-SA-18, pp. 1–17, American Society of Mechanical Engineers, New York (1955).

48. R. Beck, "Thermometric Time Lag," *Trans. ASME,* **63,** pp. 531–543 (August, 1941).

49. S. Kambara and M. Matsui, "Study on Thermostat. Part III. Research on Time Lag of Various Thermometers," *J. Soc. Chem. Ind. Japan,* **34,** no. 5, pp. 167B–172B (May, 1931).

50. B. Noyes, "The Stem Lag of Industrial Thermometers," *Instruments,* **15,** no. 11, pp. 449–452, 454, 456, 457, and 492 (November, 1942).

51. H. B. Henrickson, "Thermometer Lag of Aircraft Thermometers, Thermographs, and Barographs," *RP* 222, *J. Research Natl. Bur. Standards,* **5,** no. 3, pp. 695–709 (September, 1930).

52. H. Moreau, J. A. Hall, and V. M. Leaver, "Mercury-in-Quartz Thermometers for Very High Accuracy," *J. Sci. Instr.,* **34,** no. 4, pp. 147–154 (April, 1957).

53. H. C. Anderson, "A Simple Carbon Dioxide Vapor Pressure Thermometer," U. S. Atomic Energy Commission, MDDC-535, 5 pp. (September, 1945).

54. K. H. Stokes and R. C. Whitehead, Jr., "Ambient Temperature Errors in a Gas-Filled Thermal System for Pneumatic-Balance Instruments," *Paper* 54-A-159, 9 pp., American Society of Mechanical Engineers, New York (1954).

55. Trans-Sonics Inc., "Bulb Temperature Pick-Ups," *Rev. Sci. Instr.,* **21,** no. 11, pp. 942–943 (November, 1950).

56. N. P. Bailey, "The Response of Thermocouples," *Mech. Eng.*, **53**, no. 11, pp. 797–804 (November, 1931).

57. F. I. Badgley, "Response of Radiosonde Thermistors," *Rev. Sci. Instr.*, **28**, no. 12, pp. 1079–1084 (December, 1957).

58. H. H. Lowell, "Response of Two-Material Laminated Cylinder to Simple Harmonic Environment Temperature Change," *J. Appl. Phys.*, **24**, no. 12, pp. 1473–1478 (December, 1953).

59. M. Jakob and G. A. Hawkins, *Elements of Heat Transfer*, 3d ed., 317 pp., John Wiley & Sons, New York, 1957.

60. D. P. Timo, "Thermocouple Errors During Temperature Transients," *Industrial Laboratories*, **10**, no. 6, pp. 6–10 (June, 1959); **10**, no. 10, pp. 110–111 (October, 1959).

61. Ruge Associates, Inc., Hudson, N. Y., "Resistance Temp Probe," *Instruments*, **32**, no. 12, p. 1880 (December, 1959).

62. M. W. Carbon, H. J. Kutsch, and G. A. Hawkins, "The Response of Thermocouples to Rapid Gas-Temperature Changes," *Paper* 49-A-148; *Trans. ASME*, **72**, pp. 655–657 (July, 1950).

63. R. J. Moffat, "Designing Thermocouples for Response Rate," *Paper* 57-GTP-8 (1957); *Trans. ASME*, **80**, no. 2, pp. 257–262 (February, 1958), American Society of Mechanical Engineers, New York.

64. M. D. Scadron and I. Warshawsky, "Experimental Determination of Time Constants and Nusselt Numbers for Bare-Wire Thermocouples in High-Velocity Air Streams and Analytic Approximation of Conduction and Radiation Errors," *Technical Note* 2599, 81 pp., U. S. National Advisory Committee for Aeronautics, Washington (January, 1952).

65. J. Rabinowicz, M. E. Jessey, and C. A. Bartsch, "Resistance Thermometer for Transient High-Temperature Studies," *J. Appl. Phys.*, **27**, no. 1, pp. 97–98 (January, 1956).

66. E. A. Johnson, "The Measurement of Temperature of Sound Fields," *Phys. Rev.*, **45**, no. 9, pp. 641–645 (May, 1934).

67. W. J. Fry and R. B. Fry, "Determination of Absolute Sound Levels and Acoustic Absorption Coefficients by Thermocouple Probes—Experiment," *J. Acoust. Soc. Am.*, **26**, no. 3, pp. 311–317 (May, 1954).

68. P. Webb, "The Measurement of Respiratory Air Temperature," *Rev. Sci. Instr.*, **23**, no. 5, pp. 232–234 (May, 1952).

69. B. Luyet and F. Gonzales, "Recording Ultra Rapid Changes in Temperature," *Refrigerating Engineering*, **59**, pp. 1191, 1193, and 1236 (December, 1951).

70. M. Hollander, *An Experimental Measurement of the Temperature Distribution in the Workpiece during Metal Cutting*, Doctoral Dissertation, 243 pp., Columbia University, New York, N. Y., 1959.

71. Trott, W. J., "Welder for Attaching Fine Wires to Massive Metal Bodies," *Rev. Sci. Instr.*, **20**, no. 8, pp. 624–625 (August, 1949).

72. A. J. Mortlock, "Error in Temperature Measurement due to the Interdiffusion at the Hot Junction of a Thermocouple," *J. Sci. Instr.*, **35**, no. 8, pp. 283–284 (August, 1958).

73. H. Bernstein, "Attaching Thermocouples by Capacitance Welding," Office of Technical Services, *Technical Report*, NGT-T-21-55, Naval Ordnance 4854, (April, 1955).

74. V. Paschkis and G. Stolz, Jr., "Quenching as a Heat Transfer Problem," *J. Metal*, **8**, no. 8, pp. 1074–1075 (August, 1956).

75. C. G. Suits, "The Determination of Arc Temperature from Sound Velocity Measurements. I and II," *Physics,* **6,** no. 6, pp. 190–202 (June, 1935).

76. "Developments in Photographing Scope Traces," *Du Mont Instrument Journal,* no. 2, pp. 7–9, 14, 1957.

77. A. L. Sorem, "Developing High-Speed Film Used in Recording Oscilloscope Traces," *Du Mont Instrument Journal,* no. 2, pp. 3–5, 1957.

78. S. H. Neddermeyer, E. J. Althaus, and W. Allison, "The Measurement of Ultra-Short Time Intervals," *Rev. Sci. Instr.,* **18,** no. 7, pp. 488–495 (July, 1947).

79. E. W. Titterton, "A Microsecond Interval Timer," *Rev. Sci. Instr.,* **22,** no. 1, p. 96 (January, 1951).

80. "Time Delay Generator," *Rev. Sci. Instr.,* **22,** no. 1, p. 64 (January, 1951).

81. R. Hofstadter and J. A. McIntyre, "Note on the Detection of Coincidences and Short Time Intervals," *Rev. Sci. Instr.,* **21,** no. 1, pp. 52–53 (January, 1950).

82. V. D. Agosta, *Temperature Determinations of Nitrogen and Methane-Air Combustion Products by Velocity-of-Sound Measurements,* Doctoral Dissertation, 250 pp., Columbia University, New York, 1958.

83. V. D. Agosta and H. D. Baker, "Determination of Nitrogen Temperatures by Velocity-of-Sound Measurements," *Proceedings of the Third U. S. National Congress of Applied Mechanics,* pp. 709–715, American Society of Mechanical Engineers (June, 1958).

84. V. D. Agosta and H. D. Baker, "Temperature Determinations of Methane-Air Combustion Products by Velocity-of-Sound Measurements," *Proc. Sixth Annual Conference on Fluid Mechanics,* pp. 303–319, American Society of Mechanical Engineers (September, 1959).

85. A. L. Hedrich and D. R. Pardue, "Sound Velocity as a Measurement of Gas Temperature," American Institute of Physics, *Temperature,* Vol. II, pp. 383–392, Reinhold Publishing Corp., New York, 1955.

86. J. Hilsenrath, C. W. Beckett, W. S. Benedict, L. Fano, H. J. Hoge, J. F. Masi, R. L. Nuttall, Y. S. Touloukian, and H. W. Wooley, "Tables of Thermal Properties of Gases," *Natl. Bur. Standards Circ.* 564, 488 pp., Government Printing Office, Washington (November, 1955).

87. D. G. Marlow, C. R. Nisewanger, and W. M. Cady, "A Method for the Instantaneous Measurement of Velocity and Temperature in High Speed Air Flow," *J. Appl. Phys.,* **20,** no. 8, pp. 771–776 (August, 1949).

88. L. Bergmann and H. S. Hatfield, *Ultrasonics and Their Scientific and Technical Applications,* pp. 22 and 91, John Wiley and Sons, New York, 1939.

89. H. E. Edgerton, "Shock Wave Photography Improved," *Industrial Laboratories,* **9,** no. 7, pp. 6–8 (July, 1958).

90. A. Whetstone, "Millimicrosecond Light Source," *Rev. Sci. Instr.,* **30,** no. 6, pp. 447–450 (June, 1959).

91. Farnsworth Electronics Company, "Photomultiplier," *Rev. Sci. Instr.,* **26,** no. 10, p. 1002 (October, 1955).

92. *Encyclopedia on Cathode-Ray Oscilloscopes and Their Uses,* 2nd ed., 1356 pp., John F. Rider Publisher, New York, 1960.

93. J. D. Clem, Jr., "Development of a Special Thermocouple for Measuring Transient Temperatures within a Solid Body," *Rev. Sci. Instr.,* **31,** no. 3, pp. 334–336 (March, 1960).

94. M. D. Scadron, "Time Response Characteristics of Temperature Sensors," *Paper* 158H, 8 pp. (1960), SAE National Aeronautic Meeting, Society of Automotive Engineers, New York.

95. F. R. Caldwell, L. O. Olsen, and P. D. Freeze, "Intercomparison of Thermo-couple Response Data," *Paper 158F*, 17 pp. (1960), SAE National Aeronautic Meeting, Society of Automotive Engineers, New York.
96. J. V. Beck and H. Hurwicz, "Effect of Thermocouple Cavity on Heat Sink Temperature," *Mech. Eng.*, **81**, no. 10, p. 94 (October, 1959).
97. M. E. Barzelay, K. N. Tong, and G. Hollo, "Thermal Conductance of Con-tacts in Aircraft Joints," *Technical Note* 3167, 47 pp., U. S. National Advisory Committee for Aeronautics, Washington (March, 1954).

7

MOVING BODIES

7·1 INTRODUCTION

Neither motion nor remoteness are problems in radiation pyrometry. The angle through which the pyrometer views a moving body remains fixed. The size of the geometrical source area imaged on the sensitive element is determined by the distance and the subtended angle characteristic of the focusing device. Nonuniformities in temperature in moving bodies appear as changing temperatures. Small bodies passing through the field of view become intermittent temperatures.

When, however, it is expedient to place thermal-contact sensitive elements on a moving body, difficulties arise. If the thermometer has an integral indicating dial or graduated stem, it may be difficult to read this dial or stem while it is in motion; whereas, stopping the body to make readings may not be feasible and the temperatures may thereby be altered. If the indicating instruments are stationary, arranging satisfactory leads to the moving body often becomes a problem.

Motions may be continued, as motions of continuous rotation about an axis or of steady travel along a path. Also, they may be reciprocating along fixed guides or oscillating about pivots.

7·2 SLIDING ELECTRIC CONTACTS

If the motion is not both unidirectional and long continued, continuous leads can be used. Schultz [1] connected flexible coiled wires to a resistance thermometer mounted on the moving piston of a hot-air engine (see Sec. 6·6 and Fig. 6·7A). Similarly, Armi, Johnson, Machler, and Polster [2] used a flexible lead to a rifle bullet, pushed a few inches down the barrel by a falling weight. With a bullet-barrel-interface thermoelectric element, the other lead was joined to the barrel. For a body in continuous flight, no leads at all are possible. Either installations must be complete on the body and perhaps self-recording as in *radiosonde*, or radiation methods must be used. Thus, Riezler and Hardt [3] designed a radiation pyrometer suited to measur-

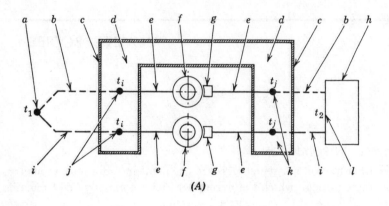

(A)

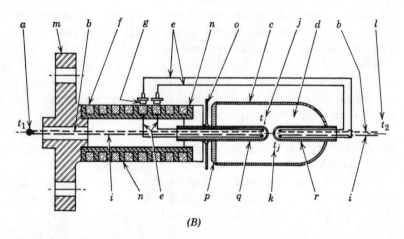

(B)

Fig. 7·1. Brush-slip-ring sliding contacts. (*A*) Schematic diagram; and (*B*) ring-and-brush assembly with steam chest. *a*, One of four junctions on rotor; *b*, thermocouple metal I; *c*, wall of stationary steam chest; *d*, steam space; *e*, copper lead wires; *f*, copper slip ring; *g*, static copper brush; *h*, indicator; *i*, thermocouple metal II; *j*, junctions to copper leads at temperature t_i, nearly steam temperature; *k*, junctions to thermocouple metals at temperature t_j, nearly steam temperature; *l*, reference junction; *m*, flange for mounting to rotor; *n*, electric insulation; *o*, fin; *p*, neoprene gasket; *q*, rotating thermowell; and *r*, static thermowell. (See Fig. 5·3 and Eq. 5·5 of Volume I.) (*By permission P. R. Tarr in Research Memorandum RME 50 J23a, 11, 12, U. S. National Advisory Committee for Aeronautics, January, 1951.*)

ing the temperatures of the "sparks," i.e., incandescent fragments thrown off from a grindstone.[1][7]

When the motion is reciprocating, oscillating, or rotating continuously, it is usually possible and often convenient to accommodate the motion by sliding or intermittent contacts. Sliding contacts may be of the *crosshead* type or of the brush-slip-ring type familiar in commutators (see Fig. 7·1A and B). The purpose of the steam box here is to permit arbitrary choice of ring and brush materials so that the metals used can be those most suitable for sliding contacts. Intermittent contacts may be of the *pushrod type* (see Fig. 7·2A), or they may include "wiping" action past a *contact button* (see Fig. 7·2B). Here the contactors must be of the thermocouple metals. In either case, the contacts may be retractable to avoid wear except when taking readings.[8-25]

In a rapid-response system, the contact button or pushrod may maintain a circuit of sufficient time duration in each stroke for oscillographic indication of the entire phenomenon of interest. When source-body changes are more gradual and significant only over five or more elapsed cycles, a slow-response null-balance system is feasible. Then, although unbalance persists in the bridge-circuit arrangement used, a series of pulses affect the indicator. The time-average impulse determining the deflection is proportional to the closed-circuit fraction of the cycle. Intermittent contact thus effectively reduces the bridge-indicator sensitivity.

In resistance thermometry, variable and uncertain contact resistances are a source of error. The attaining of sufficiently small and constant contact resistances, with suitable durability, is then essential. Since this requirement is discussed in Secs. 2·18 to 2·20, nothing further need be said here.

In thermoelectric circuits, spurious or parasitic emfs tend to arise at sliding contacts. Thus, when the contact materials are other than the metal of the lead, two or more junctions occur. Heat generation in rubbing friction complicates efforts to maintain the junctions at the same uniform temperature, particularly when one junction is at the sliding interface. Unfortunately, the usual thermocouple-wire materials are not those which are used for sliding contacts in ordinary electric machinery. Furthermore, sliding-contact pairs are usually best from a mechanical standpoint when made of differing materials.

Even where metals are identical throughout, spurious noise emfs arise at sliding contacts. These emfs are attributed to two phenomena: (1) At points where asperities are sheared off in the rubbing interface, high transient temperatures result. Thermoelectric pulses from these

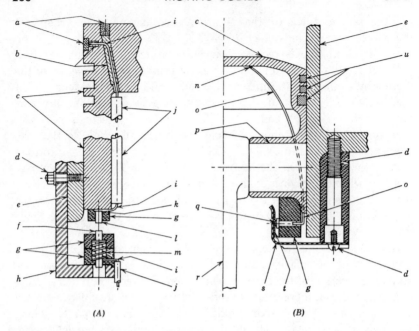

(A)   *(B)*

Fig. 7·2. Intermittent contacts. (*A*) Pushrod contact; (*B*) sliding contact. *a*, Aluminum plugs, *b*, lava tubing; *c*, piston; *d*, mounting screw; *e*, cylinder; *f*, spring-mounted contactor of thermocouple metal; *g*, electric-insulating block; *h*, steel bracket; *i*, thermocouple wire wrapped in mica tape; *j*, aluminum conduit; *k*, soldered joint; *l*, piston contactor of thermocouple metal; *m*, steel spring; *n*, thermocouple junction; *o*, double-"spaghetti" insulated thermocouple wire; *p*, wrist pin; *q*, pure-silver contact button; *r*, connecting rod; *s*, heat-treated steel spring; *t*, pure-silver electric-contact slide; and, *u*, piston rings. (*By permission P. V. Keyser and E. F. Miller, J. Inst. Petroleum,* **25**, *no. 194, 781, December, 1939; and A. F. Underwood and A. A. Catlin, S. A. E. Trans.,* **48**, *no. 1, 20–27, January, 1941.*)

random "hot spots" effect a noise-power level. (2) Junctions to semi-conducting tarnish films and intermittent *puncturing* of insulating films are sources of *semiconductor noise*. Resultant noise emfs, for several combinations measured by Horton,[26] are given in Table 7·1. It may be noted that noise emfs tend to be largest for the most widely differing and highest-graphite-content materials, i.e., for those combinations usually preferred in electric-machine design.[13, 26]

Tarr[14] found that pure copper-to-copper sliding contacts could be used with low-gumming lubricants for contact periods not exceeding about 30 sec. Under scoring conditions, the brushes maintained fresh-ened surfaces with low contact resistances. Brush wear was severe, but, with suitable lubricants, several-hundred-hour service lifetimes were possible. Light instrument oil containig 1 g/l of colloidal graphite lubricated suitably; however, film temperatures had to be limited to 300°F. Iron-to-iron sliding contacts with sulfurized extreme-pressure lubricants were also used. These sliding one-metal contacts were found to introduce errors of less than ±45 μv at sliding speeds up to 5400 ft/min. A pure-copper brush-and-slip-ring arrangement, operated at 3200 ft/min, generated only 10 μv.

Gorton and Miller [27] used chromel and alumel rollers to contact chromel and alumel rings, respectively, on gas-turbine rotor shafts. One-metal contacts to the stationary leads occurred where spring-loaded cones were pressed into conical depressions at the ends of the

Table 7·1. Generated noise voltage of brushes on solid rings. Two ¼-in. by ¼-in. brushes on each ring; sliding speed: 35 cm/sec

Ring Material	Brush Material	Normal Force, g	Generated Noise, μv
Clean silver	Natural graphite	~50	0.3
Clean silver	Silver graphite, fine texture, low silver content	~50	0.3
Clean silver	Silver graphite, coarse texture, high silver content	~50	2.5
Clean rhodium	Natural graphite	30	0.8
Clean rhodium	Silver graphite, fine texture, low silver content	60	0.5
Clean rhodium	Silver graphite, coarse texture, high silver content	50	0.4
Clean gold	Natural graphite	40	0.6
Oxidized copper	Natural graphite	~50	11 to 1
Rhodium coated with silver sulfide	Silver graphite, fine texture, low silver content	60	14
Electrographitic carbon	Natural graphite	900	1 to 9

*By permission B. M. Horton in Rev. Sci. Instr., **20**, no. 12, 930 December, 1949.*

roller jackshafts. The assembly was enclosed and oil-mist lubricated. Limiting speeds were determined by excess increases in circuit resistance at the roller and cone contacts. The limiting speeds were found to be 5000 and 15,000 rpm for single and double roller followers, respectively.

It may not be necessary to limit consideration to contacts made from the thermocouple-lead materials. Similar-material combinations of low thermoelectric power may often generate sufficiently small spurious emfs. For example, gold-silver junctions are of low thermoelectric power, and each metal is "low" with respect to copper; also, gold-silver sliding contacts have low contact resistances. Chaplin [13] used silver-graphite brushes, containing 80 to 90 per cent silver, sliding on sterling silver slip rings. During 40 hr of continuous operation at 7000 rpm, the equivalent resistance of the contact ranged from about 0.02 to less than 0.04 ohm with a maximum potential difference across the contact of 0.00035 v. Air pressure was used to provide brush pressure and to blow away conducting abrasion products.

At high speeds, bounce, chatter, and fatigue effects become dominant problems in sliding-contact design. Adequate mechanical ruggedness is also often difficult to attain in assemblies mounted on rapidly reciprocating parts such as engine pistons.

7·3 INDUCTIVE-COUPLED COMMUTATORS

Problems and errors peculiar to sliding contacts are eliminated by substituting noncontact inductive couplings.

For thermoelectric temperature measurement on bodies at high rotational speeds, Gnam [28, 29] proposed the arrangement shown in Fig. 7·3A and B. Here, both the "hot" and the "cold" junctions are on the rotating shaft. The circuit is a closed loop that includes the primary or armature winding of an electric converter. Balance of the thermoelectric emfs is effected by adjusting the thermostated "cold"-junction to the "hot"-junction temperature. Null indication in the secondary or field-coil circuit is observed in the oscillatory emf output, amplified on the screen of a cathode-ray oscilloscope. When zero current is indicated for the thermocouple loop, the location temperature is read on the thermostat thermometer.

Dahl and Freeze [30] investigated the precision to be expected from the Gnam [28, 29] arrangement. Laboratory-model sensitivities (shown in Fig. 7·4) were found to be dependent on the magnetic-circuit air-gap thickness in the converter and on the rotational speed. At the high speeds, where slip rings and roller contacts become most troublesome, inductive coupling is most precise. Figure 7·3B shows a con-

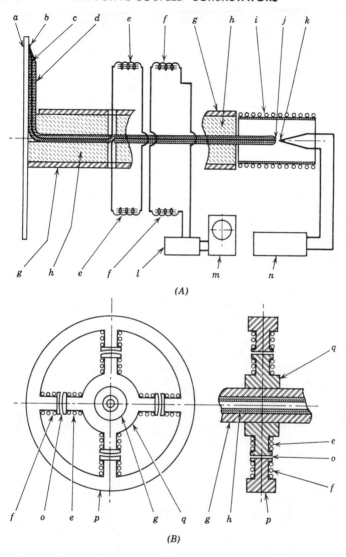

Fig. 7·3. Gnam method. (A) Dahl-Freeze laboratory model; and (B) converter design for full-scale application. *a*, Balanced disk; *b*, measuring thermoelectric junction; *c*, chromel-P thermocouple wire embedded in electric insulation; *d*, nickel tube; *e*, rotating converter coils; *f*, stationary converter coils; *g*, rotating hollow shaft; *h*, porcelain tube; *i*, electric tube furnace; *j*, rotating thermoelectric junction coaxial with shaft; *k*, stationary thermoelectric junction to indicate furnace temperature; *l*, impedance-matching transformer; *m*, cathode-ray oscilloscope; *n*, potentiometer; *o*, air gap; *p*, stator; and *q*, rotor. (*By permission A. I. Dahl and P. D. Freeze in J. Research Natl. Bur. Standards*, **41**, *no. 6, 602 and 606, December, 1948*.)

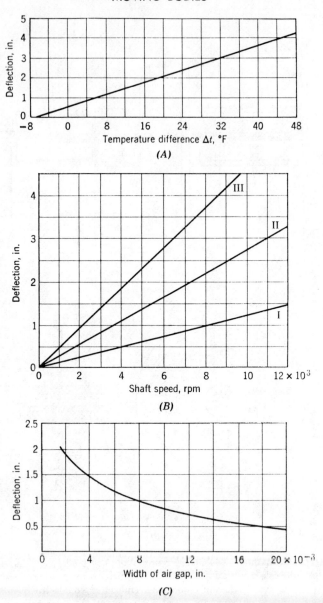

Fig. 7·4. Gnam method sensitivities. (*A*) Sensitivity, i.e., deflection versus difference Δt between disk temperature and furnace temperature at 5000 rpm and
0.003-in. air gap; (*B*) curves for sensitivity, i.e., deflection versus shaft speed at
0.003-in. air gap: (I) $\Delta t = 20°$F; (II) $\Delta t = 10°$F; and (III) rotating circuit open;
and (*C*) sensitivity, i.e., deflection versus width of air gap at 6000 rpm and $\Delta T =$
10°F. (*By permission A. I. Dahl and P. D. Freeze in J. Research Natl. Bur.
Standards, 41, no. 6, 604–606, December, 1948.*)

verter design for full-scale application. It is believed that 10°F sensitivity is feasible in a unit with a 0.01-in. air gap at a 6000-rpm shaft speed.[28-30]

Gnam [28,29] and Tarr [14] described sliding-collar-operated selector switches for successive readings on up to twenty-four temperature locations. Tarr also showed solenoid-relay-operated brush selectors for multiple-location measurements.[14,28,29]

The Greenough-Marzetta-Bayhi [31,32] radio-frequency circuit (indicated in Fig. 7·5) adapts the inductive-coupling technique to resistance thermometry. No thermostat adjustment is required, and the sensitivity is independent of the rotational speed. In the basic circuit (Fig. 7·5A), the resistance-temperature-sensitive element r_e is in effect a "short-circuiting," i.e., a *shunting*, resistor. Small changes in its value, due to temperature variations, alter the coupling between the 160,000-cycle/sec power-supply oscillator and the radio-frequency output indicator. When the design is optimum, the indicated-output emf is very nearly a linear function of the element resistance r_e. Since the output emf is necessarily also proportional to the power input, which may drift, reference to a standard resistor is required for maintaining the input in adjustment.

The schematic *block diagram* in Fig. 7·5B shows five resistance units, each with two inductive-coupling coils, constituting five thermometer units, similar to the one in Fig. 7·5A, as they are mounted on a rotor. They, each in turn, pass the fixed input and output coils once every revolution. For selective indication, the fixed input coil is powered only during the time the "dialed" thermometer unit passes. This is effected by the five fixed synchronizing coils being successively "cored" by a magnetic-strip *gating* segment, which is mounted in a definite orientation on the rotor but not in a position to influence the thermometer-unit coils. Thus, when the selector switch connects a given synchronizing coil into the input circuit, the fixed input coil is "powered" only while the magnetic-strip gating segment is opposite this coil. The thermometer unit, passing between the fixed input and output coils at this angularity of the rotor, is then the one whose temperature effects the output indication.[31,32]

One of the units is reserved as a fixed standardizing resistor r_b. The power supply is then adjusted so as always to give the same indication when the constant resistor r_b is "dialed." The resistance of any temperature-sensitive element r_e is then given by

$$r_e = r_b E_e / E_b \qquad (7·1)$$

where r_e is the resistance of the temperature-sensitive element, ohms; r_b is the resistance of the standardizing resistor, ohms; E_e is the output

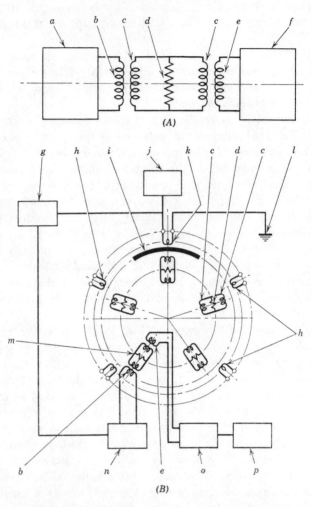

Fig. 7·5. Radio-frequency inductive coupling for resistance thermometry. (A) Basic circuit; and (B) block diagram for rotor carrying five thermometer units. a, Radio-frequency oscillator; b, stationary input coil; c, moving coupling coil; d, temperature-sensitive electric-resistance element r_e installed on rotor; e, stationary output coil; f, radio-frequency voltmeter; g, synchronizing pulse amplifier; h, stationary synchronizing coils not dialed and not gated on; i, magnetic strip mounted on rotor; j, synchronizing pulse generator; k, stationary synchronizing coil switched into circuit, i.e., dialed and when gated on; l, ground; m, thermometer unit being indicated; n, gated 160,000-cycles/sec excitation oscillator; o, peak-voltage detector; and, p, meter. (By permission Natl. Bur. Standards, U. S. Tech. News Bull., 38, no. 12, 180–181, December, 1954.)

emf for r_e, v; E_b is the output emf for r_b, v; and E_e/E_b is the ratio of the indications for the two "dialings." [31,32]

Davis and Bowman [31,32] developed a 0.040-in.-outside-diameter platinum-resistance thermometer element for use on high-speed rotors. The inconel-cased 24-turn ⅛-in. long 0.001-in. diameter wire platinum helix is embedded in ceramic cement to operate at 1600°F in the absence of force, or at 1400°F in centrifugal-force fields of up to 40,000 g. The centrifugal force on the element is then 40,000 times that which would result from gravity and corresponds to being located at a 3.5-in. radius on a rotor spinning at 20,000 rpm. The effect of temperature changes in lead resistance is minimized with the 4-lead construction of Fig. 2·4. Here the "current" leads are connected across the moving input coil, while the "potential" leads are across the moving output coil (see Fig. 7·5A).

Static tests at temperatures up to 1500°F have demonstrated precision to within ±10°F; whereas, in force fields of up to 30,000 g and temperatures up to 1400°F, precision to within ±15 to ±25°F is expected. [31,32]

There is no wear problem with this type of coupling. Large vibration amplitudes or the presence of oil and water vapor have virtually no effect on the signal transfer. The shaft can be run in either direction without modification of the device, and the electronic components can be up to 50 ft distant from the rotor. [31,32]

7·4 GUN-BARREL TEMPERATURES

Gun-barrel motion is limited to discharge-shock vibrations and recoil. However, the passage of the bullet in firing complicates measurements. The luminosity, corrosiveness, and opacity of the interior flame also cause difficulties.

Interest tends to be greatest for interior-surface barrel temperatures, especially during actual firing. Here, the use of any sort of indicating paint is prevented by the scraping action of the bullet. Sighting a radiation pyrometer on a bore-surface patch would imply a window-closed "peep" hole in the opposite wall. The window surface would be exposed to the flame gases only during firing, which need not be a continuous operation even on a machine gun. Hence, the combustion-chamber window problems do not appear fundamentally more difficult than those solved by Bridgeman and by Corry. [33] To obtain a radiant signal dependent only on the wall-patch surface temperature would, however, be a problem. Passage of the bullet prevents ambient-radiation shielding, such as that devised by Hollander. [34,55] Dependence would have to rest on spectral discrimination. Thus, Bayle and

Hübner have surmounted difficult problems with this technique (see Sec. 5·15). Since flame-radiation spectra extend in lines and bands from the ultraviolet to beyond 10 μ in the infrared, it would be necessary to work somewhere within this range, taking advantage of the "gaps" characteristic of discontinuous spectra. Suspended incandescent solid particles radiate in a continuous spectrum. However, in a suitably "smokeless" flame, the continuous fraction might be small.[33,34,55]

The Bendersky[35] gun-barrel thermoelectric element shown in Fig. 7·6 is based on principles originally reported by Hackemann.[36] Other workers have successfully applied similar devices in the measurement of gun-barrel temperatures.[35-39]

A difficulty inherent in this sort of method is that it is not the bore-surface temperature which is measured. The temperature indicated is that in the junction plane of the element. For Bendersky's design, this plane is very near to the surface, i.e., within 1 μ (0.000039 in.). However, its temperature will depend on the rate of heat flow into the surface and on the outflow to the metallic interior. The outflow will depend on the thermal diffusivity of the backing material and the heat-flow path to the ambient. In frictional abrasion, such as that which occurs at the bullet-bore interface, surface asperities often heat to their melting temperatures. It appears questionable to what extent a 1-μ thick junction layer can be subjected to such abrasion. Also, a small flush-mounted button of material other than that of the gun barrel might be abraded differently and with greater or less surface-

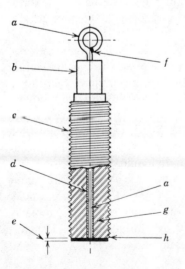

Fig. 7·6. Gun-barrel thermocouple. a, 0.012-in. diameter "A"-nickel wire; b, SAE 4130 steel tubing; c, $\frac{5}{32}$-in. diameter mounting threads; d, nickel oxide electric-insulation film formed on nickel wire by heating in carbon dioxide at 2000°F for 1 hr; e, 1-μ (0.000039-in.) thick layer of nickel plating; f, soldered joint; g, steel tube "wire-drawn" into firm contact with nickel oxide film; and, h, thermoelectric-emf plane. (*By permission D. Bendersky in Mech. Eng., 75, no. 2, 118, February, 1953.*)

heat generation. Heat inflow by flame-radiation absorption would depend on the button reflectance, probably different from that of the gun barrel. The comparative surface condition of the button will depend on relative amounts of bullet abrasion and dirt deposit and on its original texture. Gas-contact heat inflow will probably be about the same for the button as for the virgin wall surface, and this conduction may be the dominant transfer mechanism. Also, the backing material is mostly of the same sort as the gun barrel.[35-39]

The comparatively large diameter and lateral-interface thermal resistance do not adapt this installation to response for adjacent-area surface or near-surface temperatures. Nevertheless, the installations have the necessary convenience and ruggedness to withstand the severe gun-barrel operating conditions, and they have supplied much useful information. A ten-round service lifetime appears to be the limit because of the erosive effects of the powder gases. The Bendersky [35] device, in particular, has demonstrated the remarkable response rate of 800,000°F/sec, and the junction plane appears to have very nearly the same temperature as the mean for the element surface.[35-39]

7·5 ELECTRIC-MOTOR TEMPERATURES

Limitation of "hot-spot" temperatures in motor windings is a control task in manufacturing design. For squirrel-cage induction motors, the windings are stationary; therefore, temperature surveys by inserted thermocouples and mercury-in-glass thermometers are feasible. Such studies have shown that the mean temperature of the coil, as indicated by its own electric-resistance rise, although below that of the warmest zone or "hot-spot," is a fair criterion of performance. Such coil temperatures are measured after shutdown and are time-extrapolated back to the moment of switching-off. This procedure also permits measurements on coil-wound armatures.[40-45]

Rotor-mounted thermoelectric, or wire-wound electric-resistance, thermometers can be applied to the measurement of armature temperatures. Thermoelectric-lead-metal brush-and-slip-ring contacts or inductive couplings are required. However, since electric-winding temperatures are not above those accessible to thermistor temperature-sensitive elements, the use of thermistors proves to be simpler. The high element-resistance values obtainable in thermistors render slip-ring contacts noncritical, and the relatively large output emfs reduce errors from spurious theremoelectric emfs so that rings and brushes of ordinary materials can be used.[45]

Thomas and Horvat [46] installed a thermistor to measure armature temperatures on a three-phase wound-rotor induction motor. Disconnecting the secondary terminals and joining them on the rotor, they operated the motor as a squirrel-cage type, freeing the slip rings for use in the thermistor circuit. The thermistor used was a 1-mm diameter 100,000-ohm-room-temperature-resistance glass-coated-bead element with well-insulated, magnetically shielded leads. A Wheatstone-bridge indicating circuit (see Fig. 2·1) to be operated at constant setting was adjusted for balance at 85°C (185°F) with 2.5×10^{-6} amp through the element r_e. Indications, oven-calibrated to within 0.2°C, were read on a microammeter in the thermistor arm of the bridge. Precision, as reduced by variations in slip-ring contact resistances, was estimated as to within 1°C.

7·6 SLIDING-CONTACT THERMOELECTRIC JUNCTIONS

When two clean different-metal surfaces are pressed together in sliding or rubbing contact, the interface can be regarded as a thermoelectric junction. If the circuit is then closed through a reference-temperature "cold" junction, the emf indications are measures of the interface-junction temperature. In metal cutting, the tool may be one member and the workpiece the other of such a thermocouple (see Fig. 7·7A). Similarly, in friction tests, the slider and track materials form the combination (see Fig. 7·7B).[22,47-54]

Bowden[47,48,52] and Ridler[52] found that for sliders of low-melting metals—such as gallium, lead, and Wood's metal—rubbing on mild steel the indicated temperature rose in linear proportion to the frictional-heat generation until the slider-material melting temperature was reached. At all higher thrusts and rubbing speeds, the indication remained constant. For less fusible materials, such as constantan, the linear rise continued unabated. When, however, rubbing had smeared a film of the slider metal onto the track, indications dropped to low values. ·The explanation given for these phenomena is that contact and heating occur only at the asperities (see Fig. 7·8A), even for the smoothest surfaces. These points rise to their melting temperatures, after which further frictional effects in the liquid metal are small. When, because of smearing, the asperities become of the same metal, no thermoelectric junctions exist and their temperatures effect no emf indications.

To explore these phenomena, Bowden,[47,48,52] Stone, and Tudor visually observed a slider surface in the dark through a transparent-disk track. They found that numerous tiny stars of light appear at the interface. The stars were reddish in color at low speeds, becoming whiter and brighter as the speed or load was increased. Bowden[47,48,52] and Thomas[47] replaced the human eye with a lead sulfide photocon-

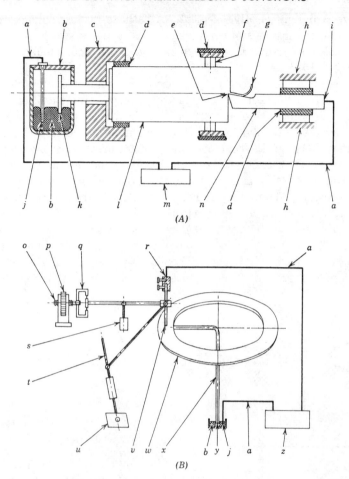

Fig. 7·7. Sliding-contact thermocouples. *A*, Tool–workpiece junction; and, *B*, sliding surface-temperature junction. *a*, Copper leads; *b*, mercury-bath moving-contact unit; *c*, chuck; *d*, electric insulation; *e*, measuring junction at the tool–workpiece interface; *f*, steady rest; *g*, chip; *h*, tool post; *i*, reference junction where tool metal joins copper leads; *j*, copper-mercury stationary junction; *k*, reference junction where workpiece metal spins in mercury bath; *l*, workpiece; *m*, potentiometer; *n*, cutting tool; *o*, screw; *p*, knurled traversing nut; *q*, gimbals; *r*, reference junction where sliding-cylinder metal joins to copper leads; *s*, weight; *t*, linkage; *u*, base; *v*, measuring junction at cylinder-disk sliding contact; *w*, rotating metal disk; *x*, wire of disk material; *y*, reference junction where disk metal contacts mercury bath; and, *z*, Einthoven galvanometer. (*By permission F. P. Bowden and K. E. W. Ridler in Proc. Roy. Soc. London A,* **154**, *644, May, 1936; and M. C. Shaw, J. D. Pigott, and L. P. Richardson in Paper 50-SA-19, Trans. ASME,* **73**, *45–47, January, 1951.*)

ductive radiation-sensitive element. A cathode-ray-oscilloscope trace then indicated myriads of sharp peaks. At a higher sweep speed, one such peak was resolved, as shown in Fig. 7·8B, and found to be of about 2×10^{-6} sec duration.[47, 48, 52]

The electric contact is thus at a very large number of tiny momentary welds, which effectively become thermoelectric junctions connected in parallel. Since the electric resistances in the shunts differ, circulatory currents arise, and the resultant emf may not correspond to the arithmetic mean of the contact-point temperatures. Gaylord, Hughes, Appl, and Ling[50] have calculated the resultant indication expected for the scintillating myriads of effectively parallel-connected asperity temperatures. Their analysis has demonstrated that, with massive-backing conductors, measurement is of the average of the asperity temperatures, weighted by the square roots of their respective contact areas. They assumed, what appears to be established, that contact emfs are due primarily to the temperatures produced and not to other effects of the motion. Temperatures of asperities may, however, de-

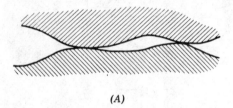

(A)

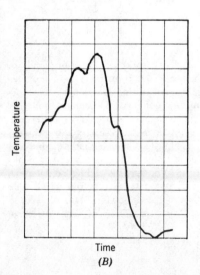

Temperature

Time

(B)

Fig. 7·8. Surface temperature of sliding solids. (*A*) Microscopic geometry of surface contacts; and (*B*) radiant energy received from a single hot spot, developed between a steel slider and a rotating glass disk. Duration was about 2μsec (2×10^{-6} sec) at a load of 350 g and sliding speed of 700 cm/sec (22.9 ft/sec). (*By permission F. P. Bowden in Thomas Hawksley Lecture, 41, 6–7, The Institution of Mechanical Engineers, London, 1954.*)

pend on their size, and small areas may, in that sense, be more heavily weighted.

In metal-cutting tool-workpiece junctions, when the interface pressure is that for plastic mass flow, the contact area may be a substantial fraction of the total area. Here ambiguities in the significance of the indicated temperatures may be less important. This method has been widely used in the metal-working industries. For gear teeth, however, and other frictional members interpretation of measurements will require care.[47–54]

7·7 RADIATION-TECHNIQUE APPLICATIONS— METAL-CUTTING TEMPERATURES

With radiation technique, motion in the source body is not a problem. Design calculations by the methods of Ch. 4 are routine, subject to the chronic difficulty of obtaining actual, as compared to *apparent*, temperatures.

The reflecting-objective optical arrangement used by Hollander [34, 55] to measure metal-cutting temperatures is shown in Figs. 4·2C and 5·11A. Radiation from 0.002- and 0.0004-in.-square source areas was focused on a 0.020-in.-square thermistor-flake bolometer (see Fig. 3·8). Modulation of the incident beam, by a mirrorized chopper disk, interposed alternately reflected flashes from a portable blackbody source (see Fig. 3·1B). The resulting a-c difference signal was then amplified, rectified, and recorded by a penwriter. Over-all sensitivities were to within 0.02°C at 927°C and to within 3°C at 27°C with 13.1-fold image magnification and 0.375-sec response time, and to within 1.7°C at 927°C with 50-fold image magnification and 0.025-sec response time.

The pyrometer, mounted in a fixed relation to the stationary cutting tool (see Fig. 5·3B), imaged a source area on the moving workpiece. The transient-temperature pattern, generated by the cutting action, remained in position about the tool and presented a constant source-area temperature to the stationary pyrometer. Curve-plotting data resulted from measurements at successive positions.[34, 55]

The conical shield, described in Sec. 5·16 and Fig. 5·11A, limited radiation to the "bundle" of rays emanating from the source area, eliminating ambient radiation. In Hollander's [34, 55] work, it was possible further to reduce reflection errors by blackening the workpiece surface.

Calibration was performed on an actual workpiece electrically heated to a uniform temperature, all geometrical and ambient effects remaining the same as during measurements. Indications were thus referred to the workpiece-metal temperatures, all "zero" effects being eliminated. Actual, and not apparent, temperatures were thus determined.[34, 55]

Overlap in successive measurements between the pyrometer determinations and the thermoelectric measurements, described in Sec. 5·2, for the same operating conditions provided a check of the resultant precision.[34, 55]

Mechanical convenience involved using a sector rather than a full-circle workpiece. The radiant signal was intermittent, as that of a passing body. The "on-off" ratio was, however, constant, i.e., that of the respective arcs. Adjusting the amplifier time constant for full response during an "on" interval increased noise passage to such extent that greater precision was obtained by accepting half response and including this constant attenuation factor in the calibration.[34, 55, 56]

7·8 RADIATION-TECHNIQUE APPLICATIONS—BRAKING TEMPERATURES

Parker[57, 58] and Marshall[57, 59] employed a lead sulfide photoconductive radiation-sensitive element to measure local surface heating during braking on railroad tires. To avoid working on a traveling locomotive, they simulated train inertia with twelve flywheels driven by a 100-hp 1000-rpm variable-speed electric motor. The same shaft carried the tired wheel, equipped with two brake blocks. Electronic instrumentation was mounted on a pair of dollies wheeled up alongside.

They did not attempt to make measurements under the brake blocks. However, by sighting their pyrometer on a tire-surface source area close to the point of emergence from under a block (see Fig. 7·9A), the cool-down time was limited to 0.0002 sec. To resolve the mottled tire-surface temperature pattern at 60-mph "train" speed, response to within 10^{-4} sec was required. A Wheatstone-bridge circuit (see Fig. 2·1) was used at fixed settings with the lead sulfide element as r_e and storage-battery power supply. The amplified unbalance output was photographed from the screen of a cathode-ray oscilloscope.[57–59]

By mounting their lensless massive-copper sighting tube very close to the tire, they achieved shielding from ambient sources, and blanketing was minimized by the motion of the tire. The close proximity sufficed also to prevent any hot wear products from being blown across the optical path. Mechanism was also provided for traversing the tire width.[57–59]

Whereas tire-surface emissivities varied with oxidation and wear effects in braking, Parker and Marshall[57, 59] chose to investigate the

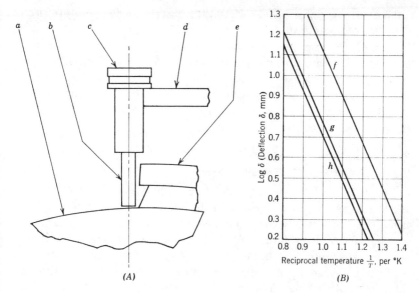

Fig. 7·9. Railway-tire braking temperatures. (A) Pyrometer installation; and (B) relation between cathode-ray-oscilloscope deflection and absolute temperature of radiating tire-surface source. a, Railway-wheel tire periphery; b, massive copper sighting tube; c, lead sulfide photoconductive radiation-sensitive-element pyrometer head; d, steel mounting bracket; e, brake-shoe block; f, blackbody; g, oxidized steel; and, h, bright steel. (By permission R. C. Parker and P. R. Marshall in Inst. Mech. Engrs. London, J. and Proc., **158**, no. 2, 7–9, September, 1948.)

correction independently. Furnace studies on tire specimens indicated emissivities, in the characteristic wavelength band of the sensitive element, ranging from 0.27 to 0.32. The emissivities were for bright and 800°C-oxidized steels, respectively. The variation corresponded to apparent-temperature deviations of 68°C (154.4°F) at 800°C (1472°F) and 13°C (55.4°F) at 200°C (392°F). Over-all blackbody calibration was performed and followed by emissivity analyses. The sensitivity and error range of their system is suggested by the curves plotted in Fig. 7·9B.

Kratz [60] used a lead sulfide element in a similar application to measure the temperature pattern in a 12-ft diameter 300-rpm segmented-copper short-circuiting-bar ring on a 30,000-kw electric generator.

Huggins, Roll, and Udin [61] used a lead sulfide element technique to plot the transient-temperature pattern during electric spot-welding of a 0.002-in. thick steel sheet. Here they observed a temperature rise of 2100°F occurring in 0.1 sec.

Keinath [62] has proposed using the magnetic properties of a moving surface to indicate its own temperature. The poles of an electromagnet, spaced by a small air gap, replace the lead sulfide cell, and the patch of opposing surface becomes the *armature*. Including the *field* coil, i.e., that of the electromagnet, in an a-c Wheatstone-bridge circuit provides for indication.

7·9 RADIATION-TECHNIQUE APPLICATIONS— TURBINE-ROTOR TEMPERATURES

Figure 7·10 illustrates a device designed by the authors for measuring local operating temperatures of the blades on gas turbines. Thickness D can be suited to the gap between blading stages, thus permitting radial traverse from hub to blade tips. Water circulation maintains structural rigidity and is also intended to prevent the sighting-tube wall from becoming a variable ambient radiation source. Properly adjusted, the flushing-air supply is expected to prevent dirtying of the gold-surface mirror and to eliminate absorbing and emitting gases from the optical path. Although design calculations were completed and the device built, tests in operation did not occur. Similar calculations for any design modification, such as one depending on applications of the radiation-sensitive elements described in Ch. 3, can be conducted by using the procedures of Ch. 4.

For the stators, choice could be from among all spots facing axially. On the moving blade circles, an average temperature at the given radius might be accepted. Here, radiation would also be received from the background gases as seen through interblade spaces. These weighted contributions would affect the resultant indication.

However, an element of short time constant τ and sufficiently high responsivity S_t with cathode-ray-oscilloscope indication would permit resolution of the circumferential patterns yielding local-area blade temperatures.

Berg [63] and Head [64] have described similar radiation pyrometers intended for measuring gas-turbine blade temperatures, using Moll and Stack elements, respectively (see Fig. 3·6A and B). These devices cannot, however, reach in between multiple stages to determine radial distributions and to avoid combustion-gas radiation and absorption effects. Because of the relatively slow response attained by the types of radiation-sensitive elements which they used and because galvanometer indication was used, over-all time constants extended into seconds. Thus, only circumferentially averaged temperatures were

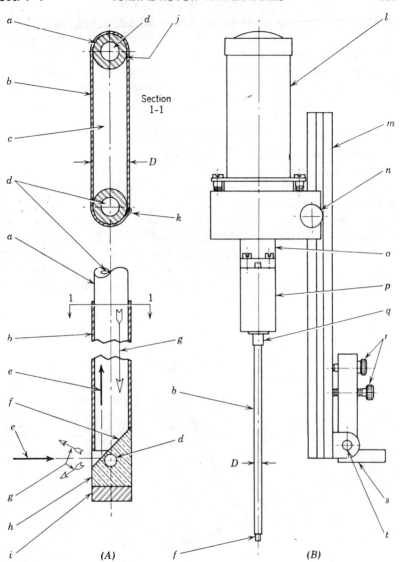

Fig. 7·10. Turbine-blade pyrometer. (A) Detail of tip construction; and (B) assembly with adjustable mount. a, Two 0.188-in. outside diameter 0.093-in. inside diameter stainless-steel tubes; b, 0.01-in. thick Z-nickel housing with folded lock seam; c, tubular radiation space flushed with air; d, cooling-water streams; e, radiant signal ray; f, gold-plate-surface plane mirror; g, flushing-air stream; h, brass mirror block; i, stainless-steel mirror mounting; j, soft-solder seam; k, folded lock seam pressed tight; l, radiation-pyrometer unit; m, base; n, clamping screw; o, support fitting; p, head; q, support; r, adjusting screws; s, mounting bracket; and, t, pivot.

attempted. Flushing air in Berg's device did not entirely exclude corrosive combustion-gas products from his objective-mirror surface. Rhodium coating was found to have the largest and most constant reflection coefficient under these severe conditions. Calibration was effected on a furnace-heated blade-material specimen, whose temperature was measured with a thermocouple.

7·10 RADIATION-TECHNIQUE APPLICATIONS— MOVING-LINE PROCESS CONTROL

When heating is required in successive operations performed on products as they pass along a conveyor line, most successful processing occurs when the proper temperatures can be maintained. Figure 7·11 shows Gorrill's [65] arrangement for measuring the 400 to 700°F seam temperatures during the soldering of tin cans. This measurement occurs as they move past the instrument at rates as high as 6 cans per second. A pyrometer of design similar to Hollander's [34, 55] described in Sec. 7·7 is focused so that the heated seams successively pass

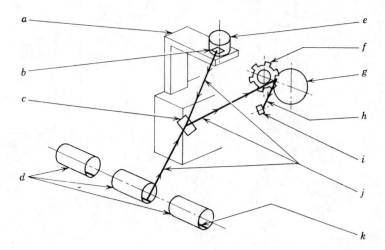

Fig. 7·11. Conveyor-belt solder-seam pyrometer. a, Bracket; b, sample of tin heated for calibration; c, mirror can be rotated 90 degrees to "look" at either the cans below or the calibration heater above; d, line of tin cans moving to the right on conveyor belt; e, calibration heater and thermocouple; f, 15-slot 1200-rpm sectored chopper disk; g, front-surface parabolic mirror; h, 300-cycles/sec pulsating radiation beam; i, thermistor-bolometer radiation-sensitive element; j, thermal-radiation signal rays; and, k, soldered seam whose temperature is indicated on cathode-ray oscilloscope screen. (*By permission W. S. Gorrill in Electronics, 22, no. 3, 112, March, 1949.*)

through the imaged source area. The temperatures thus successively presented are indicated on the screen of a cathode-ray oscilloscope. A skilled operator learns to recognize the portion of the oscilloscope trace representing the can-seam temperature. An arrangement is included in the device for over-all calibration against a specimen of the can surface currently in process. By flipping a mirror, the operator can alter the focus to an electrically heated sample, whose temperature is measured with a thermocouple.[34, 55, 65]

Cox [66] has described similar equipment for indicating the successive temperatures of seamless alloy-steel tubes passing through a 73-ft line of thirteen furnaces. The tubes move at a rate of 150 ft/min.

Package instruments commercially available suffice for many similar tasks.[67-69]

REFERENCES *

1. B. H. Schultz, "Measuring Rapidly Fluctuating Gas Temperatures," *Philips Tech. Rev.*, **13**, no. 4, pp. 104–108 (October, 1951).
2. E. L. Armi, J. L. Johnson, R. C. Machler, and N. E. Polster, "Application of the Sliding Thermocouple Method to the Determination of Temperatures at the Interface of a Moving Bullet and a Gun Barrel," *J. Appl. Phys.*, **18**, no. 1, pp. 88–94 (January, 1947).
3. W. Riezler and L. Hardt, "Temperaturmessung an Schleiffunken" (Temperature Measurement of Grinding Sparks), *Zeitschrift für angewandte Physik*, **6**, no. 11, pp. 497–499 (November, 1954).
4. A. Nägel, "The Transfer of Heat in Reciprocating Engines—III," *Engineering*, **127**, no. 3294, pp. 279–282, 627 (March, 1929).
5. L. A. Wendt and T. B. Rendel, "Some Notes on Piston Temperature and Its Measurement," *Piston Temperature Symposium*, 5 pp., Annual Meeting of Society of Automotive Engineers, Detroit, January, 1939.
6. A. B. Kaufman, "Telemetered Temperatures," *Instruments*, **28**, no. 8, pp. 1320–1322 (August, 1955).
7. C. Harmantas, "Upper-Air Temperatures Obtained by Use of Radiosonde," American Institute of Physics, *Temperature*, pp. 381–388, Reinhold Publishing Corp., New York, 1941.
8. M. A. Zipkin and J. C. Sanders, "Correlation of Exhaust-Valve Temperatures with Engine Operating Conditions and Valve Design," *Wartime Report* E-48, Fig. 3, U. S. National Advisory Committee for Aeronautics, Washington (October, 1945).
9. W. Glaser, "Measurement of Piston Temperatures Under Load," *J. Roy. Aeronaut. Soc.*, **47**, no. 111, p. 288 (February, 1943).
10. J. C. Sanders, H. D. Wilsted, and B. A. Mulcahy, "Operating Temperatures of a Sodium-Cooled Exhaust Valve as Measured by a Thermocouple," *Wartime Report* E-140, 14 pp., U. S. National Advisory Committee for Aeronautics, Washington (December, 1943).

---

* See footnote on page **26**.

11. H. P. Zoeppritz, "Reifentemperaturmessungen" (Tire-Temperature Measurement), *ATM Archiv für technisches Messen,* V2179-1, T22–T23 (March, 1942).

12. F. M. Devienne and B. Crave, "Appareil destiné à la mesure des températures et de la pression d'arrêt sur un corps en mouvement à grande vitesse dans un gaz très raréfié" (Apparatus for Measuring Temperature and Stopping Pressure on a Body Traveling in a Rarified Gas at High Speed), *Le Vide,* **11,** no. 64, pp. 163–171 (July-August, 1956).

13. R. Chaplin, "Multi-Channel Slip Rings for Stress and Temperature Measurement," *ARC Technical Report CP* 389, Memorandum M 289, Aeronautical Research Council—National Gas Turbine Establishment, Her Majesty's Stationery Office, London (1958).

14. P. R. Tarr, "Methods for Connection to Revolving Thermocouples," *Research Memorandum* RME 50J23a, pp. 1–28, U. S. National Advisory Committee for Aeronautics, Washington (January, 1951).

15. F. G. Shoemaker, "Method of Measuring Temperature of Pistons," *Army Air Forces Technical Report* 2825, 17 pp., U. S. War Department, Air Corps Materiel Division, Dayton (June, 1927).

16. A. F. Underwood and A. A. Catlin, "Instrument for the Continuous Measurement of Piston Temperatures," *S.A.E. Trans.,* Society of Automotive Engineers, **48,** no. 1, pp. 20–27 (January, 1941).

17. "Measuring Piston Temperatures," *Mech. Eng.,* **63,** no. 3, pp. 219–220 (March, 1941).

18. W. L. Bride, "Piston Crown Temperatures in a Compression-Ignition Engine with 'Comet' Head," *Inst. Mech. Engrs. London, J. & Proc., Journal,* February, 1944, *Proceedings, 150,* no. 4, p. 135 (1943).

19. B. Pinkel and E. J. Manganiello, "A Method of Measuring Piston Temperatures," *Technical Note* 765, 10 pp., U. S. National Advisory Committee for Aeronautics, Washington (June, 1940).

20. P. V. Keyser and E. F. Miller, "Piston and Piston-Ring Temperatures," *J. Inst. Petrol.,* **25,** no. 194, pp. 779–790 (December, 1939).

21. W. Oesterlin, "Messung und Registrierung von Kolben-Temperaturen am laufenden Motor" (Measurement and Recording of Piston Temperatures in a Running Motor), *Archiv für technisches Messen,* **239,** Ref. V8234-16, pp. 269–272 (December, 1955).

22. H. Shore, "Thermoelectric Measurement of Cutting Tool Temperatures," *J. Wash. Acad. Sci.,* **15,** no. 5, pp. 85–88 (March, 1925).

23. G. Flynn, Jr. and A. F. Underwood, "Adequate Piston Cooling—Oil Cooling as a Means of Piston Temperature Control," *S.A.E. Trans.,* Society of Automotive Engineers, **53,** no. 2, pp. 120–128 (February, 1945).

24. "New Technique for Measuring Piston Temperatures," *Instruments,* **22,** no. 2, p. 170 (February, 1949).

25. A. C. Scholp, G. R. Furman, and P. A. Binda, "An Instrument for Piston Temperature Measurement," *S.A.E. Annual Meeting Paper,* 9 pp., Society of Automotive Engineers, Detroit, January, 1947.

26. B. M. Horton, "Sliding Contacts to Transmit Small Signals," *Rev. Sci. Instr.,* **20,** no. 12, pp. 930–932 (December, 1949).

27. R. E. Gorton and B. E. Miller, "Instrumentation for Aircraft Gas Turbine Development," *S.A.E. Annual Meeting Paper,* 730, pp. 9–11, Society of Automotive Engineers, January, 1952.

28. E. Gnam, "Über ein neues Gerät zur Temperaturmessung an Schnelllaufenden Maschinenteilen" (A New Apparatus for Measuring the Temperatures on Machine Parts Rotating at High Speeds), *Motortechnische Zeitschrift*, **5**, no. 10, pp. 289–291 (October, 1943); also translation, *Technical Memorandum 1080*, pp. 1–6, U. S. National Advisory Committee for Aeronautics, Washington (April, 1945).

29. E. Gnam, "New Device Measures the Temperature of Machine Components Revolving at High Speed," *The Engineers' Digest*, N. Y., **2**, no. 1, pp. 12–14 (January, 1945).

30. A. I. Dahl and P. D. Freeze, "Laboratory Evaluation of a Method Proposed by Gnam for Measuring the Temperature of Rotating Parts," RP 1942, *J. Research Natl. Bur. Standards*, **41**, no. 6, pp. 601–607 (December, 1948).

31. "Turbine Blade Temperature Telemeter," *Natl. Bur. Standards U. S., Tech. News Bull.*, **38**, no. 12, pp. 180–183 (December, 1954).

32. "Turbine-Blade Temperature Telemeter," *Instruments*, **27**, no. 12, Part 1, pp. 1958–1959 (December, 1954).

33. R. T. Corry, *A Method for Detecting Chemiluminescent Radiation in an Internal Combustion Engine, and Test Results for Isooctane*, Doctoral Dissertation, 177 pp., Columbia University, New York, 1957.

34. M. Hollander, *An Experimental Measurement of the Temperature Distribution in the Workpiece during Metal-Cutting*, Doctoral Dissertation, 243 pp., Columbia University, New York, 1959.

35. D. Bendersky, "A Special Thermocouple for Measuring Transient Temperatures," *Paper 52-A-57*, 6 pp., American Society of Mechanical Engineers, New York (1952); *Mech. Eng.*, **75**, no. 2, pp. 117–121 (February, 1953); **75**, no. 7, pp. 587–588 (July, 1953).

36. P. Hackeman, *A Method of Measuring Rapidly Changing Surface Temperatures and Its Application in the Barrels of Firearms*, Hermann Göring Air Research Institute, Braunschweig, Germany (1941); Theoretical Research Translation, Armament Research Department, Office of Technical Services, Washington (1/46); British Technical Information Bureau Translation GDC 10/123 OT (January, 1941).

37. J. M. Chenoweth, J. E. Brock, C. R. St. Clair, and G. A. Hawkins, "Rapidly Fluctuating Temperatures," *Instruments*, **26**, no. 11, pp. 1714–1715, 1738 (November, 1953).

38. B. T. Willman, J. E. Brock, W. L. Sibbitt, and G. A. Hawkins, "Measurement of Gun Barrel Temperatures," *Instruments*, **28**, no. 1, pp. 106–108 (January, 1955).

39. W. H. Giedt, "The Determination of Transient Temperatures and Heat Transfer at a Gas-Metal Interface Applied to a 40-mm Gun Barrel," *Paper 177-54*, pp. 1–13, American Rocket Society, New York (1954).

40. J. W. Teker and F. H. Catlin, "Determining the Temperatures of Traction Motors," *Gen. Elec. Rev.*, **51**, no. 10, pp. 27–29 (October, 1948).

41. G. Keinath, "Temperatur-Messung an Transformatoren" (Temperature Measurement in Transformers), *ATM Archiv für technisches Messen*, V2177-1, T36–T37 (1931).

42. C. P. Potter, "Measurement of Temperature in General-Purpose Squirrel-Cage Induction Motors," *Trans. AIEE*, **58**, pp. 468–472 (September, 1939), American Institute of Electrical Engineers, New York.

43. H. M. Beede and B. M. Cain, "Accuracy of Temperature Measurements on Coil Surfaces," *Technical Paper* 47-94, pp. 1-6, American Institute of Electrical Engineers (December, 1946).

44. L. H. Hirsch, L. W. Wightman, R. F. Munier, M. L. Schmidt, F. S. Himebrook, T. C. Lloyd, C. P. Potter, and O. G. Coffman, "Investigation of Hot-Spot Temperatures in Fractional-Horsepower Motors," *Electrical Engineering,* Transactions Section, **64,** pp. 128-136 (March, 1945).

45. R. Modlinger, "Temperaturmessungen an elektrischen Maschinen" (Temperature Measurements on Electrical Machines), *Elektrotechnik Berlin,* **3,** no. 3, pp. 73-78 (March, 1949).

46. W. A. Thomas and R. J. Horvat, "Measurement of Induction-Motor Rotor Temperatures," *Instruments,* **24,** no. 4, pp. 410, 412, and 414 (April, 1954).

47. F. P. Bowden and P. H. Thomas, "The Surface Temperature of Sliding Solids," *Proc. Roy. Soc. London A,* **223,** no. 1152, pp. 29-40 (April, 1954).

48. F. P. Bowden, "Recent Studies of Metallic Friction," The Institution of Mechanical Engineers, *Thomas Hawksley Lecture,* **41,** pp. 3-12, The Institution of Mechanical Engineers, London (1954).

49. M. C. Shaw, J. D. Pigott, and L. P. Richardson, "The Effect of Cutting Fluid upon Chip-Tool Interface Temperature," *Paper* 50-SA-19, American Society of Mechanical Engineers, New York (1950); *Trans. ASME,* **73,** pp. 45-56 (January, 1951).

50. E. W. Gaylord, W. F. Hughes, F. C. Appl, and F. F. Ling, "On the Theoretical Analysis of a Dynamic Thermocouple," *Paper* 56-A-86, 4 pp., American Society of Mechanical Engineers, New York (1956).

51. H. Blok, "Measurement of Temperature Flashes on Gear Teeth under Extreme Pressure Conditions," Institution of Mechanical Engineers, *Proceedings of the General Discussion on Lubrication,* Vol. 2, pp. 14-20 (October, 1937), Institution of Mechanical Engineers, London.

52. F. P. Bowden and K. E. W. Ridler, "Physical Properties of Surfaces. III— The Surface Temperature of Sliding Metals. The Temperature of Lubricated Surfaces," *Proc. Roy. Soc. London A,* **154,** pp. 640-656 (May, 1936).

53. K. J. Trigger, R. K. Campbell, and B. T. Chao, "A Tool-Work-Thermocouple Compensating Circuit," *Paper* 56-A-90, pp. 1-5, American Society of Mechanical Engineers, New York (1956).

54. B. A. Crowder, "A Method for Measuring Tool Tip Temperature," *Technical Paper* 55, 18 pp., Engineering Experiment Station, University of Minnesota, Minneapolis (June, 1946).

55. M. B. Hollander, "An Infrared-Microradiation-Pyrometer-Technique Investigation of the Temperature Distribution in the Workpiece during Metal Cutting," *Research Report* 21, 39 pp., American Society of Tool Engineers, Detroit (February, 1959).

56. F. Schwerd, "Über die Bestimmung des Temperaturfeldes beim Spanablaut" (On the Determination of Temperature Fields during Chip Removal), *VDI Zeitschrift des Vereines deutscher Ingenieure,* **77,** no. 9, pp. 211-216 (1933).

57. R. C. Parker and P. R. Marshall, "The Measurement of the Temperature of Sliding Surfaces, with Particular Reference to Railway Brake Blocks," *Inst. Mech. Engrs. London, J. and Proc.,* **158,** no. 2, pp. 209-229 (September, 1948).

58. E. Lee and R. C. Parker, "Use of Lead Sulphide Photo-Conductive Cells for High-Speed Pyrometry," *Nature,* **158,** no. 4015, p. 518 (October, 1946).

59. P. R. Marshall and D. K. Mackenzie, "A Portable Radiation Pyrometer," *J. Sci. Instr.*, **27**, no. 2, pp. 33–36 (February, 1950).

60. J. H. Kratz, "A Radiation Pyrometer," *J. Franklin Inst.*, **259**, no. 4, pp. 362–364 (April, 1955).

61. R. A. Huggins, I. B. Roll, and H. Udin, "Measurement of Transient Surface Temperatures," *Rev. Sci. Instr.*, **23**, no. 9, pp. 467–470 (September, 1952).

62. G. Keinath, "Induktive Temperaturmessung" (Temperature Measurement by Induction), *ATM Archiv für technisches Messen*, V215-2, T1 (January, 1934).

63. H. H. Berg, "Verfahren zur Läufertemperaturmessung von Gasturbinen" (Methods for Measuring Operating Temperatures in Gas Turbines), *VDI Zeitschrift des Vereines deutscher Ingenieure*, **84**, no. 19, pp. 329–330 (May, 1940).

64. V. P. Head, "Radiation Pyrometry in Turbosupercharger Testing," *Trans. ASME*, **66**, pp. 265–269 (May, 1944), American Society of Mechanical Engineers, New York.

65. W. S. Gorrill, "Industrial High-Speed Infrared Pyrometer," *Electronics*, **22**, no. 3, pp. 112–114 (March, 1949).

66. H. W. Cox, "High-Speed Reheating of Seamless Steel Tubes," *Instrumentation*, **4**, no. 3, pp. 3–6 (Fourth Quarter, 1949).

67. "Instantaneous Temperature Measurement of Fast-Moving Objects," *Instrumentation*, **3**, no. 3, pp. 25–26 (Second Quarter, 1948).

68. J. R. Leslie and J. R. Wait, "Detection of Overhead Transmission Line Joints by Means of a Bolometer," *Trans. AIEE;* **68**, pp. 969–973 (November, 1949), American Institute of Electrical Engineers, New York.

69. L. E. Hildebrand, B. M. Cain, F. D. Phillips, W. R. Hough, J. G. Rosswog, and C. P. Potter, "Investigation of Hot-Spot Temperatures in Integral Horsepower Motors," *Technical Paper* 45-33, pp. 1–10, American Institute of Electrical Engineers (December, 1944).

8

TRANSPARENT BODIES

8·1 INTRODUCTION

Transparent bodies may be in the solid, liquid, or gaseous states. Thus, the various glasses are regarded as transparent solids; water, gasoline, alcohol, etc., as transparent liquids; and air, ammonia, hydrogen, etc., as transparent gases. Transparent substances on changing phase often remain transparent. Thus, molten glass, liquid air, ice, and water vapor are also transparent substances. Transparency in matter is associated with electrical conductivity. Thus, electrical insulators are often transparent, whereas metals are never so.

Transparency is a property whereby heat energy can radiate through the body whose temperature it is desired to measure. This process affects means for measuring temperature at a point in the body. Difficulties arise whether the attempt be by thermal-contact thermometry or by radiation pyrometry. Thus, a temperature-sensitive element immersed in the body is not merely affected by the temperature of those portions of the body with which it is in direct contact. It also receives heat by radiation from more distant parts of the body and perhaps also from the ambient. It is thus affected by the temperatures of the other regions. Similarly, a radiation-sensitive element whose associated optical system is focused on the surface of a transparent body is not affected merely by the temperature of the source-body surface area. Nor is the reflection of ambient radiation from this surface the only difficulty. Radiation from various depths in the interior of the source body pass out through this area to the radiation-sensitive element. The pyrometer response is thus influenced by the temperatures at the depths in the source body as well as those of the ambient.

We see that with both radiation and thermal-contact methods the indication corresponds to the temperatures of various portions of matter external to the spot to which the technique is presumably applied.

8·2 ABSORPTION, TRANSMISSION, AND OPACITY

What we call *transparency* is a relative concept. No material is completely transparent. Absorption, however, depends on the depth of the absorbing layer and varies in amount for different wavelength ranges. Ordinary glass absorbs very little radiation in the range of wavelengths to which the human eye responds. It is, however, quite opaque in the ultraviolet and to infrared radiation of wavelengths greater than around 3 μ. On the other hand, very thin films, i.e., of the order of 0.01 μ (4×10^{-7} in.), of metals are semitransparent.[1]

Referring to Fig. 8·1, let $J_\lambda \Delta\lambda$ be the radiant power per unit solid angle, w/steradian, in the wavelength range λ to $\lambda + \Delta\lambda$, μ, converging on the receiving surface. Then, the portion of this radiant energy absorbed in passing through a layer of thickness Δx, cm, is given by

$$\Delta J_\lambda = \alpha_\lambda J_\lambda \, \Delta x \qquad (8\cdot1)$$

where α_λ is the absorption coefficient, cm^{-1}, in the wavelength range λ to $\lambda + \Delta\lambda$, μ.

Let $J_{o,\lambda} \Delta\lambda$ be the radiant power, w, per unit time per unit solid angle in the wavelength range λ to $\lambda + \Delta\lambda$ converging from an emitting surface upon the receiver through a depth D of uniformly absorbing material. Then the integration of Eq. 8·1 yields the Bouguer-Lambert law of absorption

$$J_{i,\lambda} = J_{o,\lambda} e^{-\alpha_\lambda D} \qquad (8\cdot2)$$

where $J_{i,\lambda}$ is the radiant power, w, per unit solid angle incident upon the receiving surface. The absorption coefficient α_λ, cm^{-1}, is the average for the wavelength range λ to $\lambda + \Delta\lambda$, μ; and D is the absorbing depth, cm. The receiving surface may be that of a thermometer element, or it may be the objective lens or mirror of an optical system (see Fig. 4·2). Similarly, the emitting surface may be that of an ambient solid, or it may be an interior surface in the transparent source body.

Equation 8·2 is integrated as

$$\int_{\lambda_1}^{\lambda_2} J_{i,\lambda} \, d\lambda = \int_{\lambda}^{\lambda_2} J_{o,\lambda} e^{-\alpha_\lambda D} \, d\lambda \qquad (8\cdot3)$$

In general, both $J_{o,\lambda}$ and $e^{-\alpha_\lambda D}$ will depend on the wavelength λ. Thus, $J_{o,\lambda}$ may be given by Planck's law (Eq. 4·2) multiplied by a wavelength-dependent emissivity factor, or it may be the result of selective absorption in previous layers of material. The absorption coefficient α_λ affecting $e^{-\alpha_\lambda D}$ may be very large in certain absorption wavelength bands and small elsewhere. If the two functions $J_{o,\lambda}$ and $e^{-\alpha_\lambda D}$ are plotted as curves on coordinate paper, convenient graphical methods, described by Czerny [2] and by Tea,[3] can be employed for evaluating the integral expressed in Eq. 8·3.[2,3]

Opacity occurs when the radiant beam is entirely absorbed in the given depth. Thus, for opacity in the wavelength range λ to $\lambda + \Delta\lambda$,

$$J_{i,\lambda}/J_{o,\lambda} = 0 \tag{8.4}$$

This implies, according to Eq. 8·2, that $e^{-\alpha_\lambda D}$ is zero or that $\alpha_\lambda D$ becomes infinite. Thus, no finite thickness D of any material is ever entirely opaque. However, even in very thin layers, the transmission may be exceedingly small if the absorption coefficient α_λ is large. Thus, for a layer of the metal bismuth to transmit less than one ten thousandth of the incident radiation, the thickness needs to be only ten millionths of an inch.

If $\alpha_\lambda D = 1$ or $\alpha_\lambda = 1/D$, the ratio $J_{i,\lambda}/J_{o,\lambda} = 1/e = 0.368$ where e is the base for natural logarithms. For the transmission to be reduced to 10 per cent, i.e., $J_{i,\lambda}/J_{o,\lambda} = 0.1$, it is necessary that $\alpha_\lambda D = 2.3$. Similarly, for transmissions of 1, 0.1, 0.01, and 0.001 per cent, respectively, the required values of $\alpha_\lambda D$ are 4.61, 6.91, 9.21, and 11.51. Thus, if the absorption coefficient α_λ in a given wavelength range is appreciable, the degree of opacity increases rapidly with depth in the layer D. On the other hand, if α_λ is small, a very great depth D will be required for appreciable absorption. For example, air is quite transparent in great depths.

8·3 KIRCHHOFF'S LAW

An opaque body tends to radiate in accord with Planck's law (see Fig. 4·1) or

$$W_\lambda = c_1/\lambda^5(e^{c_2/\lambda T} - 1) \tag{4·2}$$

where $W_\lambda \Delta\lambda$ is the total hemispherical emission or *radiancy* in the wavelength range λ to $\lambda + \Delta\lambda$, ergs/cm² sec: λ is the wavelength, cm; T is the uniform absolute temperature, °K; $c_1 = 3.740 \times 10^{-5}$ erg cm²/sec; and $c_2 = 1.438$ cm °K.

The resulting radiant power $J_{o,\lambda} \Delta\lambda$ per unit solid angle or *steradiancy*, w, in the wavelength range λ to $\lambda + \Delta\lambda$, is given by

$$J_{o,\lambda} \Delta\lambda = 10^{-7}(A/\pi)W_\lambda \Delta\lambda \tag{8·5}$$

where A is the projection of the radiating source area, cm², normal to the beam (see Figs. 4·2 and 8·1, and W_λ is taken from Eq. 4·2, ergs/cm² sec).

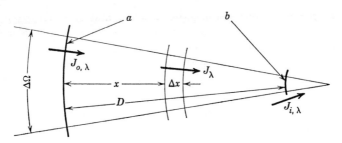

Fig. 8·1. A radiant beam. a, Emitting surface; and, b, receiving surface. D is the depth of absorbing material.

If this radiation is to emanate from a partially reflecting surface, the amount is reduced by an emissivity factor ϵ. The emissivity factor ϵ is proportional to the *absorptance* a for the surface. These quantities are related to the reflection coefficient ρ by the equation

$$\epsilon = a = 1 - \rho \qquad (8 \cdot 6)$$

or

$$\epsilon_\lambda = a_\lambda = 1 - \rho_\lambda \qquad (8 \cdot 7)$$

in the wavelength range λ to $\lambda + \Delta\lambda$.

If the body is not opaque, the radiation is also less than that given by Planck's law. It is then reduced by an *absorption*, i.e., transmission, *factor* which is given by

$$F_a = 1 - J_i/J_o = 1 - e^{-aD} \qquad (8 \cdot 8)$$

or

$$F_{a,\lambda} = 1 - J_{i,\lambda}/J_{o,\lambda} = 1 - e^{-\alpha_\lambda D} \qquad (8 \cdot 9)$$

where F_a is the absorption factor; $F_{a,\lambda}$ is the absorption factor in the wavelength range λ to $\lambda + \Delta\lambda$, μ; J_i/J_o is the ratio in which the radiant power per unit solid angle is reduced in traversing the thickness D of the body, whose absorption coefficient is α, cm^{-1}; and $J_{i,\lambda}/J_{o,\lambda}$ is this ratio for the wavelength range λ to $\lambda + \Delta\lambda$, where α_λ is the absorption coefficient, cm^{-1}, in this wavelength range, μ (see Fig. 8·1).

The absorption coefficient α_λ may be large at some wavelengths and small in other parts of the spectrum. Thus, a body or a depth of body material may be opaque and thereby radiate according to Eqs. 4·2 and 8·5 in certain wavelength ranges, although it radiates very little elsewhere.

In the preceding paragraphs, absorption in and radiation from semi-transparent bodies have been discussed separately. Thus, absorption has been treated as occurring for radiation passing through a nonradiating body. Similarly, Planck's law applies to a body of the same uniform temperature throughout its depth and describes the radiation emitted by that body exclusive of any radiation from other sources.

In temperature-measurement problems for semitransparent bodies, the two processes of absorption and emission must usually be thought of as occurring together. Thus, for a uniform-temperature absorbing material, the converging radiant beam J_λ is decreased by a fraction $\alpha_\lambda \Delta x$ in each element Δx of traverse, cm. This loss tends, however, to be compensated by an increment in radiant power emitted by the layer Δx. Thereby, for an opaque depth, the beam J_λ converges to a constant quantity which is the amount given by Planck's law for a uniform body temperature. Thus, if radiation from another body at a different temperature enters such an opaque depth, it is progressively eliminated by absorption and replaced by radiation corresponding to the traversed-body temperature. Then, after traversing an opaque depth, it is reduced or augmented to the amount specified by Planck's law (Eqs. $4 \cdot 2$ and $8 \cdot 5$).

Let us suppose now that the depth D in Fig. $8 \cdot 2A$ is not sufficient for opacity and that the radiant beam $J_{o,\lambda}$ emanates from a body at the temperature T_o, which is different from T. Here, the radiation

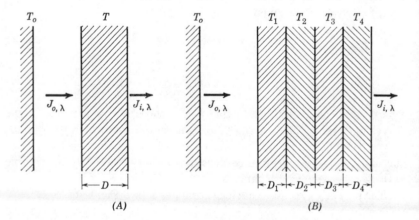

Fig. $8 \cdot 2$. Radiation in semitransparent media. (A) One layer at a uniform temperature T differing from that of the source body T_o; and (B) four successive layers at differing temperatures T_1, T_2, T_3, and T_4.

$J_{o,\lambda}$ is not entirely replaced by that for the temperature T. If T_o is greater than T, then $J_{i,\lambda}$ will be greater than the amount given by Planck's law for the temperature T. Similarly, if T_o is less than T, then $J_{i,\lambda}$ will be less than this amount. Thus, the comparison between $J_{o,\lambda}$ and $J_{i,\lambda}$ directly reveals which body is at the higher temperature and when the two bodies are at the same temperature. If the temperature of one of the two bodies is known or can be independently determined, this comparison becomes the basis of the Kurlbaum or Féry line-reversal method for measuring the temperature of the other. Thus, T_o may be the temperature of a standard blackbody source (see Fig. 3·1), whereas T is that of a stream of hot gases. Similarly, T may be the temperature of a slab of semitransparent solid material such as glass.

If the temperature differs in each of two or more semitransparent layers (see Fig. 8·2B), the emergent beam $J_{i,\lambda}$ will not correspond to Planck's law for any of the temperatures. Rather, the radiant power will be influenced in amount by all of the temperatures T_1, T_2, T_3, T_4, etc. However, it will not correspond to their arithmetic mean.

Suppose that in the wavelength range λ_1 to $\lambda_1 + \Delta\lambda$ the nearest layer is of absorbing depth $\alpha_{\lambda_1} D_4 = 4.61$ sufficing for 99 per cent absorption. The emergent beam J_{i,λ_1} would then closely approximate the radiation given by Planck's law for the temperature T_4. On the other hand, suppose that in the wavelength range λ_2 to $\lambda_2 + \Delta\lambda$ the nearer layers are nearly transparent such that each transmits 99 per cent. For this condition, their absorbing depths $\alpha_{\lambda_2} D_2$, $\alpha_{\lambda_2} D_3$, $\alpha_{\lambda_2} D_4$ would each be less than 0.01. Then, if the most distant layer is of absorbing depth $\alpha_{\lambda_2} D_1 = 4.61$ sufficing for 99 per cent absorption, the emergent beam J_{i,λ_2} will correspond to that given by Planck's law for a temperature nearly equal to T_1. Suppose that the radiant power per unit solid angle $J_{i\lambda}$ is taken as a criterion of temperature. Then, for this example in the wavelength range λ_1 to $\lambda_1 + \Delta\lambda$, the temperature indicated will approximate that of layer D_4; whereas, in the wavelength range λ_2 to $\lambda_2 + \Delta\lambda$, the temperature will be nearly that of D_1.

Suppose a body to be one of homogeneous composition such that α_λ is nearly the same at all depths. Then in a given wavelength range λ to $\lambda + \Delta\lambda$, an absorbing-depth magnitude $\alpha_\lambda D$ will depend entirely on the thickness D. If α_λ is large, D can be small for near opaqueness, i.e., for $\alpha_\lambda D = 4.61$. Thereby, the temperature deduced from $J_{i,\lambda}$ will be that of a surface layer. However, if α_λ is small, D must be large; and therefore, the indicated temperature will be that at a correspondingly great depth in the body.

8·4 RADIATION METHODS

The Kurlbaum or Féry line-reversal method mentioned in Sec. 8·3 has had its most extensive applications in flame-temperature studies. It thus seems appropriate to defer further discussion until the treatment of the methods used in those studies (see Secs. 13·22 to 13·24).

Successful techniques have also been based on variations of the absorption coefficients α_λ with wavelength. Thus, in certain wavelength ranges, depths of the material may be transparent, while the particular layer whose temperature it is desired to measure may be both opaque and black. Such a layer can be dealt with in this wavelength range as though the other material were absent. The methods of Chs. 3 and 4 then apply. However, it may be necessary to take account of absorption in the intervening material in calibration and in computing the transfer factor F_t or F_i (see Eqs. 4·25 to 4·28).

The achievements of Hübner [4] and Bayle [5] in their precision radiation measurements of electric-light bulb and cloud temperatures, respectively, are illustrations of what can be done by employing this technique (see Sec. 5·15).

8·5 BODY ITS OWN THERMOMETER—SOLIDS

When a transparent body can be so disposed that temperature variations in its own properties serve as means for the indication of its temperature, transparency is not a problem. Thus, the electric resistance of a body or the local value of its resistivity at a point may be the property used. Similarly, the thermal expansion along some linear dimension in a solid or the volume expansion of a fluid may be used to determine its temperature.

The variation in the distance between marked points on a rigid surface can be precisely measured by means of a *microscope* or *micrometer comparator*. Similarly, mechanical-multiplier *extensometers* and *magnetic* or *electric-resistance strain gages*, such as those used to indicate elastic strains in *experimental stress analysis*, can be used to determine thermal expansion. The temperature is then given by

$$t - t_o = (D - D_o)/\beta_D D_o \qquad (8·10)$$

where $t - t_o$ is the temperature change, °F; $D - D_o$ is the thermal expansion, in.; D_o is the original or *gage length* between marked points, in.; and β_D is the linear coefficient of thermal expansion, per °F.

If suitable precautions can be included to correct for thermal variations in the refraction of light rays, microscope determinations need not be limited to surface lengths. Thus, interior markers may be viewed through transparent layers of the body. Thereby, internal temperatures of transparent solids may also be indicated.

When temperatures are nonuniform, *temperature stresses* tend to arise. The corresponding *elastic deformations* or *strains* may then partly counteract the thermal expansions. The strain gage indicates the resultant change in the gage length L_o which is the algebraic sum of the thermal expansion and elastic strain. It is not then evident to what extent the expansion may be due to local temperature change. The portion of the expansion due to elastic strain represents the effect of the temperatures in other parts of the body. The indication intended as that of local temperature is thus affected by the average.

8·6 BODY ITS OWN THERMOMETER—LIQUIDS

By disposing the liquid overflow in a graduated capillary such as that provided in the stem of a liquid-in-glass thermometer, exact measure of volume changes can be made. Various other precise means are available for measuring small changes in liquid volumes. For example, an electrically conducting mercury surface in a liquid column can be dial-indicated by use of make-and-break electric contact points touching the liquid surface. A self-balancing servomechanism, operated by the amplified contact current, maintains the contact point at about the liquid level and also drives the indicating or recording mechanism. Float balls with mechanical-multiplier linkages and *optical levers* can also be precise indicators of surface levels. Thus, a pencil of light reflected from a mirrorized link can serve as a sensitive arm and also operate a galvanometer-amplifier photoelectric relay with effects similar to those with make-and-break contact points.

In general, the containing vessel will undergo temperature changes and corresponding expansions whereby the overflow becomes a differential effect. The vessel may be of low thermal diffusivity such that its temperature changes are small, or it may assume a temperature near to that of the contained liquid. The vessel temperature is independently measured using the methods described in Volume I.

The average temperature in the liquid is then given by

$$t = t_o + \Delta V/\beta_V V_o + 3 \Delta t_D \beta_D/\beta_V \qquad (8·11)$$

where t is the average temperature of the liquid body, °F; t_o is its initial temperature, °F, at its initial volume V_o, in.³; ΔV is the overflow, i.e., differential volume expansion, in.³; β_V is the volume coefficient of thermal expansion for the liquid, per °F; β_D is the average linear coefficient of thermal expansion for the vessel wall, per °F; and Δt_D is the average rise in vessel-wall temperature, °F.

Corrections must be applied for any elastic deformations in the vessel because of pressure changes with rise of liquid in a capillary indicator. Calibration can be performed by substituting a liquid of known coefficient of thermal expansion whose temperature can be independently determined.

8·7 BODY ITS OWN THERMOMETER—GASES

When the body is gaseous, it is usually more convenient to measure the change in pressure than in volume. If gas is confined in a rigid container at constant volume, Bourdon gages or electric *transducers* can be used. Commercial devices are available in a wide assortment adapted to this purpose. They include those of short response times τ, with output signals suited to electronic amplification. Indication of rapidly changing temperatures is thus feasible. The temperature is given by the *equation of state* for the gas as

$$T = pV/CmR = p/\rho CR \qquad (8·12)$$

where T is the average temperature, °K; p is the absolute pressure, dynes/cm²; V is the volume, cm³; m is the mass of the gaseous body, g; ρ is the average density, g/cm³; C is the *compressibility factor*, dimensionless; and R is the gas constant per unit mass, ergs/g °C.[6,7]

The compressibility factor C is unity for ideal gases. For many actual gases, the deviations from unity do not exceed 1 per cent and are often less than 0.1 per cent. This occurs when the temperatures are well above the *critical temperature* and the pressures are well below the *critical* pressure for the substance. In general, these conditions are satisfied when the gas is far from its point of condensation into the liquid state. For example, room air or the products of combustion of a flame are usually far from their condensation points (except for the water-vapor contents). Steam or ammonia are, however, likely to be near to their condensation points. Curves are given by Lyderson, Greenkorn, and Hougen [7] for the compressibility factor C in terms of the critical properties of the gas. Critical properties for most known substances are listed in published tables.[6,7]

The gas constant R can be computed from

$$R = R_m/M \qquad (8·13)$$

where R_m is the gas constant for one mole of the substance, 8.3136 × 10⁷ ergs/gram molecule °K; and M is the molecular weight. Values of M for particular gases are readily available in published tables. The average values of M for gaseous mixtures are given by Eqs. 6·20 and 6·21.

8·8   THERMAL-CONTACT METHODS—SHIELDING

Measurement of temperature in transparent bodies by direct contact often requires shielding.   Thus, a temperature-sensitive element intended to assume the local body temperature by conductive or convective heat transfer may be shielded from radiant heat exchange with more distant portions of the body and with the ambient.

Figure 8·3 indicates the *heat balance* for an element of length Δx in a uniform-temperature transparent body where shielding is interposed.   Thus,

$$U_{c,e}(t' - t) - U_{r,e}(t - t_1) = -q_e = q_a - q_b = 0 \qquad (8·14)$$

The measurement error is then

$$t' - t = (t - t_1)U_{r,e}/U_{c,e} \qquad (8·15)$$

Similarly, at the shields,

$$2U_{c,1}(t' - t_1) + U_{r,1}(t - t_1) = U_{r,1}(t_1 - t_2) \qquad (8·16)$$

$$2U_{c,2}(t' - t_2) + U_{r,2}(t_1 - t_2) = U_{r,2}(t_2 - t_3) \qquad (8·17)$$

$$\cdot \ \cdot \ \cdot \ \cdot \ \cdot \ \cdot \ \cdot \ \cdot \ \cdot \ \cdot \ \cdot \ \cdot \ \cdot \ \cdot \ \cdot \ \cdot \ \cdot$$

$$2U_{c,n}(t' - t_n) + U_{r,n}(t_{n-1} - t_n) = U_{r,n}(t_n - t_a) \qquad (8·18)$$

where t is the temperature of the immersed length Δx of the temperature-sensitive element or its leads, °F; t' is the uniform temperature of the transparent fluid body, °F; t_1, t_2, $\cdots$, and t_n are the temperatures of the successive shields, respectively, °F; $U_{c,e}$, $U_{c,1}$, $U_{c,2}$ $\cdots$, and $U_{c,n}$ are the thermal-contact boundary conductances along the length Δx referred to the exposed surfaces of the element, the first shield, the second shield, $\cdots$, and the nth shield, respectively, Btu/hr ft² °F; $U_{r,e}$, $U_{r,1}$, $U_{r,2}$, $\cdots$, and $U_{r,n}$ are the radiation boundary conductances along the length Δx referred to the exposed surfaces of the element, the first shield, the second shield, $\cdots$, and the nth shield, respectively, Btu/hr ft² °F; and t_a is the effective mean temperature of the ambient, °F.[8,9]

Absence of longitudinal conduction and end radiation is assumed in this simplified discussion.   Also, radiation and fluid boundary conductances $U_{c,n}$ and $U_{r,n}$ are taken as the same on both sides of a given shield.   A more complete analysis is to be provided in Secs. 10·15 to 10·18.

Such a shielding arrangement is of value only when the body is a fluid that can be caused to circulate through the spaces between

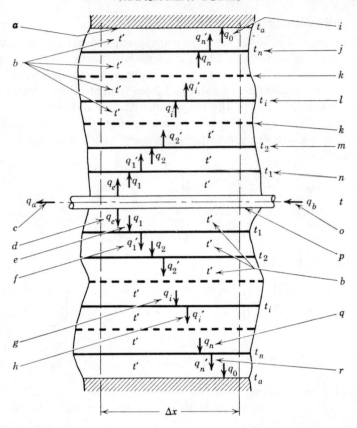

Fig. 8·3. Heat-balance diagram for an element of length Δx, ft, of a multiple-shielded element. a, Ambient solid surface at temperature t_a, °F; b, transparent medium at uniform temperature t', °F; c, axial heat flow in thermometer tube, Btu/hr; d, radial heat flow from thermometer tube, Btu/hr; e, radial heat flow into first shield, Btu/hr; f, radial heat flow leaving first shield, Btu/hr; g, radial heat flow into ith shield, Btu/hr; h, radial heat flow leaving ith shield, Btu/hr; i, radial heat flow to ambient, Btu/hr; j, nth shield at uniform temperature t_n, °F; k, intermediate shields; l, ith shield at temperature t_i, °F; m, 2nd shield at temperature t_2, °F; n, 1st shield at temperature t_1, °F; o, axial heat flow in thermometer tube, Btu/hr; p, thermometer tube at temperature t, °F; q, heat flow into nth shield, Btu/hr; and, r, heat flow leaving nth shield, Btu/hr.

shields. The flow of fresh material tends to counteract the effect of the shield temperatures on the local source-body temperature t'. If the transparent body were a solid, such flow could not occur, and the local material would be reduced by conduction to the shield temperatures. It would then receive radiant energy absorbed by the shields.

Thus, it would rarely if ever be worthwhile to attempt shielding in solid transparent bodies.

The conductances $U_{c,e}$, $U_{c,1}$, $U_{c,2}$, etc., will be the fluid-boundary conductances for the prevailing flow configurations. Formulas and charts in the textbooks on heat transfer permit their estimation. If the transparent-body material departs sufficiently from ideal transparency to radiate significant amounts in the thin layers between shields, the conductances $U_{c,e}$, $U_{c,1}$, $U_{c,2}$, etc., may be increased to allow for these effects. Charts and formulas for this purpose are available in the handbooks and heat-transfer textbooks. The radiative effects can also be computed from Eqs. 4·2, 8·5, and 8·9 if data are available for the absorption coefficients α_λ. The depth D in each case is then the distance between shields.[8, 9]

If the transparent-body temperature is nonuniform, the location error may approximate the corresponding linear dimension of the shield system.

The shields are usually cylindrical and pumping provides longitudinal flow to maintain the intershield fluid temperature t'. The flow rate also tends to increase the fluid boundary conductances $U_{c,e}$, $U_{c,1}$, $U_{c,2}$, and $U_{c,n}$ and thereby to lower the ratio $U_{r,e}/U_{c,e}$. In Eq. 8·15, the temperature-measurement error $t' - t$ is proportional to this ratio of the radiation to thermal-contact boundary conductances. Large flow rates thus provide means to minimize this error. Detailed discussion of this method is, however, deferred to Secs. 10·15 to 10·18.[8, 9]

8·9   UNSHIELDED THERMAL-CONTACT ELEMENTS

When shielding combined with pumping is not feasible, as in the case of solid transparent bodies, another principle must be employed, namely, that of suppressing radiant transfer to the temperature-sensitive element in comparison with thermal-contact heat transfer, by making the diameter of the element sufficiently small.

A temperature-sensitive element, exposed through transparent media to radiant heat exchange with opaque ambient bodies, will almost inevitably be much smaller in diameter than the distance to the bodies. For this case, the ambient assumes blackbody behavior, and the radiation-boundary conductance assumes the maximum value given by

$$U_{r,e} = \epsilon\sigma(T_a^3 + T_a^2 T_e + T_a T_e^2 + T_e^3) \qquad (8·19)$$

where $U_{r,e}$ is the radiation boundary conductance referred to the element surface, Btu/hr ft² °F; ϵ is the emissivity of the element surface; σ is the Stefan-Boltzmann constant, 0.172×10^{-8} Btu/hr ft²

$°R^4$; T_a is the effective-mean-absolute ambient temperature, $°R$; and T_e is the absolute temperature of the element, $°R$. This computation for $U_{r,e}$ neglects the effect of the element diameter and gives the maximum value of conductance that is nearly attained by very small diameters.[8, 9]

For radiant exchange with absorbing layers in a surrounding semi-transparent body, Eqs. $4\cdot2$, $8\cdot5$, $8\cdot8$, and $8\cdot9$ apply. Here also, the exchange per unit area of element surface is not dependent on the element diameter.[8, 9]

For immersion in solid media, the thermal-contact boundary conductance is given by

$$U_{c,e} = 3k/[d \sinh^{-1}(2L/d)] \qquad (6\cdot13)$$

where $U_{c,e}$ is the thermal-contact boundary conductance at the element surface, Btu/hr ft^2 $°F$; k is the thermal conductivity of the body material, Btu/hr ft $°F$; L/d is the length–diameter ratio of the immersion; and d is the element diameter, ft.

As d becomes small, the factor $\sinh^{-1}(2L/d)$ increases slowly. Thus, for $2L/d = 74$, $\sinh^{-1}(2L/d)$ has barely reached the value 5. Hence for smaller diameters d, the main effect arises from the factor d in the denominator. Thereby, if the element diameter d is made sufficiently small, the thermal-contact boundary conductance $U_{c,e}$ can be made arbitrarily large.[8, 9]

It was noted in Sec. $6\cdot5$ that fluid-boundary conductances also increase as the element diameter decreases.[8, 9]

Rewriting Eq. $8\cdot15$ for the case where no shields are interposed between the element and the ambient

$$t' - t = (t - t_a)U_{r,e}/U_{c,e} \qquad (8\cdot20)$$

where t', t, and t_a are the temperatures of body material in contact with the element, the element itself, and the mean ambient, respectively, $°F$; and $U_{r,e}/U_{c,e}$ is the ratio of the radiation to thermal-contact boundary conductances at the element surface.

Thus, by making the element diameter d sufficiently small, the ratio $U_{r,e}/U_{c,e}$ can be made arbitrarily small. The temperature-measurement error $t' - t$ can thereby usually be reduced to a permissible magnitude.

8·10 EXAMPLE

The effective thermal conductivity of a variety of glass is to be measured for temperatures up to 500°F. Only the average value over a range of 100°F at each mean temperature is, however, expected. The apparatus available is a 15-in. diameter parallel-plate heat-flow meter. Lateral thermal insulation provides for establishing sufficiently uniform temperature fields at the centers of circular-slab specimens if the slabs do not exceed 2 in. in thickness (see Fig. 8·4).

The *effective average thermal conductivity* is defined by

$$k = qD/(t_x - t_y)A \qquad (8·21)$$

where the *effective conductivity* k, Btu/hr ft °F, includes the flow by radiant heat transfer through the semitransparent body; t_x and t_y are the temperatures of the glass, °F, at the termini of the gage length D, ft; and q is the heat-flow rate, Btu/hr, through the area A, ft², measured by the electric-power dissipation at the center heating coil.

Since planes parallel to the heater plates are nearly isothermal, it is necessary merely that the location error be small normally to these planes. Thus, thermoelectric or electric-resistance thermometer wires, lying in such planes, can be of any required lengths, provided that their diameters are sufficiently small. It is decided to use platinum resistance wire fused into the glass in a single-strand or grill arrangement sufficing for the required element resistance. Potential leads tap in at points of sufficient immersion. This adequately reduces the error due to conduction of heat along the leads from the ambient. At the

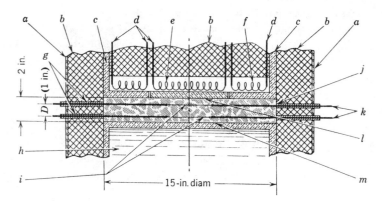

Fig. 8·4. Thermal-conductivity-of-glass apparatus. *a*, Cylindrical steel shell; *b*, thermal insulation; *c*, copper guard-ring shells; *d*, heater-coil leads; *e*, electric-heater coil; *f*, guard-ring heater coil; *g*, ceramic electric-insulator tubes; *h*, circulating coolant fluid; *i*, platinum electric-resistance thermometer elements fused into glass specimen; *j*, glass specimen; *k*, electric-resistance thermometer leads; *l*, copper heat-source surface; and, *m*, copper heat-sink surface.

maximum temperature 500°F, the glass remains of sufficient electric resistivity for insulation.[10]

Figure 3·3 indicates that, in thicknesses of less than 0.05 in., glass may be nearly transparent in wavelengths up to 4 μ. The ambient radiant body of highest temperature is the upper plate whose maximum operating temperature must be somewhat above 500°F. It is assumed to be 1000°R. Then, for the 1000°R source, Fig. 4·1 indicates about 10 per cent of the radiant emission to be in the wavelength range 0 to 4 μ, i.e., to $\lambda T = 4000 \, \mu$ °R. Design must hence assume appreciable transmission through 0.05-in. depths. This transmission must be considered in locating the gage length D, Fig. 8·4, and in design calculations for the temperature-sensitive elements.

For a 0.5-in. thickness, Fig. 3·3 indicates a cutoff wavelength at around 2 μ. At $\lambda = 2 \, \mu$ and $T = 1000$°R for the 1000°R plate, $\lambda T = 2000 \, \mu$ °R. Then, according to Fig. 4·1 in the remaining wavelength range 0 to 2 μ, i.e., for λT from 0 to 2000 μ °R, only 0.1 per cent of the total radiant energy occurs to be transmitted. Thus, a 0.5-in. thickness is essentially opaque. Transmission of heat in the glass beyond this depth may be regarded as exclusive of radiation transmitted from ambient hot bodies. It is assumed that, if the termini of the gage length D are each at least 0.5 in. from the glass surface, heat transfer must result from the average temperature gradient $(t_x - t_y) \, D$ and the property k of the glass (Eq. 8·21).

Locations t_x and t_y are hence chosen as 0.5 in. from the surfaces at a separation gage length of 1 in. For a 1 per cent location error, the wire diameter must not then exceed 0.01 in. (No. 30 B & S gage).

A trial calculation of temperature-measurement error is hence based on 0.01-in. wire diameter. Although location to within 0.01 in. is required, radiation from transparent depths of up to 0.05 in. or more must be regarded as contributing to the error. For simplicity, the contribution is greatly exaggerated and assumed to be 10 per cent of the radiation from the hottest of the neighboring bodies. Calculations are based on Eqs. 8·19, 6·13, and 8·20 for the ambient and element temperatures, respectively: $T_a = 1000$°R and $T_e = 900$°R. Then assuming $\epsilon = 0.3$ for platinum wire immersed in glass and substituting into Eq. 8·19 gives

$$U_{r,e} = 0.1 \times 0.3 \times 0.174 \times 10^{-8} \times [\,(1000)^3 + (1000)^2 \times 900$$

$$+ (1000) \times (900)^2 + (900)^3\,]$$

$$= 0.18 \, \text{Btu/hr ft}^2 \, \text{°F}$$

Similarly, with $k = 0.5$ Btu/hr ft °F for glass and if the effective installed length-diameter ratio L/d is assumed to be at least 10 for 0.01-in. diameter wire, Eq. 6·13 becomes

$$U_{c,e} = 3 \times 0.5/[(0.01/12) \sinh^{-1} 20]$$

$$= 1.5/(0.000833 \times 3.69)$$

$$= 488 \text{ Btu/hr ft}^2 \text{ °F}$$

Then, $U_{r,e}/U_{c,e} = 0.18/488 = 0.00037$, and Eq. 8·20 gives the temperature-measurement error as

$$t - t' = (1000 - 900) \times 0.00037$$

$$= 0.037°F$$

This is 0.037 per cent of the assumed 100°F temperature difference $t_x - t_y$ in Eq. 8·21. Since a 1 per cent error is accepted for D, such a temperature-measurement error is negligible.

By the use of 0.001-in. diameter wire, both location and temperature-measurement errors would be reduced by a factor of 10, and 0.1 per cent precision attained.

Hübner [4] effected wetted contact with the glass bulbs of operating electric incandescent lamps through glycerine and silicone oil, as transparent heat conductors. The high-filament-temperature radiation and his 0.02- to 0.03-in. diameter thermocouple wires resulted in somewhat larger temperature errors. The errors were, however, regarded as acceptable in the lamp industry.

8·11 OTHER METHODS

The velocity-of-sound method, the orifice method, and others mentioned in Ch. 2 of Volume I permit the body to serve as its own thermometer. Thus, these methods are applicable for transparent bodies. Discussions of these techniques are, however, deferred to the more specific problems to which they most directly relate in Chs. 10 to 14.

REFERENCES *

1. M. Czerny, W. Kofink, and W. Lippert, "Bolometer geringer Trägheit" (Bolometer of Low Inertia), *Annalen der Physik*, **8**, Series 6, nos. 1–2 (1950).

---

* See footnote on page 26.

2. M. Czerny, "Zur Integration des Planckschen Strahlungsgesetzes" (On Integrating Planck's Law of Radiation), *Zeitschrift für Physik,* **139,** no. 3, pp. 302–308 (1954).

3. P. L. Tea, "Mechanical Integraph for the Numerical Solution of Integral Equations," *J. Franklin Inst.,* **245,** no. 5, pp. 403–420 (May, 1948).

4. H. J. Hübner, "Messung der Oberflächentemperatur von Gläsern, die durch Strahlung erhitzt werden" (Measurement of the Surface Temperature of Glass Heated by Radiation), *Zeitschrift für angewandte Physik,* **7,** no. 6, pp. 273–279 (1955).

5. A. Bayle, "Récepteur pour la mesure de la temperature des nuages" (Receiver for Measuring the Temperature of Clouds), *Revue d'optique,* **33,** no. 10, pp. 507–513 (October, 1954).

6. J. Hilsenrath, C. W. Beckett, W. S. Benedict, L. Fano, H. J. Hoge, J. F. Masi, R. L. Nuttall, Y. S. Touloukian, and H. W. Wooley, "Tables of Thermal Properties of Gases," *Natl. Bur. Standards Circ.* 564, 488 pp., Government Printing Office, Washington (November, 1955).

7. A. L. Lyderson, R. A. Greenkorn, and O. A. Hougen, "Generalized Thermodynamic Properties of Pure Fluids," *Engineering Experiment Station Report* 4, 99 pp., University of Wisconsin, Madison (October, 1955).

8. M. Jakob, *Heat Transfer,* Vol. I, 758 pp., 1949; M. Jakob and S. P. Kezios, Vol. II, 652 pp., 1957, John Wiley & Sons, New York.

9. M. Jakob and G. A. Hawkins, *Elements of Heat Transfer,* 3rd ed., 317 pp., John Wiley & Sons, New York, 1957.

10. R. C. Mason, "A New Thermocouple," *Rev. Sci. Instr.,* **8,** no. 7, p. 265 (July, 1937).

9

LIQUIDS

9·1 INTRODUCTION

Having the body, whose temperature it is desired to measure, in the liquid state more often facilitates than hinders temperature measurement since wetted thermal contact can then occur. For liquid materials, volume heat capacities are comparable to those occurring in solids. Heat transfer is not only aided by substantial thermal conductivities but usually increased by convection and often multiplied by rapid forced flow. Boundary conductances thus tend to be high. These fortunate factors make it easier to minimize temperature-measurement errors by proper design. In fact, where the liquid is water in a well-stirred thermostated bath, the problems may reduce essentially to those of building the temperature-sensitive element itself. The highest precision is attained in these circumstances. Thus, errors may be reduced to the effects of irregularities and uncertainties in bath control. For example, Rossini and Frandsen [1] using a platinum-resistance thermometer in a thermostated water bath, estimated their error at 0.0001°C in measuring a small temperature change. [1-7]

9·2 VELOCITY EFFECTS

When flow velocities are high and irregular, corresponding temperature variations result. Discrepancies due to these phenomena are, however, less often serious in liquid-temperature measurement than in gas-temperature measurement. Hence, a more complete discussion will be deferred to the chapter on gases. However, it should be noted here that similar phenomena occur in liquids.

Thus, Geldbach and Müller [8] observed local temperature changes in streams of water at points where the flow was disturbed by obstacles. For stream velocities of up to around 7 m/sec (23 ft/sec), temperature rises were of the order of 0.02 to 0.04°C (0.036 to 0.072°F) and appeared to be proportional to the square of the undisturbed-stream velocity. [8,9]

It is thereby evident that too vigorous stirring of a thermostated

279

bath will tend to increase, rather than to reduce, the residual non-uniformities in temperature.[8, 9]

9·3 LENGTH OF IMMERSION

The analyses described in Ch. 7 of Volume I for installations in solids are fully applicable to insertions in liquids. For the given character of the leads or exposed stem, insulation and thermowell construction, physical properties of the liquid, and prevailing flow conditions, the necessary length of immersion can be calculated to conform to the precision requirements for the problem.

The term $1/(U_b + U_{rb})$ in Eq. 7·12 of Volume I corresponds here to the thermal resistance between unit exterior area of the protecting tube and portions of the liquid sufficiently distant not to be affected by the flow q of heat through the installation to the ambient. If the sensitive element is inserted bare without a protecting tube, the exterior surface is that of the element itself.

For insertions in liquids, the quantity U_b usually becomes the fluid-boundary conductance U_f over this external surface. U_{rb} has the same meaning and is computed in the same way for transparent liquids as for transparent solids. In the case of insertions in extremely viscous liquids, where circulation and convection currents are negligible, heat transfer may be primarily by conduction. In this case, the fluid-boundary conductance U_f may closely approximate U_b as computed from Eq. 7·14 or scaled from Fig. 7·7 of Volume I. Equation 6·13 can also be used. For the usual flow conditions, values for U_f can be obtained by reference to the standard textbooks on heat transfer.[10, 11]

9·4 SPURIOUS VOLTAIC EFFECTS

Emfs, arising from chemical reactions between electrically conducting solutions and the metals of the sensitive element, have been discussed in Sec. 5·4 of Volume I. Such spurious emfs become confused with those effecting the temperature indications, and large errors may occur. Thus, voltaic emfs tend to the order of magnitude of a volt, whereas signals may be measured in millivolts or microvolts. Obviously, any incipient voltaic emfs can have disastrous consequences.

Liquids containing water and dissolved substances generally behave as electrolytes, even though the percentages of solutes and water are exceedingly small. Molten salts and ceramics, such as the various fluxes and slags occurring in metallurgical processes, may behave similarly.

Electric temperature sensitive elements—such as thermoelectric junctions and electric-resistance thermometers—require protection tubes when immersed in electrolytes of even the weakest sorts. It is indispensable that these tubes be sufficiently impervious to prevent diffusion of moisture or chemicals into the space containing the element. Condensation of any vapors entering along the stem with the leads must similarly be prevented.

Liquid-in-glass thermometers are immune to these effects. This is also the case for gallium-in-fused-silica thermometers and for expansion or pressure systems generally. Here, electrical phenomena are not the bases of temperature sensitivity, and small electric emfs have no effects. Although thermistors are electric-resistance thermometers, they are frequently furnished embedded in glass beads and with identical platinum leads. These elements are but slightly affected by electrolytes and are often used without protection tubes.

For temperature measurements in acid- and alkali-free oils or similar liquids that are chemically inert and electrically insulating, spurious voltaic effects do not occur. Hence, no protection tubes or protective coatings are required. However, one cannot assume in general that oils, such as engine-crankcase oils, are chemically neutral.

9·5 CONTAMINATION

Thermoelectric powers and temperature coefficients of electric resistance are usually affected by small changes in the chemical compositions of the sensitive-element wire materials. When the materials are subjected to the actions of chemically reactive liquids or vapors, such changes tend to occur. Similar effects may also result from surface adsorption. One result is that of sensitivity drift requiring more-frequent recalibrations. However, such *contamination* may also be nonuniform over the geometrical extent of an element and its leads. The result then will usually be a sensitivity to the exact temperature pattern pervading the details of the geometry.

A contaminated element thus requires that, during calibration, exactly the same temperature pattern be maintained as that occurring in service. This requirement is usually difficult or impossible to satisfy. Thus, contamination rates must be minimized by employing the most impervious protection tubes or protective coatings available. Substances to be used for such application are discussed in Ch. 10 of Volume I.

Mercury-in-glass thermometers and other expansion or pressure systems are generally unaffected by contamination. Elastic elements, such as those employing bimetals, are not, however, thus immune.

9·6 TRANSPARENT LIQUIDS

Liquids may be transparent, and, if a particular material transmits in a wavelength range extending into the infrared or if ambient sources radiate sufficient amounts in the shorter wavelengths, appreciable radiant heat transfer may occur through the liquid. For example, water in layers up to 1 mm thickness transmits in wavelengths to beyond 2 μ in the infrared. In this case, the analyses and techniques described in Ch. 8 must be applied. Spectrally discriminative methods may be used. Similarly, shielding of thermal-contact elements is a possibility. Shielding technique is described in Secs. 8·8 and 10·15 to 10·18. Fortunately, the high values of liquid-boundary conductances tend to minimize radiation errors.[12]

Transparency in liquids does not affect a large fraction of the practical work. Thus, liquid metals are never transparent. Liquids containing water—as, for example, acid or alkali solutions and various other chemical reagents—tend to be strongly absorbing in the infrared beyond 2 μ where most radiant heat transfer occurs. Except for the molten ceramics and the metals, most liquids are too volatile for use in the presence of high-temperature radiant sources. Thus, a combination of conditions, when appreciable radiation occurs in a transparent wavelength range, is the exception rather than the rule.[12]

9·7 CORROSIVE LIQUIDS

Liquids are more often destructively corrosive than either gases or solids. Wetted contact, high concentrations of reacting constituents, and kinetic mobility of the primary particles contribute to the tendency to dissolve and chemically combine with the surface layers of inserted devices. Elevation of temperature rapidly aggravates these effects. Thus, reaction rates increase exponentially with temperature in accord with van't Hoff's equation. Thereby, corrosion problems are most severe in measurement on hot liquids.

Temperature-sensitive elements intended for insertion in corrosive liquids are usually provided with protection tubes. The wall thicknesses in these tubes as designed for sufficient *corrosion allowances* are often quite heavy, and multiple tubes are frequently used (see Figs. 1·9 and 6·1). Materials suitable for use in these protective walls are discussed in Sec. 6·5 and in Ch. 10 of Volume I. Besides surviving exposure to the corrosive liquids, such tubes must be impervious to the diffusion of any gases or vapors that might contaminate the sensitive-element material. Electric-resistance elements are usually more sensitive to the effects of such contamination than thermoelectric elements and therefore require more effective protection.

Suitably resistant metals and ceramics are available for most liquid chemicals occurring in the laboratory and in industrial processes. The liquids include molten glass and the more fusible metals such as brass, typemetal, and the diecasting alloys. Figure 9·1A illustrates a commercial product intended for semipermanent immersions in molten nickel, silver, phosphor bronze, and copper. Similarly, the design indi-

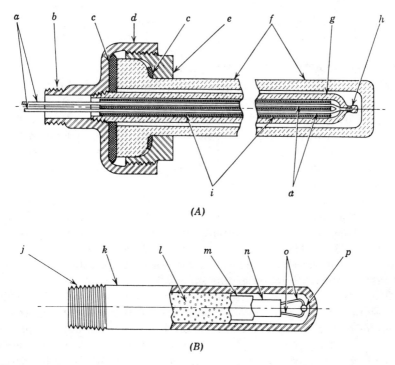

(A)

(B)

Fig. 9·1. Thermocouple assemblies for high-temperature corrosive liquids. (A) Design for semipermanent immersions in molten nickel, silver, phosphor bronze, copper, etc.; and (B) design for installations in 1700°F (927°C) molten carburizing and other salt baths. a, No. 8 B & S gage (0.128 in.) chromel-against-alumel thermocouple wires; b, ¾-in. mounting threads; c, asbestos washers; d, malleable-iron holder; e, malleable-iron hexagon locknut; f, 1.75-in.-outside-diameter 1-in. inside diameter Carbofrax tube, 18 to 36 in. long; g, Metalast, furnished by Elematic Equipment Corporation (Chicago, Ill.), protection tube; h, thermo-electric junction; i, porcelain-and-lavite two-hole insulators; j, 1.062-in. outside diameter mounting threads; k, alloy-steel tube, 12 to 18 in. long; l, tightly packed Carborundum granules; m, Sillimanite inner protecting tube; n, two-hole porcelain insulators; o, No. 14 B & S gage (0.064 in.) chromel-against-alumel thermocouple wires; and, p, electric-butt-welded thermoelectric junction. (*By permission Elematic Equipment Corporation, Chicago, Ill., and Minneapolis-Honeywell Regulator Co., Bulletin 5602, Philadelphia, Pa., May, 1952.*)

cated in Fig. 9·1*B* is for installations in carburizing and other salt baths at temperatures up to 1700°F.[13-18]

Liquid iron and its alloys at furnace temperatures tend to be more destructively reactive. Graphite protection tubes can be successfully used in molten pig iron; graphite is also resistant to attack in the several-inch layer of highly reactive floating slag. Ferrodure, a self-glazing clay-graphite protection tube, available from Pyrometer Company of America (Penndel, Pa.), is said to withstand molten iron for 48 hr. There is, however, no known substance which will withstand the action of molten steel indefinitely.[17,19]

9·8 OPEN-HEARTH AND ELECTRIC FURNACES

An open-hearth furnace consists of a roofed oblong ceramic basin in which batches of up to perhaps 275 tons of steel are melted. Heat is supplied by a flame burning in the space between the metal and the roof. The surface of the liquid metal is protected by several inches of viscous molten slag floating on the top. *Tapping* temperatures are of critical significance. **Cooling between tapping and** *teeming* **results** in the waste of skull in the *ladle* if the tapping temperature is too low. Chemical reactions in the *bath* are very sensitive to temperature. Thus, the time-temperature pattern in the last stages of refining affects the quality of the steel. Uniformity of temperature to within a range of around 20°F is attained over the extent of even the largest baths. Proper determination of the mean requires local-temperature measurements to within a fraction of this spread.[20,21]

The electric furnace is usually smaller than the gas-fired open-hearth furnace. Capacities may range from 1000 lb to 100 tons. It is used for high-grade special and alloy steels. Heat is usually supplied from an electric arc burning between a pair of large carbon electrodes extending vertically down through the furnace roof nearly to the surface of the metal. Induction heating, by eddy currents in the metal itself as generated by electric currents in external solenoids, is also used in some of the smaller furnaces. Temperature-measurement difficulties in the electric furnaces are similar to those in the gas-fired open-hearth furnaces.

The fundamental economic responsibility of the steel industry lends peculiar significance to successes in coping with its technical problems. The almost overwhelming difficulties obstructing temperature measurement in liquid steel lend this task extraordinary interest; therefore, most of the present chapter will be devoted to this problem.[22-25]

9·9   RADIATION MEASUREMENTS ON LIQUID STEEL

The elevation of the prevalent temperatures alone, where the temperatures range from 2800 to 3100°F, had suggested radiation techniques long before any other methods were thought of. In fact, for hundreds of years, the furnaceman's eye has been regarded as a reliable optical pyrometer. He wears his cobalt-blue *Pugh-glass* goggles presumably for protection. However, proposals that green or amber glass more suitable for this function be substituted overlook the fact that Pugh glass really constitutes the *color* filter for his improvised *intensity-ratio* pyrometer. Thus, the transmitted visible radiation is limited to a blue and a red band. The resulting purple hue changes rapidly with temperature. Over-all accuracy may range from within ±30 to ±75°F.[26,27]

Conventional optical pyrometry is commonly associated with the steel industry. Difficulties in its application are however fundamental. Being a metal, clean steel has a low emissivity, i.e., usually less than 0.5; whereas, any slag or dirt floating on its surface has an uncertain but much higher emissivity as well as a variable and somewhat different temperature. The only point in the process at which the bare surface of the molten steel is exposed is during pouring. Then, because of the great elevation above ambient temperatures and the low emissivity of the metal, apparent-temperature corrections run into several hundreds of degrees. Although, following the early authority of Burgess,[28,29] American custom has assumed the value of 0.4 for the emissivity of liquid steel, later data indicate this assumption to have resulted in a displaced temperature scale. When actual emissivities are somewhat above 0.4, the proper emissivity correction should be less and the actual temperatures lower. For example, the original determination of Burgess for molten iron was 0.37, whereas Goller[30] reports values of from 0.4 to 0.75 for molten stainless steels. Carbon content appears to have little effect on emissivity, and values in the range 0.4 to 0.5 are found for carbon steels. It has been estimated that the displacement of the scale is from 35 to 65°F above the actual.[28-32]

Permanently installed automatic radiation-pyrometer recorders focused on the furnace roofs serve as useful control devices. In continuous operation, they merely reveal related conditions, not the actual steel temperatures. However, in the *bath-equalization method*, a determination of the average bath-furnace temperature is effected. Here, the flame, arc, or induction heater is shut off, and time allowed for the floating slag to attain the bath-metal temperature and for the inner roof surface to reach radiative equilibrium with the surface slag. The furnace interior thus becomes an approximately uniform-temperature cavity with blackbody behavior. No emissivity correction is required. Since the equilibrating time allowance is less than a minute, the average bath temperature will not have dropped appreciably. Remaining nonuniformities in temperature, due to active heat-flow processes and in the absence of stirring, effect uncertainties requiring interpretation. Precision has, however, been estimated as being within ±5°F (±2.8°C).[33,34]

By dipping and pouring from a test spoon inserted through the *wicket,* an optical pyrometer can be sighted on the bare metal. Apparent temperatures are affected by reflections from the roof and slag surfaces so that an emissivity correction is required. Also, the metal rapidly cools during the pouring, and the reading must be taken quickly. Consistent results have been attained by applying a correction of 25 to 30°C (45 to 54°F).[34,35]

9·10　STEEL-FURNACE IMMERSION PYROMETERS

The corrosive action of liquid steel is so destructive that no kind of thermowell can be installed permanently immersed in the bath. To take a reading, it is customary for the furnaceman to reach into the furnace with a sufficiently long-stemmed device to penetrate into the metal through the several-inch-thick layer of viscous floating slag. The flame—or arc in an electric furnace—may be turned off during this operation. However, the furnace space remains at 2900 to 3000°F and sparks from splashing on insertion might injure the furnaceman were not the wicket opening covered by a splash guard similar to the shield around the gun breech of a field-artillery gun to protect the crew.[36-38]

For open-hearth furnaces, the required length of the thermometer may be from 6 to 14 ft. However, portable units designed to be held in one hand for manual immersion in ladles and pouring streams are made as short as 24 in.; extension lengths are available as accessories. In blast-furnace tapping, 22-ft assemblies are used.[19,39,40]

The intense furnace heat tends to warp the long stem and to soften it. Thus, it may bend under its own weight or because of the force required to insert the end through the viscous floating slag. Such warpage and bending tend to damage any contained instruments and are particularly destructive if optical elements are thereby thrown out of alignment. Rotating the stem during insertion has been found helpful. However, in all designs, the stem is made thick and strong. Frequently an inner tube is also used. The inner tube is shielded from the furnace heat by the outer casing but spaced sufficiently not to sustain mechanical injury from warpage of the casing.[34,36-38,41,42]

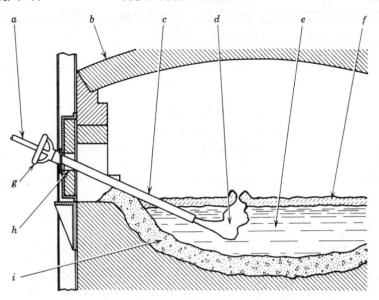

Fig. 9·2. Blow-tube pyrometer in open-hearth furnace. *a*, Stem from which air hose and rubber-covered flexible leads from the sensitive element to wall-mounted recorder emerge; *b*, silica-brick furnace roof; *c*, air-purged sighting tube, i.e., immersion unit; *d*, air bubble; *e*, open-hearth steel bath; *f*, floating layer of molten slag; *g*, handle; *h*, wicket; and *i*, furnace lining of magnesia and dolomite for basic open-hearth furnace or of siliceous material for acid open-hearth furnace. (*By permission H. T. Clark and S. Feigenbaum in Metals Technology, Am. Inst. Mining Met. Engrs., Technical Publ. 2031, 3, June, 1946.*)

The resulting device may weigh from 20 to 90 lb and is often mounted on a carriage for wheeling up to the furnace (see Figs. 9·2, 9·3B, 9·5, 9·6 and 9·7). The manual effort in handling is, however, still not negligible, and the necessity of consummating a reading during the small fraction of a minute to which feasible immersion time is limited causes a degree of mental strain. Automatic recording and signaling to notify the operator when to retract tend to ease this tension.[27, 34, 36–38, 41, 43]

9·11 BLOW-TUBE PYROMETER

The blow-tube pyrometer originated as a laboratory method used by Rosenhain [44] and was later developed for industrial use by Collins and Oseland.[45] It is intended to expose a clean molten-metal surface for radiation measurements, at the same time establishing blackbody conditions. As indicated in Fig. 9·2, the open end of an iron tube is inserted beyond the slag layer into the molten steel. Gas under 8 to 10 lb/in² pressure, blown out through the tube end, maintains a well-stirred undulating cavity in the *bath*. A radiation-sensitive element focused on a patch of surface area within this cavity serves to indicate temperatures.[32, 35-38, 41, 44-48]

Since the steel-tube temperature is not that directly indicated, it need not be made to attain the bath temperature. Thus, the end may be protected by a graphite tip, while the shank is sheathed in an expendable cardboard *mailing tube*. The lower temperature of the tube together with the insulating slag coating picked up during insertion permits satisfactory tube-service lifetimes. The sensitive element, leads, and indicating instruments need not be overheated or exposed to corrosive conditions. Occasional replacement of tubes is cheaply effected.[19, 32, 35-38, 41, 45, 47, 48]

The precision attained is reduced to below the ideal by practical considerations. Thus, although air is cheap as a blowing gas, its oxygen content chemically combines with the steel in the cavity. The heat released in this combustion reaction raises the temperature of the metal surface. Substitution of commercial nitrogen with much lower, but still appreciable, oxygen content reduces the error by about 100°C (180°F). The expense is however not trifling, and this objection has tended to discourage its use.[49, 50]

Although the source-body surface area is on a cavity in the metal, the radiation received at the element is not true blackbody radiation. The relatively cool tube end forms part of the cavity surface. The effect of the cool fraction of the inner cavity surface is aggravated: (1), by the high reflectivity, i.e., low emissivity of the clean molten metal focused on; and, (2), by the relatively high emissivities of the cooler solid surface areas coated with oxides, slag, and dirt. An uncertain emissivity correction is thus necessary, without which too-low temperature indications will result.[35-37, 42, 51, 52]

Early corrections based on an assumed emissivity of 0.61 gave high readings. It has been suggested that the total error resulting from the combination of the combustion heating and the departure from blackbody behavior effects about the right elevation to produce agreement with the erroneously displaced temperature scale. The blow tube has, however, been calibrated against the immersion thermocouple to within ±20°C (±36°F) spread in the readings.[45, 46, 49, 50, 53-55]

In one form (see Fig. 9·3), the inserted end of this device is closed by a thin quartz or silicon carbide tube which attains the molten-metal temperature. The inner tube surface has an emissivity much higher than that of the metal, and many diameters of tube length are brought

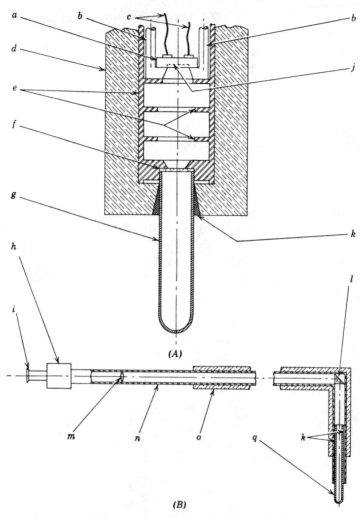

(A)

(B)

Fig. 9·3. Immersion radiation pyrometer. (A) Head design with photoelectric cell; and (B) immersion-tube assembly with disappearing-filament optical pyrometer. a, Photoelectric cell; b, circulating-water inlet and outlet tubes; c, electric lead wires; d, refractory thermal insulation; e, steel diaphragm unit to limit field of view of photoelectric cell to the walls of the radiating tube where the walls are in contact with the molten metal; f, silica window; g, 5-mm-bore 0.5-mm-wall, or 7-mm-bore 0.8-mm-wall, silica or silicon carbide radiating tube; h, pyrometer lamp house; i, eyepiece; j, photosensitive receiving surface; k, asbestos packing; l, reflecting prism; m, objective lens; n, steel tube; and, o, diatomite thermal insulation. (*By permission F. H. Schofield and A. Grace in American Institute of Physics, Temperature, 943, 944, Reinhold Publishing Corp., New York, 1941.*)

to the metal temperature. This procedure effects very nearly true cavity conditions, i.e., blackbody behavior, and no emissivity correction is considered necessary. Likewise, no combustion heating occurs. Readings must be taken quickly, i.e., within about 20 sec, which is difficult with visual instruments. Structural problems in the end-closure are also severe, but they are essentially those accepted with the immersion thermocouple and lack the additional complication of the thermocouple itself. The use of a thermocouple also lengthens the heating and thereby the required immersion time. Change to automatic indication eliminates the reading difficulty. Flushing with pressurized transparent gases prevents accumulation of absorbing constituents in the optical path such as those that may result from any porosity in the immersed tube end.[17, 27, 38, 45, 46, 51, 52]

Jenkins and Gaylor,[46] working in a laboratory, used baffles to help establish cavity conditions in their closed-tube device (see Fig. 9·4). The diameters of the sighting holes in the baffle plugs were restricted to one eighth of the length of immersion. Omitting the baffles had caused errors of 20 to 23°C (36 to 41.4°F); the low readings were attributed to departure from true blackbody behavior. When the baffles were used, the determinations confirmed the value 1527°C (2780.6°F), which they regarded as correct to within ±3°C (±5.4°F)

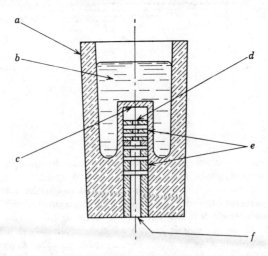

Fig. 9·4. Melting-temperature pot. *a*, Pure-alumina refractory crucible; *b*, molten iron; *c*, blackbody sighting surface; *d*, aperture of collimating baffles; *e*, flat surface-ground refractory baffles; and, *f*, sighting hole. (*By permission C. H. M. Jenkins and M. L. V. Gaylor in Proc. Roy. Soc. London A,* **129,** *no. 809, 96, September, 1930.*)

for the melting temperature of their specimens of iron. Other determinations for iron are higher by 8 to 11.9°C (14.4 to 21.4°F). These other data suggest residual departure from blackbody behavior even with their baffles. However, this discrepancy may also have been caused by contamination of the specimens. Immersion without flushing gases for periods of 24 to 48 hr was found to cause errors of 1.8°C (3.24°F) through radiant absorption by condensed metallic vapors in the optical path. The Rosenhain [44] *bubble* method gave values of 1527°C (2780.6°F) for the same iron specimens.[42,44,46,52,56]

9·12   THERMOELECTRIC IMMERSION PYROMETERS

Guthmann [51] has ably reviewed the development of methods for measuring molten-steel temperatures. Since only fragments of that review can be mentioned here, the reader is referred to Guthmann's excellent paper for more complete information.

The problems are in two categories: (1), to obtain thermoelectric materials of satisfactory performance at steel-furnace temperatures, i.e., at up to around 3200°F (1760°C); and, (2), to provide protection-tube walls which will exclude metallic and other contaminating vapors and also withstand the temperatures and corrosive action of the molten steel. Failure to find materials to fulfill these conditions on any but a temporary basis has resulted in the *quick-immersion* technique. Here, the sensitive element is plunged into the bath for a dwell usually not exceeding around 20 sec. During this brief interval, the junction must be heated to bath temperature and a reading taken. This rapid-response requirement necessitates thin tube walls (see Table 9·1). The consequent thermal-shock stressing imposes severe demands on the mechanical properties of the protection-tube materials.[17,51,57-68]

Table 9·1. Relative response times for thermocouples with quartz protection tubes, sec, for different proportions

Wall thickness		Tube diameter		
		3 mm	4 mm	5 mm
mm	in.	(0.118 in.)	(0.158 in.)	(0.197 in.)
1.0 to 1.2	0.039 to 0.047	—	16 to 21	18 to 25
0.7 to 0.9	0.027 to 0.035	10 to 14	11 to 15	12 to 16
0.4 to 0.6	0.016 to 0.023	6 to 9	7 to 10	9 to 11

After removal from the bath, the device can be reconditioned at leisure in preparation for the next determination. Besides scraping off incrustations of slag, the reconditioning usually involves replacing the protection tube. After a limited number of immersions, a fraction of an inch of the thermocouple wires must also be cut off and a new junction formed. The expense of the reconditioning operation is rarely ignored, nor is the tendency to intrude on other furnace activities overlooked. The effect is a limitation on the number of readings taken and the temperature data made available to the furnaceman.[27, 39, 51]

Thermoelectric materials suitable for service at these elevated temperatures are discussed in Ch. 5 of Volume I. Similarly, the properties of refractories available for protection tubes, casings, and insulators are reviewed in Ch. 10 of Volume I. Additional data are also to be found in the references. The following sections will provide descriptions of certain designs tested by experience.[17, 19, 39, 57–82]

9·13 THE SCHOFIELD-GRACE DESIGN

The original Schofield-Grace [53–55] development is indicated in Fig. 9·5. A carriage was provided to wheel the device up before the furnace. The carriage supported its weight while the tip was inserted through the wicket, dipped down through the floating-slag layer into the molten steel, and a reading taken. Oliver and Land,[83] Manterfield,[43, 84] and others have applied this device in survey investigations of the temperature variations in acid and basic open-hearth and electric furnaces. Accuracies were estimated to be within ± 1 to $\pm 2°C$ (± 1.8 or $\pm 3.6°F$) at different depths during the same immersion or to be within $\pm 4°C$ ($\pm 7.2°F$) for different thermocouples. Absolute local temperatures were believed to have been determined to within $\pm 5°C$ ($\pm 9°F$). However, it was recognized that, because of the observed scope of the temperature variations over the depth and lateral extent of the bath, a determination at one point might differ from the average by as much as ± 10 or occasionally by $\pm 20°C$ (± 18 or $\pm 36°F$).[47, 51, 53–55, 83–87]

9·14 IMMERSION THERMOCOUPLES—MODIFIED DESIGNS

Many successful quick-immersion thermocouples have been built since the original due to Schofield and Grace.[53–55] They are usually characterized by variations in detail. Thus, although the small-diameter thin-walled protection tube remains and is usually of fused silica or quartz, it is occasionally replaced by a similar tube of another material. Similarly, the thermoelectric junction is usually of platinum against platinum with 10 or 13 per cent rhodium. Occasionally, how-

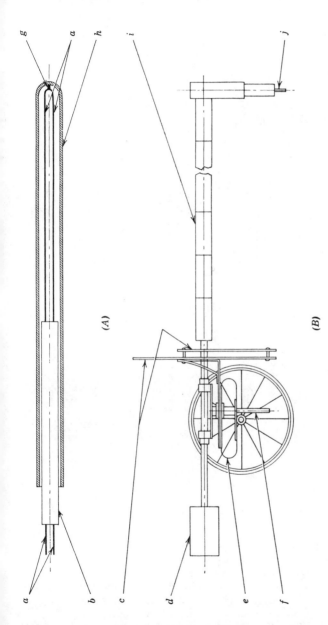

Fig. 9·5. Schofield-Grace immersion thermocouple. (A) Tip design; and (B) trolley-mounted thermocouple assembly. a, 0.5-mm (0.02 in.) diameter, platinum against platinum with 13 per cent rhodium thermocouple wires; b, twin-bore silica electric-insulator tube; c, Uralite shield; d, lead counterweight; e, leaf springs; f, swivel shaft; g, thermoelectric junction; h, 0.5- to 1.0-mm (0.02- to 0.04-in.) wall silica sheath; i, diatomite-block-insulation–encased 1.25-in. steel pipe stem; and j, tip unit shown in A. (By permission F. H. Schofield and A. Grace in American Institute of Physics, Temperature, 938, 939, Reinhold Publishing Corp., New York, 1941.)

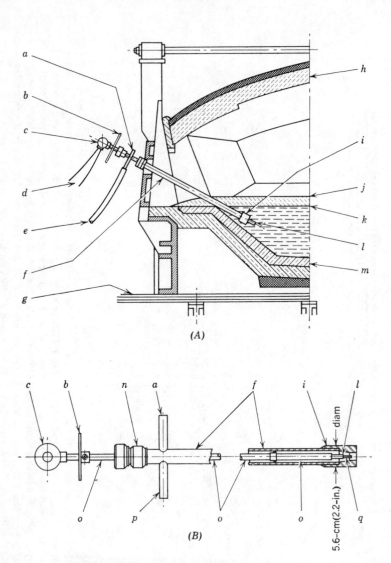

Fig. 9·6. Kotsho's design. (A) Thermocouple immersed in bath for measurement; and (B) combination thermocouple. a, Handle; b, handwheel; c, terminal box; d, leads to galvanometer; e, compressed-air hose; f, steel tube; g, floor; h, refractory furnace roof; i, steel, refractory, or graphite end piece; j, slag level; k, molten-metal level; l, quartz tube; m, lining; n, stuffing box; o, internal metal tube; p, nipple for compressed-air-hose connection; and, q, inner quartz tube. (By permission V. S. Kotsho in The Engineers' Digest, **3**, no. 4, 169, April, 1946.)

ever, other high-temperature combinations are used. They may be tungsten against molybdenum or a tungsten-molybdenum alloy. The wire diameters remain about the same, i.e., 0.3 to 0.5 mm (0.012 to 0.02 in.) in diameter. Similarly, the two-holed insulators are usually of quartz, and the long-stem housing is a thick-walled steel pipe. A wealth of inventive effort has been expended in devising outer sheathings to protect the immersed portion of the housing from heat, abrasion, and erosion, while increasing its stiffness and reducing its weight.[19, 31, 33, 43, 85–95]

One variation has been to surround the end initially with a massive graphite cylinder. The graphite quickly dissolves in the molten steel but survives long enough to "cushion" the thermal shock. Within the slag layer the graphite remains to protect the thermocouple tube which can then be made of porcelain.[34]

Figure 9·6 indicates a design described by Kotsho.[31] Here, the quartz-tube-protected thermoelectric junction is retracted to within the stem during insertion. Compressed air at 0.5 to 1.0 kg/cm^2 (7.1 to 14.2 lb/in.^{2}) prevents slag and metal from entering the annular interspace. After the device has been correctly positioned in the furnace (see Fig. 9·6A), the operator advances the handwheel causing the thin thermocouple tube to protrude into the metal. This arrangement has been successfully applied in both basic and acid furnaces and in alloy as well as carbon steel.[31, 51]

Figure 9·7A illustrates a form, which is commercially available, complete with automatic recording and colored-light signal-flashing apparatus. Audible alarms are also furnished to direct the operator in the successive stages of the standardizing, preheating, immersion, and retraction procedure. These conveniences—enhanced by the reduction to less than 40 lb of device weight to be maneuvered at the furnace—reduce the nerve tension in taking a reading. Servicing usually involves little beyond changing the replaceable plug assembly. Reserve thermocouple wire is stored in an inner tube to provide for periodically cutting-off and rewelding the junction. While a 90-degree immersion end is shown, 60-degree ends are also available. A strip-chart record shown in Fig. 9·7B illustrates the reading-taking process. Accuracies of within ±10 to ±15°F (±5.5 to ±8.3°C) are obtained.[92, 96, 97]

Manterfield [43, 84] and Thurston [43] have described a hand-winch arrangement for lowering the immersion thermocouple into the bath. It is mounted on the furnace back wall out of the way of chargers, locomotives, etc. It also hinges to swing flush when not in use. A special back-wall hole is provided and 30-degree sloping rails guide the tip to the proper depth of immersion.[43, 84]

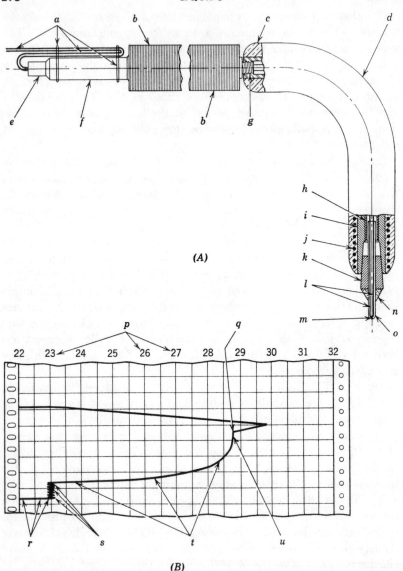

Fig. 9·7. Molten-steel thermocouple. (A) Structural details; and, (B) typical strip-chart record from molten-steel recorder. a, Extension wire taped to handle; b, baling-wire sheathing wound over refractory sleeving; c, refractory sleeving; d, 90-degree bend for immersion depth; e, 0.375-in. pipe; f, 1.125-in. outside diameter tubing; g, detachable screw connection between handle assembly and interchangeable immersion end; h, steel inner pipe; i, graphite sleeve; j, asbestos wrapping; k, graphite plug; l, platinum against platinum with 13 per cent rhodium thermocouple wire; m, thermoelectric junction; n, refractory cement; o, silica thermo-

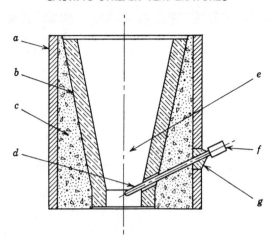

Fig. 9·8. Thermocouple-adapted runner box. *a*, Cylindrical cast-iron case; *b*, 0.75-in. thick conical refractory lining; *c*, rammed "compo"; *d*, 0.5-mm (0.020-in.) wire-diameter, platinum against platinum with 13 per cent rhodium thermocouple in 0.7-mm (0.028-in.) wall, 6.5-mm (0.26-in.) outside diameter silica sheath; *e*, passage for casting stream; *f*, thermocouple-unit head protected from splashes of hot metal by asbestos tubing; and, *g*, "Sairset" cement. (*By permission D. A. Oliver and T. Land in J. Iron Steel Inst. London,* **149**, *no. 1, 516P, 1944.*)

9·15   CASTING-STREAM TEMPERATURES

In blast-furnace runners, tapping, and casting, where the metal is poured over the *lip* of a *ladle,* either an optical pyrometer or short-stemmed quick-immersion thermocouple can be used. When, however, metal is bottom-poured, these methods are not feasible. The velocity of the moving stream is then such that any device inserted into this open *jet* merely sprays metal in all directions.

Figure 9·8 indicates an arrangement for measuring temperatures in casting streams. The ring is inserted between the ladle and the mold. It thereby serves to transmit the stream. Pouring must be continuous through this device for at least 15 sec to permit taking a reading. Consequently, measurements cannot be taken in pouring castings of

couple protecting tube; *p*, temperatures, hundreds of °F; *q*, thermocouple removed from metal at this point; *r*, green light on, indicating that thermocouple circuit is complete and recorder is standardized; *s*, yellow light flashing, indicating that thermocouple is preheating to 2300°F, chart motor is energized intermittently; *t*, yellow light on, indicating that thermocouple has been preheated, chart motor is energized continuously; *u*, red light on, indicating that true temperature has been reached. (*By permission Minneapolis-Honeywell Regulator Co., Instrumentation Data Sheet No. 64-8a, Philadelphia, Pa., June, 1952.*)

less than around 500 lb. The temperature indicated is that at the location of the thermocouple in the stream. If sufficient length and time of immersion are provided, the precision at this point may be of the same order as that for other types of immersion thermocouples.[20, 21, 98]

9·16 TWO-COLOR OR RATIO PYROMETRY

In the two-color method (see Secs. 4·11 and 4·12), the ratio of the radiant-power emissions over two wavelength ranges is measured. This ratio, instead of the actual value in one wavelength range, becomes the criterion of source-body temperature. Thus, in Fig. 4·5, ratios of this sort are plotted against the corresponding temperatures.[24]

It is often implied that the two-color method eliminates the need for an emissivity correction. This is not in general true. It is shown in Sec. 4·14 and Eqs. 4·52, 4·54 and 4·55 that in two-color or ratio pyrometry the relation between the actual and apparent temperatures depends on the ratio of the emissivities in the two wavelength bands, respectively. Exemption then from the need to compute an emissivity correction—in the absence of complete blackness—occurs in general only for a *gray* body. Grayness is an ideal concept. It is that of a body for which this ratio is always unity, i.e., a body for which the emissivity is the same at all wavelengths. Price and Lowery [99] have assembled data on the emissivity characteristics of several liquid metals as well as of various solids. Their curves indicate variations of emissivity with wavelength which are often quite rapid. Thus, the emissivity of liquid iron is found to decrease from 0.6 at about 1.6 μ to approximately 0.28 at 4 μ. These data then indicate that one cannot blindly omit the emissivity correction in two-color or ratio pyrometry.[24, 99, 100]

Available data for the particular molten metal may, however, permit empirical evaluation of the slope of the emissivity curve between a pair of wavelength ranges. From the slope the mean ratio ϵ/ϵ' will then be determined for the wavelength ranges corresponding to the two colors. Thus, values for ϵ/ϵ' are the form in which emissivity data are used in two-color pyrometry.[24, 35, 99, 100]

There is much evidence that reliable molten-metal measurements can be made with the two-color pyrometer. Comparative independence of emissivity-ratio variations due to films of oxide and slag is one of the advantages attributed to this method.[24]

Inspection of the emissivity curve may reveal a wavelength at which there is a maximum or a minimum value. Then, for wavelength ranges symmetrically disposed about this peak, the emissivity ratios will approximate unity. By proper design, it may be possible to utilize a pair of wavelength ranges close enough together to insure small uncertainties in the emissivity ratio but so located that the device retains adequate sensitivity. Figure 4·9 and Eq. 4·46 show that the sensitivity depends sharply on the choice of wavelength ranges. A happy combination may perhaps occasionally be found. Care must however be taken that a temperature rate of change of the emissivity ratio at such a null point does not defeat this purpose.[99, 100]

9·17 EMISSIVITIES

Although thermal radiation-sensitive elements are almost uniformly sensitive at all wavelengths, the photo elements have characteristic passbands which differ among individual specimens. Transmission bands for the lenses and windows used may further limit the wavelength range to which the pyrometer system reacts. When the emissivity of a given source-body surface varies over the spectrum, the average value within the passband of a particular system will depend on the wavelength limits of the passband for the system. Thus, the value to be used for the emissivity of a given source body, such as the bare surface of a molten steel, depends not only on the steel but on the pyrometer.

The Price-Lowery [99] curves further indicate that at 0.65 μ the emissivity of liquid iron increases from around 0.35 at the melting point 1792°K (1519°C or 2766°F) to 0.55 in the neighborhood of 2500°K (2227°C or 4041°F). Thus, the value to be used for the emissivity correction depends on the actual temperature of the source body. The use of an established emissivity value then leads to correct temperature determinations only if the determinations are within the range for which this value is a satisfactory average.[99, 100]

REFERENCES *

1. F. D. Rossini and M. Frandsen, "The Calorimetric Determination of the Intrinsic Energy of Gases as a Function of the Pressure. Data on Oxygen and Its Mixtures with Carbon Dioxide to 40 Atmospheres at 28°C," *RP* 503, *J. Research Natl. Bur. Standards*, **9**, no. 6, pp. 733–747 (December, 1932).
2. C. W. Waidner and H. C. Dickinson, "On the Standard Scale of Temperature in the Interval 0 to 100°C. II. Mercurial Thermometry," *Bulletin of the Bureau of Standards*, **3**, no. 4, pp. 667–674 (October, 1907).
3. H. Moreau, J. A. Hall, and V. M. Leaver, "Mercury-in-Quartz Thermometers for Very High Accuracy," *J. Sci. Instr.*, **34**, no. 4, pp. 147–154 (April, 1957).

* See footnote on page 26.

4. Z. S. Garvitch, "A Field Instrument for Measuring Temperatures of Natural Boiling Pools," *J. Sci. Instr.*, **32**, no. 7, pp. 261–263 (July, 1955).

5. S. J. Borgars, "A Meniscus Thermometer for the Measurement of Small Temperature Differentials," *J. Sci. Instr.*, **30**, no. 12, p. 487 (December, 1953).

6. R. E. Kitson and J. Mitchell, Jr., "Differential Thermometer," *Anal. Chem.*, **21**, no. 3, pp. 401–403 (March, 1949).

7. A. F. Spilhaus, "Bathythermograph and Sea Sampler," *U. S. Patent Office* 2396724, 4 pp., Government Printing Office, Washington (1946).

8. A. Geldbach and W. Müller, "Über den Einfluss der Geschwindigkeit einer Wasserströmung auf die Thermometeranzeige" (Effect of Water-Flow Velocity on Thermometer Readings), *Zeitschrift für technische Physik*, **14**, no. 9, pp. 362–367 (1933).

9. L. Trefethen, "Measurement of Mean-Fluid Temperatures," *Paper* 54-A-113, 9 pp., American Society of Mechanical Engineers, New York (1957).

10. M. Jakob and G. A. Hawkins, *Elements of Heat Transfer*, 3rd ed., 317 pp., John Wiley & Sons, New York, 1957.

11. M. Jakob, *Heat Transfer*, Vol. I, 758 pp., 1949; M. Jakob and S. P. Kezios, Vol. II, 652 pp., 1957, John Wiley & Sons, New York.

12. J. Strong, H. V. Neher, A. E. Whitford, C. H. Cartwright, and R. Hayward, *Procedures in Experimental Physics*, pp. 363, 369–370, Prentice-Hall, Englewood Cliffs, N. J.

13. H. B. Gardner, "Temperature Measurement of Red Brass (85-5-5-5) during Melting and Casting," American Institute of Physics, *Temperature*, 968–973, Reinhold Publishing Corp., New York, 1941.

14. J. R. Green, "Instrumentation and Control of Glass Melting Operations," *The Glass Industry*, **30**, no. 3, pp. 149–154, 174 (March, 1949).

15. "The Carbucouple—For Liquid Carburizing and Other Salt Baths," *Bulletin* 5602-21M, 2 pp., Minneapolis-Honeywell Regulator Co., Philadelphia, Pa. (May, 1952).

16. C. R. Bingham and C. C. Roberts, "Design and Application of Thermocouples for Specific Needs," *Instrumentation*, **4**, no. 3, pp. 25–27 (Fourth Quarter, 1949).

17. W. F. Roeser, "The Passage of Gas through the Walls of Pyrometer Protection Tubes at High Temperature," *RP* 354, *J. Research Natl. Bur. Standards*, **7**, no. 3, pp. 485–494 (September, 1931).

18. E. M. Kline and A. M. Hall, "Nickel and Inconel Thermocouple Protection Tubes," *Metals & Alloys*, **21**, no. 2, pp. 401–404 (February, 1945).

19. H. T. Clark, "Recent Developments in the Pyrometry of Liquid Iron and Steel," *Iron and Steel Engineer*, **23**, no. 2, pp. 55–63, 80 (February, 1946).

20. T. Land, "The Ladle Cooling of Liquid Steel," *J. Iron Steel Inst. London*, **145**, no. 2, pp. 157P–182P (1941).

21. V. Paschkis and J. W. Hlinka, "Temperature Drop in Pouring Ladles—Part II," *Preprint* No. 57-41, *Trans. American Foundrymen's Society*, **64**, pp. 565–576 (1956).

22. G. K. Burgess, "Report of Pyrometer Committee of National Research Council," *Pyrometry*, pp. 3–36, American Institute Mining and Metallurgical Engineers, New York, 1920.

23. C. H. Lorig, "Fluidity and Temperature Measurements in Steel Melting Practice," *Industrial Heating*, **8**, pp. 28, 30, 42–43 (January, 1941).

24. K. Guthmann, "Vergleichende Temperaturmessungen an Roheisen- Guss-eisen- und Stahlschmelzen" (Comparative Measurements of Temperature on Molten Pig Iron, Cast Iron, and Steel), *Stahl und Eisen,* **57,** no. 44, pp. 1245–1248; **57,** no. 45, pp. 1269–1279 (November, 1937).

25. J. R. Green, "Measurement of Temperature in the Open Hearth," *Blast Furnace Steel Plant,* **35,** no. 4, pp. 443–447 (April, 1947).

26. R. Sosman, *The Pyrometry of Solids and Surfaces,* 98 pp., American Society for Metals, Cleveland, 1940.

27. H. J. Hoge, "Temperature Measurement in Engineering," *Temperature,* Vol. II, pp. 287–325, Reinhold Publishing Corp., New York, 1955.

28. G. K. Burgess, "Temperature Measurements in Bessemer and Open-Hearth Practice," *Technologic Paper* 91, 29 pp., U. S. Bur. Standards, Washington (May, 1917).

29. G. K. Burgess and R. G. Waltenburg, "The Emissivity of Metals and Oxides," *Scientific Paper* 242, no. 4, pp. 591–605, U. S. Bur. Standards, Washington (May, 1915).

30. G. N. Goller, "The Emissivity of Molten Stainless Steels," *Trans. Am. Soc. Metals,* **32,** pp. 239–254 (1944), American Society for Metals, Cleveland.

31. V. S. Kotsho, "Methods for Measuring the Temperature of Liquid Steel in the Open-Hearth Furnace," *The Engineers' Digest, N. Y.,* **3,** no. 4, pp. 169–170 (April, 1946); *Stal',* no. 9/10, pp. 273–278 (1944).

32. L. H. Veiock, "Bath Temperature Pyrometry," *Instruments,* **26,** no. 5, pp. 722–723, 754 (May, 1953).

33. J. R. Green, "Measurement of Temperature in the Open Hearth," *Blast Furnace Steel Plant,* **35,** no. 3, pp. 344–347 (March, 1947).

34. L. O. Sordahl and R. B. Sosman, "The Measurement of Open-hearth Bath Temperature," American Institute of Physics, *Temperature,* pp. 927–936, Reinhold Publishing Corp., New York, 1941; *Instruments,* **13,** no. 5, pp. 127–130 (May, 1940).

35. K. Guthmann, "Amerikanische Temperaturmessungen im Stahlbad des Siemens-Martin-Ofens" (American Temperature Measurements in the Steel Bath of the Siemens-Martin Furnace), *Stahl und Eisen,* **60,** no. 18, pp. 395–396 (May, 1940).

36. E. D. Martin, "Plant Test and Use of Equipment for Measuring Molten-Metal Temperature," *Twenty-Second Open-Hearth Proceedings,* pp. 199–201 (1939), American Institute of Mining and Metallurgical Engineers, New York.

37. M. J. Bradley, "Measuring Temperature Beneath Surface of Molten Metal," *Twenty-Second Open-Hearth Proceedings,* pp. 192–198 (1939), American Institute of Mining and Metallurgical Engineers, New York.

38. D. Robertson, "Radiation Pyrometry in the Steel Industry," *Mech. Eng.,* **73,** no. 3, pp. 198–202 (March, 1951); *Paper* 50-IIRD-4, 7 pp., American Society of Mechanical Engineers, New York (1950).

39. G. R. Fitterer, "Pyrometry of Liquid Steel and Pig Irons," American Institute of Physics, *Temperature,* pp. 946–957, Reinhold Publishing Corp., New York, 1941.

40. "Bristol's Portable, Immersion-Type Molten Metal Thermocouple with Metal-Ceramic LT-1 Protection," *Bulletin* P1273, 4 pp., The Bristol Co., Waterbury, Conn. (May, 1957).

41. H. T. Clark and S. Feigenbaum, "A Radiation Pyrometer for Open-Hearth Bath Measurements," *Technical Publication* 2031, Class C, no. 433, 13 pp., Iron and Steel Division; *Metals Technol.*, **13**, no. 4, 13 pp. (June, 1946); *Proceedings of Open-Hearth Conference*, **29**, pp. 229–240 (1946); American Institute of Mining and Metallurgical Engineers, New York.

42. L. O. Sordahl, "Radiation Pyrometer Device," *U. S. Patent Office* 2184169, 3 pp., Government Printing Office, Washington (1939).

43. D. Manterfield and J. R. Thurston, "Improvement in Design of Immersion Pyrometers for Liquid Steel," *Blast Furnace Steel Plant*, **34**, no. 12, pp. 1520–1521, 1535–1536 (December, 1946).

44. W. Rosenhain, "Some Methods of Research in Physical Metallurgy," *J. Inst. Metals*, **42**, no. 2, pp. 36–37 (June, 1929).

45. F. L. Collins and C. Oseland, "Apparatus for Measuring High Temperatures," *U. S. Patent Office* 2020019, 3 pp., Government Printing Office, Washington (1935).

46. C. H. M. Jenkins and M. L. V. Gaylor, "The Optical Determination of High Metallurgical Temperatures—The Melting Point of Iron," *Proc. Roy. Soc. London A*, **129**, no. 809, pp. 91–114 (September, 1930).

47. J. W. Percy, "Comparison of Methods for Measuring Temperature of Molten Metals," *Instruments*, **20**, no. 7, pp. 766–768 (July, 1951); "Instrumentation for the Iron & Steel Industry," *Proceedings of the First Annual Conference*, pp. 33–36 (1951), Instruments Publishing Čo., Pittsburgh.

48. H. B. Emerick, "Open Hearth Bath Pyrometers," *Blast Furnace and Steel Plant*, **38**, no. 12, pp. 1425–1427 (December, 1950).

49. L. O. Sordahl and J. W. Bain, "Temperature Scale of the Blowing-Tube Bath Pyrometer," *Iron and Steel Engineer*, **24**, no. 6, pp. 60–61 (June, 1947).

50. C. B. Post and D. G. Schoffstall, "Temperature Measurement in Basic Arc Furnaces," *Journal of Metals*, **1**, no. 10, pp. 12–17 (October, 1949).

51. K. Guthmann, "Temperaturmessung an Metallschmelzen" (Temperature Measurement in Molten Metals), *ATM Archiv für technisches Messen*, no. 166, Ref. V2164-1, T96–98 (November, 1949).

52. H. Wagenbreth, "Über die schwarze Temperatur der Tauchstrahler beim Goldpunkt" (On the Blackbody Temperature of an Immersion Radiator at the Gold Point), *Zeitschrift für angewandte Physik*, **10**, no. 11, 521–525 (November, 1958); *Sci. Abstr. A*, **62**, no. 739, p. 652 (July, 1959).

53. F. H. Schofield and A. Grace, "A 'Quick-Immersion' Technic for High-Temperature Measurements on Fluids," American Institute of Physics, *Temperature*, pp. 937–945, Reinhold Publishing Corp., New York, 1941.

54. F. H. Schofield, "Report on Heterogeneity of Steel Ingots," *Special Report* 16, p. 215, Iron and Steel Institute, London (1937).

55. F. H. Schofield and A. Grace, "8th Report on Heterogeneity of Steel Ingots," *Special Report* 25, p. 239, Iron and Steel Institute, London (1939).

56. J. Chipman and S. Marshall, "Some New Measurements of the Melting Point of Iron and of Ferrous Oxide," American Institute of Physics, *Temperature*, pp. 958–962, Reinhold Publishing Corp., New York, 1941.

57. R. R. Ridgway, "Thermocouple," *U. S. Patent Office* 2152153, 3 pp., Government Printing Office, Washington (1935).

58. G. R. Fitterer, "Thermoelectric Apparatus," *U. S. Patent Office* 2094102, 3 pp., Government Printing Office, Washington (1937).

REFERENCES 303

59. H. A. Wilhelm, H. J. Svec, A. I. Snow, A. H. Danne, "High Temperature Thermocouples," *U. S. Atomic Energy Commission,* AECD-3275, 8 pp. (June, 1948).

60. M. Pirani and G. F. von Wangenheim, "Ein Thermoelement für höchste Temperaturen" (A Thermoelement for the Highest Temperatures), *Zeitschrift für technisches Physik,* **6,** no. 7A, pp. 358–359 (1924).

61. H. L. Watson and H. Abrams, "Thermoelectric Measurement of Temperatures above 1500°C," *Trans. Electrochem. Soc.,* **54,** pp. 19–36 (September, 1928).

62. A. Schulze, "Über die Auswahl und das Verhalten metallischer Werkstoffe für Thermoelemente" (Choice and Behavior of Metallic Materials for Thermoelements), *Elektrotechnik Berlin,* **3,** no. 3, pp. 65–70 (March, 1949); *Metallische Werkstoffe für Thermoelemente* (Metallic Materials for Thermocouples), 100 pp., J. W. Edwards, Ann Arbor, 1946.

63. D. A. Davies, "Two Thermocouples Suitable for Measurement of Temperatures up to 2800°C," *J. Sci. Instr.,* **37,** no. 1, pp. 15–17 (January, 1960).

64. H. R. Wisely, "Thermocouples for Measurement of High Temperatures," *Ceramic Age,* **66,** no. 1, pp. 15–16 (July, 1955).

65. M. K. McQuillan, "Some Observations on the Behavior of Platinum/ Platinum-Rhodium Thermocouples at High Temperatures," *J. Sci. Instr.,* **26,** no. 10, pp. 329–331 (October, 1949).

66. N. Fuschillo, "Inhomogeneity E.m.f.s in Thermoelectric Thermometers," *J. Sci. Instr.,* **31,** no. 4, pp. 133–136 (April, 1954).

67. "Thermoelemente für hohe Temperaturen" (Thermoelements for High Temperatures), *VDI Zeitschrift des Vereines deutscher Ingenieure,* **83,** no. 23, p. 702 (June, 1939).

68. H. Shenker, J. I. Lauritzen, Jr., and R. J. Corruccini, "Reference Tables for Thermocouples," *Natl. Bur. Standards Circ.* 508, 71 pp., Government Printing Office, Washington (1951).

69. P. R. Morris, "Inductance-Type Thermocouple Tester," *Instruments,* **29,** no. 11, pp. 2217–2219 (November, 1956).

70. A. Sherman, "The Thermocouple Circuit Restorer," *Instruments,* **27,** no. 1, pp. 124–125 (January, 1954).

71. T. M. Dauphinee, "An Apparatus for Comparison of Thermocouples," *Can. J. Phys.,* **33,** no. 6 (June, 1955).

72. G. Haase and G. Schneider, "Untersuchungen an Thermoelementen aus dem System Iridium-Rhenium" (Experiments on Thermocouples Made from the Iridium-Rhenium System), *Zeitschrift für Physik,* **144,** no. 1–3, pp. 256–262 (1956).

73. O. Feussner, "Neue Edelmetall-Thermoelemente für sehr hohe Temperaturen" (New Noble-Metal Thermocouples for Very High Temperatures), *Elektrotechnische Zeitschrift,* **54,** no. 7, pp. 155–156 (February, 1933).

74. B. Osannjun and E. Schröder, "Temperaturmessungen mit Wolfram-Molybdan-Thermoelementen" (Temperature Measurement with Tungsten-Molybdenum Thermocouples), *Archiv für das Eisenhüttenwesen,* **7,** no. 2, pp. 89–94 (August, 1933).

75. A. R. Anderson and D. J. MacKenzie, "Materials for High (2500°–4000°F) Gas Engine Temperature Measurements," *Paper* 158B, 8 pp., 1960, S.A.E. National Aeronautic Meeting, Society of Automotive Engineers, New York.

76. C. T. Sims, G. B. Gaines, and R. I. Jaffee, "Refractory-Metal Thermocouples Containing Rhenium," *Rev. Sci. Instr.*, **30**, no. 2, pp. 112–115 (February, 1959).

77. "The Development of High Temperature Thermocouples," *U. S. Atomic Energy Commission*, AECU-42, 1 p., Washington, August, 1948.

78. M. E. Ihnat and W. C. Hagel, "A Thermocouple System for Measuring Turbine-Inlet Temperatures," *Paper* 59-IRD-1, 6 pp., American Society of Mechanical Engineers, New York (1959).

79. W. F. Roeser and S. T. Lonberger, "Methods of Testing Thermocouples and Thermocouple Materials," *Natl. Bur. Standards Circ.* 590, 21 pp., Government Printing Office, Washington (February, 1958).

80. C. Zener, "Thermoelectricity—Its Impact on Science and Technology," *Industrial Laboratories*, **9**, no. 11, pp. 30–33, 35, 36, 38, 39 (November, 1958).

81. Committee AE-2, Temperature Measuring Devices, "Thermoelectric Circuits and the Performance of Several Aircraft Engine Thermocouples," *S.A.E. Aeronautical Information Report* 65, 16 pp., Society of Automotive Engineers, New York (August, 1958).

82. J. C. Lachman, "Calibration of Thermocouples to 4000°F, *Instruments*, **32**, no. 7, pp. 1030–1032 (July, 1959); "Refractory Metal Thermocouples," *Paper* 59-HT-21, 10 pp. (1959); *Mech. Eng.*, **81**, no. 10, p. 95 (October, 1959), American Society of Mechanical Engineers, New York.

83. D. A. Oliver and T. Land, "The Temperature Distribution in the Liquid Steel in Various Steelmaking Furnaces," *J. Iron Steel Inst. London*, **145**, no. 1, pp. 245P–277P (1942).

84. D. Manterfield, "Survey of Liquid Steel Temperatures in Basic Open-Hearth Furnaces," *J. Iron Steel Inst. London*, **149**, no. 1, pp. 467P–479P (1944).

85. L. F. Weitzenkorn, "A Method for the Determination of Bath Temperatures," *Electric Furnace Steel Proceedings*, **2**, pp. 143–150 (October, 1944), American Institute of Mining and Metallurgical Engineers, New York.

86. R. W. S. Freeman, "High Temperature Measurements of Liquid Steels Using the Quick-Immersion Thermocouple Technique," *Canadian Metals and Metallurgical Industries*, **7**, pp. 23–25 (December, 1944).

87. T. B. Winkler, "Liquid Iron and Steel Temperatures in Practice," *Blast Furnace Steel Plant*, **37**, no. 5, pp. 536–542 (May, 1949).

88. F. S. Swaney, "Open-Hearth Bath Temperature Measurement," *Instruments*, **26**, no. 2, pp. 256–258, 288, 290 (February, 1953).

89. V. G. Gruzin, "Thermocouple for the Measurement of Steel Bath Temperatures," *The Engineers' Digest*, N. Y., **10**, no. 10, p. 344 (October, 1949); *Zavodskaya Laboratoria*, no. 11, pp. 1396–1397 (1948).

90. R. C. Baker, "Installation and Use of Instruments on Open-Hearth Melting Furnaces," *J. Iron Steel Inst. London*, **157**, Part 1, pp. 84–86 (September, 1947).

91. W. A. Spindler, "Immersion Thermocouple Simplified Protection Tube," *American Foundryman*, **11**, no. 4, pp. 125–126 (April, 1947).

92. "Immersion Thermocouple Takes Molten Steel Temperature in 45 Seconds," *Iron and Steel Engineer*, **22**, no. 12, pp. 129–130 (December, 1945); "Expendable Immersion Thermocouple," *Mech. Eng.*, **82**, no. 2, p. 77 (September, 1960).

93. L. H. Veiock, "A Thermocouple System for Molten-Metal Temperature Measurement," *Instruments*, **24**, no. 7, pp. 769–770, 794 (July, 1951); "In-

strumentation for the Iron & Steel Industry," *Proceedings of the First Annual Conference*, pp. 36–38 (1951), Instruments Publishing Co., Pittsburgh.

94. R. F. Wright and E. Scorah, "A Period Immersion Pyrometer," *J. Iron Steel Inst. London*, **169**, pp. 243–244 (November, 1951).

95. G. Leiber, "Temperaturmessungen im Stahlbade des basischen Siemens-Martin-Ofens" (Temperature Measurements in the Steel Bath of the Basic Siemens-Martin Furnace), *Archiv für das Eisenhüttenwesen*, **11**, pp. 63–66 (August, 1937).

96. "New Immersion Thermocouple for Molten Steel Temperature Measurement," *Instrumentation Data Sheet*, no. 6.4-8-37.5C, 3 pp., Minneapolis-Honeywell Regulator Co., Philadelphia, Pa. (July, 1950).

97. "Bath Temperature Measurement," *Instrumentation Data Sheet*, no. 6.4-8a-4M, 4 pp., Minneapolis-Honeywell Regulator Co., Philadelphia, Pa. (June, 1952).

98. D. A. Oliver and T. Land, "A Thermocouple Method for the Measurement of Liquid Steel Casting-Stream Temperatures," *J. Iron Steel Inst. London*, **149**, no. 1, pp. 513P–521P (1944); *The Engineers' Digest, N. Y.*, **1**, no. 12, pp. 667–668 (November, 1944).

99. D. J. Price and H. Lowery, "The Emissivity Characteristics of Hot Metals, with Special Reference to the Infra-Red," *J. Iron Steel Inst. London*, **149**, no. 1, pp. 523P–546P (1944).

100. D. Y. Svet, "Radiation Pyrometry in the Near Infrared Region of the Spectrum" (in Russian), *Doklady Akademii Nauk SSSR*, **130**, no. 1, pp. 61–63 (January, 1960).

10

10·1 INTRODUCTION

Temperatures of bodies in the gaseous state are among those measurements most commonly desired as well as often those most difficult to achieve. The abundance of circumstances in which interest in gas temperatures arises is probably sufficiently obvious not to require elaboration. However, the types of difficulties encountered in their measurement may be more numerous than is always realized. Thus, to a novice, it might seem very simple to immerse a thermometer in the gaseous body and note the reading on an indicator.[1]

Gases even at quite-high pressures have low thermal capacities. Thereby, the necessary heat to bring a temperature-sensitive element to the local gas temperature cannot be supplied by a thin contiguous layer. An appreciable volume of gas is required. This implies that the heat to overcome an element's thermal capacity must come from a larger gaseous region. This heat is ordinarily brought to the immediate vicinity of the thermal element by convective currents or forced circulation. However, the surface of a solid immersed in a fluid stream is surrounded by a quiescent layer called the *film*. Transmission of heat through the film must occur essentially by conduction. Gases are generally poor conductors of heat, and fluid-boundary conductances for gases tend to be low. The difficulties in establishing effective local thermal contact tend to accentuate the problems of temperature measurement.

Thus, heat conducted to the sensitive element along the leads must be removed by transfer from the element to the gas. Low values of the gas-boundary conductances imply larger temperature differences to transfer such amounts of heat. The effect is to increase errors due to the conduction of heat along the leads.[2,3]

Efforts to increase the local values of the gas-boundary conductances by forced circulation tend to accentuate errors due to *velocity effects*. Thus, a limit is usually reached beyond which no further improvement can be effected in this manner.

10·2   LENGTH OF IMMERSION

The necessary length of immersion of a temperature-sensitive element and the adjacent portions of its leads can be calculated according to the methods of Ch. 7 in Volume I.   The temperature-measurement error is given by Eq. 7·9 in that chapter.

The surface-boundary conductance U_b for immersion in a gas becomes the gas-boundary conductance.   Values for gas-boundary conductances can be estimated from the data and formulations given in the standard textbooks on heat transfer.   The values will depend not only on the particular gas and its condition but also on the flow geometry and velocities.   The geometry and velocity patterns may be determined by the shielding and pumping arrangements surrounding and supplementing the element itself.[2-9]

Since gases are always at least partially transparent, the term U_{rb} in Eq. 7·12 of Volume I can never be neglected.   Commonly, radiation exchange with ambient bodies is so important that shielding is provided to reduce or minimize its effects.   The principles of such shielding are discussed in Ch. 8.   Regardless as to whether radiation exchange occurs directly with the ambient or with the artificial environment provided by the shielding arrangements, the term U_{rb} must be evaluated for what constitutes the actual surroundings of the temperature-sensitive element and its leads.

Bodies in radiant exchange with the element are often at substantially different temperatures from those of the gas in contact.   For purposes of estimation of the required length of immersion, a mean-ambient temperature can usually be used.   When this sort of approximation is considered inadequate, more elaborate calculation procedures may be attempted.   However, if feasible, it will usually be more effective to reduce the difficulties by providing sufficient shielding.   Calculations to determine the features of an adequate shielding design are then required.[7,8]

Means for computing the emissivity and configuration factors used in predicting radiation exchange for a given geometry and temperature pattern are given in the standard textbooks on heat transfer.   For more exact determinations, model or analogue-computer and also digital-computer methods are available.[2,3,10-13]

10·3   SPURIOUS OR PARASITIC EMFS

Parasitic voltaic effects are discussed in Sec. 5·4 of Volume I.   Fortunately, in a large part of the work with gases, errors due to voltaic effects are not serious, because gases are very poor conductors of electricity.   Unless ionized in an **arc** or chemical reaction, they ordinarily do not serve as electrolytes in the formation of voltaic cells with the metals of the temperature-sensitive element and its leads. Voltaic effects in gas-temperature measurement usually arise from condensation of vapors to form electrically conducting liquid films. These films may cover insulator surfaces to provide conducting paths from one metal to another. Even though the liquid in its pure state is a fair electric insulator, dissolved substances absorbed from the condensation surface may produce conductivity. Films may be invisible, perhaps being merely *adsorbed* molecular layers and yet of sufficient electric conductivity to cause serious errors.

Water is the usual condensation product. Consequently, difficulties tend to occur in the temperature ranges for which water exists appreciably in the liquid or adsorbed states. The scopes of such temperature ranges depend not only on the vapor pressures in the gases but also on the properties of the solid surfaces. *Wettability* is thus a factor; similarly, *adsorption affinities* may be important. Both tend to be affected by dirt and other surface deposits. Thus, *deliquescent* salts tend to adsorb moisture, whereas *nonwetting* coatings tend to prevent condensation.

Proper choice of insulating materials or their surface coatings, when they are exposed to the gases, is thus a useful design technique. When such means are regarded as inadequate, hermetical sealing-in of the electric circuit becomes a necessity.[14]

Generally, regions of elevated temperature tend to be those in which moisture condensation does not occur. Similarly, at sufficiently low temperatures, condensation products are in the solid state and inactive as electrolytic vehicles.

10·4 CORROSIVE GASES

Except at very high pressures, the concentrations of reacting constituents tend to be low in the gaseous state. Thereby, in accord with the *law of mass action*, the chemical reactivities for gases tend to be less than for liquids and in proportion to the lower prevailing densities. The *mobilities* of the active particles are, however, greater for gases and increase with rising temperatures. Also, in accord with van't Hoff's equation, the reaction velocities themselves increase exponentially with rising temperatures.

The effect is that gases are often highly corrosive. In dry air at room temperature, thermoelectric elements can safely be used bare, and even platinum-resistance elements are sometimes so used. At elevated temperatures and in chemically reactive gases, such as oxygen, ammonia, hydrogen chloride, superheated steam, and sulfur dioxide, protection tubes must be employed.[14-17]

Failures to prevent corrosive attacks on the sensitive element result in spurious or parasitic thermoelectric effects for thermoelectric thermometers. Thus, composition changes tend to occur in portions of the lead wires in which temperature gradients occur. Errors arising in this way are discussed in Sec. 5·3 of Volume I.

Calibration drifts occur in electric-resistance thermometers when the elements are exposed to corrosive gases. Such drifts necessitate excessive frequency of recalibrations and may invalidate the readings entirely. Resistance elements are much more critical in this respect than thermoelectric elements. Liquid-in-glass thermometers and gas- and vapor-pressure thermometers are usually immune to errors arising from corrosive effects, although in severe service such units may disintegrate altogether.[18]

10·5 SLIP OR TEMPERATURE JUMP

A phenomenon tending to introduce obscure errors is that of *slip* or *temperature jump*. At the surface of a solid or liquid immersed in a gas, there is a discontinuity in the temperature field. Thus, at the bounding surface, the gas is at a temperature t_o which is different from the temperature t of the body with which it is in contact (see Fig. 10·1). It is known that

$$t' - t = Dg \qquad (10·1)$$

where t' is that temperature which would occur in the gas at the surface of the wall if the temperature gradient continued undistorted to the wall surface, °F; t is the wall-surface temperature, °F; g is the component normal to the wall of the temperature gradient in the gas, °F/in.; and D is the *temperature-jump distance*, in.[19, 20]

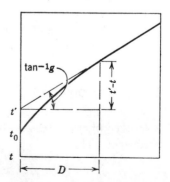

Fig. 10·1. Temperature gradient near a wall. t is the wall-surface temperature; t_o is the gas temperature at the wall surface; g is the undisturbed temperature gradient in the gas; and D is the temperature-jump distance.

The temperature-jump distance D is of the order of magnitude of the *mean free path* between *collisions* for the molecules of the gas. This is, of course, a short distance at ordinary gas-molecule densities. For example, with nitrogen at atmospheric pressure and a temperature of 20°C (68°F), the mean free path is given as 9.3×10^{-6} cm (3.66×10^{-6} in.). However, this distance becomes very much longer at reduced pressures.

The temperature-jump distance is given approximately by

$$D = 2G[(2 - \alpha_c)/\alpha_c](T/T_o p)L_o \qquad (10\cdot2)$$

where T is the gas temperature, °R; p is the gas pressure, atm; L_o is the mean free path at 1 atm and T_o, °R, in.; α_c is the *thermal accommodation coefficient;* and G is a factor of the general order of magnitude of unity but depending on the properties of the particular gas.[19, 20]

The *accommodation coefficient* α_c describes the tendency of gaseous molecules to acquire the wall temperature on collisions with the wall. Their failure to do so completely partly accounts for the temperature jump from the wall temperature to that of the surface layer of colliding molecules. The accommodation coefficient depends on the gas, the wall-surface material, and its condition. The maximum value for α_c is unity, corresponding to complete equalization. For ordinary "technical" surfaces, Wiedmann and Trumpler [21] found values ranging from 0.87 to 0.97. However, Thomas and Schofield [22] measured the accommodation coefficient for helium on clean tungsten as less than 0.02.[19-22]

10·6 TEMPERATURE-JUMP ERROR

Even though the temperature-jump error is usually negligible, it becomes important in certain circumstances. Thus, with surfaces not specially cleaned and at atmospheric temperature and pressure, the temperature-jump distance D will usually be less than 10^{-5} in. Then, for the temperature jump to become 0.01°F, it is necessary that the temperature gradient in the gas normal to the surface of the thermometer element be 1000°F/in. However, at a pressure of 10^{-4} atm, the temperature-jump distance may be about $\frac{1}{10}$ in., and an error of 1°F would result from a temperature gradient of only 10°F/in.

10·7 THERMODYNAMICS

When a gas undergoes an *adiabatic expansion*, without performing *external work*, the temperature change is given by the *free-expansion* coefficient. Thus

$$\eta = (dt/dp)_u \qquad (10\cdot3)$$

where η is the free-expansion coefficient, °C/atm; and $(dt/dp)_u$ is the rate of change of temperature, °C, with pressure, atm, at constant *internal* or *intrinsic energy u*, ergs/g of gas. Such an expansion is realized when a gas, confined at a given initial pressure and temperature, is allowed to expand into an evacuated vessel. Any change in temperature would then be measured prior to subsequent heat exchange with the walls of the vessel.[23, 24]

When a gas is in *steady-state adiabatic* flow along a *duct* or *streamline*, such that net changes in kinetic energies of *mass motion* are negligible while *gravitational potential energies* remain constant, the process is said to be *isenthalpic*. The temperature change from one point to a second point further downstream is then given by the Joule-Thomson coefficient. Thus

$$\mu = (dt/dp)_{u + pv} \qquad (10·4)$$

where μ is the Joule-Thomson coefficient, °C/atm; and $(dt/dp)_{u + pv}$ is the rate of change of temperature, °C, with pressure, atm, at constant *enthalpy u + pv*. In $u + pv$, u is the *intrinsic energy*, ergs/g; p is the gas pressure, dynes/cm²; and v is the specific volume, cm³/g. Thus, v is the volume occupied by unit mass of gas, i.e., $v = 1/\rho$ where ρ is the density, g/cm³.[23, 25]

Both the *free expansion* coefficient η and the Joule-Thomson coefficient μ have zero values for ideal gases. For actual gases, except when near to condensation, the values for η and μ are usually small. Thus, for air in the vicinity of room temperature and pressure, μ and η are both of the order of 0.25°C/atm.[23, 24]

Free expansions are irreversible and *nonisentropic*. Isenthalpic expansions through porous partitions, where hundreds of atmospheres pressure change may occur, are likewise highly irreversible and nonisentropic. Thus, the above expressions are valid whether or not entropy changes occur. Such entropy changes may be those associated with viscous friction. It is thus to be noted that neither pressure changes nor viscous friction necessarily result in substantial temperature changes. Small temperature changes may, however, occur through nonvanishing values of η and μ, i.e., of the *free-expansion* and Joule-Thomson effects, respectively.[23–25]

Gas densities are low enough that gravitational-potential energies do not ordinarily vary appreciably, except perhaps with considerable changes in altitude.

Temperature changes occur: (1), when energy is added to the gas from outside sources; and, (2), when kinetic energy of mass motion in the gas is converted into random thermal energy. In both cases, the effect is to increase the *intrinsic* or *internal energy u* to which the temperature *t* is directly related.[25-29]

The intrinsic energy *u* consists of the kinetic energies of random translational motion for the individual gas molecules and of their *quantized* internal-energy states. The states include *rotational, vibrational, electronic,* and *nuclear* energies. For any definite quantity of energy in equilibrium random distribution among these modes of energy storage, the temperature has a uniquely determined corresponding value.

Energy can be added to a unit mass of gas from outside sources by heat transfer. The process is then *nonadiabatic*. Energy can also be added by the effect of external mechanical forces. Thus, a confined gas may be compressed by a piston which then does work on the gas. The same effect will result if the piston is replaced by surrounding masses of gas. Similarly, the gas may be in viscous shear between solid surfaces driven by external forces. Thus, a body of gas might occupy an annular space between two cylindrical surfaces rotating in opposite directions. The energy supplied by the driving motor would be expended in churning, thereby heating the gas by viscous friction. One or both of the surfaces could be replaced by an external stream of gas without changing the result. Regardless of the form or manner in which energy from external sources is conveyed to, and dissipated as random thermal energy in, the gas, the temperature rise corresponds to the increase in the intrinsic energy u.[25-29]

Kinetic energy of mass motion, whether of translation or of rotation, is not intrinsic energy and bears no direct relation to the temperature of the gas. In fact, such motion is always relative. Thus, atmospheric air, when no wind is blowing, may appear motionless to an observer standing on the earth. However, to the occupant of an airplane in flight, it appears to be in rapid motion.[25-27]

The kinetic energy of a unit mass of gas moving at velocity V, cm/sec, is given by

$$KE = V^2/2 \qquad (10 \cdot 5)$$

where KE is the kinetic energy in ergs/g; and V is the mass-motion velocity, cm/sec. If the kinetic energy KE is dissipated into thermal energy in the same unit mass of gas, the effect is identical whether a "moving" gaseous mass is brought to rest by a "stationary" obstacle or a "moving" object accelerates the gas to its own "velocity." "Moving" and "stationary" are thus recognized as relative terms. Nor is the amount of energy, along with the corresponding temperature rise, affected by the detailed mechanics of its manner of conversion into random thermal energy.[25-29]

In a gas flow where a definite pressure p rather than a definite specific volume v prevails, any rise in temperature of the gas is accompanied by a corresponding expansion, i.e., an increase in the specific volume v. External work is performed in such an expansion, by which part of any energy added to the gas is expended in performing the external work. Therefore, in computing the local temperature rise, one divides by the specific heat at constant pressure C_p rather than by that at constant volume C_v. The larger value of C_p automatically corrects for the loss of energy in external work. Thus

$$\Delta t = V^2/2JC_p \qquad (10·6)$$

where Δt is the temperature rise, °C; V is the initial relative mass-motion, cm/sec; C_p is the specific heat at constant pressure, cal/g °C; and J is the mechanical equivalent of heat, 4.18×10^7 ergs/cal.[25-29]

Similarly, if the energy is received by heat transfer,

$$\Delta t = q/C_p \qquad (10·7)$$

where Δt is the local temperature rise, °C; q is the heat energy received by unit mass, cal/g; and C_p is the specific heat at constant pressure, cal/g °C. [25-29]

Likewise

$$\Delta t = W/JC_p \qquad (10·8)$$

where Δt is the local temperature rise, °C; W is the mechanical work performed by external agencies upon unit mass of gas, ergs/g; J is the mechanical equivalent of heat, 4.18×10^7 ergs/cal; and C_p is the specific heat at constant pressure, cal/g °C. The work W may be performed in viscous shear, i.e., friction.[25-27]

If W is the net work in compression and the usual work of expansion accompanying a temperature rise is included in W, the specific heat at constant volume is used; thus

$$\Delta t = W/JC_v \qquad (10·9)$$

Actually, these phenomena cannot occur adiabatically. The local temperature changes result in gradients with the consequent flow of heat. The values for Δt observed in practice are thus numerically smaller than those given by Eqs. 10·6 to 10·9.[26-29]

10·8 STATIC AND TOTAL TEMPERATURE

If an attempt is made to use a solid thermometer element or *probe* to measure temperatures in a body of gas moving relatively to the apparatus, the heating effects listed in Sec. 10·7 tend to result in erroneous determinations. Thus, the gaseous layer contiguous to the surface of the sensitive element is warmed according to Eqs. 10·6 to 10·9. The resulting discrepancy is usually described in terms of Eq. 10·6, i.e., as a fraction of $V^2/2JC_p$. This fraction is always appreciable. It is rarely less than about 63 per cent, and, in parallel flow, values up to at least 87 per cent occur. For dry atmospheric air, the magnitude of $V^2/2JC_p$ ranges from 0.11°C at 50 ft/sec (1525 cm/sec) to 42.7°C at 1000 ft/sec (30,500 cm/sec) (see Fig. 10·2). Hence, although this effect can be neglected in much work, it becomes important at high velocities.[3, 25, 26, 28–37]

By ingenuity in design, probes can be made for which, under specified conditions, the discrepancy approaches 100 per cent of the quantity $V^2/2JC_p$. If an independent measurement is made to determine V, the discrepancy can then be calculated and subtracted.[25–29]

The actual temperature, as thus corrected for this change resulting from the presence of the thermometer, is often called the *static* temperature. The name arises from the idea that it is the reading that would occur were there no relative velocity between the gas and an

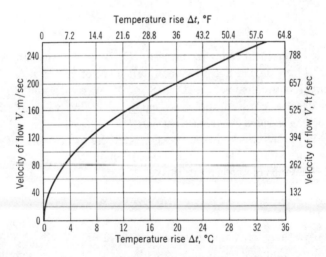

Fig. 10·2. Relation between velocity of flow and stagnation temperature rise for dry air and adiabatic conditions. (*By permission A. E. Hintermann, The Engineers' Digest, 2, no. 7, 359–360, July, 1945.*)

error-free thermometer. A better definition might perhaps be to say that the static temperature is that which would prevail in the absence of the thermometer.[25-29]

Similarly, the sum of the actual temperature and the quantity $V^2/2JC_p$ is often called the *total temperature*. Thus

$$t_t = t + V^2/2JC_p \qquad (10 \cdot 10)$$

where t_t is the total temperature, °C; t is the temperature, i.e., the static temperature, °C; V is the free-stream velocity, cm/sec; J is the mechanical equivalent of heat, 4.18×10^7 ergs/cal; and C_p is the specific heat at constant pressure, cal/g °C (which is assumed to be constant).

The total temperature is of interest as a quantity that can be directly measured. In a suitably designed *probe*, the gas can be brought nearly to rest at the location of a thermocouple junction, which thereby serves to indicate this *stagnation* or *total temperature*. The fraction r of the quantity $V^2/2JC_p$, which is included in the temperature indication for a particular probe design, is called the *recovery factor*. Thus

$$r = (t_i - t)/(t_t - t) \qquad (10 \cdot 11)$$

where r is the recovery factor; t_i is the indicated temperature, °C; t is the free-stream temperature, i.e., the static temperature, °C; and t_t is the total temperature, °C. Values for r as high as 0.998 have been achieved for limited ranges of velocities and *yaw angles*.[25-29,38]

It should be mentioned that the total temperature is often a useful quantity in itself. This application is independent of its service as a step in the determination of the temperature, i.e., the static temperature.

10·9 TOTAL PRESSURE AND STATIC PRESSURE

These two pressures are regarded as analogous to the total and static temperatures. Specifically, the pressure measured by a manometer connected to a hole in the duct wall (see Fig. 10·3A) is called the *static pressure* p_s. On the other hand, if a tube opening is arranged with its plane normal to the flow (see Fig. 10·3B), the manometer will indicate the *total* or *stagnation pressure* p_t. The observed elevation of the total pressure with respect to the static pressure results from the deceleration effect as the gas is brought to rest in the *impact tube*.

The static pressure results from the thermal motion of the gas molecules and is the actual pressure in the same sense that the static

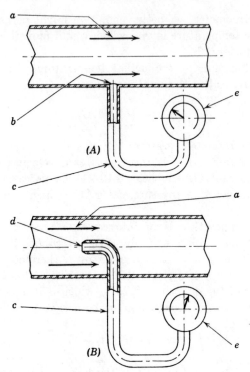

Fig. 10·3. Pressure probes. (A) Static tube, and (B) pitot tube. a, Direction of flow; b, static-pressure tap; c, connecting tube; d, total-pressure tap; and, e, pressure gages.

temperature is the temperature. The total pressure is thus larger by an *impact* term proportional to the square of the relative velocity V between the measuring tube and the stream.

For a full discussion of the techniques for measuring total and static pressures, the reader is referred to the various treatises on aerodynamic measurements.[28, 29, 39]

10·10 DETERMINATION OF STATIC TEMPERATURE

The temperature, i.e., the static temperature, is given by

$$t = t_i - rV^2/2JC_p \qquad (10·12)$$

where t and t_i are the temperature and indicated temperatures, respectively, °C; r is the calibrated value of the recovery factor for the given operating conditions; V is the free-stream velocity, cm/sec;

$J = 4.18 \times 10^7$ ergs/cal; and C_p is the specific heat at constant pressure, cal/g °C.[28,29,39]

To apply Eq. 10·12 it is necessary to measure the velocity V. Various methods for doing this are described in the books on aerodynamic measurements. One of the simplest methods is based on pressure measurements in the stream.[28,29,39]

Eckert and Weise [40] have proposed the equation

$$V^2 = 2[\gamma/(\gamma - 1)]RT_i[1 - (p_s/p_t)^{(\gamma-1)/\gamma}]/$$
$$\{1 - (1 - r)[1 - (p_s/p_t)^{(\gamma-1)/\gamma}]\} \quad (10·13)$$

where $\gamma = C_p/C_v$ is the average ratio of the specific heat at constant pressure to that at constant volume for the gas; T_i is the indicated temperature, °K; R is the gas constant for the particular gas, ergs/g °C; r is the recovery factor; p_s/p_t is the ratio of the static pressure to the total pressure for the free stream; and V is the free-stream velocity, cm/sec.[28,29,40,41]

A probe may be supplied in calibration with a correction curve to yield total temperature in terms of indicated temperature and *Mach* number M. The temperature T can then be computed by using a relation suggested by Lindsey.[41]

$$T = T_t/[(\gamma - 1)M^2/2 + 1] \quad (10·14)$$

with M given by

$$M^2 = 2[(p_t/p_s)^{(\gamma-1)/\gamma} - 1]/(\gamma - 1) \quad (10·15)$$

where T is the free-stream temperature, °K; T_t is the total temperature, °K; p_s is the free-stream *static pressure*; p_t is the total or stagnation pressure; γ is the ratio of the specific heat at constant pressure to that at constant volume; and M is the Mach number. The ratio of the free-stream velocity V to the local velocity of sound a is called the Mach number.[28,29,39,41] Thus

$$M = V/a \quad (10·16)$$

10·11 RELAXATION TIME

In the random translational motions of the molecules of a gas, the velocities range from zero to infinite speeds. The velocity-distribution pattern in this state of molecular chaos is described by *Maxwell's law* and is called the *Maxwellian distribution*.[19]

When the Maxwellian distribution of energies in the translational motions of the molecules is disturbed, the time for restoration of the normal pattern is called the *translational relaxation time*. This time depends on the temperature and pressure, being briefer at higher temperatures and higher pressures. However, under atmospheric conditions, the order of 0.001 μsec (10^{-9} sec) is usually sufficient for resumption of translational equilibrium. This time is so short that translational equilibrium can almost always be assumed.[42-49]

However, if the local condition in a body of gas is caused to change with great rapidity, a departure from *internal equilibrium* may result. Thus, if energy is added to the translational motions of the gaseous molecules by sudden compression, the energy is not immediately shared with the *quantized* internal energy states. Thereby, the rotational, vibrational, electronic, and nuclear energies are not instantly augmented by the fraction of this energy they would possess at equilibrium. Similarly, if energy is directly subtracted from the kinetic energy of the random thermal translational motions of the gas molecules, the internal quantized states do not at once fully replace this loss. In this condition of a body, the thermodynamic temperature becomes an undefined quantity.[42-48, 50]

When such a disturbance has occurred, the time for re-establishing equilibrium is called the *relaxation time* or *heat-capacity lag*. Relaxation times are characteristic of the energy transitions involved. They differ for the various *rotational* and *vibrational energies* and for different *molecular species*. Relative to the time intervals usually involved in work with gases, the relaxation times are brief. Thus, they are conveniently measured in microseconds. Values range from less than 0.01 μsec (10^{-8} sec) to around 10 μsec (10^{-5} sec); much larger times are rare.[42-49]

For chemically stable gases, relaxation effects are usually important only in very sudden phenomena such as in *jets* and *shocks*. It is only here that temperature lacks its usual definition, with the consequent perplexity in any attempt at its measurement. For chemically active mixtures of gases, flames, sparks, arcs, and nuclear reactions, non-equilibrium effects may be of great importance.[42-48, 50]

10·12 RADIATION ERRORS

When a temperature-sensitive element is immersed in a body of gas, it does not necessarily assume the temperature of the gas. For a sufficient length of immersion, the error that might result from conduction of heat along the stem or lead wires can be made as small as desired. However, if the surrounding opaque bodies, such as the walls, "viewed" by the element are at temperatures different from that of the gas, the element will assume a temperature intermediate between that of the gas and that of the walls. Thus

$$(t' - t)/(t - t_1) = U_{r,e}/U_{c,e} \qquad (8·15)$$

where (see Fig. 8·3) t', t, and t_1 are the mean temperatures of the gas, the element, and the surrounding opaque bodies, respectively, °F; and $U_{r,e}$ and $U_{c,e}$ are the effective radiation and fluid-boundary conductances referred to the element surface, Btu/hr ft^2 °F. The temperature t_1 may be either the temperature of the walls or that of the first shield. When these temperatures are nonuniform, t_1 represents their properly weighted average. In the case of a shield, the portions of the ambient viewed through the open ends must be included in such an average.[1, 31, 51–53]

Fishenden and Saunders [7] have provided a convenient means for estimating the error represented by the ratio $(t' - t)/(t - t_1)$. They do not intend their method to be used for calculating corrections but rather for determining the relative adequacies of comparative designs. This procedure involves the assumption that a mean value t_m for the gas and wall temperatures t' and t_1 can be used in computing the effective boundary conductances $U_{r,e}$ and $U_{c,e}$. Naturally, the nearer these temperatures are to being alike, the smaller will be the error. However, when t' and t_1 differ widely, although the error of estimation will be larger, the error to be estimated will also be larger and the need for accuracy correspondingly less.

Their equation is written as

$$(t' - t)/(t - t_1) = \epsilon\psi d \qquad (10·17)$$

where ϵ is the emissivity of the sensitive-element surface, or the *emissivity factor* referred to the element surface for a closely surrounding shield; d is the diameter of the cylindrical element, in.; and ψ is a factor plotted in their family of curves, reproduced here as Fig. 10·4. Thus, ψ is given as a function of the product of the gas velocity V streaming past the element, ft/sec, and the element diameter d, in., for a succession of values of the mean wall temperature t_m, °F. Figure 10·4 is computed for air; however, it may be used for carbon monoxide, nitrogen, oxygen, carbon dioxide, and water vapor.[2, 3, 7]

Rohsenow [52] has provided a set of charts permitting a more accurate determination of the errors for unshielded thermometers. He intends his method to be used in computing corrections to readings in service.

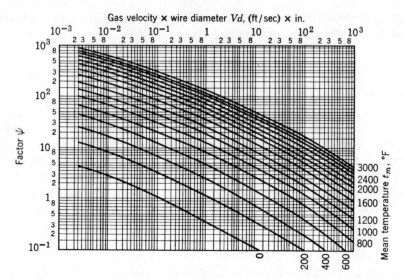

Fig. 10·4. Radiation-correction chart. (*By permission M. Fishenden and O. A. Saunders in J. Inst. Fuel,* **12,** *no. 64, S6, March, 1939.*)

10·13 REDUCTION OF RADIATION ERRORS

When a trial computation of the radiation error by the method described in Sec. 10·12 indicates the radiation error to be excessive, means must be adopted for its reduction. The variables on which the error depends are: (1), the surface emissivity ϵ of the sensitive element; (2), the diameter d of the sensitive element; (3), the mass flow ρV of the gas stream past the element; and, (4), the mean temperature t_m for the gas and the opaque ambient surfaces.[1, 53, 54]

In Sec. 8·10, an example is worked out illustrating how radiation errors can be reduced by making the element-wire diameter sufficiently small. For mobile gases Eq. 10·17 and Fig. 10·4 would be used instead of Eq. 6·13; however, the same advantage would be gained by using thin wires.[7, 9, 55, 56]

Piccard, Larsen, and Blomstrand [57] used a thin-wire element in *radiosonde* to measure upper-atmosphere air temperatures. Thermal expansion in a 4-in. long 0.005-in. diameter white-gold (gold-nickel alloy) wire actuated a pointer. Indications coupled to an electronic circuit provided Morse-code temperature messages from their *sounding balloon* to the ground station. Signals occurred at the rate of 15 per minute. The wire-element unit was suspended in the open air, mounted on a bracket extending laterally from the *gondola*. At a rated sensitivity to within 1°C, the element was found to be immune to the effects of direct sunshine, recording only the actual air temperatures.[57-61]

Dätwyler [62, 63] has proposed an ingenious means to compensate for radiant heat losses from a bare-wire electric-resistance element. The balancing magnitude of an electric heating current is determined by the condition that wire-temperature fluctuations resulting from gas turbulence will vanish when the wire is at the gas temperature. The correct heating current is thus that for which the average square of the random wire-temperature fluctuations is found to be a minimum.[62-66]

If elements of successively smaller wire diameter are used to measure the temperature of the same body of gas, the determinations can be plotted against wire diameter as points on a curve. The curve can then be extrapolated to zero wire diameter. The corresponding temperature ordinate can then be regarded as the temperature which would be indicated by a very much smaller wire than might be feasible to employ in practice.[64, 65]

Fiock [67-71] and Dahl [67, 68, 70-73] have found that, in many circumstances, it is sufficient to reduce the surface emissivity of the sensitive element. In so doing, they utilized an idea conceived a century earlier. Thus (see Fig. 10·5), they have arranged to clamp silver- or gold-foil jackets about thermoelectric junctions. The jackets fit so snugly that the thickness "splitting" the gas stream was not greatly increased. Such designs are limited to use in "clean" gases, i.e., gases which do not deposit dust, soot, fly-ash, or slag particles on the brightly polished surfaces. Although gold tarnishes very little, silver cannot be used in sulfurous or other gases in which it blackens. This type of design is usually used when gas velocities V are quite fast and when temperatures are not high.[64, 67-75]

If the gas flow is in a duct, it is sometimes practicable to bring the ambient inner wall surfaces approximately to the gas temperature. This can be done by lagging a neighboring length of the duct with external thermal insulation. Such technique is effective in reducing the radiation error and also usually simplifies means for eliminating the conduction error. Several duct diameters on each side of the thermometer installation should be insulated to minimize end-radiation.[3]

If controlling the wall temperatures is not feasible, shielding is the natural recourse. Aspiration through a cylindrical shield system then permits control of the velocity V. Thus, the combination of: (1), increasing the fluid-boundary conductance by increasing the mass flow; and, (2), suppressing radiant heat transfer by use of shields causes

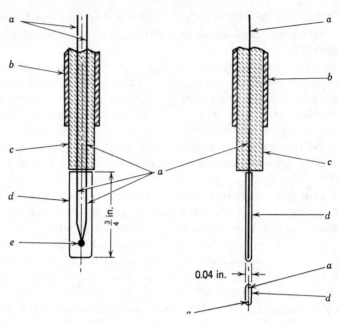

Fig. 10·5. Silver-shielded junction. *a*, No. 22 B & S gage (0.025 in.) chromel-against-alumel thermocouple wires; *b*, steel-tube sheathing; *c*, two-hole porcelain insulator; *d*, 0.020-in. thick fine-silver shield; and, *e*, thermoelectric-junction bead ground flat to wire thickness. (*By permission A. I. Dahl, Petroleum Refiner,* **29,** *118, March, 1950.*)

the element to assume an approximation to the actual gas temperature.[1, 76]

10·14 SHIELD DESIGN

A typical shield system is indicated schematically in Fig. 8·3. The various surfaces shown in cross section are usually those of cylindrical shells (see Figs. 10·6 and 10·7). Both ends may be open and the free-stream velocity may supply the flow longitudinally through the shield system. When this natural motion is insufficient to provide the necessary fluid-boundary conductances, one end is connected to a suction pump. In general, surfaces at other than the shield temperatures can be "seen" by the element—as well as by the shields themselves—through the open ends. Thus, one open end exposes the "view" of the ambient, while the other displays the stem and suction-duct surfaces which are often water-cooled. A shield length is then chosen which

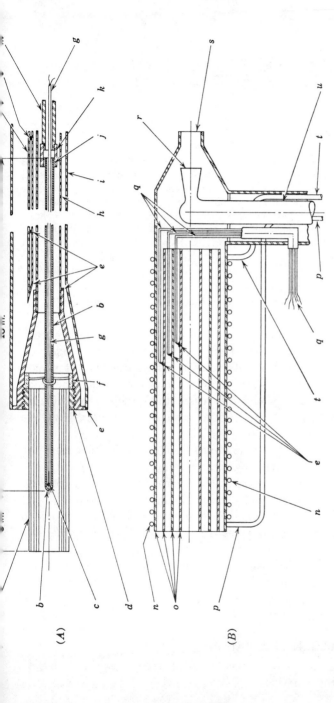

Fig. 10·6. Industrial multiple-shielded suction pyrometers. (A) Marsh's open-hearth-furnace probe; and, (B) Lucke's heated-shield design. a, Nickel radiation shields; b, 0.375-in. outside diameter porcelain protection tube; c, platinum against rhodium thermoelectric junction; d, shield adaptor ring; e, welds; f, protection-tube centering ring; g, two-hole porcelain insulators; h, 1.25-in. outside diameter steel suction tube; i, 1.75-in. outside diameter steel-tube water-cooled casing; j, glass tape; k, 0.25-in. stainless-steel coupling; l, 0.375-in.-pipe water inlet; m, 0.25-in. stainless-steel pipe; n, heating- or cooling-fluid-tube coil; o, concentric cylindrical shields; p, fluid inlet tube; q, thermocouple lead wires; r, steam or air ejector nozzle; s, restricted outlet; t, fluid outlet tube; and, u, steam or air inlet tube. (By permission J. S. Marsh in Instruments, **26**, no. 12, 1876, December, 1953; and C. E. Lucke, U. S. Patent Office 2006469, 3 pp, Government Printing Office, Washington, 1934.)

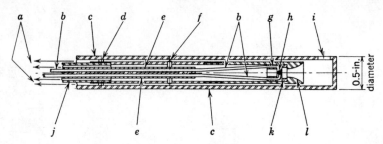

Fig. 10·7. Sonic-velocity suction pyrometer. *a*, Exit air flow; *b*, No. 18 B & S gage (0.040 in.) chromel-against-alumel thermocouple wires; *c*, heat-resisting-steel outer radiation shield; *d*, lugs welded to inner tube to centralize it; *e*, two-hole porcelain insulator; *f*, 3-pin-"spider" distance piece; *g*, ceramic-insulation locating bushing; *h*, butt-welded junction; *i*, 0.187-in. diameter inlet-air hole; *j*, heat-resisting-steel inner radiation shield; *k*, ceramic-insulation spacer bushing; and, *l*, nozzle. (*By permission E. P. Walsh and S. Allen in Paper 49-A-66, American Society of Mechanical Engineers, New York, 1949.*)

is considered to reduce the angle *subtended* by the open ends sufficiently.

Making the shields small in diameter tends to reduce the end-subtended angle for a given shield length and also reduces the external-surface area exposed to ambient radiation. Reducing the intershield spaces to less than around $\frac{1}{16}$ in., however, tends to increase the fluid-flow resistance excessively and to prevent the establishment of adequate intershield gas velocities. Excessive shield lengths have the same effect.

Increasing the gas velocity improves conditions by increasing the fluid-boundary conductance; however, only up to a certain point. For greater values, the error increases. Thus, excessive suction in reducing the gas density ρ effects a net decrease in the mass-flow rate ρV on which the conductance depends. Furthermore, cooling in accord with Eq. 10·6, when velocities are excessive, may also effect an appreciable error.

It is necessary for the designer to determine the number of shields that will be necessary to yield the required precision. However, the use of more than about five shields is usually found to effect little further improvement.[1, 64, 65, 75–90]

10·15   SHIELD-DESIGN CALCULATIONS

The conditions for heat balance at the successive shields shown in Fig. 8·3 yield the equations

$$U_{c,e}(t' - t) = U_{r,e}(t - t_1) \tag{8·14}$$

$$2U_{c,1}(t' - t_1) + U_{r,1}(t - t_1) = U_{r,1}(t_1 - t_2) \tag{8·16}$$

$$2U_{c,2}(t' - t_2) + U_{r,2}(t_1 - t_2) = U_{r,2}(t_2 - t_3) \tag{8·17}$$

$$2U_{c,i}(t' - t_i) + U_{r,i}(t_{i-1} - t_i) = U_{r,i}(t_i - t_{i+1}) \tag{10·18}$$

$$2U_{c,n}(t' - t_n) + U_{r,n}(t_{n-1} - t_n) = U_{r,n}(t_n - t_a) \tag{8·18}$$

To calculate the error $t' - t$ in gas-temperature measurement by use of Eq. 8·14, it is necessary to have values for the gas- and radiation-boundary conductances $U_{c,e}$ and $U_{r,e}$, respectively, and for the temperature t_1 of the first shield.

For the range of gas temperatures to which the device is intended to be applicable and for the flow conditions contemplated, values for $U_{c,e}$ can be estimated from the formulations given in the heat-transfer textbooks. Similarly, for surface emissivities corresponding to the intended construction, an assumed shield-element mean-temperature value for $U_{r,e}$ can be computed.[2, 3, 9]

Solution of Eq. 8·14 for the error $t' - t$, however, depends on having a value to use for the first-shield temperature t_1. Obtaining the value for t_1 depends in turn on the simultaneous solution of the system of equations Eqs. 8·14, 8·16 to 8·18, and 10·18. Exact execution of this task is tedious. Fortunately, Bartas and Mayer [91] have provided a simple closed form which is subject only to certain stated simplifying assumptions. An approximate trial set of shield temperatures is thus made conveniently available at once. Their formula is

$$(t' - t_i)/(t' - t_a) = \cosh i\phi/\cosh(n + 1)\phi \tag{10·19}$$

where

$$i = 0 \text{ for the thermometer element} \tag{10·20}$$

and

$$i = 1, 2, \cdots, i, \cdots, n \tag{10·21}$$

for the successive shields. The quantity ϕ is given by the relation

$$\cosh \phi = (U_c + U_r)/U_r \tag{10·22}$$

Here, U_c and U_r are the fluid- and radiation-boundary conductances, respectively. They are assumed to have the same values throughout the shield system. Thus, U_r is given by

$$U_r = 4\sigma\epsilon T_m^3 \tag{10·23}$$

where ϵ is the surface emissivity approximated by one mean value applying to all surfaces; T_m is the mean absolute temperature of the shield system, °R; $\sigma = 17.20 \times 10^{-10}$ Btu/hr ft² (°R)⁴; and U_r is the mean radiation-boundary conductance, Btu/hr ft² °F.[91]

The error is given directly by letting $i = 0$ in Eq. 10·19; thus

$$t' - t = (t' - t_a)/\cosh(n+1)\phi \qquad (10\cdot24)$$

Other assumptions tacit in Fig. 8·3 and Eqs. 8·14 to 8·18 and 10·18 are that the gas, wall, and shield temperatures can be regarded as sufficiently uniform to be represented by the mean-value symbols t', t_a, and $t_1 \cdots t_i \cdots t_n$, respectively.[91]

Equation 10·19 takes no account of the curvatures and open-end effects in the shields. Thus, this calculation views Fig. 8·3 as though the shields were a set of infinite parallel planes with the element Δx at the center. Bartas and Mayer [91] have performed a more rigorous analysis taking account of the usual cylindrical shape and of the open ends exposed to the ambient. The curvature error was found to be of no importance in this approximate calculation. However, end effects were sufficiently significant to be plotted as a set of correction curves (see Fig. 10·8B).

The possible effects of gas radiation were included in this extended analysis, but no curves were provided.[91, 92]

Equation 10·24 is plotted in Fig. 10·8A against the number of shields for three values of the ratio U_c/U_r of the fluid- to the radiation-boundary conductances. The order of magnitude of the error $t' - t$ to be expected with a given installation can thus be obtained directly. In Fig. 10·8B, the effect of open ends is given. Thus, the curves of Fig. 10·8A are each replaced by a family of curves for various values of the *end-radiation factor* F_e. This quantity F_e is a *geometric-ratio factor* giving the ratio of the amount of radiation passing out the open ends of the center shield to the amount of radiation perpendicular to the shields. Means for estimating such *radiation-configuration factors* are given in the textbooks on heat transfer and in the literature. Tea [10, 12] and Baker [12] have provided a model method for exact solution without the use of mathematics. Values of 0.01 to 0.02 for F_e commonly occur in nonaspirated shield systems. When suction is employed, smaller end apertures are feasible with correspondingly reduced values of F_e.[2, 3, 10-14, 91-94]

Land [81, 86-88] and Barber,[86-88] Fishenden [7, 95] and Saunders,[7] Schack,[8] Moffatt,[93] Rohsenow [52, 96] and Hunsaker,[96] and others have described procedures for making more refined performance calculations. The

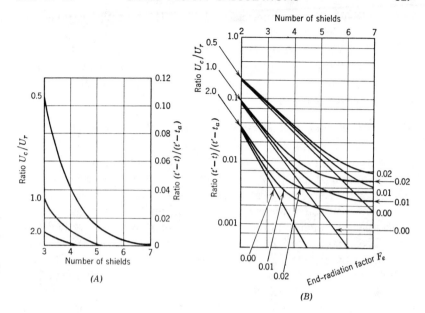

Fig. 10·8. Calculated-error curves for cylindrical shielding. (*A*) Ratio of measurement error $t' - t$ to difference between gas and wall temperatures $t' - t_a$ versus number of shield elements for three values of the ratio U_c/U_r of the fluid-to the radiation-boundary conductances; and (*B*) same as *A* except that curve for each value of the ratio U_c/U_r is split by three values of the end-radiation geometric factor F_e. (*By permission J. G. Bartas and E. Mayer Paper 56-A-130, American Society of Mechanical Engineers, New York, 1956.*)

procedures are usually based on a tentative shield design. Because of the complexity of the problem, such methods tend to be iterative and numerical or graphical in character. As such, their presentation would require more space than is available here. Hence, the reader is referred to the original papers in which the techniques are fully detailed.[7, 8, 52, 75, 86-88, 93, 95, 96]

As a plan of attack, it is suggested that a tentative design be found at the outset by using Eqs. 10·19 to 10·24 and Fig. 10·8. This design can then be studied in any degree of detail which appears warranted, either by applying special methods or by resorting to common-sense application of the standard textbooks on heat transfer. One can thus successively balance the equations Eqs. 8·14 to 8·18 and 10·18. The full set of approximate shield temperatures given by Eq. 10·19 will be a convenient starting point. These values can then be adjusted to correspond to successively more refined values of the radiation-

and fluid-boundary conductances U_r and U_c over the various surfaces.[2, 3, 7, 8, 86–88, 91, 93, 96]

It will be noted, however, that the computational errors of the Bartas and Mayer [91] Eqs. 10·19 to 10·24 are in proportion to measurement errors for the design. They thus tend to become less as the precision of the instrument is improved.[64, 75, 77–85, 91]

10·16 INDUSTRIAL MULTIPLE-SHIELDED SUCTION PYROMETERS

These instruments are variously termed *aspirated*, *velocity*, *high-velocity*, and *suction* pyrometers. Also, since the sensitive element is usually of that type, they are commonly called *thermocouples*, i.e., high-velocity thermocouples. They are not, however, to be confused with devices intended for measurements in high-velocity gas streams. Their most common application is in still or slowly moving bodies of gas. The original design due to Assman appeared in 1887, whereas most of the possible variations have seen industrial service in Germany in the period beginning around 1908. American interest dates from about the time of an excellent review paper by Haslam and Chappell [75] in 1925. Ramifications in this field are too extensive to be described here. Hence, for a full account, the reader is referred to Mullikin's [64, 77] excellent survey, with attention to his bibliography of 113 references.[1, 17, 55, 64, 71, 75–78, 86–90, 95]

Three representative designs are indicated in Figs. 10·6 and 10·7. The device of Fig. 10·6A was developed for measuring inlet-air temperatures in open-hearth furnaces, where it was found that each additional 100°F of air preheat shortened the furnace-heating time by about three-quarters of an hour. The device is used by insertion to a length of about 40 in. through a hole in the *uptake wall* on the *pit* side just above the floor level. A sliding-fit Transite shield prevents air leakage through that part of the hole not occupied by the instrument. Several units each survived some hundreds of individual measurements at temperatures up to 2600°F with no damage other than to protection tubes and shields. Indirect evidence lent confidence in the results; however, no rigorous calibration was performed.[79, 90]

The heated-shield technique is attributed to Wentzl and Schulze (1926) who used, however, only one shield with an axial thermocouple protection tube and one junction on the shield. Lucke's [80] version shown in Fig. 10·6B is characterized by multiple shields in conjunction with aspiration and by thermoelectric junctions welded to each shield. Radiation is said to be *neutralized* when the readings on the junctions are equal. Variations in the gas velocity should then have no effect on the readings. Electric heat input at the outer shield is intended to compensate for radiation loss to the ambient when the latter is below gas temperature. If, however, the ambient is warmer, liquid- or gas-flow cooling must replace heating.[76,77,80]

The heated-shield method is criticized as being cumbersome, expensive, and slow. Nonuniformities in shield temperatures, affecting the shield-junction readings, have been said to introduce added errors. There can be no question, however, that full radiation compensation is thereby possible, whereas this is not always otherwise the case. Taking a reading requires a *balancing* operation similar to that in using a potentiometer. The heater current is thus altered to equalize the readings on the shield junctions. Suitable design will minimize thermal lag, and the balancing can be performed by rapid automatic means.[76,77,80,93,97]

The design of Walsh and Allen [97] (see Fig. 10·7) is intended for use at low gas densities where velocity errors may also be a problem. Adequate mass flow is obtained by accelerating the gas in a *nozzle* to *sonic velocity*. The bare-wire thermoelectric junction is thus sufficiently affected to attain local gas temperatures, although there are only two shields. The local temperatures at the junction are, of course, not those in the free stream. The gas flow is largely "stopped," yielding temperatures nearer to the total or stagnation values. The recovery factor r does not, however, closely approach unity, having a value of about 0.87. This value is anticipated in a theoretical treatment but finally determined by calibration. Since the nozzle velocity is that of sound, it is independent of *yaw angles* and free-stream velocities. Hence, the recovery factor is regarded as known with great accuracy. The indicated absolute temperatures are then corrected by an empirical factor of 1.0154 to yield total temperatures. The actual stream temperature, i.e., static temperature, must be obtained by subtracting the quantity $V^2/2JC_p$ per Eq. 10·10. This implies an independent determination of the free-stream velocity V as done, for example, by using Eq. 10·13. Equations 10·14 and 10·15 can, however, be substituted where the Mach number then becomes the intermediate quantity. In either case, the total and static pressures must be measured in the stream at the location of temperature determination.[64,75,77-85,97,98]

10·17   PERFORMANCE OF SHIELDED PYROMETERS

Although no one set of experimental studies can reveal the effects of conditions encountered in practice, certain results are of interest. Marsh [79] constructed a series of pyrometers of increasing complexity and compared their performance. His data are indicated in Fig. 10·9A and tend to confirm the theoretical conclusion portrayed in Fig. 10·8 that usually little is gained by using more than five shields.[76, 79, 81-88, 90]

The reduction of error with increase in aspiration rate is shown in Fig. 10·9B. It will be noted that there is a rate for which the reading is a maximum. This reading may, however, still be lower than the actual gas temperature. Further increase in gas velocity merely increases the error. Land [81, 86-88] recommends velocities of 500 to 700 ft/sec despite the fact that cooling according to

$$\Delta t = V^2/2JC_p \qquad (10·6)$$

may be appreciable for V as large as 21,350 cm/sec (700 ft/sec), but he adds that, with available equipment, one must often be content with 100 or 200 ft/sec.[81, 86-88]

Mullikin [64, 77] and Osborn [77] performed extensive tests on a single-

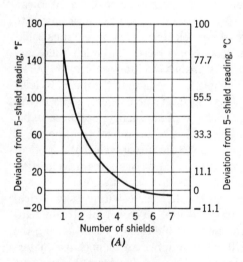

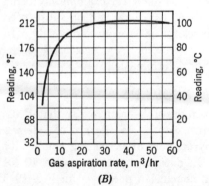

Fig. 10·9. Experimental-error curves for cylindrical shielding. (A) Error versus number of shields; and (B) reading versus gas velocity measured in cubic meters per hour at 0°C and 1 atm pressure (1 m³ = 10⁶ cm³ = 35.31 ft³). (By permission T. Land in Instruments, 29, no. 7, 1316-1317, July, 1956.)

Table 10·1. Comparative readings of different types of thermocouples in a four-inch-square duct

Instrument or Condition	Reading, °F
Estimated true gas temperature	2105
Multiple-shield, high-velocity thermocouple temperature	2103
Multiple-shield, high-velocity thermocouple shield temperature	2090
Bare No. 28 B & S gage (0.013 in.) thermocouple temperature	1995
Single-shield, high-velocity thermocouple temperature	1963
Bare No. 22 B & S gage (0.025 in.) thermocouple temperature	1951
Bare No. 14 B & S gage (0.064 in.) thermocouple temperature	1922
Bare No. 8 B & S gage (0.128 in.) thermocouple temperature	1863
Single-shield, high-velocity shield temperature	1817
Optical-pyrometer "hot-wire" temperature	1607
Wall temperature	311

By permission, Mullikin and Osborn in Temperature, p. 815, Reinhold Publishing Co., 1941.[37]

ceramic-shielded design suitable for withstanding fly-ash conditions in boiler furnaces. They also studied a modification in which the annulus between the ceramic shield and the thermocouple protection tube is filled with a cluster of parallel small-diameter ceramic tubes. This arrangement is regarded as providing the equivalent of many concentric shields. The data demonstrated that, for simulated boiler-furnace conditions, the device indicated actual gas temperatures to within ±14°F. Mullikin [64,77] and Osborn,[77] however, believed its accuracy to be higher. Their various comparison data are listed in Table 10·1.[17,64,75,77–85,90]

10·18 TEST METHOD

Land [81,86–88] has suggested a simple test which can be performed in actual plant operation. This consists in first halving the gas flow and then shutting it off altogether. The indicated temperature then departs from that of the gas and more and more approximates that of the radiant surrounding bodies as the gas flow is reduced. This change occurs in two steps corresponding to the two valve changes. A curve of indicated temperature is then plotted against time during the course of the valve changes to show the two steps. Land's criteria are: (1), that, if the big (i.e., second) step is less than seven times as high

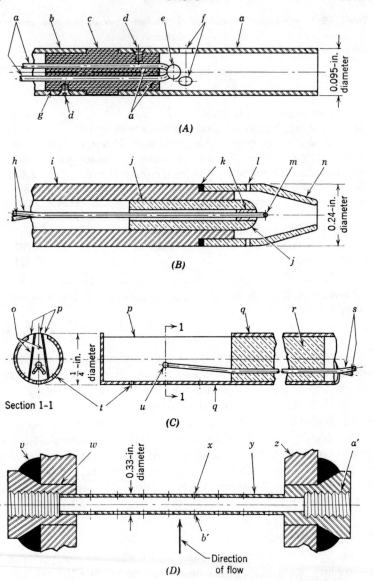

Fig. 10·10. Total-Temperature Probes. (A) Pratt & Whitney probe; (B) Winkler probe; (C) Scadron design; and (D) Murdock-Fiock steam well. a, No. 30 B & S gage (0.01 in.) iron-against-constantan thermocouple wires; b, 18 per cent nickel with 8 per cent chromium stainless-steel tube; c, plastic; d, two 0.014-in. diameter screws; e, 0.025-in. diameter spherical junction; f, three 0.023-in. diameter vent holes; g, tight fit; h, fiber-glass-insulated No. 30 B & S gage (0.01 in.) iron-against-constantan thermocouple wires; i, stainless-steel holder; j, silica tube with

as the (first) small one, the pyrometer is not operating with accuracy and the error exceeds the height of the small step; and, (2), that, if the ratio of the step heights exceeds 7:1, the height of the small step is a good estimate of the error of the pyrometer operating with full suction.

It is to be noted that, when there is an appreciable pressure differential across the furnace wall, it may be necessary to plug the outlet to stop the flow.[81, 86–88]

10·19   STAGNATION-TEMPERATURE PROBE DESIGN

Invention has been prolific in devising instruments for the indication of total temperatures. Among these instruments, however, the stagnation-probe type is represented by a group of designs somewhat similar except as to detail. The construction usually consists of a stem protruding into the gas stream with a thermoelectric junction in some sort of a cup at its tip. The junction is located in the *stagnation zone* of the gas-flow disturbance produced by this cup. Thus, in general, these devices are characterized by flow restrictions suited to nearly stopping the gas flow at the location of the measuring thermoelectric junction.[1]

Such baffles retarding the flow usually also serve as radiation shields. However, this shielding tends to be rather inadequate. In addition, errors are augmented by conduction of heat along the leads. Compactness in design, intended to effect minimum disturbance in the gas-flow pattern under investigation, tends to insufficient lengths of immersion, together with limitations on the number of shields provided.[71]

Since the radiation and conduction heat-flow paths are thus left at substantial magnitudes, it is indispensable that the gas-boundary conductances at the junction surfaces be made as large as possible. This requires, in turn, that the flow not be fully stagnated at the junction

---

platinum-coated spherical surface; *k*, W. V-B. Ames Co. (Fremont, Ohio) Technical-B Copper Cement; *l*, two vent holes; *m*, thermocouple junction; *n*, silica shield, both surfaces platinum coated; *o*, Inconel shields; *p*, three 0.025-in. wide by 0.5-in. long slots; *q*, 0.25-in. outside diameter Inconel tubing; *r*, ceramics; *s*, 0.012-in. diameter thermocouple wires; *t*, nine 0.032-in. diameter vent holes; *u*, thermocouple junction; *v*, weld; *w*, steel fitting; *x*, 0.04-in. diameter holes on 0.375-in. centers; *y*, 0.33-in. outside diameter 0.23-in. inside diameter tube; *z*, wall of steam main; *a'*, ⅛-in. pipe thread; *b'*, 0.129-in. diameter holes on 0.375-in. centers. (*By permission, H. C. Hottel and A. Kalitinsky, J. Appl. Mech.,* **12**, *A-30, March, 1945; E. M. Winkler, J. Appl. Phys.,* **25**, *no. 2, 231, February, 1954; M. D. Scadron, C. C. Gettleman, and G. J. Pack, Research Memorandum RME 50129, 8, U. S. National Advisory Committee for Aeronautics, Washington, December, 1951; J. W. Murdock and E. F. Fiock, Paper 50-S-36, Trans. ASME, 72, no. 11, 1155–1161, November, 1950.*)

but rather that appreciable motion be maintained. Recovery factors can thus never become 100 per cent.

The rate of flow required at the junction to sufficiently reduce radiation and conduction errors depends on the temperature level and on its difference from the ambient. The possible magnitudes of recovery factors r are thereby determined. The effect is obviously a compromise intended to balance these sources of error for a given range of operating conditions. The balance is so delicate that it has always been necessary to work out the best adjustment of factors in experimental testing. The resulting instrument is then valid only for the ranges provided by its calibration curves. A few sample designs of stagnation total-temperature probes are indicated in Fig. 10·10.[1, 26-29, 31, 39, 41, 53, 54, 67, 69, 70, 74, 99-106]

10·20   STAGNATION PROBES

The Pratt & Whitney probe (Fig. 10·10A) is intended as a simple and durable construction which is practicable in small sizes. The

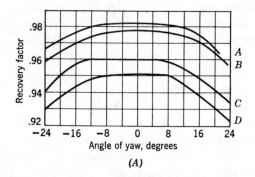

(A)

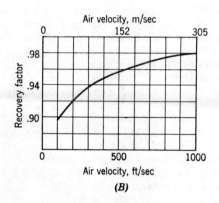

(B)

Fig. 10·11. Performance of Pratt & Whitney probe. (A) Recovery factor versus angle of yaw; and (B) recovery factor versus air velocity. Velocities are for curves: A, 1040 ft/sec; B, 940 ft/sec; C, 595 ft/sec; and D, 425 ft/sec. (By permission H. C. Hottel and A. Kalitinsky, J. Appl. Mechanics, **12**, A-30, March, 1945.)

dependence of the recovery factor on the free-stream air velocity and on the *angle of yaw* is given in Fig. 10·11A and B. It is to be noted that, to read correctly, the axis of the device must be aligned with the stream direction to within ±10 degrees angle of yaw. The radiation error is found to be around 0.5°F for ambient walls at 300°F above the gas temperature. However, this accuracy applies only to air at room temperature. The unit is not intended for service at elevated temperatures.[105,107]

Winkler's [38,108] design shown in Fig. 10·10B is adapted to high supersonic speeds and elevated temperatures. The use of nonmetallic shield material with platinum plating reduces radiation errors and permits application at gas temperatures of up to 670°K (746°F). The recovery factors attained are plotted in Fig. 10·12A. Units of this type have been built as small as 2.5 mm (0.1 in.) diameter. Replacing the platinum coating with gold and increasing the length-diameter ratio of the thermocouple wires is expected to increase precision in the higher temperature ranges.

The design of Scadron, Gettelman, and Pack [109] (see Fig. 10·10C) is arranged to provide multiple shielding, with gas flow between the successive shields as in suction pyrometers. The leads are also immersed to an appreciable length in the shielded flow, tending to limit conduction losses. Performance curves for such probes are given in Fig. 10·12B and C. It is to be noted that the recovery factor is independent of yaw angle over the range ±30 degrees, as well as of the free-stream velocity over the range 0.3 to 1.0 for the Mach numbers. Although the tests were conducted at room temperature, the all-Inconel construction permits operation at elevated temperatures.

The construction of Murdock [110] and Fiock [67-71,110] (see Fig. 10·10D) is available for indicating average temperatures in high-velocity steam mains. The steam cannot be *wet*, i.e., contain suspended droplets of water. It must be *superheated* steam which behaves similarly to air. However, calibration tests were performed in steam over the ranges of 450 to 625°F, 20 to 200 lb/in.², and velocities of 725 to 1150 ft/sec. Accuracy to within ±2°F for total absolute temperatures was demonstrated throughout this range of conditions for both uniform flow and the velocity gradients characteristic of fully developed pipe turbulence.[17,67-71,110]

Since these four designs are merely representative of the variety available, it is suggested that the reader consult the references for constructions that may better suit his purpose.[1,18,26-29,38,39,41,51,54,67-70, 72,73,85,93,100-102,105-107,111-113]

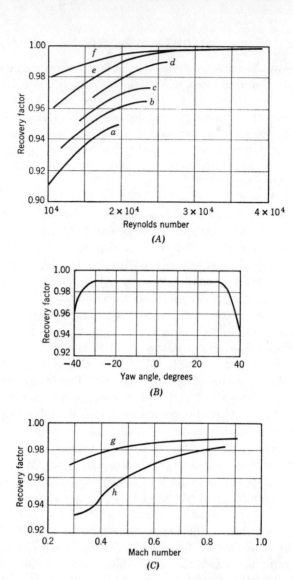

Fig. 10·12. Performance of Winkler and Scadron-Gettleman-Pack probes. (A) Recovery factor versus probe Reynolds number for Winkler probe at various free-stream temperatures and Mach numbers; (B) recovery factor versus yaw angle for Scadron et al. probe; and (C) recovery factor versus free-stream Mach number for Scadron et al. probe. a, M = 7.6, T = 670°K (1206°R); b, M = 6.95, T = 610°K (1098°R); c, M = 6.6, T = 590°K (1062°R); d, M = 5.75, T = 570°K (1026°R); e, M = 5.3, T = 550°K (991°R); f, M = 4.9, T = 330°K (594°R); g, free stream density = 0.10 lb/ft³ (0.0016 g/cm³); and, h, free-stream density = 0.04 lb/ft³ (0.00064 g/cm³). (By permission E. M. Winkler, J. Appl. Phys., 25, no. 2, 232, February, 1954; M. D. Scadron, C. C. Gettleman, and G. J. Pack, Research Memorandum RME 50129, 15–16, U. S. National Advisory Committee for Aeronautics, Washington, December, 1951.)

10·21   VORTEX-TUBE THERMOMETER

The vortex-tube thermometer, introduced by Vonnegut,[114] utilizes the Ranque-Hilsch cooling phenomenon to counteract the stagnation-heating effect. As indicated in Fig. 10·13A, the stream of *ram air* enters tangentially at the inner periphery of a tube, resulting in a whirling of the air about the tube axis. In this rotary motion, the consequent

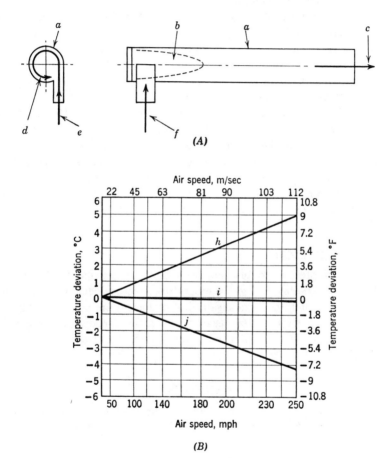

Fig. 10·13. Vortex-tube thermometer. (A) Uniflow design; (B) performance curves at 3000 ft (914 m) altitude. a, Vortex tube; b, cold-air core at which thermometer element is located; c, discharge; d, rotary motion of air in vortex tube; e, tangential air entry; f, ram air; h, conventional thermometer; i, vortex thermometer in housing with valve adjusted; and, j, vortex thermometer in housing with valve wide open. (*By permission L. S. Packer and H. C. Box in Paper 52-A-22, American Society of Mechanical Engineers, New York, 1955; B. Vonnegut in Rev. Sci. Instr., 21, no. 2, 138, February, 1950.*)

centrifuging effect causes a reduction of pressure along the axial zone with a temperature decrease in proportion to the corresponding adiabatic expansion. The pressure reduction can be made as much as twice the difference between the total and the static pressures. Consequently, the temperature can be reduced to well below the free-stream or static temperature. This margin permits compensation for extraneous energy transfers, nonadiabatic effects, etc.[114–116]

It can be shown that the pressure drop along the axis of the vortex tube is proportional to V^2, i.e., to the square of the free-stream velocity. Similarly, the usual impact or stagnation pressure p_t exceeds the static pressure p_s by an amount proportional to V^2. Thereby, the vortex cooling remains proportional to the stagnation heating as the free-stream velocity changes, and this actually occurs over wide velocity ranges. Thus, if the valve is adjusted so that the axial thermometer element indicates the free-stream temperature at one speed, it will continue to do so as the speed is varied (see Fig. 10·13B).[114–116]

Although this device has no value as a primary instrument, it is convenient in yielding the free-stream temperature directly. The alternative stagnation probes require calculations based on supplementary measurements of static and total pressures and Eqs. 10·13 or 10·14 and 10·15.[114–116]

10·22 CONCLUSION

In this chapter, an effort has been made to outline the principal problems and methods of gas-temperature measurement. Other techniques applicable to gases generally but of special importance for gases at very low or very high temperatures or in the nonequilibrium conditions of flames, arcs, and nuclear reactions will be discussed in subsequent chapters.[1, 117–124]

REFERENCES *

1. P. D. Freeze, "Bibliography on the Measurement of Gas Temperature," *Natl. Bur. Standards Circ.* 513, 14 pp., Government Printing Office, Washington (1951).
2. M. Jakob and G. A. Hawkins, *Elements of Heat Transfer*, 3rd ed., 317 pp., John Wiley & Sons, New York, 1957.
3. M. Jakob, *Heat Transfer*, Vol. I, 758 pp., 1949; M. Jakob and S. P. Kezios, Vol. II, 652 pp., 1957, John Wiley & Sons, New York.
4. "The Preparation and Use of Chromel-Alumel Thermocouples for Turbojet Engines," *S.A.E. Aeronautical Information Report* 46, 40 pp., Society of Automotive Engineers (May, 1955).

* See footnote on page 26.

5. M. T. Cichelli, "Design of Temperature Measuring Elements," *Ind. Eng. Chem.,* **40,** no. 6 (June, 1948).

6. N. R. Johnson, A. S. Weinstein, and F. Osterle, "The Influence of Gradient Temperature Fields on Thermocouple Measurements," *Paper* 57-HT-18, 20 pp., American Society of Mechanical Engineers, New York (1957).

7. M. Fishenden and O. A. Saunders, "The Errors in Gas Temperature Measurement and Their Calculation," *J. Inst. Fuel,* **12,** no. 64, pp. S5–S14 (March, 1939).

8. A. Schack, "The Theory and Application of the Suction Pyrometer," *J. Inst. Fuel,* **12,** no. 64, pp. S30–S38 (March, 1939).

9. W. Kraus, *Messung des Temperatur- und Geschwindigkeitsfeldes bei freier Konvektion* (Measurement of Temperature and Velocity Fields in Free Convection), 147 pp., Verlag G. Braun, Karlsruhe (1955).

10. P. L. Tea, *Determination of Configuration Factors for Solid-to-Solid Radiation by Use of Model Chambers,* Doctoral Dissertation, Columbia University, New York, 1955.

11. B. T. Chao, "On a Generalized Procedure for the Calculation of Thermal Radiation Transfer," *Paper* 55-SA-61, pp. 1–11, American Society of Mechanical Engineers, New York (1955).

12. P. L. Tea, Jr. and H. D. Baker, "A Model Method for Determining Geometric Factors in Solid-to-Solid Radiation Heat Transfer," *Paper* 57-SA-10, 9 pp. (1957); *Trans. ASME,* **80,** no. 2, pp. 367–372, American Society of Mechanical Engineers, New York (February, 1958).

13. D. C. Hamilton and W. R. Morgan, "Radiant-Interchange Configuration Factors," *Technical Note* 2836, 110 pp., U. S. National Advisory Committee for Aeronautics, Washington (December, 1952).

14. J. P. Vollrath, "Transparent Thermocouple Protecting Tubes Improve Control," *Instrumentation,* **1,** no. 2, pp. 14–15 (May–June, 1944).

15. F. H. Getman, *Outlines of Theoretical Chemistry,* 4th ed., pp. 365–367, 438, John Wiley & Sons, New York, 1927.

16. "High-Velocity-Stream TC," *Instruments,* **31,** 30th Anniversary Issue, pp. 133–134 (January, 1958).

17. *Steam—Its Generation and Use,* 37th ed., pp. 6.1–6.21, The Babcock & Wilcox Company, New York, 1955.

18. E. F. Fiock and A. I. Dahl, "Temperature Measurements in High-Velocity Streams of Hot Gas," *Report* 3164, 46 pp., Natl. Bur. Standards, Government Printing Office, Washington (1953).

19. E. H. Kennard, *Kinetic Theory of Gases,* pp. 110–113, 177–180, 311–315, McGraw-Hill Book Co., New York, 1938.

20. I. Estermann, "Gases at Low Densities," F. D. Rossini, "Thermodynamics and Physics of Matter," *High Speed Aerodynamics and Jet Propulsion,* **1,** nos. I16–I19, pp. 759–771, Princeton University Press, Princeton, N. J. (1955).

21. M. L. Wiedmann and P. R. Trumpler, "Thermal Accommodation Coefficients," *Trans. ASME,* **2,** pp. 57–64, American Society of Mechanical Engineers (January, 1946).

22. L. B. Thomas and E. B. Schofield, "Thermal Accommodation Coefficient of Helium on a Bare Tungsten Surface," *J. Chem. Phys.,* **23,** no. 5, pp. 861–866 (May, 1955).

23. M. W. Zemansky, *Heat and Thermodynamics*, 4th ed., pp. 116–120, 280–283, McGraw-Hill Book Co., New York, 1957.

24. H. D. Baker, "The Joule Effect in Air," *Phys. Rev.*, **64**, nos. 9 and 10, pp. 302–311 (November, 1943).

25. H. W. Emmons, "Recovery Factors," *Heat Transfer Lectures*, **1**, AECU-116, NEPA-804, pp. 59–79 (December, 1948).

26. W. Wimmer, "Stagnation Temperature Recording," *Technical Memorandum* 967, 27 pp., U. S. National Advisory Committee for Aeronautics, Washington (January, 1941); "Die Messung der Stautemperatur," *Ingenieur-Archiv*, **11**, no. 1, pp. 1–23 (February, 1940).

27. H. J. Van der Maas and S. Wynia, "Corrections on the Thermometer Reading in an Air Stream," *Technical Memorandum* 956, 17 pp., U. S. National Advisory Committee for Aeronautics, Washington (October, 1940); *Correctie voor stuwing en wrijving op thermometeraanuijzingen*, no. 8, Report V834, pp. 28–33, National Luchtvaartlaboratorium, Amsterdam, Holland, 1939.

28. R. C. Dean, Jr., *Aerodynamic Measurements*, 272 pp., Massachusetts Institute of Technology, Cambridge, 1953.

29. R. W. Ladenburg, B. Lewis, R. N. Pease, and H. S. Taylor, *Physical Measurements in Gas Dynamics and Combustion*, 578 pp., Princeton University Press, Princeton, 1954.

30. F. Simmons, "Recovery Corrections for Butt-Welded, Straight-Wire Thermocouples in High-Velocity, High-Temperature Gas Streams," *Research Memorandum*, RME 54G22a, 19 pp., U. S. National Advisory Committee for Aeronautics, Washington (September, 1954).

31. G. E. Glawe, F. S. Simmons, and T. M. Stickney, "Radiation and Recovery Corrections and Time Constants of Several Chromel-Alumel Thermocouple Probes in High-Temperature, High-Velocity Gas Streams," *Technical Note* 3766, U. S. National Advisory Committee for Aeronautics, Washington (October, 1956).

32. W. R. Wimbrow, "Experimental Investigation of Temperature Recovery Factors on Bodies of Revolution at Supersonic Speeds," *Technical Note* 1975, 20 pp., U. S. National Advisory Committee for Aeronautics, Washington (October, 1949).

33. J. R. Stalder, M. W. Rubesin, and T. Tendeland, "Determination of the Laminar-, Transitional-, and Turbulent-Boundary-Layer Temperature-Recovery Factors on a Flat Plate in Supersonic Flow," *Technical Note* 2077, 20 pp., U. S. National Advisory Committee for Aeronautics, Washington (June, 1950).

34. J. Kaye, "Survey of Friction Coefficients, Recovery Factors, and Heat-Transfer Coefficients for Supersonic Flow," *Annual Meeting Paper*, 29 pp., Inst. of Aeronautical Sciences (January, 1953).

35. J. R. Jack and B. Moskowitz, "Experimental Investigation of Temperature Recovery Factors on a 10° Cone at Angle of Attack at a Mach Number of 3.12," *Technical Note* 3256, 15 pp., U. S. National Advisory Committee for Aeronautics, Washington (July, 1954).

36. K. W. Woodfield and R. Bloomfield, "Determine the Static and Total Temperatures of a High Temperature High Velocity Gas Stream," *General Motors Engineering Journal*, **5**, no. 3, pp. 53–54 (July–August–September, 1958).

37. A. C. Hintermann, "Temperature Measurement of Air and Gases at High Velocity of Flow," *The Engineers' Digest, N. Y.*, **2**, no. 7, pp. 359–360 (July, 1945).

38. E. M. Winkler, "Design and Calibration of Stagnation Temperature Probes for Use at High Supersonic Speeds and Elevated Temperatures," *J. Appl. Phys.*, **25**, no. 2, pp. 231–232 (February, 1954).

39. R. J. Sweeney, *Measurement Techniques in Mechanical Engineering*, 309 pp., John Wiley & Sons, New York, 1953.

40. E. Eckert and W. Weise, "Die Messung der Lufttemperatur im Schnellflug" (The Measurement of Air Temperature in Rapid Flight), *Jahrbuch 1941 der deutschen Luftfahrtforschung*, pp. 1723–1726 (1941).

41. W. F. Lindsey, "Calibration of Three Temperature Probes," *Wartime Report* L-273, 6 pp., U. S. National Advisory Committee for Aeronautics, Washington (April, 1942).

42. R. N. Schwartz, "Vibrational Relaxation Times in Gases (Three-Dimensional Treatment)," *J. Chem. Phys.*, **22**, no. 5, pp. 767–773 (May, 1954).

43. W. Griffith, "Vibration Relaxation Times in Gases," *J. Appl. Phys.*, **21**, no. 12, pp. 1319–1325 (December, 1950).

44. T. D. Rossing, R. C. Amme, and S. Legvold, "Heat Capacity Lag of Gaseous Mixtures," *Technical Note* 3558, U. S. National Advisory Committee for Aeronautics, Washington (March, 1956).

45. H. A. Bethe and E. Teller, "Deviations from Thermal Equilibrium in Shock Waves," *BRL Report No.* X-117, Ballistics Research Laboratories, Department of the Army, Aberdeen Proving Ground, Md.

46. R. Walker, "Heat Capacity Lag in Gases," *Technical Note* 2537, U. S. National Advisory Committee for Aeronautics, Washington (November, 1951).

47. R. N. Schwartz, Z. I. Slawsky, and K. F. Herzfeld, "Calculation of Vibration Relaxation Times in Gases," *J. Chem. Phys.*, **20**, no. 10, pp. 1591–1599 (October, 1952).

48. K. F. Herzfeld, "Relaxation of Partial Temperatures," American Institute of Physics, *Temperature*, Vol. II, pp. 233–248, Reinhold Publishing Corp., New York, 1955.

49. J. G. Parker, "Rotational and Vibrational Relaxation in Diatomic Gases," *Physics of Fluids*, **2**, no. 4, pp. 449–462 (July–August, 1959); *Sci. Abstr. A*, **62**, no. 742, p. 1021 (October, 1959).

50. M. Rudin, "Criteria for Thermodynamic Equilibrium in Gas Flow," *Physics of Fluids*, **1**, no. 5, pp. 384–392 (September–October, 1958).

51. W. Tewes, "Temperaturmessfehler in strömenden Gasen und Dämpfen" (Error in Temperature Measurement of Flowing Gases and Vapors), *Zeitschrift für technische Physik*, **22**, no. 7, pp. 160–167 (1941).

52. W. M. Rohsenow, "A Graphical Determination of Unshielded-Thermocouple Thermal Correction," *Trans. ASME*, **68**, pp. 195–198, American Society of Mechanical Engineers, New York (April, 1946).

53. E. M. Moffatt, "Methods of Minimizing Errors in the Measurement of High Temperatures in Gases," *Instruments*, **22**, no. 2, pp. 122–132 (February, 1949).

54. W. J. King, "Measurement of High Temperatures in High-Velocity Gas Streams," *Trans. ASME*, **65**, pp. 421–431, American Society of Mechanical Engineers, New York (July, 1948).

55. L. J. Lina and H. H. Ricker, Jr., "Measurements of Temperature Variations in the Atmosphere Near the Tropopause with Reference to Airspeed Cali-

bration by the Temperature Method," *Technical Note* 2807, 23 pp., U. S. National Advisory Committee for Aeronautics, Washington (October, 1952).

56. J. L. Sloop and G. Morrell, "Temperature Survey of the Wake of Two Closely Located Parallel Jets," *Research Memorandum* E 9121, 37 pp., U. S. National Advisory Committee for Aeronautics, Washington (February, 1950).

57. J. Piccard, H. Larsen, and J. Blomstrand, "Thin-Wire Thermometer for Radiosondes," *Rev. Sci. Instr.,* **25,** no. 10, pp. 959–963 (October, 1954).

58. D. A. Mazzarella and D. K. Kohl, "Air-Temperature on a 420-foot Tower," *Instruments,* **27,** no. 8, pp. 1306–1309 (August, 1954).

59. T. Hayashi, "Periodic Variation of Temperature Caused by Sound Wave," *ETJ Electrotechnical Journal* (Denki-Gakkwai) Tokyo, **3,** no. 5, pp. 103–106 (May, 1939).

60. N. W. Spencer, H. F. Schulte, and H. S. Sicinski, "Rocket Instrumentation for Reliable Upper-Atmosphere Temperature Determination," *Proceedings of the IRE,* **42,** no. 7, pp. 1104–1108 (July, 1954), The Institute of Radio Engineers, New York.

61. W. H. Corcoran, B. Roudebush, and B. H. Sage, "Temperature Gradients in Turbulent Gas Streams," *Chem. Eng. Progr., Trans.,* **43,** no. 3, pp. 135–142 (March, 1947).

62. G. Dätwyler, "Mesure de températures élevées dans les écoulements de gaz" (Measurement of Elevated Temperatures in Flowing Gas), *Compt. rend.,* **233,** pp. 131–133 (July, 1951).

63. G. Dätwyler, "Applications nouvelles de l'anemomètre à fil chaud" (Novel Applications of the Hot-Wire Anemometer), *Compt. rend.,* **235,** pp. 1101–1103 (November, 1952).

64. H. F. Mullikin, "Gas-temperature Measurement and the High-Velocity Thermocouple," American Institute of Physics, *Temperature,* pp. 775–784, Reinhold Publishing Corp., New York, 1941.

65. R. Jackson, "Newer Methods of Gas Temperature Measurement—Review Series No. 105," *Bull. Brit. Coal Utilisation Research Assoc.,* **15,** no. 7, pp. 245–256 (July, 1951).

66. W. G. Spangenberg, "Heat Loss Characteristics of Hot-Wire Anemometers at Various Densities in Transonic and Supersonic Flow," *Technical Note* 3381, 82 pp., U. S. National Advisory Committee for Aeronautics, Washington (May, 1955).

67. E. F. Fiock and A. I. Dahl, "The Measurement of Gas Temperature by Immersion-Type Instruments," *J. Am. Rocket Soc.,* **23,** no. 3, pp. 155–164 (May–June, 1953).

68. E. F. Fiock and A. I. Dahl, "The Use of Thermocouples in High-Velocity Gas Streams," *J. Am. Soc. Naval Engrs.,* **60,** no. 2, pp. 139–162 (May, 1948).

69. E. F. Fiock, L. O. Olsen, and P. D. Freeze, "The Use of Thermocouples in Streaming Exhaust Gas," *Third Symposium on Combustion, Flame, and Explosion Phenomena,* pp. 655–662, The Williams & Wilkins Co., Baltimore, 1949.

70. A. I. Dahl and E. F. Fiock, "Thermocouple Pyrometers for Gas Turbines," *Paper* 48-SA-29, 11 pp., American Society of Mechanical Engineers, New York (1948).

71. A. I. Dahl and E. F. Fiock, "Shielded Thermocouples for Gas Turbines," *Trans. ASME,* **71,** pp. 153–161, American Society of Mechanical Engineers, New York (February, 1949).

72. A. I. Dahl, "Thermocouple Junction with Radiation Shield," *U. S. Patent Office* 2472808, 3 pp., Government Printing Office, Washington (1946).

73. A. I. Dahl, "Measurement of High Temperatures in Gas Streams," *Petrol. Refiner,* **29,** pp. 115–122 (March, 1950).

74. "New Thermocouple Assembly for Gas Turbines and Jet Engines," *Instruments,* **20,** no. 3, pp. 258, 260 (March, 1947).

75. R. T. Haslam and E. L. Chappell, "The Measurement of the Temperature of a Flowing Gas," *Ind. Eng. Chem.,* **17,** no. 4, pp. 402–408 (April, 1925).

76. G. Srikantiah and A. Ramachandran, "Temperature Measurements in Low Velocity High Temperature Gas Streams," *J. Indian Inst. Sci., B,* **37,** no. 1, pp. 41–57 (January, 1955).

77. H. F. Mullikin and W. J. Osborn, "Accuracy Tests of the High-Velocity Thermocouple," American Institute of Physics, *Temperature,* pp. 805–829, Reinhold Publishing Corp., New York, 1941.

78. F. Mayer, "Die Wärmetechnik der Siemens-Martin Oefen" (The Temperature Technique of the Siemens-Martin Furnaces), *Stahl u. Eisen,* **28,** no. 22 (May, 1908).

79. J. S. Marsh, "Significance of Air Temperature in Open-Hearth Operation," *Instruments,* **26,** no. 12, pp. 1876–1878, 1908, 1910 (December, 1953).

80. C. E. Lucke, "Apparatus for Measuring Gas Temperatures," *U. S. Patent Office* 2006469, 3 pp., Government Printing Office, Washington (1934).

81. T. Land, "Suction Pyrometry," *Instruments,* **29,** no. 7, pp. 1314–1320 (July, 1956).

82. P. Cohen, R. C. Corey, and J. W. Myers, "Methods and Instrumentation for Furnace Heat-Absorption Studies: Temperature and Composition of Gases at Furnace Outlet," *Trans. ASME,* **71,** no. 8, pp. 965–978, American Society of Mechanical Engineers, New York (November, 1949).

83. H. F. Mullikin, "Accurate Measurement of High Gas Temperatures," *Power,* **78,** p. 565 (October, 1934).

84. G. V. Parmelee and R. G. Huebscher, "The Shielding of Thermocouples from the Effects of Radiation," *Heating, Piping, & Air Conditioning, ASHVE* Journal Section, **18,** pp. 144–146 (February, 1946).

85. E. M. Moffatt, "Errors in High Temperature Probes for Gases," *Paper* 48-A-52, 19 pp., American Society of Mechanical Engineers, New York (1948).

86. T. Land and R. Barber, "The Design of Suction Pyrometers," *Trans. Society Instrument Technology,* **6,** no. 3, pp. 112–130 (September, 1954).

87. T. Land and R. Barber, "Suction Pyrometers in Theory and Practice," *J. Iron Steel Inst. London,* **184,** pp. 269–273 (November, 1956).

88. R. Barber, R. Jackson, T. Land, and G. G. Thurlow, "A Suction Pyrometer for Measuring Gas Exit Temperatures from the Combustion Chambers of Water-tube Boilers," *J. Inst. Fuel,* **27,** no. 163, pp. 408–416 (August, 1954).

89. R. Jackson, "The Measurement of Gas Temperature by Thermocouples— Review Series No. 87," *Bull. Brit. Coal Utilisation Research Assoc.,* **14,** no. 2, pp. 33–39 (February, 1950).

90. J. S. Marsh, "Significance of Air Temperature in Open Hearth Operation," *Yearbook of the American Iron and Steel Institute,* pp. 185–205, American Iron and Steel Institute, New York, 1951.

91. J. G. Bartas and E. Mayer, "Estimation of Temperature Patterns in Multiply-Shielded Systems," *Paper* 56-A-130, pp. 1–11, American Society of Mechanical Engineers, New York (1956).

92. H. C. Hottel and E. S. Cohen, "Radiant Heat Exchange in a Gas-Filled Enclosure," *Paper* 57-HT-23, pp. 1–36, American Institute of Chemical Engineers, New York (1957).

93. E. M. Moffatt, "Multiple-Shielded High-Temperature Probes," *S.A.E. Quart. Trans.*, Society of Automotive Engineers, **6**, no. 4, pp. 567–580 (October, 1952).

94. H. Leuenberger and R. A. Person, "Compilation of Radiation Shape Factors for Cylindrical Assemblies," *Paper* 56-A-144, pp. 1–19, American Society of Mechanical Engineers, New York (1956).

95. M. Fishenden, "The Use of Thermocouples for Temperature Measurement," *Journal of the Institution of Heating Ventilating Engineers,* **7**, pp. 15–35 (March, 1939).

96. W. M. Rohsenow and J. P. Hunsaker, "Determination of the Thermal Correction for a Single-Shielded Thermocouple," *Paper* 46-A-53, pp. 1–5 (1946), *Trans. ASME,* **69**, no. 6, pp. 699–704 (August, 1947), American Society of Mechanical Engineers, New York.

97. E. P. Walsh and S. Allen, "A Pyrometer for Measuring Total Temperatures in Low Density Gas Streams," *Paper* 49-A-66, 13 pp., American Society of Mechanical Engineers, New York (1949).

98. K. Terada and G. Yamamoto, "Method for Measuring Air Temperature on a High-Speed Airplane," *Journal of Meteorology,* **4**, pp. 201–202 (December, 1947).

99. H. W. Sibert, "Determination of Airplane Thermometer Recovery Factors in Flight," *Journal of Aeronautical Sciences,* **14**, no. 6, pp. 364, 367 (June, 1947).

100. D. L. Goldstein and R. Scherrer, "Design and Calibration of a Total-Temperature Probe for Use at Supersonic Speeds," *Technical Note* 1885, 17 pp., U. S. National Advisory Committee for Aeronautics, Washington (May, 1949).

101. H. M. Beede and C. R. Droms, "A Simplified Thermocouple for Temperature Measurements in High Velocity Gas Streams," *Instruments,* **7**, no. 3, pp. 41–44 (March, 1951).

102. J. D. Humphreys, "Probe Recovery Factor," *Instruments,* **27**, no. 2, p. 283 (February, 1954).

103. Rosemount Engineering Company, "Temperature Probe," *Rev. Sci. Instr.,* **27**, no. 10, p. 894 (October, 1956).

104. E. Cartotto, "Instrumentation for Rocket Testing," *Instruments,* **26**, no. 4, pp. 585–587 (April, 1953).

105. G. Srikantiah and A. Ramachandran, "Measurement of High Temperatures in Gas Streams," *Electrotechnics Bangalore,* **25**, pp. 26–38 (1955).

106. S. J. Markowski and E. M. Moffatt, "Instrumentation for the Development of Aircraft Power Plant Components Involving Fluid Flow," *S.A.E. National Aeronautical Meeting Paper,* 15 pp., Soc. Automotive Engineers, New York (April, 1947).

107. H. C. Hottel and A. Kalitinsky, "Temperature Measurements in High-Velocity Air Streams," *J. Appl. Mechanics,* **12**, no. 3, pp. A25–A32 (March, 1945).

108. E. M. Winkler, "Stagnation Temperature Probes for Use at High Supersonic Speeds and Elevated Temperatures," *Navord Report* 3834, 16 pp., U. S. Naval Ordnance Laboratory, White Oak, Maryland (October, 1954).

109. M. D. Scadron, C. C. Gettelman, and G. J. Pack, "Performance of Three High-Recovery Factor Thermocouple Probes for Room-Temperature Operation," *Research Memorandum* RM E 50129, 18 pp., U. S. National Advisory Committee for Aeronautics, Washington (December, 1950).

110. J. W. Murdock and E. F. Fiock, "Measurement of Temperatures in High-Velocity Steam," *Paper* 50-S-36, 13 pp. (1950), *Trans. ASME,* **72,** no. 11, pp. 1155–1161 (November, 1950), American Society of Mechanical Engineers, New York.

111. L. Maimquist, "Temperature Measurements in Gases Flowing at High Velocity," *The Engineers' Digest, N. Y.,* **10,** no. 3, p. 104 (March, 1949).

112. F. D. Werner, "Total Temperature Measurements," *Paper* 58-AV-17, 12 pp., American Society of Mechanical Engineers, New York (1958).

113. C. H. Bosanquet, "The Wall Effect in Gas Temperature Measurement," *J. Inst. Fuel,* **12,** no. 64, pp. S14–S18 (March, 1939).

114. B. Vonnegut, "Vortex Thermometer for Measuring True Air Temperatures and True Air Speeds in Flight," *Rev. Sci. Instr.,* **21,** no. 2, pp. 136–141 (February, 1950).

115. J. E. Lay, "An Experimental and Analytical Study of Vortex-Flow Temperature Separation by Superposition of Spiral and Axial Flows—Parts I and II," *Papers* 58-SA-71 and 58-A-90, 13 and 9 pp., American Society of Mechanical Engineers, New York (1958).

116. L. S. Packer and H. C. Box, "Vortex-Tube Free-Air Thermometry," *Paper* 55-A-22, 9 pp., American Society of Mechanical Engineers, New York (1955).

117. L. B. Haig, "A Design Procedure for Thermocouple Probes," *Paper* 158C, 15 pp. (1960), SAE National Aeronautic Meeting, Society of Automotive Engineers, New York.

118. J. D. Meador, "Dynamic Testing of Gas Sampling Thermocouples," *Paper* 158G, 7 pp. (1960), SAE National Aeronautic Meeting, Society of Automotive Engineers, New York.

119. R. J. Moffat, "A Stable High Temperature Thermometry Rig," *Paper* 158E, 9 pp. (1960), SAE National Aeronautic Meeting, Society of Automotive Meeting, Society of Automotive Engineers, New York.

120. J. F. Potts and D. L. McElroy, "Basic Studies on Base-Metal Thermocouples," *Paper* 158A, 5 pp. (1960), SAE National Aeronautic Meeting, Society of Automotive Engineers, New York.

121. F. S. Faizullov, N. N. Sobolev, and E. M. Kudryavtsev, "Temperature of Nitrogen and Air Behind a Shock Wave" (in Russian), *Doklady Akademii Nauk SSSR,* **127,** no. 3, pp. 541–544 (July, 1959).

122. S. A. Losev and N. A. Generalov, "Measurement of the Gas Temperature Behind a Shock Wave" (in Russian), *Pribory i Tekhnika E'ksperimenta,* no. 3, pp. 108–110, May–June, 1959.

123. G. Charatis and T. D. Wilkerson, "Excitation Temperature of Chromium in the Shock Tube," *Physics of Fluids,* **2,** no. 5, pp. 578–579 (September–October, 1959).

124. R. P. Benedict, "Temperature Measurement in Moving Fluids," *Paper* 59-A-257, American Society of Mechanical Engineers, New York (1959).

11

HIGH-TEMPERATURE GASES

11·1 INTRODUCTION

At sufficiently high temperatures, all substances evaporate completely and assume the gaseous state. Thereby, the problems in measuring high temperatures are inevitably those where the work is with high-temperature gases. Usually, it is the effects of chemical or nuclear reactions which raise gases to the very high temperatures, and it is the circumstances attending such reactions which result in the most serious difficulties confronting measurement. However, such reactions are not always in progress, and, even when they are, the specific difficulties peculiar to high temperature levels alone constitute an important class of problems. Dissociation effects resulting from elevated temperatures will be discussed for the most part in Ch. 14.

In the present chapter, the term *high temperature* will be taken to imply a temperature at which the use of any solid thermometer probe is impracticable or impossible. Even when made of the most refractory materials, a device will survive only at temperatures below a certain limit. At higher temperatures, it will be destroyed. Thus, there are temperature regions where no instrument can be used which depends for its indication on an element attaining thermal equilibrium with the source-body temperature.[1-9]

A certain popular view supposes that radiation techniques are inevitably the recourse when temperatures are too high for the use of solid thermometer elements; however, ideally *transparent* bodies do not radiate. Therefore, measurement of the temperatures of ideally transparent gases by optical or radiation pyrometry is impossible. At best, many actual gases can only be made sufficiently absorbing by subsidiary *coloring* techniques. Such recourse, however, is not always possible and is often undesirable. Many common gases, as, for example, air, hydrogen, oxygen, nitrogen, argon, helium, and neon, are of the transparent variety. These gases neither radiate nor absorb extensively outside the visible and ultraviolet regions; whereas, temperatures attainable by the combustion of fuels do not suffice to produce much radiation in these wavelength ranges. In this sense, such gases are for many practical purposes to be regarded as transparent.[10]

Fortunately, however, for use with gases, there are several alternative methods, and it is the objective in the present chapter to describe the more important of these procedures. None of them depends on requiring any part of the apparatus to attain the gas temperature. Although optical devices may be applied, measurement of thermal radiation from the gas is not generally involved. Density variation in the gas resulting from temperature change is usually the underlying principle. However, the means for indication of the density variations differ widely.[11]

11·2 DENSITY OF A CONFINED GAS

The relative values of the pressure p, temperature T, and density ρ (specific volume $v = 1/\rho$) for any pure substance in the gaseous state are governed by a functional relationship called the *equation of state*. For gaseous mixtures, the concentrations of the various constituents behave as additional variables in this equation. Thus

$$T = \phi(p, \rho, c_1, c_2, c_3, \cdots, c_n) \tag{11·1}$$

where T is the temperature, °K; p is the pressure, dynes/cm² (1.013 $\times 10^6$ dynes/cm² = 1 atm); ρ is the density, g/cm³; and c_1, c_2, c_3, $\cdots$, c_n are the concentrations of the various constituents in the mixture, g/gram of mixture. The exact form of the function ϕ is never known; therefore, application is limited to the use of experimental data plotted as curves and charts and to approximate formulas. Many such data and many such formulas are available.[12-15]

The simplest of these formulas is

$$T = pV/CmR = p/\rho CR \tag{8·12}$$

where T is the average temperature, °K; p is the absolute pressure, dynes/cm²; V is the volume, cm³; m is the mass of the gaseous body, g; ρ is the density g/cm³; C is the compressibility factor, dimensionless (see Sec. 8·7); and R is the gas constant per unit mass, ergs/g °K. The gas constant R is given by

$$R = R_m/M \tag{8·13}$$

where R_m is the gas constant for one mole of the substance, 8.3136 $\times 10^7$ ergs/gram molecule °K; and M is the molecular weight.

When the gas consists of a mixture of different-molecular-weight molecules, M is approximated by

$$M = 1/(c_1/M_1 + c_2/M_2 + c_3/M_3 + \cdots) \qquad (6\cdot20)$$

where M_1 is the molecular weight of constituent 1; and c_1 is the number of mass units of constituent 1 per unit mass of gas, etc.[16]

Means for measuring the average temperature of a body of confined gas through pressure indications according to Eqs. $11\cdot1$, $8\cdot12$, $8\cdot13$ and $6\cdot20$ are described in Sec. $8\cdot7$. In transient phenomena, such as those that occur in the cylinder space of an internal-combustion engine, the containing vessel need not acquire the gas temperature. Under such circumstances, this method can be used for the measurement of high temperatures.[17,18]

11·3　THE VELOCITY OF SOUND

The velocity of sound in gases is given by the equation

$$a = (\gamma RT)^{\frac{1}{2}} \qquad (11\cdot2)$$

where a is the velocity of sound, cm/sec; γ is the ratio of the specific heat at constant pressure to that at constant volume for the gas; R is the gas constant for the particular gas, ergs/g °K; and T is the absolute temperature, °K.[19,20]

In applying this equation to the measurement of temperature T through measurement of the velocity a, one must beware of the limits of its applicability. It is derived for the theoretical case of a small disturbance propagated adiabatically in an ideal gas. Deresiewicz [21] notes that very high frequency waves occur isothermally rather than adiabatically. For this case, the factor γ would be absent. At pressures high with respect to the pressure at the critical point and temperatures low relatively to the critical temperature, nonideal behavior must be expected and the compressibility factor C of Eq. $8\cdot12$ (assumed constant) applied such that [19-21]

$$a = (\gamma CRT)^{\frac{1}{2}} \qquad (11\cdot3)$$

Waves generated by sharp high-intensity pulses, such as electric arcs and sparks, are not generally good approximations to small disturbances. Suits [20,22,23] has shown that sound waves initiated by 30-kv 1-μf condenser discharges through 0.05-mm (0.002-in.) diameter 5-cm long copper fuses traverse the first centimeter at speeds of several times the normal velocity of sound. Attenuation is, however, rapid in the first few centimeters. With spark intensities adequate for temperature-measurement applications, he found the normal velocity to be very nearly attained after 1-cm travel of the wave.[19, 20, 22, 23]

At high frequencies f, the velocity of sound a is greater than that given by Eq. 11·2. The increase results from several factors. As an isothermal disturbance, the velocity would tend to be reduced. However, if the period of oscillation, i.e., $1/f$, is short relatively to the relaxation time τ, the effective value of γ is increased. Thus, for times of the order of magnitude of τ, the internal-energy states do not attain equilibrium. Thereby, in effect, the specific heats lack the contributions corresponding to the internal-energy states. Then

$$\gamma = c_p/c_v = (c_v + R)/c_v \qquad (11·4)$$

increases as c_v decreases, since the gas constant R remains unchanged. The increase in γ results in a corresponding increase in the sonic velocity a. Since τ may be as long as 10^{-5} sec, abnormal sonic velocities tend to arise at frequencies greater than 10^5 cycles/sec.[19, 20, 24, 25]

In a high-temperature gas, the speed of sound depends also upon the chemical composition and chemical reaction rates. Thus, two limiting sound speeds are normally distinguished: (1), that of "frozen" or constant chemical composition; and, (2), the "equilibrium" sound speed. The latter assumes that the reaction can keep pace with the temperature and pressure fluctuations as the sound wave passes.[25]

A more obscure effect is demonstrated with monatomic gases such as helium and argon. For these gases, energy storage in the internal-energy states is small. Thereby, relaxation lags cannot explain abnormal sonic velocities. This phenomenon is briefly described as a selective behavior on the part of the faster molecules in propagating pressure pulses. There is also a tendency to abnormal velocities at low pressures. Thus, Abbey [26, 27] and Barlow [26] observed a progressive increase in a for air at pressures below 15 cm of mercury, amounting to about 2 per cent at a few millimeters pressure. For methane, the effect was a decrease at 1 cm followed by a slight increase at pressures of less than 0.5 cm of mercury.[26-28]

11·4 VELOCITY-OF-SOUND METHODS

Two techniques based on the temperature dependence of acoustic velocities in gases were described in Sec. 6·9. From the character of the procedures indicated, it is evident that no part of the apparatus is required to attain the gas temperature.

Thus, the *transmitting* and *detecting* electrodes or crystals can be protected by thin sheets of cooler gas. Such protecting gas layers may

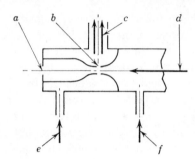

Fig. 11·1. Pneumatic window. *a*, Aperture; *b*, effective plane of window; *c*, exhaust gases to suction pump; *d*, line of sight; *e*, hot gases; and, *f*, transparent cool gases. (*By permission H. C. Hottel and H. G. Mangelsdorf in Trans. Am. Inst. Chem. Engrs.*, **31**, *517, September, 1935.*)

occur naturally as when the sound wave is passed through an open flame. Otherwise, the electrodes can be recessed and the recesses cooled by circulating air so directed (see Fig. 11·1) as not to disturb the body of gas under investigation. The end layers of cool gas must be treated as sources of error. Thus, they may be maintained constant in path length and density and included in a calibration; or by varying thicknesses in measured amounts, their effect can be subtracted out in successive readings.[29]

The Suits [20, 22, 23] method is better adapted to high-temperature work than the oscillating-quartz-crystal technique, since the Suits electrodes can be made of refractory metals and coupled by massive heat-flow paths to water jackets.[20, 22, 23, 30]

The method of Livengood,[31–34] Taylor,[31–33, 35] Wu,[31–33] Rona,[34] and Baruch [34] was developed for measuring temperatures in the combustion chambers of piston internal-combustion engines. Here, the quartz crystals used by Marlow, Nisewanger, and Cady are replaced by water-cooled brass rods mounted so that their opposing ends are flush with the inner surface of the wall (see Fig. 11·2). Oscillating barium titanate ceramic "crystals" mounted on the outer ends of the rods are the sensitive elements. Electric pulses from a 2.5-megacycle (2.5 × 10⁶-cycles/sec) oscillating circuit cause the "crystals" on the transmitter rod to vibrate. This mechanical motion is conducted to the rod which then starts a sound-wave pulse across the cavity. On reaching the detector, the wave stimulates mechanical vibrations in the detector rod which are then converted to electric oscillations by the second barium titanate "crystal." Both the transmitter pulse and that absorbed by the detector are applied to a cathode-ray tube. The time lag between them can then be displayed as a measurable horizontal distance on the oscilloscope screen. However, it is more satisfactory to employ a delay circuit whereby the locations of the two signal traces can be adjusted to coincide on the screen. The time delay thus ap-

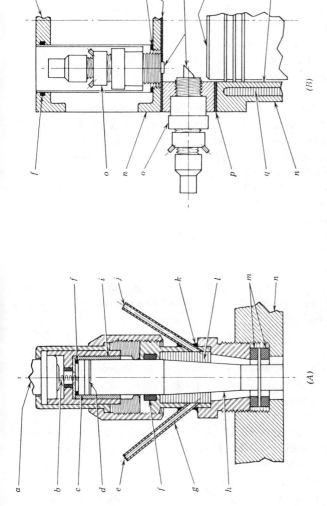

Fig. 11·2. Velocity-of-sound apparatus. (A) Sending and receiving transducer design; (B) transducers installed in engine cylinder. a, Coaxial-cable fitting; b, contact spring; c, backing plate; d, barium titanate ceramic "crystal"; e, cooling-water inlet; f, O-ring gasket; g, stainless-steel tube; h, brass coupling rod; i, ground connection; j, cooling-water outlet; k, silver-solder joint; l, water jacket; m, acoustical isolation; n, engine-cylinder wall; o, transducer assembly; p, gasket; q, engine-wall water jacket; r, piston; and, s, cylinder wall.   (By permission J. C. Livengood, C. F. Taylor, and P. C. Wu in S.A.E. Annual Meeting Paper 3C, 20 pp., Society of Automotive Engineers, January, 1958.)

plied is then read on a dial and can be determined to within about 0.05 μsec (0.5×10^{-7} sec).

The measured time lag consists essentially of the interval required for the sound wave to cross the cavity. However, internal lags in the electric circuit and in the mechanical components of the system are additive quantities. These increments are characteristic of the instrument and can be calibrated by varying the sound path.[31-36]

After all corrections have been made, the remaining error in the measurement of the sound-wave transit time is estimated to be around 0.1 μsec (10^{-7} sec). For the 0.6-in. (1.55-cm) sound path used, this corresponded to a precision to within about 1 per cent in the measurement of temperature.[31-35]

Moeckel and Evvard[37] have developed a method using the combustion chamber itself as the measuring device. A loud source of noise, resulting from detonating combustion of the charge (i.e., *knock*) or artificially produced by the explosion of a *pistol primer*, sets the cavity gases in vibration. Analysis indicates that only one of the natural modes for a cylindrical gas column of the proportions occurring in an engine cylinder lies below 10,000 cycles/sec. A filter in the leads of the *magnetostrictive-element* detector limits the *passband* to a frequency range of 4000 to 10,000 cycles/sec. The 4000-cycle/sec *threshold* then excludes ordinary engine-cycle frequencies. Thereby, only one frequency is transmitted for display on the oscilloscope screen. The corresponding wavelength λ in the gas is then fixed by the cavity dimensions, and the concurrent velocity a of the acoustic wave in the gas column is given by

$$a = f\lambda \qquad (6 \cdot 22)$$

where a is the velocity of sound, cm/sec; λ is the resonant wavelength, cm; and f is the frequency, measured by display on a cathode-ray-oscilloscope screen, cycles/sec. The corresponding temperature is computed from Eqs. $6 \cdot 19$, and $6 \cdot 20$ or $6 \cdot 21$.

The resulting determinations of engine-gas temperatures were self-consistent to within 25 or 50°F (14 or 28°C) and in agreement with those obtained by the *spectral-line-reversal* method. It was estimated that errors of 3.5 and 14 per cent, respectively, in the absolute temperatures would result from neglecting the variations in the ratio of specific heats γ with fuel-air ratios and temperature and the variations in the mean molecular weight M with temperature.[37]

Various other methods of measuring the velocity of sound have been used for temperature measurement. Thus, Barrett and Suomi,[38] in quest of a balloon-borne device for *telemetering* upper-air temperatures, produced an instrument which *broadcasts* a continuous signal. The instantaneous frequencies in the signal wave are characterized by the absolute temperatures at the location of the balloon. The transmitter and detector transducers are piezoelectric crystals spaced about 16 in. (41 cm) apart in the open air. In the *pulse-feedback system* used, an electrically generated pulse, after traversing the sound-wave path in air, *triggers* the next pulse. Thus, successive pulses occur at time intervals determined by the time lag of the system. This time lag, as in the method of Livengood [31–35] et al., consists of the interval required for the sound to traverse the air space plus that corresponding to the instrument constant. The original high-frequency-pulse oscillations are then filtered out, leaving an envelope wave of temperature-dependent frequency f in the order of 1000 cycles/sec. This wave, after amplification, is broadcast to the ground.[19, 26, 31–35, 38]

The velocity of sound at the balloon is then

$$a = D/(1/f - \tau_i) \qquad (11 \cdot 5)$$

where a is the velocity of sound, cm/sec; D is the sound-wave path, cm; f is the broadcast frequency, cycles/sec; and τ_i is the circuit-delay time of the instrument, sec. With τ_i calculated as 33.7 μsec. (33.7 $\times$ 10^{-6} sec) and $1/f$ ranging from 1000 to 1200 μsec, the instrument correction can be made with precision. Temperatures are then computed from Eqs. 6·19, and 6·20 or 6·21.[19, 38]

11·5   ORIFICE METHODS—SUBSONIC-PROBE THEORY

If a stream of gas passes in low subsonic motion through two successive orifices (see Fig. 11·3), the mass-flow rate W is given by

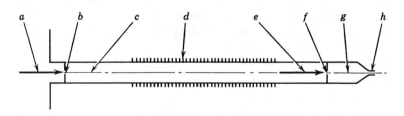

Fig. 11·3. Two-orifice system. *a*, Entering gas stream at temperature T_1 and pressure p_1; *b*, first measuring orifice; *c*, hot gases at pressure p_2; *d*, cooling fins to reduce temperature of hot gases to more conveniently measured value T_2; *e*, gas stream at temperature T_2 and pressure p_2; *f*, second measuring orifice; *g*, gases at pressure p_3; and, *h*, control valve. (*By permission Fairchild Camera and Instrument Corp., Jamaica, N. Y.*)

$$W = K_1 A_1 [(p_1 - p_2) p_1 / T_1]^{1/2} = K_2 A_2 [(p_2 - p_3) p_2 / T_2]^{1/2}$$
$$(11 \cdot 6)$$

where W is the mass-flow rate, g/sec; p_1 and T_1 are the absolute (static) pressure, dynes/cm^2 (1 atm = 1.013×10^6 dynes/cm^2; 1 bar = 10^6 dynes/cm^2) and the absolute (static) temperature, °K, respectively, before the first orifice; p_2 and T_2 are these quantities before the second orifice, p_3 is the exit pressure at the second orifice, dynes/cm^2; A_1 and A_2 are the effective areas of the two orifices, respectively, cm^2; and K_1 and K_2 are the orifice coefficients for the two orifices, respectively.

Solving Eq. 11·6 for T_1, we have

$$T_1 = (K_1 A_1 / K_2 A_2)^2 [(p_1 - p_2) p_1 / (p_2 - p_3) p_2] T_2 \qquad (11 \cdot 7)$$

The pressure drop $p_1 - p_2$ can usually be kept small enough so that the ratio p_1/p_2 varies by only small percentages. Since Eqs. 11·6 and 11·7 apply accurately only when p_1/p_2 and p_2/p_3 are thus each close to unity, it is good design practice to arrange matters this way. The orifice areas and constants A_1, A_2, K_1, and K_2 remain substantially constant. Hence, these quantities can be grouped into one coefficient K to be determined by calibration. The temperature T_1 is then given by

$$T_1 = K[(p_1 - p_2) / (p_2 - p_3)] T_2 \qquad (11 \cdot 8)$$

Since adiabatic flow has not been assumed, cooling arrangements can be introduced between the two orifices. By these means, T_2 can always be reduced to a conveniently measured temperature level.

What remains then for the determination of T_1 is the task of measuring the static-pressure drops $p_1 - p_2$ and $p_2 - p_3$ across the two orifices, respectively. Static-tube openings in the duct wall suffice to transmit the pressures p_1, p_2, and p_3 to indicators which can then be operated at room temperature. Thus, no portion of the apparatus is required to assume the temperature T_1.[13, 39-46]

If the free-stream velocity relative to that of the instrument exceeds 100 ft/sec (3050 cm/sec), i.e., a Mach number of $M = 0.09$ or at most $M = 0.25$, corrections are necessary. Thus, in the customary operation of an orifice probe, the velocity before the first orifice is reduced to a low value. Thereby, the static temperature T_1 and static pressure p_1 correspond approximately to their stagnation values, i.e., to the total temperature and the total pressure at this point. The calibrated values for the recovery factor r would have to be applied to determine the free-stream total temperature. The free-stream (static) temperature would then be computed from Eqs. 10·12 to 10·15.[43, 44, 46, 47]

11·6 SONIC-FLOW ORIFICE PROBE—THEORY

When the pressure drop across an orifice exceeds a certain critical value, the flow velocity through the orifice is that of sound. For the sonic-flow nozzle or orifice, the mass-flow rate is given by

$$W = K\psi(\gamma)p_t A/(RT_t)^{1/2} \qquad (11·9)$$

where

$$\psi(\gamma) = \gamma^{1/2}/[(\gamma + 1)/2]^{(\gamma + 1)/2(\gamma - 1)} \qquad (11·10)$$

and where W is the mass-flow rate, g/sec; T_t is total absolute temperature, °K; p_t is the total pressure, dynes/cm²; A is the nozzle-throat orifice area, cm²; γ is the ratio of the specific heat at constant pressure to that at constant volume for the gas; R is the gas constant for the particular gas, ergs/g °K; and K is the discharge coefficient.[43–45, 48, 49, 51]

It is to be noted that the values for T_t, P_t, γ, and R are those upstream or before entering the orifice.

When the same mass flow passes through two successive nozzles or orifices (see Fig. 11·3) and the restrictions are such that the critical-pressure ratio is exceeded across each, the sonic-flow relation Eq. 11·9 applies in both cases. Then.

$$W = K_1\psi(\gamma_1)p_{t_1}A_1/(R_1 T_{t_1})^{1/2} = K_2\psi(\gamma_2)p_{t_2}A_2/(R_2 T_{t_2})^{1/2} \qquad (11·11)$$

and

$$T_{t_1} = (K_1/K_2)^2[\psi(\gamma_1)/\psi(\gamma_2)]^2[R_2 A_1^2/R_1 A_2^2](p_{t_1}/p_{t_2})^2 T_{t_2} \qquad (11·12)$$

The ratio of specific heats γ for gases varies with temperature and degree of dissociation. Hence, when the temperature drop from T_1 to T_2 is large, the factor $\psi(\gamma_1)/\psi(\gamma_2)$ may differ substantially from unity and may become a function of both static and stagnation pressures and temperatures at stations 1 and 2. These static temperatures depend in turn on the local values of the flow velocities (see Eq. 10·11) at successive points in the progress through the instrument.[43, 44, 46, 48]

If the gas dissociates appreciably at the higher temperature T_1 so that recombination occurs in the temperature drop from T_1 to T_2, the concentrations c_1, c_2, c_3, $\cdots$, etc., of the various constituent gases will change. These gases will have differing molecular weights: M_1, M_2, M_3, $\cdots$, etc. Consequently, the mean-value gas constant R will vary according to the relation

$$R = R_m/M \qquad (8·13)$$

where R_m is the universal gas constant, 8.3136×10^7 ergs/mole °K; and M is the mean molecular weight given by

$$M = 1/(c_1/M_1 + c_2/M_2 + c_3/M_3 + \cdots) \qquad (6 \cdot 20)$$

Thus, in the temperature drop T_1 to T_2, R may change such that R_2/R_1 differs appreciably from unity and is a function of both temperatures T_1 and T_2.

In general, the effects of changing values of γ and R are best determined by over-all calibration. When over-all calibration is regarded as inconvenient or impossible, calculations based on tabulated data constitute means for the estimation of corrections. The corrections include the effects of nonideal-gas behavior. They thus tend to be significant at high pressures and low temperatures. For carefully designed and precisely constructed nozzles, however, the discharge coefficients K_1 and K_2 have values near unity. If the calculated corrections are not too large, the results may suffice for primary temperature determinations.[16,44,48,49]

Blackshear[48] has made calculations showing that, if the vibrational relaxation time is as long as 10^{-5} sec, the rate of change of translational temperature in passing through an orifice may be so great that the vibrational-energy storage does not "keep pace" with the process. Thereby, the *populations* in the vibrational-energy states may not change much during the expansion. Under these circumstances, the gas behaves as though the vibrational-energy contributions to the specific heats were absent or "frozen." In the range from room temperature up to nearly 10,000°K (18,000°R), the specific heat c_v then remains effectively almost unchanged across the orifice. If the gas constant R also remains unchanged, i.e., if no dissociation occurs, the ratio of specific-heats γ behaves as a constant. Blackshear suggests that, for air in the vicinity of room temperature and a suitable orifice arrangement, the factor $\psi(\gamma_1)/\psi(\gamma_2)$ may be regarded as a constant corresponding to the value $\gamma = 1.4$.

Vibrational relaxation times, however, are not in general as long as 10^{-5} sec. Hence, this simplification cannot be assumed as a general rule applying to all gases.

When R and γ do behave as constants to a satisfactory approximation, Eq. 11·12 can be simplified as

$$T_{t_1} = K(p_{t_1}/p_{t_2})^2 T_{t_2} \qquad (11 \cdot 13)$$

where K is a coefficient to be determined in calibration.[43]

Since adiabaticity has not been assumed, cooling can be provided and T_{t2} reduced to a conveniently measured temperature. The remaining task is that of measuring the ratio of total pressures p_{t1}/p_{t2}. Pitot tubes or other impact openings will suffice to transmit these pressures to indicators. Such instruments can of course be placed at suitable distances and allowed to assume room temperature.[48]

The impact-tube openings, the first orifice, and the mouth surfaces of the probe are exposed to gases at the temperature T_1. It is not, however, necessary that the mouth surfaces assume any approximation to the gas temperature. Thus, they can be cooled in whatever degree is necessary for their preservation.

The stream diameter contracts proportionately as the velocity rises to the sonic level at the orifice. If adequate precautions are not taken in design, gas may be drawn from layers sweeping the outer probe surfaces. When the inflow thus unduly sweeps the cooled surfaces before entering the first orifice, gas-cooling will occur. Such cooling will constitute a measurement error. It must, therefore, be restricted to within suitable limits.[48]

Wildhack [44] has estimated that the per cent error in absolute temperature resulting from an inaccuracy in the measurement of pressure is not more than three times the per cent error in the absolute pressure. For an initial pressure of 1 atm, he finds maximum sensitivities to within 0.6°C (1.1°F) per 0.1 mb at 1650°C (3002°F) and to within 0.1°C (0.18°F) per 0.1 mb at 300°C (572°F). (*Note:* 1 mb = 10^{-3} bar; 1 bar = 1/1.013 atm = 10^6 dynes/cm^2.) In the range from 5 to 10°K (9 to 18°R) for helium, he estimates a sensitivity to within 0.005°C (0.009°F) per 0.1 mb in pressure measurement.[17,18,44]

The areas A_1 and A_2 of the restrictions can be of any convenient sizes. Large areas tend to decrease the lag time τ but require larger-capacity suction pumps. Very small holes, on the other hand, are subject to plugging with dirt and to diameter variations through erosive wear and corrosion. Nozzles as small as 0.05 mm (0.002 in.) diameter have, however, been used.[44]

11·7 ORIFICE-PROBE DESIGNS

Ueling and Steinbart patented a two-orifice thermometer in Germany in 1893. Many designs have appeared since that time, of which only two examples are described here.[40,44]

A subsonic form due to Godridge, Jackson, and Thurlow [39,42] is shown in Fig. 11·4. The Inconel tip, quartz first orifice, and water-cooled stem adapt it to high-temperature service. It has been used up to 1550°C (2822°F); however, this limit was for the calibrating unit not for the probe. Careful calibration studies indicated that temperatures determined according to Eq. 11·6 are accurate to within ±5 per cent. However, dust blockage of both orifice plates was experienced during tests in pulverized-coal flames. Also, probes of this general variety have not been found entirely reliable when free-stream velocities exceed 100 ft/sec (3050 cm/sec).[39, 42-44, 46, 47]

The sonic-flow orifice probe of Havill and Rolls [49] is indicated in Fig. 11·5. A laboratory high-vacuum pump located in the nose of the airplane, connected to the probe by an 0.75-in. (1.9-cm) diameter tube, assures sonic velocity through both orifices. Calculations indicated a lag time τ' of 0.006 sec for the probe itself; however, the pressure-measuring system increased the over-all lag to about 0.045 sec. In a controlled-furnace static calibration, the error was inferred from a standard deviation of ±10.5°F (5.8°C).[49]

Lalos [50] describes a design that can be made as small as 0.5 in. (12.7 mm) in diameter. It is rated as accurate to within 3°F (1.7°C) for temperatures up to 1500°F (815°C) when approximate values for

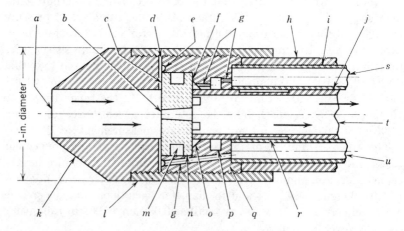

Fig. 11·4. Two-orifice thermometer. *a*, Gas inlet; *b*, 0.1-in. diameter first orifice; *c*, quartz disk; *d*, six radial pressure-tap grooves; *e*, circular pressure-tap groove; *f*, tin-, copper-, or gold-wire O-ring gasket in shallow groove; *g*, drilled-hole pressure taps; *h*, water-cooled 0.875-in. outside diameter steel-tube probe body; *i*, 0.188-in. outside diameter steel tube to downstream pressure taps; *j*, 0.375-in. outside diameter central suction tube; *k*, Inconel (by H. Wiggin and Co., Ltd., England) head; *l*, steel casing; *m*, groove in quartz orifice plate to provide flexible webs for gas-sealing; *n*, flexible web; *o*, countersunk pressure-tap passage; *p*, circular-recess pressure-tap passage; *q*, steel orifice-containing block; *r*, grooved cooling-water passage; *s*, downstream pressure tap; *t*, suction gas outlet; and, *u*, upstream pressure tap. (*By permission A. M. Godridge, P. R. Jackson, and G. G. Thurlow in J. Sci. Instr.*, **32**, *no. 7, 280, July, 1955.*)

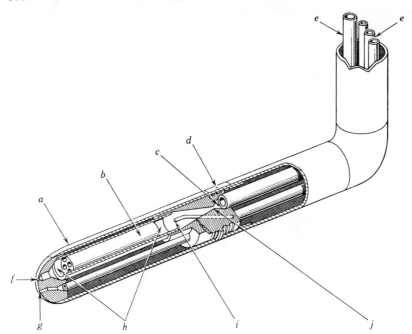

Fig. 11·5. Sonic-flow orifice probe. *a*, Outer skin of heat-resistant metal; *b*, heat-source cooler consisting of a honeycomb metal block; *c*, iron-against-constantan thermocouple; *d*, static-pressure tap; *e*, ducts leading to orifices and total- and static-pressure taps; *f*, first sonic-flow orifice; *g*, total-pressure tap before first orifice; *h*, chamber; *i*, total-pressure tap before second orifice; and *j*, second sonic-flow orifice. (*By permission C. D. Havill and L. S. Rolls, Technical Note 1509, 10, U. S. National Advisory Committee for Aeronautics, Washington, January, 1948.*)

γ are available. In turbine exhaust gases, where no knowledge of γ is assumed, the accuracy is still to within about 15°F (8.3°C) for this temperature range.[51]

Simmons and Glawe [52] made comparison studies on a water-cooled sonic-flow probe at temperatures up to 4000°R (3540.3°F or 1946.8°C). Within the range of scatter in the readings of alternative instruments, their device was found to be in agreement.

Various other designs have been proposed.[39, 53]

11·8 CLARK-ROHSENOW METHOD

One form of the Clark-Rohsenow [47] device is indicated in Fig. 11·6. It is seen to be similar in construction to the orifice probes

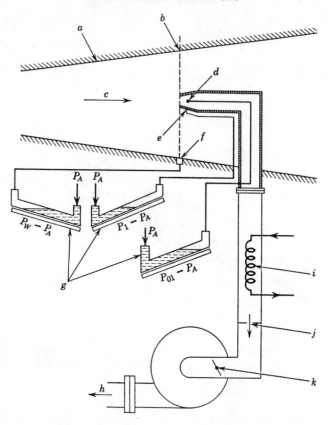

Fig. 11·6. Clark-Rohsenow method. P_A = atmospheric pressure; P_1 = static pressure inside probe; P_{01} = stagnation pressure inside probe; P_W = static pressure in stream. a, Combustion tube; b, position 1; c, stream of hot gases; d, stagnation-pressure-tube orifice; e, static-pressure orifice inside probe; f, static-pressure orifice; g, manometers; h, exhaust; i, heat exchanger; j, position 2, calibrated orifice; and, k, control valve. (*By permission J. A. Clark and W. M. Rohsenow in Trans. ASME*, **74**, *no. 2, 222, February, 1952*.)

described in preceding sections. In particular, the temperature measurement T_2 is made, as before, after the gases have been cooled to a convenient level. The other measurements are of pressure and do not require that the pressure-probe parts attain the high gas temperatures. In the Clark-Rohsenow method five quantities must be measured; whereas, to apply Eqs. 11·8 or 11·13, only three are needed, the additional two being pressures. The compensating virtue attributed to the Clark-Rohsenow method is that the determinations appear to be peculiarly independent of variations in the value of the ratio of the specific heats γ. In products of combustion, where the composition of the gases may be unknown or changing and difficult to determine, this feature becomes a marked advantage.

The observation equation used is given as

$$T_1 = K[\gamma_1/(\gamma_1 - 1)](R_2/R_1)(A_1/A_2)^2[(p_{s_1}^2/(p_{s_2} \Delta p_{s_2})]$$
$$\times [(p_{t_1}/p_{s_1})^{(\gamma_1-1)/\gamma_1} - 1]T_2 \qquad (11\cdot14)$$

where T_1 is the (static) absolute temperature to be determined, i.e., that at position 1 (see Fig. 11·6), °K; K is a numerical calibration factor which includes the discharge coefficient for the orifice at position 2; γ_1 is the ratio of specific heats for the gas at position 1; R_1 and R_2 are the gas constants for the particular gas at positions 1 and 2, respectively, ergs/g °K; A_1 and A_2 are the effective orifice areas at positions 1 and 2, respectively, cm^2; p_{s_1} and p_{s_2} are the static pressures at positions 1 and 2, respectively, dynes/cm^2 (10^6 dynes/cm^2 = 1 bar = 1/1.013 atm); p_{t_1} is the total or impact pressure at position 1, dynes/cm^2; Δp_{s_2} is the static-pressure drop across the orifice at position 2, dynes/cm^2; and T_2 is the (static) absolute temperature at position 2, °K.[47]

Collecting the properties for the given gas and the constants for the apparatus into one calibration coefficient K, we have [43,47]

$$T_1 = K(p_{s_1}^2/p_{s_2} \Delta p_{s_2})[(p_{t_1}/p_{s_1})^{(\gamma_1-1)/\gamma_1} - 1]T_2 \qquad (11\cdot15)$$

The ratio R_2/R_1 of the gas constants at positions 1 and 2, respectively, appears as a factor in Eq. 11·14. Thereby, any uncertainty in the value of R_2/R_1, resulting from dissociation, recombination, and chemical reactions, will result in a relative error of the same magnitude in the measurement of T_1. The value of γ_1 appears only for position 1; therefore, variations in T_2 have no effect on γ_1. Also, the occurrence of the quantity $\gamma_1/(\gamma_1 - 1)$ both as a factor and as an exponent in Eq. 11·14 has the effect that changes in γ_1 affect T_1 to the extent of only about 1 per cent of its absolute value.[47]

It is to be noted, however, that subsonic probes do not depend on the value of γ either. Furthermore, in sonic-velocity orifice probes, vibrational energy states may remain effectively "frozen" by not "keeping pace" with temperature changes. Here again, temperature changes in γ may cause little error. On the other hand, subsonic probes are not reliable in high-velocity gas streams, and not all gases have sufficiently long relaxation times to suppress changes in γ.[41,46,48]

The Clark-Rohsenow [47] method thus finds a place for high-velocity high-temperature gases of unknown but constant composition and unknown or short vibrational relaxation times. Calibration studies have verified the comparative independence of temperature levels and properties.

11·9 FLOW STREAM—ITS OWN THERMOMETER

The orifice methods described in preceding sections have each been realized in terms of a probe inserted into the gas stream. Such a probe draws off a sample of the gas flow either by impact pressure or through a suction pump at the outlet end.

Instead of applying flow equations to pressure and temperature data taken in such a sample of the stream, these or similar equations can be applied to the flow in the main duct. The resulting determination is, of course, an average value over the entire cross section at the given position. Likewise, measurements of quantities which vary laterally in the stream require traversing to obtain the corresponding *profiles*. Total-pressure and total-temperature measurements must thus be obtained as representative or average values.[43, 46, 54, 55]

For use in such a main-stream determination, Cesaro, Koenig, and Pack [54] have proposed the following as an observation equation

$$T_{t_2} = KT_{t_1}(p_{s_2}/p_{s_1})[(p_{t_2} - p_{s_2})/(p_{t_1} - p_{s_1})] \qquad (11\cdot16)$$

where T_{t_1} and T_{t_2} are the average total absolute temperatures at positions 1 and 2, respectively, °K; p_{s_1} and p_{s_2} are the static pressures at positions 1 and 2, respectively, dynes/cm^2; p_{t_1} and p_{t_2} are the average total or impact pressures at positions 1 and 2, respectively, dynes/cm^2; and K is a calibration constant including the effects of cross-sectional area changes, gas properties, and additions to the stream resulting from fuel injection between positions 1 and 2.[43, 46, 54]

This method has been proposed for determining the average temperatures of product gases while limiting temperature measurements to those on the inlet air stream. Pressure measurements are required at both positions 1 and 2. Conversion of total temperatures to static temperatures requires application of velocity or Mach-number data, using such formulations as Eq. 10·12 to 10·15.[43, 46, 54]

Data obtained by this method have been found to be in agreement to within around 2 per cent with those obtained in measurements made with thermocouples.[46, 54]

11·10 THE INTERFEROMETER METHOD

The velocity-of-sound techniques described in Secs. 6·9 and 11·4 depend in their measurements on indications of the time required for a sound-wave pulse to traverse a known distance through the gas.

This time interval may be measured by the phase shift produced in an electric circuit that is coupled to the sound path. Sonic devices thus depending on phase shifts are called *sonic interferometers*.[19, 26, 56, 57]

The *optical interferometer* (see Fig. 11·7A) depends on the time required for a *light wave* to traverse a definite distance through the gas. Such a distance may be varied in measured amounts by a micrometer screw. An initial beam *oa* is "split" by a *half-silvered mirror* at *a* so that one ray passes through the gas while the second ray passes around the test section containing the gas. These two rays are then brought together on a screen, i.e., at *e* or *e'*. If the respective distances traversed are such that the two rays arrive in phase, reinforcement occurs. If, however, the separate paths differ such that the waves arrive out of phase, interference results. Thereby, as a micrometer screw is advanced, changing either path, i.e., the path difference, by successive wavelengths, *brightness* and *darkness* alternate on the screen.[58]

Thus, let us assume (see Fig. 11·7A) the adjustments to be such that the geometrical path length *abce* is equal to the path length *adce* and that path *ab'c'e'* is equal to path *ad'c'e'* for any point *e'*. Then, if the medium is uniform throughout, the light rays will reunite in the same phase at both *e* and *e'*, i.e., everywhere on the screen. This is called adjustment for *infinite fringe width*.

If the pressure is uniform throughout, the density and thereby the *optical thickness* for a given path length depend on the temperature of the gas. With a heated plate inserted (see Fig. 11·7B), the paths *abce* and *ab'c'e'* still remain in the same uniform medium. However, the ray paths *adce* and *ad'c'e'* traverse the test section and in different temperature strata. The different densities corresponding to the differing temperatures in the two test-section paths and the resulting difference in *optical thickness* effect a shift in the phase relations between the pairs of rays reuniting at points *e* and *e'*, respectively. Thus, if the two rays are in *unison* at *e*, this is the location on the screen of a *bright fringe*. Then, if the phase shift from the ray *adce* to *ad'c'e'* is a half wavelength, the rays are in opposite phase at *e'*, and *e'* is the location of a *dark fringe*.

When, as shown in Fig. 11·7B, the distance *ee'* is one fringe width, the effective path difference from *adce* to *ad'c'e'* is one wavelength. This effective path difference results from an increment in density corresponding to a decrease in temperature between the isothermal strata *fg* and *f'g'*. In general, such a decrement in temperature corresponds to each fringe, and the difference in temperature between

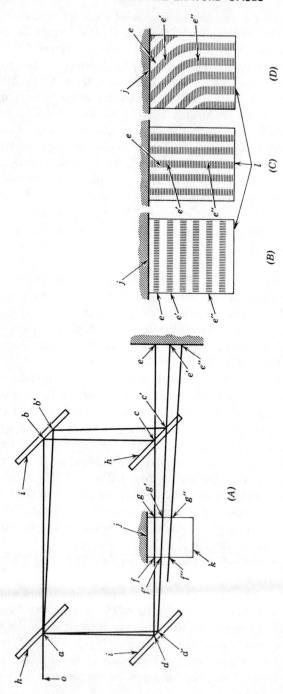

Fig. 11·7. Mach-Zehnder interferometer. (A) Optical system; (B) fringe shift for parallel mirrors; (C) nonparallel-mirror fringe pattern; and, (D) fringe shift for nonparallel mirrors. *oabce*, bypassed-ray path; *oab'c'e'*, alternate bypassed-ray path; *oadfge*, transmitted-ray path; *oad'f'g'e'*, alternate transmitted-ray path; *f"g"e"*, nth transmitted-ray path; *h*, half-silvered plane-mirror surface; *i*, full-reflecting plane-mirror surface; *j*, hot surface; *k*, test section; and, *l*, screens. (By permission C. D. Coulbert in Mech. Eng., **74**, no.12, 1005, December, 1952.)

any two strata fg and $f''g''$ is proportional to the number of fringes counted between the corresponding points e and e'' on the screen. Thus

$$\Delta T = T \, \Delta N / [(n - 1) D / \lambda - \Delta N] \qquad (11 \cdot 17)$$

where ΔT is the difference in temperature between two strata, such as fg and $f''g''$ on Fig. $11 \cdot 7A$, °K; T is the absolute temperature at stratum $f''g''$, °K; ΔN is the number of fringes counted from point e to point e'' on the screen (see Fig. $11 \cdot 7B$); D is the path length fg, $f'g'$, or $f''g''$ in the gas, cm; λ is the wavelength in vacuo for the monochromatic light used; and n is the index of refraction of the gas at temperature T for this light.[57-60]

Figure $11 \cdot 8$ shows the fringe pattern for a two-dimensional temperature distribution. The fringes here correspond to isothermal surfaces. Unfortunately, three-dimensional temperature patterns are not dealt with by the interferometer method. It has been assumed that the rays traverse isothermal paths. If the paths were not isothermal, fringe shifts would merely correspond to mean-temperature differences between ray paths such as those through fg and $f''g''$. Refractive bending of rays would further increase the ambiguity of the results.

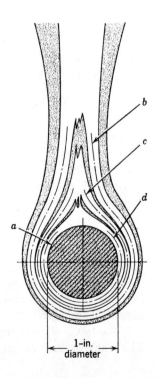

Fig. $11 \cdot 8$. Interferogram for heated cylinder in free convection. a, 1-in. diameter heated cylinder; b, 77°F isotherm; c, 80°F isotherm; and d, 83°F isotherm. Ambient-stream temperature is 74°F. (*By permission C. D. Coulbert in Mech. Eng.*, **74**, *no. 12, 1006, December, 1952.*)

Figure 11·7A and B show the Mach-Zehnder interferometer adjusted for parallel fringes. If the mirrors or screen are tilted very slightly from their orientations of perfect alignment, the respective ray paths to successive points on the screen will differ. As the differences increase to multiples of the wavelength, a pattern of interference fringes results (see Fig. 11·7C). Micrometer-screw motion or changes in gas-column temperature, to change the phase relations between the respective rays at any one point, cause successive changes of light to darkness at that point. However, this result comes about through lateral shifting of the entire fringe pattern. In these movements, light and dark fringes successively cross that point.

Suppose that the inclinations of the various mirrors are adjusted to produce the initial pattern shown in Fig. 11·7C. Here, the fringes are parallel to the plane of Fig. 11·7A, i.e., parallel to the line ee''. The brightness is then the same at the successive points e, e', and e''. Now, when the heated plate is inserted such that the rays fg, $f'g'$, etc., pass closely and parallel to the heated surface, they traverse isothermal strata at successively differing temperatures. The corresponding phase shifts from point e to e', etc., then have the effect of a shifting or warping of the original fringe pattern, resulting in darkness at e and brightness at e' (see Fig. 11·7D).

At a sufficient distance from the heated plate, the gas temperature remains undisturbed, and the corresponding fringe pattern resumes the parallel character of Fig. 11·7C. To obtain the temperature rise at any point e, one then counts the fringes along a normal such as $e''e$ and multiplies this number by the temperature rise per fringe. Thus, in Eq. 11·17, the temperature difference ΔT corresponds to the number of fringes ΔN.

Precision application of this method requires consideration of certain corrections that have been discussed by Kennard,[57,60] Howes [61] et al., and others.[57,58,60,61]

Although the interferometer is highly sensitive and precise in the measurement of gas temperatures, it is also ultrasensitive to mechanical disturbances. The frame carrying the mirrors must be made very rigid and may even be thermostated by water circulating inside tubular beams. The mass may be a third of a ton and is supported on vibration-isolating cushions or a Julius suspension. It is not permissible that thermal or sound-wave disturbances enter the paths of the light rays. To avoid jarring the instrument, adjustments of the mirrors may be made by remote control and with gear ratios as large as 10^6:1.

If the test section is not at atmospheric pressure, it must be enclosed. The windows then required for passage of the light rays at f and g in

Fig. 11·7A must be of the same high optical quality as that used in the interferometer mirrors. The size of the test section is limited by the diameter of the mirrors, which usually does not exceed around 8 in. (20.3 cm). However, if the instrument frame is built with a large enough *yoke,* a test section can be moved to several successive positions and the resulting fringe photographs pieced together to yield the entire pattern.

Since the gas is traversed only by light rays, its temperature pattern is not disturbed by the means of measurement. Location errors are merely those corresponding to the resolution of the optical system. The resolution may suffice to distinguish microscopic distances in the gas. Time lags are limited to those required to expose the photographic plates. Thus, with a condenser-discharge spark-light source, the time can be reduced to less than 1 μsec (10^{-6} sec); or motion pictures, at several thousand frames per second, can be recorded on 35-mm film.[30]

Since no part of the apparatus is required to assume the gas temperature, this method is adapted to the measurement of high temperatures. Luminosity in such gases will require the use of some wavelength not emitted or absorbed in the test-section gas. If windows are used, they will have to be protected by gas layers at room temperature. Great care will be required to avoid optical disturbances in any such windows, since seemingly small effects might result in obliterating the fringe pattern altogether.

An extensive survey of alternative interferometric techniques is given by Kraus.[57, 58, 62-65]

11·11 THE SCHLIEREN METHOD

The German word *schliere* refers to any local inhomogeneity in a transparent medium which results in an abrupt change in the refractive index. Thus, density variations resulting from stratifications in temperature result in such deviations in the refractive index, i.e., result in schlieren. The bending of light rays at the schlieren thus affords means for projecting images on screens or on photographic plates. These images reveal the corresponding temperature patterns in the gas. Such temperature fields are portrayed in the resulting pictures with sharp delineation of details. However, quantitative determinations of actual temperatures are not conveniently computed here. In consequence, space is not devoted to any description of the apparatus used. For a full account of these intricate optical systems, the reader is referred to books on aerodynamic measurements such as those by Ladenburg [58, 66] et al., Kraus,[62] and Dean.[67]

It may be mentioned, in passing, that the character of this equipment is similar in cost, delicacy, sensitivity to mechanical and other disturbances, field-size limitations, and general appearance to that of the optical interferometer.[22, 58, 62, 66-68]

11·12　X-RAY ABSORPTION METHOD

Beams of electrons, α-particles, β-particles, and X-rays are subject to the Bouguer-Lambert law of absorption which also applies to visible and infrared radiation, i.e.,

$$J_{i,\lambda} = J_{o,\lambda} e^{-\alpha_\lambda D} \tag{8·2}$$

where $J_{o,\lambda} \Delta\lambda$ is the radiant energy per unit solid angle in the entering beam in the wavelength range λ to $\lambda + \Delta\lambda$, ergs/sec; $J_{i,\lambda} \Delta\lambda$ is that in the emergent beam; α_λ is the absorption coefficient at wavelength λ, cm^{-1}; and D is the thickness of the absorbing layer, cm.[69, 70]

The amount of absorption, as measured by the ratio $J_{i,\lambda}/J_{o,\lambda}$, depends on the thickness D and on the absorption coefficient α_λ. This coefficient is proportional to the density. Thus

$$\alpha_\lambda = \rho\phi(\lambda, Z) \tag{11·18}$$

where ρ is the density, g/cm^3; λ is the wavelength, μ; and Z is the mean *atomic number* for the chemical elements comprising the gaseous layer. The form of the function $\phi(\lambda, Z)$ depends on the actual wavelength range and includes the effects of *scattering* as well as those of true absorption.[69, 70]

The density ρ is related in turn to the temperature T. Thus

$$T = p/\rho C R \tag{8·12}$$

where T is the temperature, °K; p is the absolute pressure, dynes/cm^2; ρ is the density, g/cm^3; C is the compressibility factor (see Sec. 8·7); and R is the gas constant per unit mass, ergs/g°K.

Thus

$$\alpha_\lambda = (p/T)\psi(C, R, \lambda, Z) \tag{11·19}$$

The sensitivity of this method is directly proportional to the value of α_λ and thereby to the pressure p and to the function $\psi(C, R, \lambda, Z)$. The function $\psi(C, R, \lambda, Z)$ is proportional to the molecular weight M, to approximately the cube of the wavelength λ, and to the fourth power of the atomic number Z. Thus, measurement is easier in *dense* gases. Because of the dependence on λ, *soft* X-rays, i.e., those of long wavelength, are usually used. Wavelengths thus tend to exceed around 2 Å (Ångstrom units), i.e., 2×10^{-4} μ.[69, 70]

Various empirical expressions are available for the function $\psi(C, R, \lambda, Z)$, from which α_λ can be computed. However, since it is impossible to exclude *end losses* at windows, etc., and since X-ray beams of suitable intensities are not monochromatic, the practical procedure is to determine the relationship between $J_{i,\lambda}$ and T by overall calibration.[69–73]

11·13   X-RAY METHOD APPLICATION

Figure 11·9 indicates an arrangement for "sighting across" the diameter of a wind tunnel. An X-ray source at one side supplies the entering beam $J_{o,\lambda}$. The energy of the emergent beam $J_{i,\lambda}$ is indicated by a Geiger-Mueller tube. This device functions on the principle of *counting* the individual *photons* incident into its sensitive space. The number of photons, i.e., *packets* of X-radiation energy, thus incident per unit of time is proportional to the energy $J_{i,\lambda}$ of the emergent beam. The accuracy with which such a count can be determined is greater for large counts. The counting rate can be increased by increasing the beam energy $J_{o,\lambda}$ up to the limit set by resolution of the tube-circuit arrangement used. However, thereafter, counting accuracy depends on using longer counting times, the times commonly running to several minutes. The X-ray method is thereby limited to measuring time-average temperatures or those which are nearly constant.[69–73]

Refraction effects are generally negligible with X-rays. Thus, ray paths are accurately straight lines despite any schlieren or density variations. This feature renders the method peculiarly well suited to the study of patterns where temperature gradients are steep, as, for example, in surface films. In such work, beam diameters as narrow as 0.025 cm (0.01 in.) have been used.[69–73]

Calibration can be performed by using atmospheric air as the reference path, or an evacuated path may be used. There is, however, an end-effect path length ΔD which includes any windows or protective gas layers. This length must be maintained constant. It is also desirable that this additive constant in the absorption path be small relative to the path length D. Therefore, the absorbing thickness D cannot be made arbitrarily short and may be a foot or more. Since Eq. 8·2 is exponential in form, i.e., not linear, the average indicated for a non-uniform-temperature path D is not an *arithmetic mean*. It is a *weighted average* and not readily interpreted when temperature variations are large. Hence, the X-ray method is best adapted to measuring temperatures which are uniform along the path D.[69–73]

X-ray beams are immune to the effects of schlieren, i.e., local density changes and fluctuations. Hence, a protective device, such as that

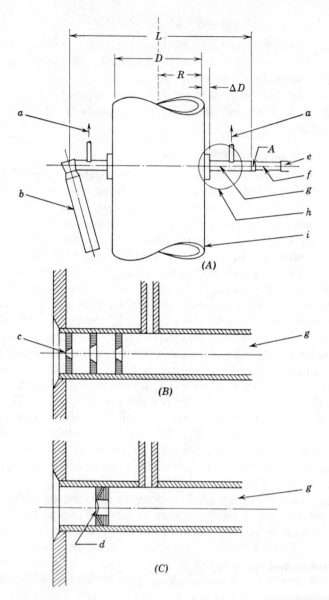

Fig. 11·9. X-ray absorption apparatus. (A) Over-all arrangement of apparatus; (B) pinhole arrangement; and (C) aluminum-foil window. L = distance from X-ray source to detector; D = path length through gas mixture, $D = 2R$; ΔD = outside profile length; may be 0.25 in. with pin holes, but not less than 1 in. with window; A = X-ray-beam area at distance L. a, Stream to vacuum pump; b, X-ray tube; c, 0.05-in. diameter pin hole; d, 0.2-in. diameter aluminum-foil window; e, leads to scaler; f, Geiger-Mueller-counter tube; g, vacuum chamber; h, detail shown in views B and C; and, i, tunnel. (*By permission R. N. Weltmann and P. W. Kuhns in Technical Note 2580, 26–27, U. S. National Advisory Committee for Aeronautics, Washington, January, 1948.*)

indicated in Fig. 11·1, can be used. In this device, the flows are so directed that a sharply defined dividing plane exists between the protective layer of cool gas and the end of the layer D (see Fig. 11·9). This arrangement accurately defines the *gage length D* without the need for any solid window material to be exposed to the hot gas. Therefore, no portion of the apparatus needs to assume the gas temperature. Furthermore, X-rays lie in a wavelength range entirely outside the spectrum emitted by any flame resulting from the chemical combustion of fuel. Thus, the radiation-sensitive elements used, i.e., the Geiger-Mueller counters, are unaffected by flame radiation. Because of these two features, the X-ray method is adapted to the measurement of high temperatures.[29, 69–73]

11·14 CONCLUSION

In the present chapter, methods have been described which can be applied to the measurement of high gas temperatures. In practice, high temperatures usually arise in flames and arcs. Thus, the temperature measurements in flames and arcs will usually employ several of the methods. However, additional difficulties are presented by the conditions of chemical nonequilibria and ionization.[9]

REFERENCES *

1. "Ceramic Coatings Prevent Exhaust-Gas Corrosion," *Natl. Bur. Standards U. S., Tech. News Bull.,* **35**, no. 6, pp. 89–91 (June, 1951).
2. Callite Tungsten Corp., "Molybdenum Tubing," *Rev. Sci. Instr.,* **18**, no. 5, p. 373 (May, 1947).
3. "Base New Company Service on Ceramic Coating Development," *Industrial Laboratories,* **6**, no. 2, pp. 36–37 (February, 1955).
4. National Bureau of Standards, "Ceramic Coating for High-Temperature Alloys," *Rev. Sci. Instr.,* **22**, no. 12, pp. 1035–1036 (December, 1951).
5. F. H. Clark, *Metals at High Temperatures,* 350 pp., Reinhold Publishing Corp., New York, 1950.
6. "Ceramic Coatings for Use in Nuclear Reactors," *Natl. Bur. Standards U. S., Tech. News Bull.,* **38**, no. 10, pp. 150–152 (October, 1954).
7. W. N. Harrison, D. G. Moore, and J. C. Richmond, "Ceramic Coatings for High-Temperature Protection of Steel," *RP* 1773, *J. Research Natl. Bur. Standards,* **38**, no. 3, pp. 293–307 (March, 1947).
8. D. G. Moore, L. H. Bolz, J. W. Pitts, and W. N. Harrison, "Study of Chromium-Frit-Type Coatings for High-Temperature Protection of Molybdenum," *Technical Note* 2422, U. S. National Advisory Committee for Aeronautics, Washington (July, 1951).
9. W. M. Cohn, "The Field of Extreme Temperatures," *Temperature,* American Institute of Physics, pp. 764–772, Reinhold Publishing Corp., New York, 1941.

* See footnote on page 26.

10. V. G. Shaw, "High Temperature Measurement," *Instruments*, **33**, no. 1, pp. 58–61 (January, 1960).

11. "High-Temperature Measurements," *Instruments*, **30**, no. 10, pp. 1896–1898 (October, 1957).

12. G. E. Uhlenbeck and L. Gropper, "The Equation of State of a Non-Ideal Einstein-Bose or Fermi-Dirac Gas," *Phys. Rev.*, **41**, pp. 79–90 (July, 1932).

13. A. L. Clark, "The Definition of a Perfect Gas," *Trans. Roy. Soc. Can. III*, pp. 293–311 (1924).

14. M. H. Cassan, "Pyromètre-densimètre à gaz" (Pyrometer and Density Meter for Gases), *Journal des usines à gaz*, **53**, pp. 527–532 (1929).

15. S. F. Pickering, "Relations between the Temperatures, Pressures, and Densities of Gases," *Natl. Bur. Standards Circ.* 279, 85 pp., Government Printing Office, Washington (1926).

16. J. H. Keenan and J. Kaye, *Gas Tables*, 238 pp., John Wiley & Sons, New York, 1948.

17. B. E. Philippsen, "Pressure Indicators in Engine Fuel Research," *Electronic Industries & Electronic Instrumentation*, **1**, no. 2, pp. 2–3 (February, 1947).

18. H. D. Warshaw, "A Gauge for Indicating Pressure Transients in a Combustion Chamber," *Rev. Sci. Instr.*, **23**, no. 9, pp. 493–496 (September, 1952).

19. A. L. Hedrich and D. R. Pardue, "Sound Velocity as a Measurement of Gas Temperature," American Institute of Physics, *Temperature*, Vol. II, pp. 383–392, Reinhold Publishing Corp., New York, 1955.

20. C. G. Suits, "High-Temperature Gas Measurements in Arcs," American Institute of Physics, *Temperature*, pp. 720–733, Reinhold Publishing Corp., New York, 1941.

21. H. Deresiewicz, "Plane Waves in a Thermoelastic Solid," *J. Acoust. Soc. Am.*, **29**, no. 2, pp. 204–209 (February, 1957).

22. C. G. Suits, "Notes on High-Intensity Sound Waves," *Gen. Elec. Rev.*, **39**, no. 9, pp. 430–43 (September, 1936).

23. C. G. Suits, "The Temperature of the Copper Arc," *Proc. Natl. Acad. Sci. U. S.*, **21**, no. 1, pp. 48–50 (January, 1935).

24. J. Hilsenrath, C. W. Beckett, W. S. Benedict, L. Fano, H. J. Hoge, J. F. Masi, R. L. Nuttall, Y. S. Touloukian, and H. W. Wooley, "Tables of Thermal Properties of Gases," *Natl. Bur. Standards Circ.* 564, 488 pp., Government Printing Office, Washington (November, 1955).

25. R. A. Gross and C. L. Eisen, "On the Speed of Sound in Air," *Physics of Fluids*, **2**, no. 3, pp. 276–279 (May–June, 1959).

26. R. L. Abbey and G. E. Barlow, "The Velocity of Sound in Gases," *Australian J. Sci. Research, Ser. A*, **1**, no. 2, pp. 175–189 (1948).

27. R. L. Abbey, "The Velocity of Sound in Gases at Low Pressures," *Australian J. Sci. Research, Ser. A*, **5**, no. 1, pp. 223–225 (1952).

28. "Propagation of Sound in Monatomic Gases," *NBS Technical News Bulletin*, **40**, no. 9, pp. 121–124, Government Printing Office, Washington (September, 1956).

29. H. C. Hottel and H. G. Mangelsdorf, "Heat Transmission by Radiation from Non-Luminous Gases II. Experimental Study of Carbon Dioxide and Water Vapor," *Trans. Am. Inst. Chem. Engrs.*, **31**, pp. 517–549 (September, 1935).

30. J. A. Fitzpatrick, J. C. Hubbard, and W. J. Thaler, "A High Intensity Short Duration Spark Light Source," *J. Appl. Phys.*, **21**, pp. 1269–1271 (December, 1950).

31. J. C. Livengood, C. F. Taylor, and P. C. Wu, "Measurement of Gas Temperature in an Engine by the Velocity of Sound Method," *S.A.E. Annual Meeting Paper* 3C, 20 pp., Society of Automotive Engineers, March, 1958.

32. Coordinating Research Council, *Four Proposed Methods of Measuring End-Gas Properties,* pp. 6–7, 43–82, Coordinating Research Council, New York, January, 1953.

33. C. F. Taylor, J. C. Livengood, G. F. Harper, E. A. Oster, T. P. Rona, T. Y. Toong, and P. C. Wu, "Development of a Method for Measuring Gas Temperatures of an Internal Combustion Engine," *Final Report on CRC Project* CF-1-49 (MIT Project DIC-7295) 171 pp.; *Progress Report on Instantaneous Temperature Measurements,* Coordinating Research Council, New York, 1955.

34. J. C. Livengood, T. P. Rona, and J. J. Baruch, "Ultrasonic Temperature Measurement in Internal Combustion Engine Chamber," *J. Acoust. Soc. Am.,* **26,** no. 5, pp. 824–830 (September, 1954).

35. C. F. Taylor, "Summary Report on Development of a Technique for Measuring Gas Temperatures in an Internal Combustion Engine," *CRC Project* CM-1-58, 50 pp., Coordinating Research Council, New York (October, 1958).

36. R. A. Brew, "Time Interval Measurement to 10^{-8} Second," *Instruments,* **31,** no. 10, pp. 1684–1685 (October, 1958).

37. W. E. Moeckel and J. C. Evvard, "Determination of Gas Temperatures from the Frequency of Knock-Induced Gas Vibrations in an Internal-Combustion Engine," *Wartime Report* NACA ARR E 6A07, 30 pp., U. S. National Advisory Committee for Aeronautics, Washington (January, 1946).

38. E. W. Barrett and V. E. Suomi, "Preliminary Report on Temperature Measurement by Sonic Means," *J. Meteorol.,* **6,** pp. 273–276 (August, 1949).

39. A. M. Godridge, R. Jackson, and G. G. Thurlow, "The Venturi Pneumatic Pyrometer," *J. Sci. Instr.,* **35,** no. 3, pp. 81–88 (March, 1958).

40. H. Schmick, "Über die Bestimmung von Gastemperaturen mittels Druckdifferenzmessung" (Determination of Gas Temperatures by Means of Pressure Differences), *Zeitschrift für technische Physik,* **10,** no. 4, pp. 146–147 (1929).

41. D. W. Moore, Jr., "A Pneumatic Method for Measuring High-Temperature Gases," *Aeronautical Engineering Review,* **7,** no. 5, pp. 30–34 (May, 1948).

42. A. M. Godridge, R. Jackson, and G. G. Thurlow, "A Small Pneumatic Pyrometer," *J. Sci. Instr.,* **32,** no. 7, pp. 279–282 (July, 1955).

43. E. R. Letsch and W. J. King, "Methods of Measuring High Temperatures in Gas Streams," *Paper* 51-A-143, pp. 1–10, American Society of Mechanical Engineers, New York (1950).

44. W. A. Wildhack, "A Versatile Pneumatic Instrument Based on Critical Flow," *Rev. Sci. Instr.,* **21,** no. 1, pp. 25–30 (January, 1950).

45. M. D. Scadron, "Analysis of a Pneumatic Probe for Measuring Exhaust-Gas Temperatures with Some Preliminary Experimental Results," *Research Memorandum* RM E52 A11, 26 pp., U. S. National Advisory Committee for Aeronautics, Washington (May, 1952).

46. E. F. Fiock and A. I. Dahl, "The Measurement of Gas Temperature by Immersion-Type Instruments," *J. Am. Rocket Soc.,* **23,** no. 3, pp. 155–164 (May–June, 1953).

47. J. A. Clark and W. M. Rohsenow, "A New Method for Determining the Static Temperature of High-Velocity Gas Streams," *Paper* 51-SA-33, (1951); *Trans. ASME,* **74,** no. 2, pp. 219–228 (February, 1952), American Society of Mechanical Engineers, New York.

48. P. L. Blackshear, Jr., "Sonic-Flow-Orifice Temperature Probe for High-Gas-Temperature Measurements," *Technical Note* 2167, 20 pp., U. S. National Advisory Committee for Aeronautics, Washington (September, 1950); *Paper* 52-SA-38, pp. 1–5, American Society of Mechanical Engineers, New York (1952).

49. C. D. Havill and L. S. Rolls, "A Sonic-Flow Orifice Probe for the In-Flight Measurement of Temperature Profiles of a Jet Engine Exhaust with After-burning," *Technical Note* 3714, 18 pp., U. S. National Advisory Committee for Aeronautics, Washington (May, 1956).

50. G. T. Lalos, "A Sonic-Flow Pyrometer for Measuring Gas Temperatures," *RP* 2242, *J. Research Natl. Bur. Standards*, **47**, no. 3, pp. 179–190 (September, 1951).

51. L. Viaud, "Détermination de la température moyenne dans une chambre de combustion" (Determination of the Average Temperature in a Combustion Chamber), *Recherche aéronautique, Paris*, **no. 18**, pp. 55–58 (November–December, 1950).

52. F. S. Simmons and G. E. Glawe, "Theory and Design of a Pneumatic Temperature Probe and Experimental Results Obtained in a High-Temperature Gas Stream," *Technical Note* 3893, 41 pp., U. S. National Advisory Committee for Aeronautics, Washington (January, 1957).

53. N. Celiscev and G. Held, "An Improved System for Measuring the Temperature of a Gas," *Patent Specification* 790, 393, 3 pp., The Patent Office, London (1956).

54. R. S. Cesaro, R. J. Koenig, and G. J. Pack, "Experimental Analysis of a Pressure-Sensitive System for Sensing Gas Temperature," *Technical Note* 2043, 52 pp., U. S. National Advisory Committee for Aeronautics, Washington (February, 1950).

55. I. I. Pinkel, "Determination of Ram-Jet Combustion-Chamber Temperatures by Means of Total-Pressure Surveys," *Technical Note* 2526, 10 pp., U. S. National Advisory Committee for Aeronautics, Washington (December, 1951).

56. J. L. Stewart, "A Variable Path Ultrasonic Interferometer for the Four Mega-cycle Region with some Measurements on Air, CO_2, and H_2," *Rev. Sci. Instr.*, **17**, no. 2, pp. 59–65 (February, 1946).

57. R. B. Kennard, "Temperature Distribution and Heat Flux in Air by Inter-ferometry," American Institute of Physics, *Temperature*, pp. 685–706, Rein-hold Publishing Corp., New York, 1941.

58. F. J. Weyl, "Analysis of Optical Methods," and R. Ladenburg and D. Bershader, "Interferometry," in R. W. Ladenburg, B. Lewis, R. N. Pease, and H. S. Taylor, *Physical Measurements in Gas Dynamics and Combustion, High Speed Aerodynamics and Jet Propulsion*, **9**, nos. A1 and A3, pp. 3–25, 47–78, Princeton University Press, Princeton, N. J., 1954.

59. C. D. Coulbert, "Mach-Zehnder Interferometer Applications," *Mech. Eng.*, **74**, no. 12, pp. 1005–1010 (December, 1952).

60. R. B. Kennard, "An Optical Method for Measuring Temperature Distribution and Convective Heat Transfer," *RP* 452, *J. Research Natl. Bur. Standards*, **8**, no. 6, pp. 787–805 (June, 1932).

61. W. L. Howes and D. R. Buchele, "A Theory and Method for Applying Inter-ferometry to the Measurement of Certain Two-Dimensional Gaseous Density Fields," *Technical Note* 2693, 46 pp., U. S. National Advisory Committee for Aeronautics, Washington (April, 1952).

62. W. Kraus, *Messung des Temperatur- und Geschwindigkeitsfeldes bei freier Konvektion* (Measurement of Temperature and Velocity Fields in Free Convection), 147 pp., Verlag G. Braun, Karlsruhe (1955).

63. L. Akobjanoff, "A Precise Gas Manometer," *Rev. Sci. Instr.*, **23**, no. 8, pp. 447–448 (August, 1952).

64. E. M. Winkler, "Very Accurate Measurements of Fringe Shifts in an Optical Interferometer Study of Gas Flow," *Rev. Sci. Instr.*, **24**, no. 11, pp. 1067–1068 (November, 1953).

65. C. W. Curtis, R. J. Emrich, and J. Mach, "A Chrono-Interferometer for Measuring Gas Density during Transient Flows," *Rev. Sci. Instr.*, **25**, no. 7, pp. 679–682 (July, 1954).

66. F. J. Weyl, "Analysis of Optical Methods," and J. W. Beams, "Shadow and Schlieren Methods," in R. W. Ladenburg, B. Lewis, R. N. Pease, and H. S. Taylor, *Physical Measurements in Gas Dynamics and Combustion, High Speed Aerodynamics and Jet Propulsion*, **9**, nos. A1 and A2, pp. 3–46, Princeton University Press, Princeton, N. J., 1954.

67. R. C. Dean, Jr., *Aerodynamic Measurements*, 272 pp., Massachusetts Institute of Technology, Cambridge, 1953.

68. N. F. Barnes and S. L. Bellinger, "Analyzing Airflow with Schlieren and Shadowgraph Equipment. Theory and Operation of Both Methods," *Gen. Elec. Rev.*, **47**, pp. 27–36 (December, 1944).

69. E. M. Winkler, "X-Ray Technique," in R. W. Ladenburg, B. Lewis, R. N. Pease, and H. S. Taylor, *Physical Measurements in Gas Dynamics and Combustion, High Speed Aerodynamics and Jet Propulsion*, **9**, no. A6, pp. 97–108, Princeton University Press, Princeton, N. J. (1954).

70. R. N. Weltmann and P. W. Kuhns, "An Analysis of an X-Ray Absorption Method for Measurement of High Gas Temperatures," *Technical Note* 2580, 35 pp., U. S. National Advisory Committee for Aeronautics, Washington (December, 1951).

71. J. Dimeff, R. K. Hallett, Jr., and C. F. Hansen, "X-Ray Instrumentation for Density Measurements in a Supersonic Flow Field," *Technical Note* 2845, 39 pp., U. S. National Advisory Committee for Aeronautics, Washington (December, 1952).

72. G. J. Mullaney, "Temperature Determination in Flames by X-Ray Absorption Using a Radioactive Source," *Rev. Sci. Instr.*, **29**, no. 2, pp. 87–91 (February, 1958).

73. H. T. Knight and D. Venable, "Apparatus for Precision Flash Radiography of Shock and Detonation Waves in Gases," *Rev. Sci. Instr.*, **29**, no. 2, pp. 92–98 (February, 1958).

12

12·1   INTRODUCTION

In ordinary life, one speaks of temperatures as being *low* when they are uncomfortable to the human body. Engineers may use the term *low* to distinguish temperatures that are not *high* or perhaps to refer to those used in refrigeration warehouses. To scientists, however, the term *low temperature* has a much more restricted connotation. This more limited, although still loosely defined, meaning is that intended in the present chapter.

The *low-temperature* region is thus variously regarded as: (1), that of temperatures below the oxygen point ($-182.970°C$, $-297.346°F$, or $90.18°K$) where the International Temperature Scale ends; (2), that of temperatures below around $4°K$ ($7.2°R$), for which gas thermometry is no longer feasible; (3), that of temperatures below $1°K$ ($1.8°R$) where the helium vapor-pressure thermometer becomes impractical; or, (4), that of temperatures below about $0.1°K$ ($0.18°R$) where substantial departures occur in the behavior of magnetic thermometers.

In general, although absolute zero ($0°K$ or $0°R$) is unattainable, each decade in the approach to that limit brings a new set of physical conditions, and there is a consequent new group of experimental difficulties.

12·2   ABSOLUTE ZERO

Negative absolute temperatures do not occur in any ordinary physical sense, i.e., a sense of implying conditions "colder" than those at $0°K$. It is not, however, to be fancied that bodies at absolute zero would be devoid of energy. It has been said that, at the zero point, energy is all, or to a maximum degree, in orderly form except for that minimum associated with the uncertainty principle of quantum mechanics. This "ordered" energy includes that of *orbital* motion for electrons *bound* to individual atoms. Similarly, the Fermi-Dirac-Sommerfeld statistics predict large magnitudes for random velocities in *conduction* electrons bound only to the crystal *lattice*. Other forms of energy storage consist of *chemical* and *nuclear binding energies, mass energy, electromagnetic field energy*, etc.[1-3]

Temperatures above 0°K are characterized by the *excitation* of the *energy states* of *disorder*. Thus, *nuclear-spin entropies* tend to arise as temperatures ascend above 10^{-6}°K. Similarly, *electron-spin entropies* begin to develop at about 10^{-3}°K and may be fully developed at 0.1°K. Then, at about 1°K (1.8°R), entropy begins to accumulate in the *lattice vibrations* of crystals. At higher temperatures in gaseous molecules, *translational, rotational, vibrational,* and *excited-electronic energies* arise. *Population densities* in energy states are distributed in accord with Maxwell-Boltzmann's law

$$N_1/N_2 = (g_1/g_2)e^{-(E_1-E_2)/kT} \qquad (12·1)$$

where N_1 is the number of members of a *group* occupying the energy state E_1; N_2 is the number occupying state E_2; E_1 and E_2 are the *excitation energies* for the two states, respectively, ergs; g_1 and g_2 are the *a priori probabilities* or *statistical weights* for these two states; k is Boltzmann's constant, 1.38×10^{-16} erg/°K; T is the absolute temperature, °K; and e is the natural-logarithmic base.[1-4]

Boltzmann's law (Eq. 12·1) is regarded as a definition of temperature in *statistical mechanics*. As such, it is a widely used *microscopic concept* thereof. For conditions of thermodynamic equilibrium, this definition exactly accords with that based on Carnot's theorem, i.e., Kelvin's definition (see Eq. 12·4). It is, however, to be noted that in Eq. 12·1 the temperature level T is characterized only by distribution ratios. These ratios are such as that of N_1/N_2 among the energy states E_1 and E_2. Thus, when E_1 is greater than E_2, N_1/N_2 is less than g_1/g_2 unless T is infinite or negative.[1, 2, 4, 5]

When N_1/N_2 is found to exceed g_1/g_2 for E_1 greater than E_2, one has the choice either of assuming a departure from Boltzmann's law or of allowing T to take on negative values. Such *negative temperatures*, however, would correspond to conditions "hotter" than at infinite temperature, not "colder" than absolute zero of temperature. This concept is more readily accepted if one thinks in terms of the reciprocal temperature $1/T$. Then the possible range of values for $1/T$ would be from infinity (0°K) continuously through zero (infinite Kelvin temperature) into negative values. Cases where N_1/N_2 has exceeded g_1/g_2 have been observed for isolated *nuclear-spin systems*.[1, 4, 6-8]

The temperature concept is fraught with other theoretical difficulties in the approach to absolute zero. Thus, there is a *critical temperature* for crystals below which the laws of thermodynamics do not apply.

Here, the number of degrees of freedom for one granule of the crystalline substance no longer suffices for *statistical uniformity*. Thus, 0.1-mm grains of diamond powder, cooled to 0.001°K (0.0018°R) by external means subsequently removed, would be subject to "wild" *fluctuations*. Most grains would have no vibrational quantum; a few would have one; and a very few perhaps two. For any one single grain, the concept of a thermodynamic temperature would obviously fail altogether. Such critical temperatures are dependent on the grain size and on a *characteristic temperature* for the material. A typical value of the critical temperature for crystals 1 mm on a side might be taken as about 0.0001°K (0.00018°R).[1,4]

12·3 PRODUCTION OF LOW TEMPERATURES

It is beyond the scope of the present work to describe the techniques employed in achieving low temperatures. We can merely note that essentially two procedures are used: (1) *boiling under reduced pressure*, and (2) *magnetic cooling*.[9–12]

The pressure that the vapor assumes in the presence of its liquid phase is a function of temperature. If this pressure is lowered by means of a vacuum pump, the temperature is correspondingly decreased. Heat removal occurs, in effect, as the latent heat of vaporization. When the highest feasible vacuum, i.e., that of about 10^{-3} mm of mercury (1.3×10^{-6} atm or 1.3 dynes/cm²), is pumped over the surface of liquid helium, the equilibrium temperature is approximately 0.66°K (1.19°R). Temperatures as low as 1°K (1.8°R) can be produced in this way.[9,13–15]

If a pellet of a *paramagnetic* salt is magnetized in a strong magnetic field, work of magnetization is performed. Then, if suitable *heat-exchange media* are provided to keep the temperature constant, there is an evolution of heat from the salt. The corresponding reduction in entropy is given by

$$\Delta S = \Delta Q/T \qquad (12·2)$$

where ΔQ is the heat removed, cal; T is the absolute temperature, °K; and ΔS is the entropy decrease, cal/°K.[10,16,17]

If next the heat-exchange medium is removed and a switch then opened on the electromagnet effecting a collapse of the magnetic field, adiabatic demagnetization occurs. A temperature decrease results in the salt, corresponding to the previous reduction in entropy. This temperature drop is greater in proportion to the intensity of the field used. However, to attain absolute zero, it would be necessary to perform the impossible task of establishing an infinite magnetic field.[7,10,11,16,17]

By applying this method to ordinary paramagnetic salts, temperatures down to about 0.001°K are accessible. Where a material exhibits *nuclear paramagnetism,* i.e., paramagnetic behavior resulting from *nuclear magnetic moments,* much lower temperatures can be attained. However, because of the very small *magnetic susceptibilities* of such substances, it is necessary to magnetize at very low initial temperatures. Thus, magnetizing copper at 0.01°K under 50,000 gauss has sufficed, on demagnetization, for its cooling to about 2×10^{-5}°K. Temperatures as low as 10^{-6}°K have been produced by similar procedures.[18]

12·4 LOW-TEMPERATURE MEASUREMENT

Temperature measurement, in any case, usually depends on one of three tactics: (1), a thermometer element can be made to assume the parent-body temperature; (2), a radiation-sensitive element can respond to thermal emission from the source body; or, (3), the body can serve as its own thermometer.

Radiant emission (see Eq. 4·1) is proportional to the fourth power of the absolute temperature. Thus, at the oxygen point 90.18°K (162.324°R), its amount is only a little over 1 per cent of that at the freezing point of water. Since radiation pyrometry is difficult for source bodies even as cool as room temperature, it is hardly to be expected at this much lower temperature. At temperatures below 10°K (18°R), means are not available to measure thermal radiation at all. Hence, radiation methods just do not apply in the low-temperature region.

When a thermometer element is used, it must be brought to the parent-body temperature by heat transfer. Heat flow along the leads to the ambient always tends to set up a temperature discrepancy between the element and the parent body. This error is in proportion to the thermal current and to the thermal resistance between the element and the parent body (see Ch. 7 of Volume I). Similarly, the lag time for the approach of the temperature-sensitive element to the parent-body temperature is proportional to this resistance, as well as to the thermal capacity of the element (see Eq. 6·4).

The effectiveness of conductive and convective heat-transfer processes and of thermal contacts is thus always a dominant factor in installation design. This factor becomes peculiarly acute at low temperatures where coefficients tend to be so small. Since the coefficients change rapidly with temperature and other conditions, design values must be chosen for the exact circumstances. To indicate the nature of what is involved, succeeding sections will be devoted to a sketch of the salient features of the heat-transfer pattern prevailing at low temperatures.

It will be seen that, with approach to absolute zero, all modes of heat transfer decline to vanishing values. The remaining recourse then becomes that of having the body serve as its own thermometer.[10, 19]

12·5 FLUID HEAT-EXCHANGE MEDIA

It is evident that radiation exchange contributes little to thermal communication at low temperatures.

Since helium boiling under reduced pressure is the means of reducing temperatures down to about 1°K (1.8°R)—hydrogen is similarly used at higher temperatures—helium is commonly used as a heat-exchange medium. Either the liquid or its vapor can be so used. However, as temperatures decline in the region below 1°K (1.8°R), the remaining possibilities of the procedure depend on the peculiar properties of helium in this temperature range.[10, 20, 21]

As a heat-exchange gas, helium is used at pressures down to about 10^{-3} mm of mercury (1.3×10^{-6} atm or 1.3 dyne/cm^2). This pressure corresponds to the equilibrium vapor pressure at about 0.66°K (1.19°R). Convection currents are of little importance at the densities corresponding to these low pressures. Also, the conductivity of gases decreases with the temperature; and, for helium at 1°K (1.8°R), it has declined to roughly 0.2 per cent of its value at the ice point, i.e., to 6.8×10^{-7} cal/sec cm °C (1.6×10^{-4} Btu/hr ft °F).[10, 21-24]

At lower temperatures, the sparsity of vapor molecules excludes effective heat transfer. Also, adsorption effects are pronounced at these temperatures, and the paramagnetic salts used in magnetic cooling tend to serve as *getters*. The effect is further to reduce the density of the helium and its availability for heat transfer.[10, 24]

At pressures below 25 atm, helium does not solidify. The λ-point, whose coordinates are $T = 2.19$°K (3.95°R) and $p = 0.0508$ atm (38.6 mm of mercury or 51,500 dynes/cm^2), is a triple point marking the coexistence of helium vapor and two liquid phases, i.e., liquid I and liquid II. Helium liquid II occurs at the lowest temperatures and is a liquid of remarkably low viscosity. Its thermal conductivity is very much larger than that of liquid I. Thus, it is quoted as being of the order of 3×10^{-3} cal/sec cm °C (0.7 Btu/hr ft °F) at 0.5°K (0.9°R). At temperatures below the λ-point, helium II is thus available as a heat-transfer medium. However, the thermal conductivity appears to decline as at least the cube of the absolute temperature and vanishes with approach to 0°K.[9,10]

Liquid helium cannot be cooled, by boiling it under reduced pressure, to temperatures much below 1°K (1.8°R). Hence, using it as an exchange medium at lower temperatures would necessitate cooling it by external means. Its relatively large heat capacity would then limit the range of temperatures attainable.[9,10]

12·6 THERMAL CONDUCTIVITIES OF SOLIDS

As temperatures are reduced below the ice point, the thermal conductivities of solid materials increase, reaching maximum values somewhere in the range from about 5 to 50°K (9 to 90°R). For copper, the extraordinary conductivity of 7050 Btu/hr ft °F (29.2 cal/sec cm °C) occurs at 20°K (36°R).[10,25,26]

At temperatures below that for this maximum, thermal conductivities decline. Thus, at 1°K (1.8°R), the conductivity of copper has receded to around 0.5 cal/sec cm °C (120 Btu/hr ft °F). If the rate of decrease is roughly linear, values of the order of 0.1 and 0.01 times smaller are to be expected at 0.1 and 0.01°K (0.18 and 0.018°R), respectively. Values approach zero with approach to absolute zero of temperature.[19,26]

The thermal conductivities of paramagnetic salts, such as those used in magnetic cooling, decline to small values at the temperatures reached in such cooling. Crystalline ferric ammonium alum and chromic potassium alum have been observed to have thermal conductivities of the order of 10^{-5} cal/sec cm °C (2.4×10^{-3} Btu/hr ft °F) at 0.1°K (0.18°R). Since these conductivities have been found to vary as nearly the cube of the absolute temperature, much higher values are to be expected at 1°K (1.8°R), and lower or vanishing values with approach to absolute zero. The conductivities for compacts of finely ground powders are found to be 6 to 50 times lower than those for single crystals.[10]

In consequence of the low conductivity values, maintaining a uniform temperature throughout a paramagnetic body, such as that commonly used either as a magnetic thermometer or for magnetic cooling, becomes a serious experimental difficulty. Single crystals, however, when they are grown with few gross imperfections, can very rapidly attain internal thermal equilibrium. Thus, bars of crystalline quartz or high-purity copper can be used for *thermal links*. When single-crystal-link intermediate materials are used, most of the thermal resistance occurs at the *contacts* i.e., at the interfaces between bodies. Reduction of thermal resistances at such contacts is difficult.[10,19,27]

Large departures from the Wiedemann-Franz law occur. For example, in the electrically *superconducting* state, the thermal conductivity is less than in the normal state. Thus, for tantalum and tin at temperatures of around 0.5°K (0.9°R), the thermal conductivities are about 50 times larger in the *normal* than in the superconducting state. It has been estimated that for tin this ratio would increase to the order of 10^5 at 0.01°K (0.018°R). Since the normal state can be restored by immersing the body in a magnetic field of at least the *threshold* intensity, this property can be used for "switching." In this technique, an electrical switch in the field coil of an external electromagnet becomes, in effect, a means of opening and closing a "switch" in a thermal-circuit link within the *cryostat*.[10]

12·7 THERMAL CONTACTS

Application of heat-exchange media is dependent on thermal contacts at the bodies between which heat is exchanged, i.e., at the thermometer element and the parent body. At low temperatures, such contact resistances tend to be the *controlling resistances*.

When the heat-exchange medium or one of the bodies is a gas, the contact resistance assumes the aspect of *temperature jump*. This topic is discussed in Secs. 10·5 and 10·6; hence, it need only be mentioned here that, at low temperatures, the low-density conditions prevail at which temperature-jump tends to become important (see Eq. 10·2). When the contact is to the liquid, i.e., to helium II, the temperature jump may also be substantial. Thus, the fluid boundary conductance for such contacts has been measured as of the order of 3×10^{-2} cal/sec cm² °C (222 Btu/hr ft² °F) at 1°K (1.8°R). Since this conductance appears to decline as about the cube of the absolute temperature, values a thousandfold smaller are to be expected at 0.1°K. Thereby, in the region below 0.1°K (0.18°R), these contacts may be the *controlling resistances* in thermal circuits.[10, 24]

Berman [29] showed that, for clean copper surfaces pressed together, the thermal conductance of the contact was proportional to the thrust and independent of the total area. Also, at these low temperatures, he found that the Wiedemann-Franz law does not hold.

Wheatley, Griffing, and Estle [19] have developed a very practical method for making thermal contacts between solids, as, for example, between paramagnetic crystals and copper thermal links. It consists of cementing the surfaces together. Contact conductances are thus achieved comparable to those for clean copper under 100 lb thrust. They describe their technique in these words:

The glue most commonly used in these experiments consisted of a one to one mixture by volume of General Electric 7031 varnish * and Toluene. The Toluene seems to improve the mechanical properties of the bond. Other solvents such as alcohol or acetone do not. The surfaces to be joined are ground with No. 320 grit carborundum or carborundum paper. A fresh layer of glue is then applied, and the surfaces are immediately pressed together. On the other hand, a layer of glue should not be applied, allowed to dry, and then a second layer applied to make the bond. In this case, the crystal frequently drops off on cooling. It appears that when the technique is properly followed, the glue separating the bonding surfaces never completely hardens. This property is essential to the use of glue at low temperatures. Thus, with ferric ammonium alum in particular, the glue painted over the outside of the crystal as a protective layer invariably flakes off on cooling to low temperatures. However, the glue between the crystal and the link forms a very strong bond. The bond is sometimes so strong that if one attempts to remove the crystal, the crystal itself frequently breaks before the bond yields. In some crystals, no particular care need be taken in technique. This is particularly true of copper potassium Tutton salt. †

Joints produced by this method have been found to have contact conductances at 0.2°K (0.36°R) of the order of 6.6×10^{-5} cal/sec cm² °C (0.49 Btu/hr ft² °F). Since these conductances appear to vary as nearly the square of the absolute temperature, they can be expected to be much larger at 1°K (1.8°R) and also to decline to zero with approach to absolute zero.[19]

12·8 TEMPERATURE ERROR

The temperature-measurement error is usually given as the product of a thermal resistance and a thermal current (see Ch. 7, Volume I). This error can also be regarded as of the order of the ratio R_1/R_2 where R_1 is the thermal resistance between the sensitive element and the parent body and R_2 is that between the sensitive element and the surroundings. The preceding sections have indicated orders of magnitude attainable for R_1. Some idea of the magnitudes attainable for R_2 is to be gained from the fact that heat losses to an ambient, perhaps 300°C (540°F) higher in temperature, can be reduced to below 50 ergs/min, perhaps better appreciated as 2×10^{-8} cal/sec or 2.8×10^{-7} Btu/hr. This implies over-all thermal resistances of the order of 2×10^9 °F hr/Btu.[19]

---

* General Electric Co. (Schenectady, N. Y.)

† *By permission J. C. Wheatley, D. F. Griffing, and T. L. Estle in Rev. Sci. Instr.*, **27**, *no. 12, 1077 (December, 1956).*

12·9   PRIMARY INSTRUMENTS

The International Temperature Scale, with its definitions of standard instruments and of fixed-point values for their calibration, ends at the oxygen point 90.18°K (162.324°R). Below this temperature, the primary instruments are the hydrogen or helium gas thermometer, the hydrogen or helium vapor-pressure thermometer, and the magnetic thermometer. Readings on the gas and vapor-pressure instruments are usually corrected by thermodynamic calculations based on pressure, volume, and calorimetric measurements, to determine temperatures on the thermodynamic scale. Resulting from such studies are published tables of temperatures versus gas pressures at constant specific volume and of temperatures versus specific volumes at constant pressure. Similar tables exist of temperatures versus the pressures of vapor in coexistence with its liquid phase. These tables for hydrogen and helium become the bases of measurement. The authenticity of such gas and vapor thermometers rests on the high degree of reproducibility of the working substances, i.e., of pure hydrogen and pure helium. The precisions attainable are dependent on the accuracies of the published tables. The "**1958** He⁴ Scale of Temperatures," approved by the International Committee on Weights and Measures for the range 1 to 5.2°K, is published in intervals of 0.001°K over the range of from 0.500 to 5.22°K. It is said to agree with the thermodynamic scale to within ±0.002°K.[9,18,24,30-60]

The hydrogen vapor-pressure thermometer is convenient in the temperature range from 10 to 20°K (18 to 36°R). In turn, the helium gas thermometer can be used down to about 4°K(7.2°R).[9,18,24,30-36,40-59]

Lower temperatures must be measured by means of paramagnetic bodies, applying the Curie-Weiss law and making the necessary corrections. Thus, if a single crystal or a pellet made as a compact of powdered crystals of a *paramagnetic* substance is placed in a magnetic field of intensity H, oersteds, the temperature is given by

$$I = CH/(T_m + \Delta) \qquad (12·3)$$

where I is the intensity of magnetization produced in the crystal or pellet, maxwell/cm²; T_m is the temperature on the *magnetic temperature* scale; C is the Curie constant for the salt; and Δ is a correction term.[9,11,16,61-71]

The magnetic susceptibility $X = I/H$ can be measured by any of a variety of external-circuit arrangements. Thus, the crystal or pellet may serve as a core piece affecting the mutual inductance between a primary and a secondary coil. The quantities C and Δ can be calculated from basic theory. If such calculations are carried out with sufficient rigor, the magnetic temperature T_m may approximate the Kelvin temperature. On the other hand, C and Δ may be regarded as calibration constants. For a spherical crystal of cubic structure, $\Delta = 0$ and so this term is often ignored. Such calibration can be performed on the helium vapor-pressure scale, i.e., at temperatures above $1°K$ ($1.8°R$). In use, however, at temperatures below about $0.1°K$ ($0.18°R$), deviations from the Curie-Weiss law become so large that mere extrapolation has little meaning.[9–11, 53, 61–71]

One straightforward procedure is to cause the thermometer to traverse an actual Carnot cycle, the lower isothermal stage of which is at the calibration temperature while the upper isothermal stage is in the helium vapor-pressure region. Then, Eq. 1·3 of Volume I is

$$T_1/T_2 = Q_1/Q_2 \qquad (12·4)$$

where T_1 is the temperature measured on the helium vapor-pressure scale, $°K$; T_2 is the calibration temperature, $°K$; Q_1 is the heat absorbed by the thermometer body at temperature T_1, cal; and Q_2 is the heat rejected by the thermometer body at temperature T_2, cal. Precision measurement of the heat quantity Q_2 is so difficult, however, that less direct means are usually employed.[1, 5, 9–11, 16, 33, 61–64, 66–71]

Since a proper description of any of these methods is beyond the scope of the present work, the reader is referred to the excellent treatment given by Zemansky[9] in his *Heat and Thermodynamics*. Suffice it to say that each procedure depends on intricate theoretical considerations and difficult experimental measurements. Thus, the thermodynamic formula

$$T = (C_m/R_m)/[\,(1/R_m)\,(dS/dT_m)\,] \qquad (12·5)$$

is often used, where T is the thermodynamic temperature, $°K$; R_m is the universal gas constant, ergs/mole $°K$; C_m is the molar heat capacity of the salt at zero field intensity H and in terms of the magnetic temperature T_m, ergs/mole $°K$; S is the molar entropy, ergs/mole $°K$; and T_m is the temperature on the magnetic temperature scale.[1, 9–11, 16, 55, 61–65, 67–71]

The values measured by de Klerk, Steenland, and Gorter[69] for C_m/R_m and S/R_m on chromium potassium alum are given in Fig. 12·1. Values for $(1/R_m)\,(dS/dT_m)$ were obtained as slopes of the curve in Fig. 12·1A. In Table 12·1, the resulting determinations for Kelvin temperatures T are given. The complementary Tables 12·2 and 12·3 extend this range to $1°K$ and to $0.0014°K$, respectively. It can be seen that the

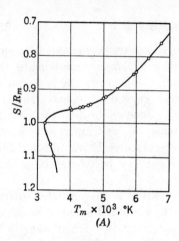 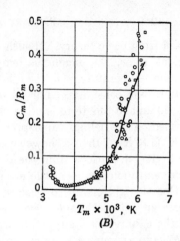

Fig. 12·1. Properties of chromium potassium alum. (A) Ratio of the molar entropy to the universal gas constant S/R_m, dimensionless, plotted against the magnetic temperature T_m, °K; and, (B) ratio of the molar heat capacity at zero magnetic-field intensity to the universal gas constant C_m/R_m, dimensionless, plotted against the magnetic temperature T_m, °K. (*By permission D. de Klerk, M. J. Steenland, and C. J. Gorter in Physica, 15, no. 7, 655, 657, August, 1949.*)

Table 12·1. Thermodynamic temperatures versus magnetic temperatures for chromium potassium alum

Magnetic Temperature T_m	C_m/R_m	$(1/R_m)(dS/dT_m)$, per °K	Thermodynamic Temperature T, °K
0.064	0.38	12.0	0.035
0.060	0.28	10.7	0.031
0.054	0.159	7.3	0.022
0.052	0.108	6.4	0.018
0.050	0.074	5.5	0.015
0.048	0.050	4.5	0.012
0.046	0.034	3.6	0.010
0.044	0.023	2.7	0.0088
0.042	0.016	2.25	0.0075
0.040	0.012	2.05	0.0065
0.038	0.011	2.6	0.0056
0.036	0.011	4.1	0.0047
0.034	0.024	6.1	0.0041
0.033	0.047	8.5	0.0039

By permission, de Klerk, Steenland, and Gorter, Physica, 15, no. 7, p. 654 (August, 1949).

Table 12·2.   Thermodynamic temperatures versus magnetic temperatures
for chromium potassium alum

Magnetic Temperature T_m	Thermodynamic Temperature T, °K
1.000	1.000
0.604	0.600
0.485	0.460
0.406	0.400
0.368	0.360
0.330	0.320
0.291	0.280
0.252	0.240
0.215	0.200

By permission, Bleaney in Proc. Royal Soc. A, 204, no. 1077, p. 219 (December, 1950).

Table 12·3.   Thermodynamic temperatures versus magnetic temperatures
for diluted chromium alum

Magnetic Temperature Uncorrected T_m	Magnetic Temperature Corrected T_m	Thermodynamic Temperature T, °K
0.0286	0.0211	0.0186
0.0222	0.0172	0.0124
0.0167	0.0143	0.0081
0.0133	0.0120	0.0056
0.0111	0.0104	0.0042
0.00952	0.00901	0.0032
0.00833	0.00791	0.0026
0.00741	0.00685	0.0022
0.00667	0.00625	0.0019
0.00606	0.00568	0.0016
0.00556	0.00538	0.0014

By permission, de Klerk, Steenland, and Gorter, Physica, 16, no. 6, p. 575 (June, 1950).

magnetic temperature T_m may be several times as large as the thermodynamic temperature T.[11, 64, 66-69]

12·10 SECONDARY INSTRUMENTS

Gas and vapor-pressure thermometers are exacting and unwieldy devices. Of course, since helium is used for cooling, its vapor pressure can also be measured and thus serve to determine the temperature of the bath. However, special bulbs intended for measuring local temperatures are bulky and not well suited to surface contacts. On the other hand, most instruments commonly used at ordinary temperatures do not apply in the low-temperature region. The liquid-in-glass thermometers cannot be used at all, whereas the sensitivities of platinum-resistance thermometers and the common thermoelectric materials become too low for convenient application. In consequence, investigation has sought different electric-resistance and different thermoelectric materials.[72, 73]

12·11 ELECTRIC-RESISTANCE THERMOMETERS

The temperature coefficients of resistance of pure metals decrease at low temperatures. Thus, values below $4°K$ ($7.2°R$) may be less than one-thousandth part of those at room temperature. Sensitivities of electric-resistance elements, which are proportional to these coefficients, thus tend, below about $7°K$ ($12.6°R$), to values too low for useful application.[74-79]

Much work has been done to extend the range of platinum-resistance thermometers to the lowest feasible temperatures; however, they have not reached much below about $14°K$ ($25.2°R$). In the region below the oxygen point $90.18°K$ ($162.324°R$), resistance-temperature relationships are complex and calibration formulas correspondingly awkward. Nevertheless, it is felt that platinum-resistance temperature determinations can reproduce the thermodynamic scale to within $\pm0.02°C$ ($\pm0.036°F$) throughout this region.[46-49, 59, 76, 80]

For alloys of metals, the low-temperature coefficients of resistance often have much larger values than those for the pure materials. Thus, constantan and manganin, the compositions commonly used for laboratory resistance standards, display appreciable temperature rates of change in this region. The coefficient of manganin, for example, exceeds that of platinum by more than 100-fold at $4°K$ ($7.2°R$). The coefficients are, however, somewhat unreproducible and are affected by magnetic fields, wire diameters, and exciting-current amperages.[76]

Certain alloys containing microscopic inclusions of superconducting metals have been found to display substantial and almost-linear temperature-rates-of-resistance change. These rates appear to result from the progressive transition of the inclusions to the superconducting state. Thus, a magnetic field, proportional to the threshold value at which the inclusion-metal material reverts to the normal state, destroys this property. Moreover, annealing such that the inclusions are absorbed into solid solution reduces the temperature coefficients of resistance to small values. Leaded phosphor bronzes, which are alloys of this sort, have yielded coefficients of the order of 0.05 per °C in the range 0.1 to 7°K (0.18 to 12.6°R). The exact value depends on the measuring current and on the magnitude of any external magnetic field.[76, 81-83]

Unfortunately, in low-temperature work, magnetic fields are used so generally that the sensitivity of alloys to such fields is usually a fatal objection. Carbon resistors are not subject to this limitation.[76, 83, 84]

12·12   SEMICONDUCTOR THERMOMETERS

Among the most satisfactory devices found have been the semiconductor electric-resistance elements. For use down to about 1°K (1.8°R), they are usually paper strips painted with colloidal carbon or compressed pellets of carbon composition. However, single crystals of germanium have also been used. Reproducibilities observed for the germanium crystals have been to within 0.01°C (0.018°R) even after warming to room temperature. Semiconductor resistance elements are highly sensitive, and they increase in sensitivity with decreasing temperature. The resistances tend to become excessive at very low temperatures; however, carbon-composition elements have been calibrated down to 0.1°K (0.18°R). The principal difficulty in semiconductor application is in obtaining reproducibility. Recalibration for each low-temperature run is thus a common requirement. Since these devices are discussed in Sec. 1·4, nothing further need be said here.[77, 82, 84-92]

12·13   THERMOCOUPLES

Thermoelectric powers tend to be low at low temperatures. For example, that of copper against constantan (60 per cent copper with 40 per cent nickel) is about 4 μv/°C (2.2 μv/°F) at 10°K (18°R); whereas the familiar value at the ice point is nearly 39 μv/°C (21.6 μv/°F). If the reference junction is kept in melting ice, deviations in its temperature from 273.15°K produce emf discrepancies which, at the measuring junction, then correspond to ten-fold greater temperature variations. The reference-junction error is thus grossly magnified.[93-103]

It has further been observed that over-all departures from reproducibility may occur in magnitudes as large as 10 μv. At 4 μv/°C, this corresponds to 2.5°C. If, however, it is arranged that a liquid-helium-point calibration reading is included with every run, this discrepancy can be reduced to within about 0.5°C (0.9°F). In effect, the helium boiling point then becomes the reference temperature.[100-103]

Various thermoelectric materials intended for use at low temperatures are mentioned in Ch. 5 of Volume I. Thus, highly dilute copper alloys have been found to develop substantial thermoelectric emfs at low temperatures while behaving nearly as pure copper at the ice point (see Fig. 12·2). For example, copper with 0.005 per cent tin against pure copper develops an approximately constant thermoelectric power of some 6 $\mu v/°C$ (3.3 $\mu v/°F$) over the range 2 to 30°K (3.6 to 54°R). For this alloy, the total emf generated over the interval of from 30°K (54°R) to the ice point is less than that for the much smaller 2-to-30°K (3.6 to 54°R) interval. The low thermoelectric power at the ice point has the effect that errors due to temperature deviations at the reference junction are almost eliminated. Furthermore, the larger ratio of the signal emf to the total quantity measured tends to lessen spurious sources of error and thus to improve reproducibility. For example, parasitic emfs due to composition gradients or due to cold work from bending the leads during installation tend to be somewhat in proportion to the total emf.[100,101,104,105]

Dilute copper-indium alloys have been found to generate up to 10

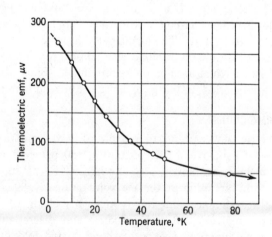

Fig. 12·2. Temperature variation of thermoelectric emf for a thermocouple composed of pure copper against copper with 0.0066 per cent tin when the constant-temperature junction is immersed in melting ice. At 273.15°K the emf is thus zero. (*By permission T. M. Dauphinee, D. K. C. MacDonald, and W. B. Pearson in J. Sci. Instr.*, **30**, *no. 11, 399, November, 1953.*)

$\mu v/°C$ (5.6 $\mu v/°F$) in the 2-to-30°K (3.6 to 54°R) range while retaining a favorable ratio of the total emf for this range relatively to
that of from 30°K (54°R) to the ice point. A particular thermocouple composed of copper with 0.0027 per cent indium against pure
platinum was reported to yield 5 $\mu v/°C$ (2.8 $\mu v/°F$) at 5°K (9°R) and
approximately 10 $\mu v/°C$ (5.6 $\mu v/°F$) at both 10 and 20°K (18 and
36°R).[101]

12·14 INSTALLATION OF TEMPERATURE-SENSITIVE ELEMENTS

Installation of thermocouples and electric-resistance elements at low
temperatures follows the same principles and procedures described in
Ch. 7 of Volume I. The calculation formulas given there are to be
used for installations in solids. When installations are in liquids, in
gases, or on surfaces, one must apply the adaptations of these methods
described in Chs. 9, 10, and 5, respectively. Since at low temperatures
the heat-transfer properties of materials differ widely from those at
ordinary and elevated temperatures, various of these peculiar characteristics have been enumerated in the present chapter. However, when
performing detailed computations, the reader will be wise to make full
use of the data contained in the references.

12·15 CONCLUSION

This chapter has sought to outline the conditions prevailing in low-
temperature work. The methods required for temperature measurement are indicated together with their limitations and the difficulties
in their application. At temperatures above the oxygen point, which
might still seem "low," problems peculiar to *low temperatures* are absent. Hence, those measurements are not discussed in this chapter.[106-111]

REFERENCES *

1. F. E. Simon, "The Concept of Temperature Near Absolute Zero," American
   Institute of Physics, *Temperature*, Vol. II, pp. 9–17, Reinhold Publishing
   Corp., New York, 1955.
2. A. J. O'Leary, "A Definition of Temperature as a Secondary Quantity,"
   Amer. J. Phys., **14**, no. 6, pp. 364–369 (November-December, 1946).
3. S. Malaker, "Behavior of Single Crystals of Cobalt-Ammonium-Sulfate below
   1 °K," in "Low Temperature Physics," *Natl. Bur. Standards Circ.* 519, pp.
   223–228, Government Printing Office, Washington (1952).
4. J. O. Hirschfelder, C. F. Curtiss, and R. B. Bird, *Molecular Theory of Gases
   and Liquids*, pp. 79–130, John Wiley & Sons, New York, 1954.

* See footnote on page 26.

5. H. C. Wolfe, "The Temperature Concept," American Institute of Physics, *Temperature*, Vol. II, pp. 3–8, Reinhold Publishing Corp., New York, 1955.

6. M. J. Klein, "Negative Absolute Temperatures," *Phys. Rev.*, **104**, no. 3, p. 589 (November, 1956).

7. K. Popaff, "Sur l'impossibilité d'atteindre le zéro des températures absolue" (On the Impossibility of Attaining the Absolute Zero of Temperature), *Compt. rend.*, **228**, pp. 908–910 (March, 1949).

8. A. Abragam and W. G. Proctor, "Spin Temperature," *Phys. Rev.*, **109**, no. 5, pp. 1441–1458 (March, 1958).

9. M. W. Zemansky, *Heat and Thermodynamics*, 4th ed., pp. 339–403, McGraw-Hill Book Co., New York, 1957.

10. E. Ambler and R. P. Hudson, "Magnetic Cooling," *Repts. Progr. in Phys.*, **18**, pp. 251–303 (1955).

11. D. de Klerk, "Magnetic Properties below 1 °K," *Physics Today*, **6**, no. 2, pp. 4–9 (February, 1953).

12. Arthur D. Little, Inc., *Low Temperature Bibliography for the Field of Cryogenics*, 63 pp., original and supplements 1–9, Arthur D. Little, Inc., Cambridge, Mass. (October, 1952–March, 1957).

13. K. R. Atkins, M. H. Edwards, and G. T. Pullan, "Booster Cryostat for Temperatures down to 0.74 °K," *Rev. Sci. Instr.*, **26**, no. 1, pp. 49–50 (January, 1951).

14. H. S. Sommers, Jr., "Two Types of Regulators and the Precision Control of Helium Bath Temperature," *Rev. Sci. Instr.*, **25**, no. 8, pp. 793–798 (August, 1954).

15. H. Forstat and J. R. Novak, "Temperature Control for Helium II," *Rev. Sci. Instr.*, **29**, no. 8, pp. 733–734 (August, 1958).

16. C. F. Squire, "Magnetic Cooling and Measurement of Temperatures below 1 °K," American Institute of Physics, *Temperature*, pp. 745–756, Reinhold Publishing Corp., New York, 1941.

17. C. V. Heer, C. B. Barnes, and J. G. Daunt, "The Design and Operation of a Magnetic Refrigerator for Maintaining Temperatures below 1 °K," *Rev. Sci. Instr.*, **25**, no. 11, pp. 1088–1098 (November, 1954).

18. J. Wilks, "Low Temperature Conference," *Physics Today*, **11**, no. 3, pp. 12–16 (March, 1958).

19. J. C. Wheatley, D. F. Griffing, and T. L. Estle, "Thermal Contact and Insulation below 1 °K," *Rev. Sci. Instr.*, **27**, no. 12, pp. 1070–1077 (December, 1956).

20. W. H. Keesom and G. Schmidt, "Researches on Heat Conduction by Rarefied Gases. III. The Thermal Accommodation Coefficient of Helium on Glass at 12 to 20 °K," *Physica*, **4**, no. 10, pp. 828–834 (October, 1937).

21. W. E. Keller, H. S. Sommers, Jr., and J. G. Dash, "Simple HeII Heat Switch," *Rev. Sci. Instr.*, **29**, no. 6, p. 530 (June, 1958).

22. N. Kurti, "The Lowest Temperature in the World," *Physics Today*, **13**, no. 10, pp. 26–29 (October, 1960).

23. National Research Council, *International Critical Tables*, Vol. 5, pp. 213–214, McGraw-Hill Book Co., New York, 1929.

24. J. Kistamaker and W. H. Keesom, "Isotherms of Helium Gas from 2.7 to 1.7 °K," *Physica*, **12**, no. 4, pp. 227–240 (July, 1946).

25. L. S. Kowalczyk, "Thermal Conductivity and Its Variability with Temperature and Pressure," *Paper 54-A-90*, 31 pp., American Society of Mechanical Engineers, New York (1950).

26. K. Mendelssohn and H. M. Rosenberg, "The Thermal Conductivity of Metals at Low Temperatures. I: The Elements of Groups 1, 2, and 3. II: The Transition Elements," *Proc. Phys. Soc. London A,* **65,** pp. 385–394 (1952).

27. M. Jakob, *Heat Transfer,* Vol. I, pp. 98–102, John Wiley & Sons, New York, 1949.

28. R. Berman, "Some Experiments on Thermal Contact at Low Temperatures," *J. Appl. Phys.,* **27,** no. 4, pp. 318–323 (April, 1956).

29. R. Berman and C. F. Mate, "Thermal Contact at Low Temperatures," *Nature,* **182,** no. 4650, pp. 1661–1663 (December, 1958).

30. W. H. Keesom and W. P. J. Lignac, "On the Temperatures of Liquid Helium," American Institute of Physics, *Temperature,* pp. 757–759, Reinhold Publishing Corp., New York, 1941.

31. C. S. Cragoe, "Slopes of the *pv* Isotherms of Some Thermometric Gases at Pressures below Two Atmospheres," American Institute of Physics, *Temperature,* pp. 89–126, Reinhold Publishing Corp., New York, 1941.

32. H. J. Hoge, "A Practical Temperature Scale below the Oxygen Point and a Survey of Fixed Points in This Range," American Institute of Physics, *Temperature,* pp. 141–156, Reinhold Publishing Corp., New York, 1941.

33. H. T. Wensel, "Temperature," American Institute of Physics, *Temperature,* pp. 3–23, Reinhold Publishing Corp., New York, 1941.

34. R. P. Hudson, "The Helium Vapor-Pressure Scale of Temperature," American Institute of Physics, *Temperature,* Vol. II, pp. 185–198, Reinhold Publishing Corp., New York, 1955.

35. J. R. Roebuck and T. A. Murrell, "The Kelvin Scale from the Gas Scales by Use of Joule-Thomson Data," American Institute of Physics, *Temperature,* pp. 60–73, Reinhold Publishing Corp., New York, 1941.

36. J. A. Beattie, "The Thermodynamic Temperature of the Ice Point," American Institute of Physics, *Temperature,* pp. 74–88, Reinhold Publishing Corp., New York, 1941.

37. H. van Dijk and M. Durieux, "On the Temperature Scale in the Liquid ^{4}He Region," *Physica,* **24,** no. 11, pp. 920–930 (November, 1958).

38. H. van Dijk and M. Durieux, "Thermodynamic Temperature Scale (T_{L55}) in the Liquid Helium Region," *Physica,* **24,** no. 1, pp. 1–19 (January, 1958).

39. F. E. Hoare and J. E. Zimmerman, "Helium Temperatures from Vapor Pressure Measurements," *Rev. Sci. Instr.,* **39,** no. 3, pp. 184–186 (March, 1959).

40. G. Schmidt and W. H. Keesom, "New Measurements of Liquid Helium Temperatures. I. The Boiling Point of Helium. II. The Vapour Pressure Curve of Liquid Helium," *Physica,* **4,** no. 10, pp. 963–977 (November, 1937).

41. F. G. Brickwedde, "The Helium Vapor-Pressure Scale of Temperatures," *Phys. Today,* **11,** no. 4, pp. 23–25 (April, 1958); F. G. Brickwedde, "The '1958 He^4 Scale of Temperatures,'" "Recommendation of the **1958**-Scale," *Physica,* **24,** Supplement, S128–S129 (September, 1958); and F. G. Brickwedde "The '1958 He^4 Scale of Temperatures,'" Part 1, H. van Dijk, M. Durieux, J. R. Clement, and J. K. Logan, Part 2, *Natl. Bur. Standards Monograph* **10,** 17 pp. (June, 1960); *J. Research Natl. Bur. Standards,* **64A,** no. 1, pp. 1–17 (January–February, 1960).

42. B. Bleaney and F. Simon, "The Vapour Pressure Curve of Liquid Helium below the λ-Point," *Trans. Faraday Soc.,* **35,** Part 9, no. 221, pp. 1205–1214 (September, 1939).

43. B. Bleaney and R. A. Hull, "The Determination of the Vapour-Pressure Curve of Liquid Helium below 1.6 °K using a Magnetic Thermometer," *Proc. Roy. Soc. London A,* **178,** no. 972, pp. 74–85 (May, 1941).

44. J. Kistamaker, "A Method for the Accurate Determination of Pressures from 100 to 1 mm," *Physica,* **12,** no. 4, pp. 217–226 (July, 1946).

45. J. Kistamaker, "The Vapour Pressure of Liquid Helium from the λ-Point to 1.3 °K," *Physica,* **12,** no. 5, pp. 272–279 (August, 1946).

46. H. J. Hoge, "A Practical Temperature Scale below the Oxygen Point and a Survey of Fixed Points in This Range," American Institute of Physics, *Temperature,* pp. 141–156, Reinhold Publishing Corp., New York, 1941.

47. H. J. Hoge and F. G. Brickwedde, "Establishment of a Temperature Scale for the Calibration of Thermometers between 14° and 83 °K," *RP* 2081, *J. Research Natl. Bur. Standards,* **22,** no. 3, pp. 351–373 (March, 1939).

48. H. J. Hoge, "Vapor Pressure and Fixed Points of Oxygen and Heat Capacity in the Critical Region," *RP* 2081, *J. Research Natl. Bur. Standards,* **44,** no. 3, pp. 321–345 (March, 1950).

49. J. C. Southard and R. T. Milner, "Low Temperature Specific Heats. II. The Calibration of the Thermometer and the Resistance of Platinum, Platinum–10% Rhodium and Constantan between −259 and −190°," *J. Am. Chem. Soc.,* **55,** no. 11, pp. 4384–4391 (November, 1933).

50. J. R. Roebuck, "The Kelvin Temperature of the Ice Point," *Phys. Rev.,* **50,** pp. 370–375 (August, 1936).

51. G. A. Slack, "Vacuum Gauge for Measuring Helium Pressures at Low Temperatures," *Rev. Sci. Instr.,* **27,** no. 4, pp. 241–242 (April, 1956).

52. S. C. Liang, "A Portable Low Temperature Thermometer," *Rev. Sci. Instr.,* **23,** no. 7, pp. 378–379 (July, 1952).

53. R. A. Erickson and L. D. Roberts, "The Measurement and the Calculation of the Liquid Helium Vapor Pressure-Temperature Scale from 1° to 4.2 °K," *Phys. Rev.,* **93,** no. 5, pp. 957–962 (March, 1954).

54. G. W. Moessen, J. G. Aston, and R. G. Ascah, "Thermodynamic Temperature Scale below 90 °K, the Normal Boiling Point of Normal Hydrogen," *J. Chem. Phys.,* **22,** no. 12, pp. 2096–2097 (December, 1954).

55. L. C. Jackson, *Low Temperature Physics,* 2nd ed., pp. 27–37, Chemical Publishing Co., Brooklyn, 1948.

56. R. Berman and C. A. Swenson, "Absolute Temperature Scale between 4.2 and 5.2 °K," *Phys. Rev.,* **95,** no. 2, pp. 311–314 (July, 1954).

57. H. van Dijk and D. Shoenberg, "Tables of Vapor Pressure of Liquid Helium," *Nature,* **164,** no. 4160, p. 151 (July, 1949).

58. W. E. Keller, "Thermodynamic Temperatures Obtained from P-V Isotherms of He Gas between 2° and 4° K," American Institute of Physics, *Temperature,* Vol. II, pp. 99–102, Reinhold Publishing Corp., New York, 1955.

59. R. B. Scott, "Low Temperature Scales from 90° to 5 °K," American Institute of Physics, *Temperature,* Vol. II, pp. 179–184, Reinhold Publishing Corp., New York, 1955.

60. J. A. Hall, "The International Temperature Scale," American Institute of Physics, *Temperature,* Vol. II, pp. 115–139, Reinhold Publishing Corp., New York, 1955.

61. D. H. Howling and F. J. Darnell, "Temperature Measurement below 1 °K," *Phys. Rev.,* **93,** no. 3, pp. 1416–1418 (March, 1954).

62. E. Ambler and R. P. Hudson, "Absolute Temperatures below 1 °K: Chromic Methylammonium Alum as a Thermometric Substance," *J. Chem. Phys.*, **27**, no. 2, pp. 378–389 (August, 1957).

63. L. D. Roberts and J. W. T. Dabbs, "A New Experimental Method for the Measurement of Temperature and Entropy at and below 1 °K," *Bull. Am. Phys. Soc.*, **26**, no. 3, p. 10 (April, 1951).

64. D. de Klerk, "Methods of Determining Very Low Thermodynamic Temperatures. Measurements with Potassium-Chromium-Alum," in "Low-Temperature Physics," *Natl. Bur. Standards Circ.* 519, pp. 211–222, Government Printing Office, Washington (1952).

65. H. B. G. Casimir, "Thermal Equilibrium at Temperatures below 1 °K," American Institute of Physics, *Temperature*, pp. 760–763, Reinhold Publishing Corp., New York, 1941.

66. D. de Klerk, "Thermometry below 1 °K, American Institute of Physics, *Temperature*, Vol. II, pp. 251–264, Reinhold Publishing Corp., New York, 1955.

67. D. de Klerk, M. J. Steenland, and C. J. Gorter, "Temperatures Obtained by Adiabatic Demagnetization of a Diluted Chromium Alum," *Physica*, **16**, no. 6, pp. 571–576 (June, 1950).

68. B. Bleaney, "Thermal Properties of Potassium Chromic Alum between 0.05 and 1 °K," *Proc. Roy. Soc. London A*, **204**, no. 1077, pp. 216–223 (December, 1950).

69. D. de Klerk, M. J. Steenland, and C. J. Gorter, "Determination of Very Low Thermodynamic Temperatures in Chromium Potassium Alum," *Physica*, **15**, no. 7, pp. 649–666 (August, 1949).

70. H. van Dijk, "Determination of Thermodynamic Temperatures between 1.5 and 0.25 °K," *Physica*, **12**, no. 6, pp. 371–395 (September, 1946).

71. H. van Dijk, "Techniques of Magnetic Thermometry," American Institute of Physics, *Temperature*, Vol. II, pp. 199–212, Reinhold Publishing Corp., New York, 1955.

72. C. Hochanadel, "A Low-Temperature Liquid-in-Glass Thermometer," *Rev. Sci. Instr.*, **25**, no. 5, p. 524 (May, 1954).

73. E. T. Patronis, Jr., H. Marshak, C. A. Reynolds, V. L. Sailor, and F. J. Shore, "Low-Temperature Thermal Noise Thermometer," *Rev. Sci. Instr.*, **30**, no. 7, pp. 578–580 (July, 1959).

74. T. M. Dauphinee and H. Preston-Thomas, "A Copper Resistance Temperature Scale," *Rev. Sci. Instr.*, **25**, no. 9, pp. 884–886 (September, 1954).

75. G. K. White and S. B. Woods, "Indium Resistance Thermometer; 4 to 300 °K," *Rev. Sci. Instr.*, **28**, no. 8, pp. 638–641 (August, 1957).

76. J. G. Daunt, "Superconductors as Thermometers," American Institute of Physics, *Temperature*, Vol. II, pp. 327–357, Reinhold Publishing Corp., New York, 1955.

77. R. D. Goodwin, "Design of Simple Resistance Thermometer Bridges for Wide-Range Control of Low Temperatures," *Rev. Sci. Instr.*, **29**, no. 6, pp. 497–501 (June, 1958).

78. G. K. White, S. B. Woods, and F. Anglin, "Indium Resistance Thermometer," *Rev. Sci. Instr.*, **29**, no. 2, pp. 181–182 (February, 1958).

79. J. W. Stewart, "Application of Indium Resistance Thermometry," *Rev. Sci. Instr.*, **30**, no. 10, p. 949 (October, 1959).

80. C. R. Barber, "A Platinum Resistance Thermometer for Use at Low Temperatures," *J. Sci. Instr.*, **32**, no. 11, pp. 416–417 (November, 1955).

81. H. A. Boorse, D. B. Cook, and M. W. Zemansky, "Superconductivity of Lead," *Phys. Rev.*, **78**, no. 5, pp. 635–636 (June, 1950).

82. A. van Itterbeek, L. de Greve, R. Lambeir and R. Celis, "Nickel Films Used as Thermometers at Low Temperatures and Superconductivity of Lead Films," *Physica*, **15**, no. 11–12, pp. 962–970 (December, 1949).

83. D. H. Parkinson and L. M. Roberts, "A Resistance Thermometer for Use at Helium Temperatures," *Proc. Phys. Soc. London B*, **68**, Part 6, pp. 386–387 (June, 1955).

84. S. A. Friedberg, "Semiconductors as Thermometers," American Institute of Physics, *Temperature*, Vol. II, pp. 359–382, Reinhold Publishing Corp., New York, 1955.

85. J. E. Kunzler, T. H. Geballe, and G. W. Hull, "Germanium Resistance Thermometers Suitable for Low-Temperature Calorimetry," *Rev. Sci. Instr.*, **28**, no. 2, pp. 96–98 (February, 1957).

86. A. H. Markham, R. G. Netzel, and J. R. Dillinger, "Carbon Resistor Thermometry below 1 °K," *Rev. Sci. Instr.*, **28**, no. 5, pp. 382–383 (May, 1957).

87. A. C. Herr, H. G. Terbeek, and M. W. Tiefermann, "Suitability of Carbon Resistors for Field Measurements of Temperatures in the Range of 35 °C to 100 °R," *Technical Note* D-264, 16 pp., U. S. National Advisory Committee for Aeronautics, Washington (February, 1960).

88. J. Millman, *Vacuum-Tube and Semiconductor Electronics*, pp. 60–91, McGraw-Hill Book Co., New York, 1958.

89. E. Ambler and H. Plumb, "Use of Carbon Resistors as Low Temperature Thermometers in the Presence of Stray rf Fields," *Rev. Sci. Instr.*, **31**, no. 6, pp. 656–657 (June, 1960).

90. J. J. Gniewek and R. J. Corruccini, "Carbon Resistance Thermometry with Mixed dc and rf Currents," *Rev. Sci. Instr.*, **31**, no. 8, pp. 899–900 (August, 1960).

91. A. R. de Vroomen, "A Practical Interpolation Procedure for Carbon Thermometry between 1.5 °K and 30 °K," *Bulletin de l'institut international du froid, Annexe*, no. 1, pp. 137–143, 1958.

92. G. B. Rodgers and F. A. Raal, "Semiconducting Diamonds as Thermistors," *Rev. Sci. Instr.*, **31**, no. 6, pp. 663–664 (June, 1960).

93. G. Borelius, "Thermoelectricity at Low Temperatures," *Physica*, **19**, no. 9, pp. 807–815 (September, 1953).

94. D. K. C. MacDonald, "Thermoelectric Power in Metals at Low Temperatures and Anomalous Impurity Scattering," *Physica*, **19**, no. 9, pp. 841–845 (September, 1953).

95. W. B. Pearson and I. M. Templeton, "Thermo-Electricity at Low Temperatures III. The Absolute Scale of Thermo-Electric Power: A Critical Discussion of the Present Scale at Low Temperatures and Preliminary Measurements towards Its Redetermination," *Proc. Roy. Soc. London A*, **231**, no. 1187, pp. 534–544 (September, 1955).

96. W. H. Keesom and C. J. Matthijs, "Thermoelectric Forces of Some Superconductors in the Neighborhood of Their Transition Points; the Influence of a Magnetic Field," *Physica*, **5**, no. 1, pp. 1–16 (January, 1938).

97. M. C. Steele, "Thermoelectromotive Force of a Superconductor versus the Same Metal in the Non-Superconductive State," *Phys. Rev.*, **81**, no. 2, pp. 262–267 (January, 1951).

98. M. C. Steele and J. Babiskin, "Magnetothermoelectric Behavior of Bismuth at Liquid Helium Temperatures," *Phys. Rev.*, **94**, no. 5, pp. 1394–1395 (June, 1954).

99. E. V. Larson and R. Mayer, "Recording and Indicating Instruments for Temperature Measurements down to 10 °K Using Copper-Constantan Thermocouples," *Rev. Sci. Instr.*, **23**, no. 12, pp. 692–694 (December, 1952).

100. T. M. Dauphinee, D. K. C. MacDonald, and W. B. Pearson, "The Use of Thermocouples for Measuring Temperatures below 70 °K. A New Type of Low Temperature Thermocouple," *J. Sci. Instr.*, **30**, no. 11, pp. 399–400 (November, 1953).

101. W. B. Pearson, "Thermocouples Suitable for Use at Low Temperature," *J. Sci. Instr.*, **31**, no. 12, p. 444 (December, 1954).

102. J.-P. Jan, W. B. Pearson, and I. M. Templeton, "Thermoelectricity at Low Temperatures. V. The Suitability of Lead as a Standard Reference Material," *Can. J. Phys.*, **36**, no. 5, pp. 627–631 (May, 1958).

103. J. W. Christian, J.-P. Jan, W. B. Pearson, and I. M. Templeton, "Thermoelectricity at Low Temperatures. VI. A Redetermination of the Absolute Scale of Thermo-electric Power of Lead," *Proc. Roy. Soc. London A*, **245**, no. 1241, pp. 213–221 (June, 1958).

104. J. F. Carlson, "Low Temperature Characteristics of Chromel-Alumel Thermocouples," *Instruments*, **33**, no. 1, p. 90 (January, 1960).

105. W. Koeppe, "On the Use of Iron-Constantan Thermocouples for Measurement of Low Temperatures," *Exper. Tech. der Physik*, **4**, no. 3, pp. 134–136 (1958); *Sci. Abstr. A*, **62**, no. 737, p. 422 (May, 1959).

106. A. H. Cooke, "The Establishment of the Absolute Scale of Temperature below 1 °K," *Proc. Phys. Soc. London A*, **62**, pp. 269–278 (May, 1949).

107. P. M. Endt, "The Use of Spontaneous Voltage Fluctuations for the Measurement of Low Temperatures," *Physica*, **16**, no. 5, pp. 481–485 (May, 1950).

108. R. A. Erickson, L. D. Roberts, and J. W. T. Dabbs, "Mutual Inductance Bridge and Cryostat for Low-Temperature Magnetic Measurements," *Rev. Sci. Instr.*, **25**, no. 12, pp. 1178–1182 (December, 1954).

109. H. J. Fink, "A New Absolute Noise Thermometer at Low Temperatures," *Can. J. Phys.*, **37**, no. 12, pp. 1397–1406 (December, 1959).

110. F. Rothwarf and J. Steinberg, "A Variable Sensitivity Gas Thermometer for Use at Low Temperatures," *Bulletin de l'institut international du froid, Annexe* no. 1, pp. 117–127, 1958.

111. H. R. Hart, Jr., and J. C. Wheatley, "Thermal Contact below 1 °K," *Bulletin de l'institut international du froid, Annexe* no. 1, pp. 311–316, 1958.

13

FLAME TEMPERATURES

13·1 INTRODUCTION

A *flame* is distinguished from any other body of hot gas by its non-equilibrium condition. Chemical reactions are in progress in a flame. *Dissociation products* occur and may be in process of *recombination* or further dissociation. The dissociation products or ions are electrically charged aggregates of atoms, and they generally contain abnormal amounts of energy.

It is known that gas-phase chemical reactions occur in *chains*. A chain is a series of steps or individual reactions occurring on collisions between pairs, or very rarely trios, of particles. Ordinarily, at least one member in any such individual reaction must be an *active particle*. An active particle is an *energy-rich* particle. Examples of such particles occurring in flames formed by the combustion of hydrocarbon fuels are individual atoms of oxygen, hydrogen, and carbon and hydroxyl (OH) and carbon monoxide (CO) ions. *Ignition* usually requires that there be present in the mixture at least a minute or residual population of these active particles.[1-4]

In an electrical discharge such as a spark or arc, charged particles are accelerated in an electric field. The charged particles consist of ions and free electrons. Ions are molecules from which one or more electrons have been removed or, occasionally, to which extra electrons have been added. The motions of the charged particles occur in opposite directions according to the respective signs of their charges. This motion is the mechanism by which electricity is conducted in sparks and arcs. Ions can be produced by the *bombarding* of *neutral molecules* by charged particles accelerated in the electric field. As these ions recombine in pairs to form neutral molecules, the ion population is replenished with new ions produced by bombardment. As in the case of ignition, to start a spark or an arc it is usually necessary that there be at least a minute initial population of charged particles.[4]

Thermodynamic temperature as discussed in Sec. 1·5 of Volume I and in Secs. 10·7, 10·11 and 12·2 of Volume II is defined only for the

condition of thermodynamic equilibrium. It is obvious that thermodynamic equilibrium does not prevail in either a flame or an arc.
Thereby, the thermodynamic temperature for such an aggregate of
matter unavoidably remains an undefined quantity.

It might thus be regarded as futile to proceed further. However,
it has been found of practical utility to perform measurements on
thermal conditions in flames. Such conditions are often described by
pseudotemperatures. The pseudotemperatures usually refer to the
amounts of storage in particular energy states. More rigorously, they
are described by the means employed in their measurement. Unfortunately, they tend to be based on certain assumptions that are often of
a speculative character.

13·2 PSEUDOTEMPERATURES

The choice of a particular pseudotemperature depends on the direction of the practical interest. However, this choice is also likely to
be dictated by the means available for measurement. For example,
interest may relate to the *sensible heat*, i.e., to that part of the intrinsic
energy of the gas occurring in *thermal form*. Energy in thermal form
is that of disorder as associated with entropy. For example, the
sensible heat may be taken as a measure of the degree of completeness
to which a combustion process has progressed, or it can be used as a
measure of the amount of mechanical work of expansion that could be
extracted from the gas.[5]

Sometimes, a pseudotemperature is described in terms of the capacity
of the gas to transmit heat to another body. This pseudotemperature
is defined by Griffiths and Awbery[6] as "the temperature of a solid
body which is in thermal equilibrium with the flame." The difficulty
with such a definition is that the temperature assumed by such a solid
body depends not only on the thermal condition of the gas but also on
the surface characteristics of the solid body in contact. Such surface
characteristics include *adsorption* properties and any others on which
catalysis or *surface combustion* may depend. Thus, active particles,
dissociated ions, fuel, and oxidizing particles tend to become condensed or adsorbed on a solid surface that is exposed to the flame
gases. Chemical reactions then occur in this adsorbed state on the
solid surface, assisted by the energy reserves of the solid. Much
of the reaction energy may then remain in the solid as the products
of combustion "re-evaporate" into the gaseous region. Also, energy-
rich particles may migrate to the solid surface and there give up their
excess energies. By these mechanisms, solids in contact with gaseous
mixtures have been known to attain temperatures hundreds of degrees

higher than those that could, at most, correspond to the sensible heat of the gas. Obviously, this sort of definition is not a reliable one, even though widely used.[1-3,5-16]

13·3 SOLID-WIRE PROBES

Techniques for the measurement of high-temperature gases by the use of fine-wire thermoelectric and electric-resistance elements were discussed in Ch. 11. These methods are simple and convenient when they are applicable. They are commonly regarded as limited to temperatures below the melting point of the wire metals. However, Hoenig [17] has shown how to use an initial rate of rise in the wire temperature quantitatively to determine gas temperatures well above the wire's melting point. Design is usually based on the heat balance among radiation to the environment, conduction along the leads, and exchanges with contiguous gaseous layers, these transfers being controlled by gas-boundary conductances. Methods thus provide for the suppression or elimination of conduction and thermal-radiation effects. In gases that are merely "hot," errors from catalytic or surface combustion do not arise; however, in flames and other mixtures of reactants not in chemical equilibrium, these effects must be considered.[5,6,10,11,17-20]

Baker,[7,19] Baker,[7] and Freudenstein [7] have reviewed a body of literature dealing with surface catalysis in relation to possible errors in the readings of solid probes. The outlook presented is somewhat discouraging, concluding in the words of Fiock et al.: [21] "Our general experience with multiple bare junctions in a region of continued chemical reaction is that such junctions usually read so high that values of combustion efficiency calculated therefrom are far above 100 percent. . . ."

Bailey [22] may have presented an example of this difficulty (although his own explanation is different) in reporting thermocouple readings of 2075 to 2325°F (1135 to 1274°C) where the theoretical temperature for 100 per cent adiabatic combustion was given as 1260°F (682°C). Alquist and Male,[23] during a series of tests on hot-spot ignition in piston internal-combustion engines, used an *engine-heated* hot spot consisting of a platinum–against–platinum-with-rhodium thermocouple. This thermocouple, when bare in the natural condition, recorded its own temperature as 1900°F (1038°C). However, when the thermocouple was treated with tetraethyl lead, either by previous dipping or by mixing tetraethyl lead in the engine fuel, the reading dropped to 1400°F (760°C). Dipping in commercial tetraethyl lead appeared to constitute a permanent treatment.

Guest,[24] in an exhaustive study of the causes of mine explosions, summarized data on surface catalysis for a large number of materials and surface conditions. The form of evidence supplied is based on the temperature of a solid surface required to ignite the gas. This temperature is found to be higher, when other factors are kept the same, by an amount proportional to the catalytic activity of the surface. The work was done on methane, which is the principal component in mine gases, and may be roughly applicable to the hydrocarbon-oxygen reactions characteristic of commercial flames.

Guest[24] clearly indicated that certain materials, particularly platinum and palladium, were much more active than the general run of substances. However, a substantial range of activity was found within a group including: gold, copper, tungsten, molybdenum, nickel, Monel metal, and stainless steel. In fact, the range of temperature elevations among the group amounted to about half of that for platinum. Hence, it does not appear safe to assume negligible catalytic activity for the above cited materials.

Quartz has been much used in surface-ignition studies because of its reputation as a poor catalyst. However, differences found in the ignition temperatures for the same fuel with different quartz surfaces have been attributed to differences in the catalytic action of the quartz surfaces.[24]

Leah,[9,25-28] Rounthwaite,[25] and Bradley,[25] following David,[29-31] used a quartz-coated, 0.0002-in. diameter, platinum with 10 per cent rhodium, electric-resistance-thermometer element to measure flame temperatures. Comparison with results on plain 0.0005-in. diameter wires of the same material showed that the bare wires read up to 300°C (572°F) higher during the period of most intense chemical reaction. Their heat-transfer analyses indicated that this difference could not be attributed to any insulating effect of the 0.00015-in. thick quartz coating but must be regarded as the effect of surface catalysis on the bare metal. Measurements by Daish, Fender, and Woodall,[32] however, have indicated that alteration of the wire's lag time by the quartz coating may account for part or all of this difference.

Klein,[33] Mentser,[33] von Elbe,[33-35] and Lewis[33-35] used thermocouples of 0.0005-in. diameter platinum against platinum with 10 per cent rhodium, dipped in molten borax, to measure combustion temperatures in nitrocellulose. Comparison with data taken with wire that was similar but uncoated indicated that peak temperatures were 382°C (720°F) higher in the bare wire. The difference was attributed to surface catalysis. Klaukens[36] and Wolfhard[36-41] found that nickel wire showed more catalytic effect than nickel-chromium wire, the latter bearing an oxide layer. Friedman[42,43] and Burke[43] used National

Bureau of Standards (Washington, D. C.) Ceramic Coating A-418 on
12-μ (4.7 × 10^{-4}-in.) diameter wires of platinum against platinum
with 10 per cent rhodium. This coating consists of eight oxides plus
a small proportion of enameler's clay. They found that one coating
permitted several complete traverses to be made with the same couple.
Reproducibility, agreement with theory, and consistency with incomplete results obtained using potassium chloride and silica coatings,
respectively, in the same sort of flame were taken as evidence that
surface-catalytic errors were not appreciable.

Most of those who have worked with coated wires have expressed the
belief that the indications thus obtained have been of "true," i.e.,
kinetic temperatures.[25, 33, 43, 44]

Apart from discrepancies between the actual wire temperatures and
those representing the thermal condition of the flame, errors arise in
bare thermoelectric and electric-resistance elements because of contamination property changes in the wire materials. This problem has
been discussed in Chs. 5 and 10 of Volume I and also in Chs. 1, 2, and
9 of Volume II. Protection tubes are usually used; they are bulky
and greatly increase lag times. Schmidt[18] chose to avoid contamination errors by using an optical pyrometer to measure the wire-probe
temperatures. Rieke[45] used a recessed blackbody probe with a
sighting tube and target surface whose temperature was then measured with an optical pyrometer.[18, 45-46]

13·4   KINETIC TEMPERATURE

The pseudotemperature in which most confidence is usually placed
is the *kinetic temperature*. The kinetic temperature is that determined
from phenomena directly dependent on the translational energies of
the gas molecules. It can be regarded as the temperature that would
prevail if all the other energy states of the gas were in equilibrium
with the translational energy states. This concept depends on the
assumption that the energies in the translational motions of the gaseous
particles are themselves in a state of statistical equilibrium. A condition is thereby implied of randomness or chaos in the distribution
of the translational energies over the range of possible values. Such
values extend in a continuum from zero to infinity, and the equilibrium
function is that of the Maxwell-Boltzmann law.

$$N/N_o = \{2\sqrt{E}/[\sqrt{\pi}(kT)^{3/2}]\}\, e^{-E/kT}\, \Delta E \qquad (13·1)$$

where N is the number of molecules with kinetic energy in the range
E to $E + \Delta E$ out of a total number N_o of molecules; E is the kinetic

energy, $\frac{1}{2}mV^2$, ergs, of translational motion for a gas molecule of mass m, g, and velocity V, cm/sec; k is Boltzmann's constant, 1.38×10^{-16} erg/°K; and T is the absolute temperature, °K.

The belief in the validity of the assumption of *translational equilibrium* is based on the relatively short *relaxation* times occurring for translational energies. They are of the order of 10^{-9} sec at atmospheric densities and temperatures and may be as short as 10^{-11} sec during the combustion stroke of an internal-combustion engine. By comparison, the relaxation times for *rotational* and *vibrational energies*, discussed in Sec. 10·11, tend to range from 10^{-8} to 10^{-5} sec.

The absence of such phenomena as *metastable states* among translational energies adds to the assurance of translational equilibrium. A metastable state is an excited energy state of indefinite lifetime, which can only be *deactivated* by temporary supply of a suitably larger quantum of energy. Such energy quanta tend most often to be available for loan in collisions of the energy-rich particles with solid walls of a containing vessel. The collisions, however, can occur only after diffusion through the intervening depth of gas. Wall collisions are thereby very much less frequent than collisions among the gas molecules. Consequently, relaxation times tend to be long for metastable states and for semistable particles in general.

Granted that the translational energy is thus a definite thing, the question then arises as to how good a criterion this energy may be of the thermal condition of the gas. We have seen that, in a flame or an arc, there are *energy-rich* particles. They have been defined as particles certain of whose energy states are excited to levels higher than would accord statistically with the Boltzmann distribution law.

$$N_1/N_2 = (g_1/g_2)e^{-(E_1-E_2)/kT} \qquad (12\cdot1)$$

In this equation, N_1 is the number of members of a group occupying the energy state E_1; N_2 is the number occupying state E_2; E_1 and E_2 are the excitation energies for the two states, respectively, ergs; g_1 and g_2 are the a priori probabilities or statistical weights for the two states; k is Boltzmann's constant, 1.38×10^{-16} erg/°K; T is the absolute temperature, °K; and e is the natural-logarithmic base.

Excited energy states not in accord with Eq. 12·1 may be electronic, vibrational, rotational, etc. However, by our assumption of translational equilibrium, they will not occur among the translational energies. Consequently, the translational energies of the particles which may be excited in their electronic, vibrational, or rotational states are assumed to be in statistical equilibrium with the translational energies of all other particles.

Where a flame is produced by the combustion of a fuel in air, nearly four fifths of the molecules present are those of nitrogen. By their inert character, they participate only to a minor degree in chemical reactions of combustion. Hence, direct *chemical excitation* of their internal energy states is less to be expected. Since they are also nearly transparent in the wavelengths in which most flame radiation occurs, excitation by radiant quanta will be of lower probability. Reaction energy will thus tend to be transmitted to these molecules only during collisions. Although it is the translational energies that are most obviously involved, transfers between higher energy states may also occur on collision. However, the probabilities for such higher-state exchanges are likely to be less and may be thousands-of-times less than in translation, where almost every collision is effective.[5, 9, 19, 37, 47]

A delay may also occur in the transmission of energy, originally received in the translational degrees of freedom, to the other energy states, even of the same molecular species. This phenomenon has been observed in jets and high-frequency sound waves and is designated by the term *excitation lag*.

Within the group of molecules participating in a chemical reaction, direct *chemical excitation* of the higher internal energy states may result. Newly formed energy-rich molecules, *free radicals*, short-lived *complexes*, and *free atoms* occur. Excitation may be in metastable states. Thus, energy states arise that are abnormal in the sense of being out of accord with the Boltzmann distribution of Eq. 12·1.

As much as one fourth of the energy of a chemical reaction has been reported to be temporarily stored in such abnormal-energy states. Radiation corresponding to deactivation of such chemically excited states, i.e., *chemiluminescent radiation*, is thus likely to be a poor criterion of the thermal condition of the gaseous body.[9, 19, 47]

In practice, it is necessary to distinguish between two zones generally prevailing in flames: (1), the *reaction zone;* and, (2), what in a *Bunsen flame* is called the *interconal region.* The zones correspond to the *flame front* and the regions of *afterburning* in a piston internal-combustion engine. In a *diffusion flame*, the two zones tend to be intermingled. In the reaction zones, highly nonequilibrium conditions are commonly found. However, in the interconal region of a well-regulated Bunsen flame, an approach to thermal equilibrium usually obtains. The reaction zone in a flame front or *luminous cone* is a thin layer, often only a few thousandths of an inch in thickness. Temperature measurements are usually not directed at this layer but are referred to the gases after the primary combustion processes have been completed. Measurements are thus generally made in regions of afterburning. Here, recombination is in process as in the interconal space, but with a certain amount of continuing primary combustion resulting partly from imperfect mixing of the original fuel components. In piston internal-combustion engines, *precombustion reactions* tend to be in progress in the region not yet traversed by the flame front.[1-3]

Exhaustive studies by Baker,[7,19] Laserson,[19] Corry,[48] and Baldo [49] have failed to demonstrate that the aggregate radiant emission from the flame gases in an internal-combustion engine differs by any large amount from what would be predicted thermally on the basis of the kinetic temperature of the same gases.[7,9,19,47-49]

The arguments, in terms of which the translational energy is taken as a criterion of the thermal condition of the gas, are then: (1), that the translational energies are usually in internal equilibrium; (2), that the translational energies commonly include a large fraction of the thermal energy of the gas; (3), that diluent gases are often present in such amounts that a large fraction of the nontranslational energy states can attain abnormal excitation only indirectly and therefore the probability of such excitation is likely to be less; and, (4), that the nontranslational energy states of the reacting constituents do not appear, in any very large fraction of their number, to be in highly abnormal energy states.

By the foregoing reasoning, it is commonly concluded that the *translational,* i.e., *kinetic, temperature* can be depended upon: (1), rarely to indicate widely erroneous magnitudes for the thermal energy; and, (2), usually to indicate with accuracy the aggregate thermal content of the gas.[50,51]

One must beware, however, of such cases as Gaydon [37-39,52-54] and Wolfhard's [36-41] finding a kinetic temperature of 4000°K (6740°F) where the theoretical maximum flame temperature was about 2700°K (4400°F). It should be added, though, that this determination was made by the relatively unreliable Doppler-line-broadening method (see Sec. 13·7).

13·5 OTHER PSEUDOTEMPERATURES

Any *mode* of energy storage can serve as the basis for a pseudo-temperature. This rule is subject to the condition that statistical equilibrium shall prevail in the body of gas for storage in this mode. For example, in

$$N_1/N_2 = (g_1/g_2)e^{-(E_1-E_2)/kT} \tag{12·1}$$

let us suppose that the states 1 and 2 are pairs of *rotational energy states.* Then, satisfying Eq. 12·1 for all such pairs implies a condition of general rotational equilibrium, and T is the *rotational temperature*. Similarly, if states 1 and 2 are any pair of *vibrational energy states*, *vibrational* equilibrium may be said to prevail, and T is the *vibrational temperature*. Likewise, the states 1 and 2 may be *electronic* energy states. Commonly, however, only a portion of a series of energy states —rotational, vibrational, or electronic—is in equilibrium. The corresponding pseudotemperature is then for this particular group of energy states.

If statistical equilibrium fails to prevail in any one mode of energy storage, the corresponding pseudotemperature remains undefined. If all the pseudotemperatures are defined and are alike, then that value is the thermodynamic temperature. If no pseudotemperature is defined, we are left without any conveniently specified term by which to designate the thermal condition of the gas.

13·6　MEASUREMENT OF KINETIC TEMPERATURE

Measurements that can be performed in the absence of thermodynamic equilibrium serve to determine individual pseudotemperatures. For example, suppose that the pressure p of a gas confined at constant volume V is to be used as the means of measurement. It is known that the pressure arises from the statistical aggregate of mechanical impacts of individual molecules upon the walls of the containing vessel. The individual impacts result from reversals of mechanical momenta in the translational motions of the gas particles. The pressure exerted is thus directly a function of the translational motions, i.e., of the statistical average of the translational energies of all the gas particles. This is what we have defined as the translational or kinetic temperature.[5]

Then, referring to the method of Sec. 8·7

$$T = pV/CmR \qquad (8·12)$$

where m is the mass of the gaseous body, g; R is the gas constant per unit mass, ergs/g°K; V is the volume, cm³; C is the compressibility factor; p is absolute pressure, dynes/cm²; and T is the kinetic temperature, °K. Leah [9, 25-28] has developed an ingenious photographic method based on this principle for which the reader is referred to his original papers.[5, 9, 25-28]

Most of the formulas and equations in gas-dynamical theory depend on Eq. 8·12. Thus, temperature measurements based on such equations are usually, in effect, measurements of pressure-volume or gas-elasticity effects. These quantities are dependent on the translational energies of the gas particles. Hence, such measurements tend to be those of translational or kinetic temperatures. Examples of these procedures are the velocity-of-sound and orifice methods and the X-ray, interferometric, and schlieren methods. These methods are discussed in Secs. 6·9, and 11·2 to 11·13.[56, 57]

13·7 DOPPLER BROADENING

The Doppler broadening of spectral lines can be taken as a measure of kinetic temperature. By this effect, the translational motion of a radiating gas particle shortens or "stretches out" the emitted wavelength. Which of these happens depends on whether the source motion is toward or away from the observer. The nominal or undisturbed frequency of a spectral line is given by

$$\nu = (E_1 - E_2)/h \qquad (13·2)$$

for a transition from energy state 1 to energy state 2, where E_1 and E_2 are the excitation energies of the initial and the final energy states, respectively, ergs; h is Planck's constant, 6.625×10^{-27} erg sec; and ν is the frequency of the emitted radiant quantum, $\sec^{-1}$.

The nominal frequency is altered to a continuous range or line width $\Delta\nu$ by several effects (see Fig. 13·1). Thus, there is the natural width resulting from the *uncertainty principle* in quantum mechanics. Then, there is *collision broadening* due to interference by neighboring molecules and *resonance* broadening due to interference by similar molecules. These effects are superimposed on the broadening due to the

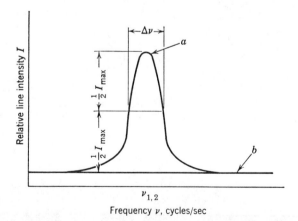

Fig. 13·1. Doppler broadening. Intensity I is plotted against frequency ν. a, peak of spectral line; and, b, continuous-background intensity.

Doppler effect. Hence, it is necessary to be assured that the broadening due to the other causes is negligible by comparison.[37, 58]

The natural width is extremely small and can safely be neglected above room temperature. The resonance pressure broadening may be serious in strong resonance lines of atomic spectra and precludes the use of such as the sodium D lines. However, in molecular spectra, resonance broadening can be neglected. Normal pressure broadening will affect all molecules to some extent at high gas pressures. However, there is evidence that this effect is not serious at atmospheric pressure and below.[37, 58]

The spectrometer used must be of very high *dispersion*. Even then, the additional line width resulting from the limitations of the instrument may be of the same order of magnitude as the broadening due to the Doppler effect. It is necessary to calibrate the instrument against lines of established contour, as, for example, those of a water-cooled mercury arc, for which the Doppler broadening is known to be small. The observed width is then corrected for the instrumental broadening to obtain that due to the Doppler effect. The half width $\Delta \nu$ (see Fig. 13·1) is measured at the points on the contour of half-peak intensity. In determining the line intensities for this measurement, it is necessary first to subtract the ordinates for the continuous background radiation.[37, 58, 59]

The Doppler broadening is given by

$$\Delta \nu_D = \Delta \nu_o - \Delta \nu_I \tag{13·3}$$

where $\Delta \nu_D$ is the Doppler broadening, sec^{-1}; $\Delta \nu_o$ is the observed half width, sec^{-1}; and $\Delta \nu_I$ is the instrumental half width. The temperature T is then determined from

$$T = 1.93 \times 10^{12} \times M (\Delta \nu_D)^2 / \nu^2 \tag{13·4}$$

where $\Delta \nu_D$ is the Doppler-broadening half width, sec^{-1}; ν is the frequency of the line, sec^{-1}; M is the molecular weight of the gas molecules; and T is the temperature, $°K$.[37]

To investigate possible departure from the Maxwell-Boltzmann distribution, i.e., from equilibrium, the observed line contour can be compared with that expected theoretically for pure Doppler broadening. To this end, the resultant curve is plotted for the combination of the instrumental and the Doppler effects. The experimental points are then superimposed on the computed curve. For an account of this difficult technique and a full discussion of the Doppler method, the reader is advised to consult Gaydon's [37-39, 52-54] original paper.[37]

The method is not sensitive, and probable errors have been estimated as from $\pm 200°C$ ($\pm 360°F$) to $\pm 400°C$ ($\pm 720°F$) even when the most precise techniques are used. There are also the hazards of possible unresolved neighboring lines which may appear as broadening. Self-absorption in outer cooler layers of the same gaseous body changes the resultant intensity distributions. Doppler determinations of kinetic temperature are not to be classed as reliable in the sense, for example, of those based on Eq. 8·12.[37,58,60]

13·8   SPECTRA

Simple particles such as free electrons and atomic nuclei are limited to *translational* and *spin* energies. Atoms have in addition the energies of orbital electrons. Molecules consist of two or more atoms. They may have thereby, besides translational, spin, and electronic energies, what are called *vibrational* and *rotational* energies. These energies arise, respectively, in the vibratory motions of the component nuclei against the "elastic" internuclear binding forces and in the "rigid-body" rotations of the molecule as a whole. The energy of the molecule is then given by

$$E = E_t + E_e + E_r + E_v + E_{es} + E_{ns} + E_{ie} \qquad (13·5)$$

where E is the total energy, ergs; E_t is the translational energy, ergs; E_e is the sum of the orbital energies of the electrons, ergs; E_r is the sum of the rotational energies, ergs; E_v is the sum of the vibrational energies, ergs; E_{es} is the sum of electron-spin energies, ergs; E_{ns} is the sum of the nuclear-spin energies, ergs; and E_{ie} is the sum of the *interaction* energies among these modes, ergs.[38,61-65]

Translational energies, whether of free electrons, atomic nuclei, or molecules, occur in a continuum. Hence, any value is possible. All other energies, i.e., spin, electronic, vibrational, rotational, and interaction energies, are quantized; thus, they occur only in discrete magnitudes. Figure 13·2 shows a partial set of energy-level diagrams for iodine vapor, which consists of diatomic molecules. It is to be noted that the steps between electronic levels are very large. Rotational levels, which are not shown, on the other hand, are spaced more closely than either the vibrational or electronic levels, which are shown.[38,61-65]

Transitions giving rise to molecular spectra can involve: (1), changes in rotational energy only; (2), changes in both rotational and vibrational energies; and (3), changes in rotational, vibrational, and electronic energies. For the first type, the energy changes $E_1 - E_2$ are very small, and, by Eq. 13·2, the frequencies ν are likewise small (i.e.,

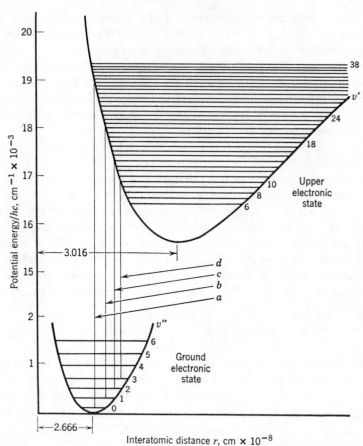

Fig. 13·2. Energy-level diagram for iodine. v' and v'' are vibration quantum numbers. a, Transition between $v'' = 0$ and $v' = 32$; b, transition between $v'' = 1$ and $v' = 21$; c, transition between $v'' = 2$ and $v' = 14$; and d, transition between $v'' = 3$ and $v' = 10$. h is Planck's constant, 6.625×10^{-27} erg sec; and c is the velocity of light in vacuo, 2.998×10^{10} cm/sec. (*By permission P. Myers, C. A. Uyehara, S. K. Chen, and N. J. Beck, Four Proposed Methods of Measuring End-Gas Properties, Appendix C, 99, Coordinating Research Council, New York, January, 1953.*)

long wavelength λ) and occur only in the far infrared. For the second type, the vibrational-energy changes also yield lines in the infrared. However, with every magnitude of vibrational change, there is associated a set of possible simultaneous rotational transitions which split these lines into bands. The closely spaced fine lines composing the bands result from the small-magnitude rotational-energy changes. The relatively large energies for electronic transitions tend to yield lines in the visible and ultraviolet, as well as in the infrared, portions of the spectrum. These lines are, however, similarly split into bands of fine lines, resulting from the simultaneous changes in vibrational and rotational energies. A *spectral band* for transitions from one of the vibrational levels in an upper electronic state is thus split into a series of finely spaced lines resulting from the various possible simultaneous rotational-energy changes. For any one electronic transition, there are then a number of such bands, i.e., a *band system,* corresponding to the number of possible vibrational-energy transitions that can occur with the same electronic transition.[38, 61-65]

The rotational lines may be further split into bands by electronic-spin-orbit interaction energies. These bands are sometimes wider than the rotational bands.[38, 61-65]

In atomic spectra, i.e., spectra from uncombined atoms, the vibrational and rotational energy states are absent. Electronic transitions then tend to result in line spectra instead of bands. Spin-splitting however occurs.

If solid particles such as carbon granules or dust occur in a flame, their radiation will be in the continuous spectrum. In the combustion of liquid or solid fuels and in the detonation of liquid or solid explosives, there usually results a background of continuous radiation upon which the lines and bands of the atomic and molecular spectra appear as superimposed. Even in the absence of any solid particles, as may occur with certain gaseous fuels, there are always ions and free electrons. In recombinations, as, for example, when a free electron enters an atom and drops to some lower energy state, its initial translational energy is added to that for the internal transition between quantized energy levels. The resulting radiation is spread into a continuum by this translational portion of the energy change. There is thus always a continuous background.[38, 61-66]

13·9   SPECTROSCOPIC TEMPERATURES

The intensities of spectral lines are often used for measurement of temperature. These line emissions arise from transitions between energy states according to

$$\nu = (E_1 - E_2)/h \qquad (13\cdot2)$$

where ν, sec^{-1}, is the frequency resulting from a transition between energy states E_1 and E_2, ergs; and h is Planck's constant, 6.625×10^{-27} erg sec.[38, 61-65]

The intensities of such lines depend on populations in the excited energy states, from which transitions can occur to result in the frequency ν, and on the *transition probabilities*. The populations of such energy states are related to the temperature by Eq. 12·1. Line intensities are then given by expressions of the form

$$I = CP\nu^4 e^{-E/kT} \tag{13·6}$$

where ν is the frequency, sec^{-1}; E is the energy of the state from which the transition occurs, ergs; P is the transition probability; k is Boltzmann's constant $= 1.38 \times 10^{-16}$ erg/°K; T is the temperature, °K; and C is an over-all instrument constant determining the units in which the intensity I is given.[38, 44, 61-65, 67]

By taking the natural logarithm of both members of Eq. 13·6, we have

$$\log (I/P\nu^4) = (-1/kT)E + \log C \tag{13·7}$$

Then, if $\log (I/P\nu^4)$ is plotted against E for the successive lines of a rotational band, a straight line should result. The slope of this line is $-1/kT$ and thereby serves to determine the temperature T, °K (see Fig. 13·3).[38, 61-65]

The relative intensities I on some arbitrary scale and the frequencies ν of the successive lines in the band are directly measured quantities. Intensity is observed as an indicator deflection or as a degree of blackening on a photographic plate. The frequency ν (or wavelength $\lambda = c/\nu$) can generally be determined directly from the dial markings on the *spectrometer* or *spectrograph* or by comparison with a familiar spectrum.[38, 61-65]

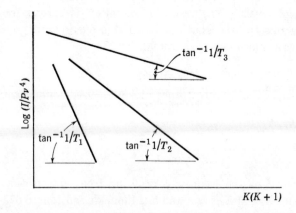

Fig. 13·3. Temperature determination from slopes.

For known spectra, the energy levels E, ergs, can be obtained from published tabulations. Established values for the transition probabilities P are also available for many spectra. For rotational spectra, the values can be calculated from formulas given by the theory. These means allow a choice of spectra from among those of the various flame constituents. However, only the less-complicated spectra are suitable, and rotational bands are usually used.[38, 61-65, 68, 69]

13·10 ROTATIONAL TEMPERATURES

Spectra resulting from rotational transitions alone are usually too far in the infrared for useful application. Spectra resulting from simultaneous rotational and vibrational transitions are also in infrared regions where measurements are difficult. However, in simultaneous electronic, vibrational, and rotational transitions, the rotational fine structure may appear in the visible or ultraviolet wavelength ranges where high resolution and rapid precision measurements are most convenient.[38, 61-65]

For diatomic molecules, the energy due to rotation is given approximately by

$$E_r = J(J + 1)Bhc \qquad (13·8)$$

where E_r is the rotational energy, ergs; h is Planck's constant, 6.625×10^{-27} erg sec; c is the velocity of light, 2.998×10^{10} cm/sec; B is given by Eq. 13·10; and J is the rotational quantum number. J takes on only discrete integral values, as [38, 61-65]

$$J = 0, 1, 2, 3, \cdots, \infty \qquad (13·9)$$

The quantity B is given by

$$B = h/(8\pi^2 c I_r) \qquad (13·10)$$

where I_r is the rotational moment of inertia of the molecule. Thus

$$I_r = D^2 m_1 m_2/(m_1 + m_2) \qquad (13·11)$$

where D is the internuclear distance, cm; and m_1 and m_2 are the masses of the two atoms, respectively, g. Since the internuclear distance D differs for different electronic-energy states, the value of B changes in electronic transitions.[38, 61-65]

Referring to Eq. 13·5, only E_r differs among the set of initial states giving rise to a rotational band. Equation 13·6 can thus be written

$$I = A_0 P \nu^4 e^{-E_r/kT} \qquad (13·12)$$

By lumping together various quantities, Eq. 13·7 can be simplified to

$$\log (I/Pv^4) = -(1/T)[A_1J(J+1) + A_2] + A_3 \quad (13·13)$$

where A_1, A_2, and A_3 are constants for the band.[38, 61-65]

By translating axes and changing scale factors, this relation can then be plotted as in Fig. 13·3 for any given temperature T, °K.[70, 71]

If the particular constituent of the flame to be used for temperature indication is a stable molecule, a gas composed of these molecules can be heated under conditions permitting reliable independent measurement of its temperature. A calibration can thus be performed on such a gas to serve as an *indicator substance*. Sets of relative intensities measured on any arbitrary scale then correspond to measured temperatures. It may be more convenient to use an additive "coloring" material as the gas than one of the constituents naturally occurring in the flame. For Eq. 13·13 to apply, a diatomic molecule can be chosen.[38, 61-65]

In preparing to plot a set of calibration curves, it is necessary first to associate the individual lines for which the frequencies v and relative intensities I are measured with the corresponding quantum numbers, i.e., with values of J or K. Rotational bands are composed of separate series that may be three or more in number. Thus, for a simple case, they may be designated as the P-branch, the R-branch, and the Q-branch, respectively.[38, 61-65]

Recourse to published tables and charts for known spectra will be helpful in identifying the successive lines in a chosen band. The correspondence between the quantum numbers J or K and frequencies v may then be verified by numerical substitutions into the formula for the particular series.[38, 54, 61-65, 68, 69]

The first curve of a family, such as that indicated in Fig. 13·3, can be drawn as a straight line of arbitrarily chosen slope and y intercept. Thus, the scale factor, in terms of which this slope represents the calibration temperature $-1/T_1$, is a free choice. Similarly, a scale factor is chosen in terms of which the y intercept represents the instrument-constant term A_3 in Eq. 13·13. The measured ordinates to the curve, at successive J or K values, then represent the quantity log (I/Pv^4) for the corresponding values of I and v. Substituting the values for I measured to some convenient scale and those for v (in sec^{-1}) into the quantity I/Pv^4 for each such spectral line yields the relative value for P for each such spectral line, i.e., for successive points on the curve. A set of transition probabilities P is thus obtained. This set is subject to the arbitrary scale factors for the plot. The same procedure can be followed for each of the other calibration temperatures T_2, T_3, $\cdots$, etc., °K; however, retaining the same set of scale factors. Thus, a set of calibration curves is obtained for the given constituent or "coloring" additive. In effect, the constant A_2 can be regarded as a displacement of the y axis, and can be ignored as is commonly done in making an experimental plot, see Fig. 13·3.[38, 54, 61-65]

To measure the temperature of a given body of gas containing the constituent for which the calibration has been made, the relative intensities I are measured for the calibrated lines. By using the corresponding v, J or K, and P values previously obtained, a group of points is plotted to the chosen scale. The points should fall along a straight line. The slope of the line then yields $-1/T$ to the scale of the plot.[38, 54, 61-65]

Scatter of the points about a straight line may be attributed to random errors that can be reduced by *fairing* or by *least-squares* analysis. If the plotted line turns out to be curved or bent, such irregularity may be interpreted as a departure from equilibrium. The rotational temperature, for this series at least, then lacks any simple definition, and a more general departure from equilibrium in the body appears probable.[38, 54, 61-65, 69]

A similar procedure can be applied to the fine structure described by either quantum number K or J when the distinction between J and K is significant.[38, 54, 61-65, 69, 71]

For a readable account of the procedures for making the required measurements of line intensity I and frequency v, the reader is referred to *Practical Spectroscopy* by Harrison, Lord, and Loofbourow.[62]

13·11   ROTATIONAL TEMPERATURE TECHNIQUES

There are various modifications of the general procedure described in Sec. 13·10. Taking advantage of the tendency of the transition probability P in the rotational structure to increase with the quantum number, Petrie,[72-74] Jones and Harrison,[70] Shepherd and Hunten,[75, 76] and others have used a simplified form of Eq. 13·13. Instead of plotting $\log(I/Pv^4)$ (see Fig. 13·3) they merely plotted $\log(I/K)$ against $K(K + 1)$ for the branch of the band used. A table of correction factors applied to the measured intensity profiles, to account for line-overlapping, was checked against a spectrograph of sufficiently high dispersion to separate all the lines. The method was verified to within a few degrees at room temperature in a hollow-cathode discharge operated with a "small" current. By applying this method, auroral temperatures were found to lie in the range of from 150 to 750°K (-190 to 890°F). Although the electronic energy levels of nitrogen were excited by electron impacts, it appeared plausible to regard these rotational determinations as near to the kinetic temperatures.[61, 69, 70, 72-77]

Methods employing only two lines are somewhat simpler. Equation 13·12 is then written as an intensity ratio

$$I_1/I_2 = (P_1\nu_1^4/P_2\nu_2^4)e^{-(E_{1r}-E_{2r})/kT} \tag{13·14}$$

In the *isointensity method* of Dieke [59, 60, 68] and Crosswhite,[59, 68] pairs of lines of equal intensity are chosen. This method merely requires the matching of intensities. It is not necessary to calibrate photographic-plate sensitivities as functions of intensity. The results are independent of the background continuum and to a first approximation are unaffected by self-absorption. The temperature is given by [59, 60, 68, 71]

$$T = (E_{1r} - E_{2r})/[k \log (P_1\nu_1^4/P_2\nu_2^4)] \tag{13·15}$$

Another method depends merely on locating the peak intensity in the band. Thus, writing Eqs. 13·8 and 13·12 with K replacing J gives

$$I = A_0 P\nu^4 e^{-K(K+1)Bhc/kT} \tag{13·16}$$

The peak, for which the slope dI/dK vanishes, yields an expression for T in terms of the peak quantum number K_m. Petrie [72-74] has used this method to measure auroral temperatures. It is not sensitive, as the peak cannot be located exactly.[72-74, 78]

Dieke [59, 60, 68] and Crosswhite [59, 68] have furnished complete and accurate tabular data for the rotational bands of OH. Rules for the application of the data in accord with the several methods are also detailed. The OH radical and its spectra are abundantly available in all flames which result from the combustion of hydrocarbon fuels; therefore this technique acquires a certain universality. Since OH is not a stable compound, direct calibration is not possible; also, rigorous calculation of transition probabilities is a specialty. Dieke and Crosswhite give numerical values for energy levels E_r, transition probabilities P, and line frequencies ν. As a result of this convenience, much work has been done and experience gained with OH rotational temperatures. Unfortunately, being intermediate products in chain reactions, the OH ions may become chemically excited. In reaction zones, large departures from equilibrium have been observed.[52, 59, 60, 68, 71, 77-85]

13·12 VIBRATIONAL TEMPERATURES

The procedures for measuring vibrational pseudotemperatures are similar to those for rotational pseudotemperatures. They are, however, usually more complicated. Intensity measurements I may be made for the initial lines in the rotational fine structures, which result from the successive electronic-vibrational transitions alone, in the various bands of the band progression. If this is done, care must be taken to segregate the proper lines. An alternative is the use of the integrated intensity of the entire rotational fine structure in each case. It involves using mean photographic-plate sensitivities for the wider assortments of intensities occurring in entire bands. The background continuum also then tends to be more of a problem. Whereas transition probabilities for rotational lines can be calculated from formulas, merely approximate graphical methods are the recourse for vibrational transition probabilities.[61, 68, 69, 77, 79, 85]

Theory indicates a comparatively direct relation between vibrational excitation and the energy of chemical union. Direct transitions within a molecule between vibrational and electronic states are also predicted by the theory. It is thereby suggested that vibrational states may occur in nonequilibrium values. Lukacs and Herman [86] thus found a vibrational temperature estimated as 15,000°K in a discharge tube, where the kinetic temperature must certainly have been much lower.[53, 76, 78, 84, 66]

13·13   SELF-ABSORPTION AND BACKGROUND INTENSITY

The measurement of relative spectral-line intensities I in spectroscopic temperature measurement is confused both by the ever-present continuous-background radiation and by the tendency to reabsorption by the gas in the wavelength of the line.[59, 80–82]

Obviously for accurate measurement of the intensity I, circumstances must be chosen for which the intensity greatly exceeds that of the background. This implies limiting measurements to sufficiently *strong* lines and to gases sufficiently free of incandescent solid particles. Likewise, the gaseous layers must be of sufficient thinness.[87]

As these layers become thicker, i.e., more opaque, both the spectral-line intensities and the intensities of the continuous background approach the distribution given by Planck's law (see Fig. 13·4). Thus, as the intensity of a line approaches that for a blackbody at the frequency of the line, the resultant value is modified more and more by self-absorption. In order that Eqs. 13·6, 13·7, 13·12 and 13·13 remain valid, the line intensity must be much lower than that for blackbody radiation.[87]

The conditions to be fulfilled are then (see Fig. 13·4)

$$I_L \gg I_c \tag{13·17}$$

$$I_L \ll I_P \tag{13·18}$$

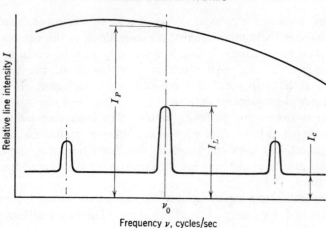

Fig. 13·4.   Line intensities. I_P is the intensity of frequency ν_0 according to Planck's law; I_c is the intensity of the background continuum; and I_L is the intensity of the given spectral line at ν_0.

where I_L is the relative intensity of a spectral line used for temperature measurement; I_c is the intensity on the same scale for the continuous background radiation; and I_P is the intensity on this scale for blackbody radiation.   Smit [87] has noted that, in order to satisfy these conditions, I_c must be at least 100 times lower than I_P for measurements with a *diffraction grating* and 1000 times less when a prism spectrograph is used.

Broida [52,71,78,88] has shown that self-absorption can result in errors of thousands of degrees when the condition of Eq. 13·18 is violated.[50,52,71,78,88]

Self-absorption may also occur in the outer layers of gas when they are at lower temperatures.   This effect tends to result in serious errors, depending on the temperatures and opacities of the layers.   Outer layers may also have different concentrations of the "coloring" constituent.   This problem is discussed to some extent in Secs. 8·2, 8·3, and 13·23.   However, the result is usually an ambiguous determination.[50,71,78]

13·14   PRECISION AND RELIABILITY
OF SPECTROSCOPIC TEMPERATURES

Broida [52,71,78,88,90] and Lalos [88] have achieved consistency in rotational-temperature measurements in flames to within around 2.5 per cent, with a total spread of 1 to 10 per cent.   Their measured points thus usually fell within $\pm 25°C$ ($\pm 45°F$) of the fairing curves.   This degree of consistency prevailed even in an acetylene flame for which the rotational temperature found was 1000°C (1800°F) higher than the *theoretical* value. The theoretical value is that for assumed thermodynamic equilibrium after adiabatic combustion of the fuel, i.e., the *adiabatic temperature.* On the other hand, Parker [89] in measuring the rotational temperature of the lower solar chromosphere estimated his error at about ±400°C (±720°F). Discrepancies attributed to measurements of temperature by rotational methods, where none of the well-known precautions has been neglected, tend to the range ±200°C (±360°F). This limited range of error of course does not apply when measurements are made in zones of intense chemical reaction. For measurements in the inner cone of a methane-and-air flame, Broida has found rotational temperatures differing by thousands of degrees. Here, nonequilibrium obviously exists, and the thermodynamic temperature is not defined.[52, 70, 71, 78, 88, 90]

13·15 ABSORPTION-SPECTRA

Observations of spectra are not limited to those of *emitted* radiation. In accord with Kirchhoff's law (see Sec. 8·3), many spectral lines can be *reversed* and made to appear as *absorption lines.* When the radiation from a *continuous* source, such as that of a blackbody, is passed through a cooler layer of gas, the spectra of the constituent atoms and molecules appear as *absorption* spectra. Relative line intensities I are then replaced by relative degrees of absorption corresponding to the quantities α_λ or $F_{a,\lambda}$ (see Eq. 8·9).

The spectroscopic methods previously described can usually also be applied in absorption. The intensity I is then replaced by the absorption factor $F_{a,\lambda}$. The conditions set by Eqs. 13·17 and 13·18 mean here that the absorption by the background continuum in the flame shall be small compared to that in the observed lines and that the absorption in these lines shall be a small fraction of the incident intensity.[87, 90]

As in the case of emission spectra, the reader is advised to consult the references for the techniques of identifying and measuring absorption spectra.[38, 54, 61–65, 68]

Myers,[91–94] Uyehara,[91–94] Chen,[91] Beck,[91] and Schweitzer [92] applied absorption-spectra technique to the measurement of *end-zone* temperatures in a piston internal-combustion engine. The gaseous charge was *colored* with iodine vapor introduced by dissolving 10.43 g of iodine per gallon in the fuel. The absorption spectra for the diatomic iodine molecule thereby appeared in the hot compressed gases. These gases, in the region not yet traversed by the flame front, are usually considered as undergoing *precombustion reactions.* Vibrational temperatures were determined from a set of calibration curves provided by heating an iodine-filled quartz absorption cell and a similar empty cell together in a furnace.[91-96]

13·16 TOTAL-RADIATION METHODS

Chapters 3 and 4 were devoted to the development of techniques for the measurement of temperature in terms of the radiant emission from a surface area on the body. Equations given there were based on the assumption that the bodies were opaque. However, a correction factor ϵ for the surface-emissivity was included. The total radiant emission is less in proportion to the factor ϵ, and the observed *apparent* temperature is correspondingly less than the actual surface temperature of the body.

Essentially the same techniques can be applied to radiating bodies of gas. In using the system of equations in Ch. 4, the emissivity ϵ must uniformly be replaced by the absorption factor F_a or $F_{a,\lambda}$ of Eqs. 8·8 and 8·9. With this interpretation, the methods of Chs. 3 and 4 can be applied to the study of flames, arcs, and stellar bodies. Unfortunately, determinations made by these procedures when applied to flames and arcs are subject to difficulties not usually encountered with solids. Thermodynamic temperatures will be obtained only when the radiation is of thermal origin, i.e., that corresponding to a condition of thermodynamic equilibrium in the gases.[7, 19, 44, 45, 48, 49, 97]

In preceding sections of the present chapter, methods discussed have depended on intensities and absorption in discrete groups of spectral lines. The condition of thermodynamic equilibrium has thus been that the energy states giving rise to these particular lines be in equilibrium with the thermal condition of the gas. However, when *total-radiation* methods are used, it is not sufficient for merely one mode of energy storage to be in equilibrium with the translational degrees of freedom. In general, all radiating modes tend to contribute, and very little of the radiation may result directly from the translational energy states. Excess radiation, such as that that might result from *chemiluminescence,* or deficient radiation from *excitation lag* in particular spectral lines might become a small fraction of the total radiation.[7, 19, 27, 34, 49, 98]

Corry[48] and Baldo[49] have shown that, for the flame gases in a piston internal-combustion engine, the excess radiation for an entire cycle does not exceed 5 per cent of that which would occur thermally. In accord with the Stefan-Boltzmann law

$$W_{0-\infty} = \sigma T^4 \tag{4·1}$$

a 5 per cent discrepancy in the observed value for $W_{0-\infty}$ corresponds approximately to a 1.2 per cent discrepancy in the value found for the absolute temperature T. Thus, if a gas-temperature level were assumed to be 3000°R, the 1.2 per cent discrepancy would become an error of 36°R (20°C).[7, 19, 34, 48, 49, 98]

Observations of total radiation always yield *apparent temperatures*. The emissivity correction must be applied in accord with Eqs. 4·47, 4·48, and 4·51 to determine the temperature T, °R. For opaque bodies, the emissivity ϵ is related to the reflection coefficient and absorptance ρ and a, respectively, by

$$\epsilon = a = 1 - \rho \qquad (8·6)$$

$$\epsilon_\lambda = a_\lambda = 1 - \rho_\lambda \qquad (8·7)$$

where ϵ_λ, a_λ, and ρ_λ are the monochromatic values.

For flames free of suspended solid particles, such as *nonluminous* or sodium-colored flames, reflection coefficients ρ and ρ_λ have been found to be too small to measure. When the luminous effect results from suspended carbon particles, values of around 1 per cent are observed. Hence, if a flame is sufficiently thick for opacity, the emissivity correction is negligible except for luminous flames.[99]

For flames which are not opaque, the absorption factor F_a replaces the usual emissivity factor in correcting apparent temperatures. Thus

$$F_a = 1 - J_i/J_o = 1 - e^{-aD} \qquad (8·8)$$

where D is the flame thickness, cm; α is the absorption coefficient, cm^{-1}; J_o and J_i are the incident and emergent radiant powers per unit solid angle, respectively, w/steradian. If surface reflection is not neglected, the product ϵF_a is used.[97-101]

Since the absorption factor F_a depends on the flame thickness D, on its composition and temperature, and on the operating conditions, it must be measured as part of the determination. Silverman[84, 102, 103] has proposed the ingenious device of interposing a rotating sectored disk, i.e., a radiation chopper, between the flame and a blackbody background. The output of a rapid-response radiation-sensitive element is then amplified by a circuit tuned to the chopping frequency. The resulting indication does not include the d-c component, which would be due to the unchopped flame radiation, but constitutes a measurement of J_i. J_o is similarly measured in the absence of the flame, yielding the ratio $J_i/J_o = e^{-aD}$ in Eq. 8·8.[84, 102-104]

13·17 MONOCHROMATIC BRIGHTNESS METHODS

The optical pyrometer described in Ch. 3 determines an apparent temperature from the brightness in a given wavelength range. This range is narrowly restricted by a filter. Either the human eye or a photocell can be used to compare this brightness with that of a blackbody in the same wavelength range. Correction of T_A to the temperature T is made by inserting the monochromatic absorption factor $F_{a,\lambda}$ or $\epsilon_\lambda F_{a,\lambda}$ into Eq. 4.51, where $F_{a,\lambda}$ is given by

$$F_{\alpha,\lambda} = 1 - J_{i,\lambda}/J_{o,\lambda} = 1 - e^{-\alpha_\lambda D} \tag{8·9}$$

and where ϵ_λ is the surface emissivity in the wavelength range λ to $\lambda + \Delta\lambda$; D is the flame thickness, cm; α_λ is the absorption coefficient in the wavelength range λ to $\lambda + \Delta\lambda$, cm^{-1}; $J_{o,\lambda}$ and $J_{i,\lambda}$ are the incident and emergent radiant powers, respectively, in the wavelength range λ to $\lambda + \Delta\lambda$ per unit solid angle, w/steradian.[44, 51, 98]

$F_{a,\lambda}$ can be measured by Silverman's [84, 102, 103] method described in Sec. 13·16 using a filter restricting radiation to the range λ to $\lambda + \Delta\lambda$ or by the similar procedure of Curcio, Stewart, and Petty [104] for which the reader is referred to their original paper.[104]

Direct evaluation of the absorption factor $F_{a,\lambda}$ is uncertain since it depends not only on the thickness of the flame but also on the concentrations of absorbing constituents. Both of these factors tend to vary and fluctuate in operation. In a method attributed to Graff [105] and developed in various forms by others, the flame is "colored" by a controlled addition of sodium atoms. The monochromatic intensity is then calibrated as a function of temperature. Continuous observations are possible using photo elements and electronic indication. With photoemissive elements, such as photomultiplier tubes of 10^{-8}-sec response time and millimicrosecond cathode-ray oscilloscopy, the most highly transient phenomena can be observed. Since the flame is thus already sodium-colored, the sodium-line-reversal method provides a convenient means for frequent static calibrations against a blackbody standard.[34, 101-103, 105-108]

In a modification of this method by Quinn,[109] the flame is made opaque at the wavelength of the sodium D lines by the coloring material introduced as sodium salt in the combustible mixture. Opacity is demonstrated by using a thickness great enough so that brightness no longer increases with flame thickness. For this purpose, a thickness of 1 cm (0.4 in.) was found to suffice. If the reflection coefficient is then regarded as being small enough to neglect, the flame becomes a blackbody at this wavelength, and no apparent-temperature correction is made. Kandya [110] has used a similar technique.

This method of course assumes the sodium-D-line emitters to be in thermal equilibrium with the flame gases. If the kinetic or translational temperature is used as a criterion, the question becomes whether the electronic-energy-state populations determining the sodium-D-line intensities are in equilibrium with the translational energies of the gas. Gaydon [37-39, 52-54, 61] has noted that these electronic states are more directly related to the vibrational energies. On the other hand, chemical reactions appear to occur in the vibrational modes. Gaydon has also noted that electronic states may become depopulated by radiation more rapidly than they are replenished by equilibrating processes. Apparently, calibration tests on these methods have been sufficiently convincing to insure the confidence of their authors. [1-3, 34, 37-39, 52-55, 61, 63, 64, 98]

13·18 THE SCHMIDT METHOD

With the Schmidt [18] method, three successive observations are made. In the original work, Schmidt used a spectrometer to limit his passband to one of the strongly emitting regions of the flame, i.e., the water-vapor or carbon-dioxide spectra at about 2.8 or 4.4 μ, respectively, in the infrared. The three observations consisted of: (1), measuring the radiation $J_{1,\lambda}$ from the flame itself, i.e., with a cool nonradiating background; (2), measuring the radiation $J_{2,\lambda}$ from a continuous-background source (Schmidt employed a Nernst lamp); and, (3), measuring the radiation $J_{3,\lambda}$ from the combination of the two, i.e., of the flame with the Nernst lamp as a background, w/steradian. [18, 111]

The radiation $J_{3,\lambda}$ from the flame backed by the lamp consists of the part $J_{1,\lambda}$ that would occur from the flame alone in the absence of the lamp, plus the portion $(1 - F_{a,\lambda})J_{2,\lambda}$ of the lamp radiation $J_{2,\lambda}$ that is transmitted by the flame. Thus

$$J_{3,\lambda} = J_{1,\lambda} + (1 - F_{a,\lambda})J_{2,\lambda} \qquad (13·19)$$

Or, solving for $F_{a,\lambda}$ gives

$$F_{a,\lambda} = [J_{2,\lambda} - (J_{3,\lambda} - J_{1,\lambda})]/J_{2,\lambda} \qquad (13·20)$$

The absorption factor $F_{a,\lambda}$ can thereby be determined from the combination of the three observations. [10, 18]

Moutet [112] has developed this method into a conveniently practicable instrument. Rotating sectored disks are provided which, together with a system of mirrors, serve to present the three monochromatic radiant beams $J_{1,\lambda}$, $J_{2,\lambda}$, and $J_{3,\lambda}$ alternately to the same rapid-response photomultiplier element. The amplified electric outputs are presented in trios of successive peaks on the screen of a cathode-ray oscilloscope. A rotating-drum camera provides photographic recording of the oscilloscope traces. Temperature determinations are then computed from the measurements of the trios of peak deflections by a graphical procedure. For this, a set of charts is provided. With Moutet's device, 4500 temperature determinations can be made per second. The labor of reducing this output of data by graphical means suggested the advantage of incorporating an electronic computer. This, in fact, was done by Myers and Uyehara.[91-94] The Moutet device also appears in a commercial form where a penwriter furnishes temperature data as a continuously inscribed curve. In this modification, however, the instrument response time is much slower, i.e., 0.1 sec. With his single-package form of the apparatus, flame diameters are limited to 25 cm (10 in.). However, when the device is built in two units, the flame space may be as great as 10 m (32.8 ft).[68, 91-94, 112]

13·19 TWO-COLOR METHODS

Ratio pyrometry (see Secs. 4·11 and 4·12) depends on observations of the ratio of intensities in two wavelength ranges. Absolute radiation measurements are not required. This independence of absolute measurements is a convenience in work with flames, since flame radiation tends to fluctuate with operating conditions.[44, 97, 101, 113]

Referring back to Eqs. 4·54 and 4·55, it is seen that the discrepancy between the actual temperature and the observed value for apparent temperature depends, by this method, on the ratio of the effective emissivities in the two wavelength ranges, respectively. Thus, when the two ranges are sufficiently narrow to permit using Wien's approximation, the temperature is given by

$$T = 1/\{1/T_A - 8.896 \times 10^{-5}[\lambda_m \lambda_m'/(\lambda_m - \lambda_m')] \log_{10}(\epsilon_\lambda F_{\alpha,\lambda}/\epsilon_{\lambda'} F_{\alpha,\lambda'})\}$$

$$(13·21)$$

where T is the corrected value for the temperature, °R; T_A is the apparent temperature, °R; λ_m and λ_m' are the mean values of the wavelengths in the two ranges, respectively, μ; and $\epsilon_\lambda F_{\alpha,\lambda}/\epsilon_{\lambda'} F_{\alpha,\lambda'}$ is the ratio of the values of the emissivity-absorption factor for the flame at the two wavelengths λ_m and λ_m', respectively, at the temperature T.

$$\epsilon_\lambda F_{\alpha,\lambda} = \epsilon_\lambda(1 - e^{-\alpha_\lambda D}) \qquad (13·22)$$

where $F_{\alpha,\lambda}$ is the absorption factor in the wavelength range λ to $\lambda + \Delta\lambda$; α_λ is the absorption coefficient for the flame gases, cm^{-1}; D is the thickness of the flame along the optical path, cm; and ϵ_λ is the surface emissivity of the flame.[34, 101]

An attraction in the two-color or ratio method lies in the hope that the ratio $\epsilon_\lambda F_{\alpha,\lambda}/\epsilon_{\lambda'} F_{\alpha,\lambda'}$ may be near to unity. This is the case for an ideal *gray body*, for which the correction vanishes and $T = T_A$.[34, 97, 101, 113]

Luminous flames emit radiation in a continuum similar to that for solid-body radiation, and wavelength ranges can be so chosen as not to include any strong spectral lines. By thus avoiding atomic and molecular emission, the danger of error due to chemiluminescent radiation is minimized. The continuum results, in part, from recombination of dissociated ions and free electrons. However, the major contribution is usually that of radiation from incandescent carbon particles suspended in the flame gases. Schack[114] has estimated that such glowing carbon or soot particles are always within $\pm 1°C$ ($\pm 1.8°F$) of the flame-gas temperature. This estimate, which is widely accepted, depends on an assumed-linear extrapolation of gas-boundary-conductance data to 330-fold larger values. The large conductances are taken to apply to the very small, i.e., 0.0003 mm (1.2×10^{-5} in.), diameter he computed for the mean particle size. Electron micrographs have shown Schack's estimates of carbon-particle size to be conservative in that actual sizes are smaller, i.e., from 0.0002 mm down to about 0.000001 mm. However, oxide particles as large as 0.001 mm have been observed in magnesium flames. The temperature to which carbon particles approach, according to Schack's estimate, is the kinetic temperature. Nevertheless, the possibility of catalytic or surface combustion occurring on the particles themselves cannot be ignored. Such reactions would tend to raise the temperatures of the particles. Schack's large values for gas-boundary conductances would seem to assure that such increases will not cause serious errors. But, Behrens[12, 100] and Rössler[12, 100, 101] have reported carbon-particle temperatures exceeding the theoretical flame temperature. This is the temperature that would result from adiabatic combustion. The observed excess temperatures ranged from 300 to 730°C (540 to 1314°F).[12, 34, 40, 41, 100, 101, 113, 114]

The surface emissivities ϵ_λ are so nearly unity that their ratio in two wavelengths can be neglected. The absorption coefficient is, however, known to vary markedly with wavelength. Thus, for carbon-particle suspensions

$$\alpha_\lambda = \alpha_T \lambda^{-n} \qquad (13·23)$$

where α_T is a constant for the flame at the given temperature T, °K; and λ is the wavelength, cm. Determinations for n have ranged from

0.65 to 1.43. Rössler [12,100,101] and Behrens [12,100] found that flame thickness, wavelength, and temperature had little effect on the value of n. Their values were distributed over this range according to the type of flame observed. Mie [115] predicted on theoretical grounds that n would depend on the mean particle size or size distribution. This is considered to be the explanation for the variation in n. The variation is not merely a property of the material. Techniques for determining luminous-flame temperatures by ratio pyrometry thereby depend on measured values for n applying to the type of flame used. The flame type will be distinguished by both the fuel variety and the operating conditions. As a suitable mean in the absence of specific knowledge, Rössler and Behrens suggest the value $n = 1$.[12,34,40,41,99-101,114-117]

13·20 EXAMPLES OF TWO-COLOR TECHNIQUES

Hottel and Broughton [116] have provided convenient charts based on their determination for the quantity n in Eq. 13·23. They use the value $n = 1.39$. With these charts, the temperature T can be read directly in terms of measured values for the apparent temperatures T_A at two stated wavelengths.

Uyehara,[91-94,118] Myers,[91-94,118] Wilson,[93,118] and Watson [93,118] have used a two-color or ratio method to measure luminous-flame temperatures. Their work was on combustion-stroke temperatures in diesel engines. In this method, two vacuum photoemissive elements respond, respectively, in two narrow wavelength ranges. The two ranges are segregated by prism dispersion. Cathode-ray-oscilloscope indication provides continuous records of the radiant intensities in the respective ranges from which point-by-point temperatures can be computed. Electronic circuitry was also provided to perform this computation, yielding continuous temperature indications.

Rössler [12,100,101,119] has used the combination of color and apparent temperatures to yield corrected values. By this technique, luminous-flame temperatures are said to be determined with accuracies of to within 1 per cent.

Bauserman, Prien, and Zandstra [120] have used a two-color method to estimate transient temperatures in explosion flames. Their flames resulted from the combustion of mixtures of metallic powders. The powders usually consisted of aluminum together with oxidizers such as barium nitrate or potassium perchlorate. The ratio of the intensities, or absorption factors, at two wavelengths for the flame was compared with that for a blackbody standard, employing an absorption or line-reversal technique. Rapid-response photoemissive elements and electronic circuitry were used. The device was set to record the time of occurrence of a preselected ratio. Determinations were made to within 3 msec and with a sensitivity of about 25°C (45°F). However, it was felt that chemiluminescence obscured the reversal points at the higher temperatures and shorter times.[40, 41, 120, 121]

Alentzev and Sobolev [122] used a *multicolor* method to measure the detonation temperature of an explosive. Here, the temperature rise is very rapid followed by a rapid decline. To obtain the peak value, determinations were made before the containing glass test tube had time to fly apart, i.e., while the detonation products continued to occupy their original volume. The spectra were photographed with a 2-mm (0.08-in.) slit width and an exposure time of 0.001 sec.

Wien's formula was used in the form

$$\log W_\lambda - \log c_1 + 5 \log \lambda = (-c_2/T)(1/\lambda) \qquad (13\cdot24)$$

where $W_\lambda \Delta\lambda$ is the total hemispherical emission in the wavelength range from λ to $\lambda + \Delta\lambda$, ergs/cm^2 sec; λ is the wavelength of the radiation, cm; T is the absolute temperature, °K; $c_1 = 3.740 \times 10^{-5}$ erg cm^2/sec; and $c_2 = 1.438$ cm °K. By plotting their measured values for the quantity $\log W_\lambda - \log c_1 + 5 \log \lambda$ against $1/\lambda$, they obtained a straight line of slope $- c_2/T$. The temperature T, °K, was determined from this slope. Since no emissivity factor had been introduced, the straightness of the plotted line indicated that the highly compressed detonation products behaved as a gray body. Penner [44, 51, 80, 82, 83, 95, 96, 123, 124] has reviewed the evidence suggesting gray-body behavior in the rocket flames resulting from solid propellants. Accuracies were estimated at to within ± 100°C (± 180°F).[44, 51, 80, 82, 83, 95, 96, 113, 122-124]

13·21 TWO-PATH METHODS

The two-path method appears to be due to Hottel and Broughton.[116] Figure 13·5 shows this arrangement. Here, the background, as "seen" through the flame, takes the form of a mirror. This mirror reflects the radiation, previously moving to the left along the flame-column thickness D, back through the flame. The reflected radiation, then proceeding to the sensitive element, tends to be added to that directly emitted by thickness D. However, a portion is absorbed in transit and does not reach the element.[10, 44, 51, 116, 124]

A second observation of the same flame thickness D can be made with a cool nonreflecting background replacing the mirror. It will be shown that, in this manner, the absorption factor $F_{a,\lambda}$ given by

$$F_{\alpha,\lambda} = 1 - e^{-\alpha_\lambda D} \qquad (8\cdot9)$$

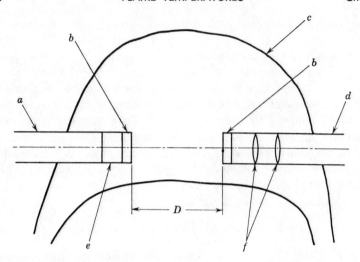

Fig. 13·5. Apparatus for two-path method. D = flame thickness, cm. a, Probe 2; b, sapphire windows; c, flame; d, probe 1; e, cool blackbody or mirror; and, f, sapphire lenses. (*By permission S. S. Penner in J. Chem. Phys.,* **19,** *no. 3, 273, March, 1951.*)

can be eliminated between the equations for the two observations, respectively. Here, α_λ is the average absorption coefficient, cm^{-1}, in the wavelength range λ to $\lambda + \Delta\lambda$, μ; and D is the flame thickness, cm.

The radiation from the single flame thickness in the wavelength range λ to $\lambda + \Delta\lambda$ is given by Eqs. 4.2 and 8.9 as

$$W_{\lambda,T_A} \Delta\lambda = F_{\alpha,\lambda} W_{\lambda,T}\, \Delta\lambda \qquad (13\cdot25)$$

Adding to this the radiation reflected by the mirror in this wavelength range, we have the total

$$W_{\lambda,T_A}{}' \Delta\lambda = (F_{\alpha,\lambda} W_{\lambda,T} + \rho_\lambda F_{\alpha,\lambda} W_{\lambda,T} e^{-\alpha_\lambda D})\, \Delta\lambda \qquad (13\cdot26)$$

where T_A is the apparent temperature, °K; ρ_λ is the reflection coefficient at the mirror surface in the wavelength range λ to $\lambda + \Delta\lambda$; and $W_{\lambda,T}$ is given by Planck's law (Eq. 4·2).

Equations 13·25 and 13·26 can be combined to yield the formula

$$W_{\lambda,T} = \rho_\lambda W_{\lambda,T_A} / (1 + \rho_\lambda - W_{\lambda,T_A}{}'/W_{\lambda,T_A}) \qquad (13\cdot27)$$

The quantities W_{λ,T_A} and $W_{\lambda,T_A}{}'$ are determined from the directly observed signals Φ_λ or H_λ by referring back to Eqs. 4·38 and 4·39. Thus

$$\Phi_\lambda = \epsilon F_t W_\lambda \qquad (13\cdot28)$$

or

$$H_\lambda = \epsilon F_i W_\lambda \qquad (13\cdot29)$$

where W_λ is successively W_{λ,T_A} and $W_{\lambda,T_A}{}'$; ϵ is the surface emissivity for the interface between the flame and the objective window (see Fig. 13.5); F_t is the total transfer factor for the optical system used, in.^{2}; F_i is the intensity transfer factor; Φ_λ is the radiant power in the wavelength range λ to $\lambda + \Delta\lambda$ incident upon and absorbed by the sensitive surface of the radiation-sensitive element, w; and H_λ is the radiant power per unit area in wavelength range λ to $\lambda + \Delta\lambda$ incident upon and absorbed by the entire surface of the radiation-sensitive element, w/in.^{2} the factors F_t and F_i are given by Eqs. 4·27 and 4·28.

The actual temperature T is determined from the thus-measured value for $W_{\lambda,T}$ by substituting into Eq. 4·2, i.e., Planck's law.

The procedure requires making the two separate observations for the same flame-thickness conditions. The reflection coefficient ρ_λ must be known; similarly, the properties ϵ and F_t or F_i for the optical system are required. However, no knowledge of the flame characteristics is assumed, and calibration of the sensitive element and optical system can be performed against any convenient standard.[10, 124–126]

Hett and Gilstein [127, 128] applied this method in their flame-temperature pyrometer. To avoid chemiluminescent errors, they limited the wavelength range to a region free from spectral lines. An interference filter, whose passband $\Delta\lambda$ was 150 Å (0.015 μ or 1.5×10^{-6} cm) wide, served to segregate the range. The background continuum in the flame, thus observed, was assumed to be in thermal equilibrium with the kinetic temperature of the gas. Radiant powers $\Phi_\lambda \, \Delta\lambda$ in the band for the two paths corresponding to $W_{\lambda,T_A} \, \Delta\lambda$ and $W_{\lambda,T_A}{}' \, \Delta\lambda$, respectively, were simultaneously recorded. Two photomultipliers were used, whose amplified outputs were displayed on two cathode-ray-oscilloscope screens. The separate traces were photographed on a 35-mm drum camera. Calibration was performed by replacing the mirror and cool blackbody backgrounds with a standardized ribbon-filament lamp. Readings without flame gases in the thickness D then included the same optical system used for measurements. Their rapid-response circuit permitted effectively "instantaneous" measurements.[10, 125–129]

13·22 LINE-REVERSAL METHODS

The functioning principle of the Kurlbaum [99, 130] and Féry [131] line-reversal methods is that of Kirchhoff's law. The essential mechanism of these techniques is described in Sec. 8·3. Although this famous law was published in 1859, the applications of Kurlbaum [99, 130] and Féry [131] did not appear until the years of 1902 and 1903, respectively.[99,130-132]

Kurlbaum [99,130] assumed flames that are made luminous by incandescent soot or glowing carbon particles. He proposed successive observations of the temperature of a blackbody as viewed through the Holborn-Kurlbaum optical pyrometer. This instrument is the now-common disappearing-filament pyrometer of wavelength passband limited by a red filter. The flame was alternately interposed between the pyrometer's objective lens and the blackbody. When, after iterative adjustments of the blackbody temperature, the pyrometer reading was the same with or without the flame interposed, the temperature was taken to be that of the flame.

Féry,[131] on the other hand, assumed nonluminous flames, i.e., flames essentially devoid of suspended carbon particles. Added sodium vapor caused such flames to emit and absorb the yellow radiation of the sodium D lines. The filament of an incandescent lamp served as a background and was imaged through the interposed flame on the slit of a spectroscope (see Fig. 13·6). When the apparent temperature of the lamp filament was higher than that of the flame, the D lines appeared as dark lines. When the lamp temperature was cooler, the lines appeared as bright lines (see Fig. 13·7). By adjusting the filament current until the lines disappeared into the continuous background of the solid-body filament radiation, the point was found at which the apparent temperature of the lamp filament was that of the flame.

Both Kurlbaum [99,130] and Féry [131] required that their respective flames be of sufficient optical thickness to produce conveniently observable absorption but not so nearly opaque as to prevent clear view-

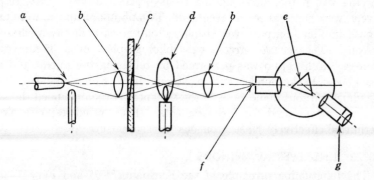

Fig. 13·6. Sodium-line-reversal apparatus. a, Carbon arc; b, lens; c, gray wedge; d, flame; e, prism; f, slit; and, g, eyepiece. (After G. Rosenthal in Archiv für technisches Messen, V2163-2, T2, January, 1942.)

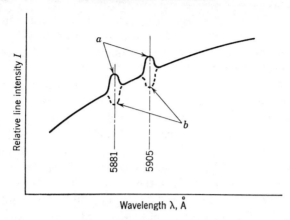

Fig. 13·7. Sodium-D-line reversal. *a*, Bright lines; and, *b*, dark lines.

ing of the backgrounds through the flame. They also assumed the surface reflectivities of their respective flames to be negligible. Kurlbaum had previously shown that the reflection coefficient was less than 1 per cent for his case. It has since been found too small to be observable for the case of Féry. Féry also tried lithium vapor, finding it to yield the same temperatures as sodium.

Neither of these methods responds directly to the kinetic temperature. The Kurlbaum [99, 130] method measures the temperatures of the suspended carbon particles. The Féry [131] method measures the electronic temperatures of the sodium atoms. Validities depend on the assumptions that the carbon particles and sodium electronic states are in thermal equilibrium, respectively, with the translational energies of the gases. The probability of finding the carbon particles in equilibrium has been discussed in Sec. 13·19. Similarly, the likelihood of deviations from the kinetic temperature on the part of the sodium electronic states is indicated in Sec. 13·17. Both methods have achieved excellent reputations in widespread applications extending through well over half a century. Nevertheless, David [29-31] has reported that the sodium-line-reversal method is commonly in error by some hundreds of degrees. The absence of any unequivocal standard for comparison, unfortunately, tends to place the basis for belief or disbelief in a somewhat speculative realm. It at least appears to have been shown that the resonance D lines of sodium, as originally used by Féry, are less prone to discrepancies than the spectra of alternative coloring metals. Most observers have found agreement among sodium, lithium, and thallium determinations. Kohn [132] found that variations in metallic-salt variety, prism dispersion, and salt density in the flame produced discrepancies of less than 5 to 8°C (9 to 14.4°F). She also verified agreement with hot-wire determinations to within an accuracy of ±10°C (±18°F).[6, 10, 29–31, 44, 131–135]

It has been shown that free sodium atoms in a flame may result both from dissociation of sodium chloride, which is a strongly endothermic process, and from chemical reactions, which tend to leave the sodium atoms in excited states. For example, Tanaka and Ogawa [136] observed strong chemiluminescence in the sodium D lines because of the reaction between ozone and sodium vapor. The possibilities of sodium D line radiation, both greater and less than that corresponding to thermodynamic equilibrium, thus exist. Henning and Tingwaldt [137] have noted that the likelihood of chemiluminescent error is less at higher flame temperatures.[19, 48, 49, 136, 137]

Another interesting effect is that certain additives, such as carbon dioxide, tend to suppress the sodium-D-line radiation whereas hydrogen tends to enhance it. This phenomenon conditions the effectiveness of the given sodium-salt concentration, but, fortunately, it does not affect the reversal temperature.[10, 136–139]

13·23 NONUNIFORM FLAMES AND LINE-REVERSAL TEMPERATURES

The usual explanations of the Féry [131] and Kurlbaum [99, 130] line-reversal methods tacitly assume that the flame temperature does not vary along the path of the light beam through the flame. Or, if the possibility of such variation is recognized, it is "hoped" that an average temperature will be determined. For this to result, it would be required that the various elements along the path length be weighted according to a linear relationship. Unfortunately, the law of Eqs. 8·8 and 8·9 is not linear, but rather it is exponential in character. The effect is that the weighting of the temperatures of successive layers of flame gases traversed by the light beam is not uniform and an arithmetic-mean temperature does not result. The discussion in Sec. 8·3 reveals that what is determined tends to be the temperature of a surface layer.

If the flame is uniformly luminous or colored by a uniform density distribution of sodium atoms, the temperature determined is that of the layer nearest to the pyrometer or spectrometer. The thickness of such an effective layer is proportional to the degree of transparency. For a high concentration of absorbing particles, this layer is thin, and the temperature determined is heavily weighted by that of the thin surface layer. If the concentration used is weak allowing a higher degree of transparency, the layer is thicker, and a larger proportion of the flame depth contributes to the determination of temperature.

The sodium-vapor method lends itself to the possibility of coloring only that portion of the flame whose temperature it is desired to measure. Thus, sodium vapor may be introduced only in certain stream lines of the flame-gas flow pattern. By this procedure, for example, a determination may be made essentially weighted for the hottest central core of an open flame, such as a Bunsen flame. Difficulties result from turbulence, and it is not generally possible to limit the coloring material in any precise manner to the flame region of interest.[140]

Bundy and Strong [141-144] have proposed the exploiting of an additional variable in the application of the sodium-line-reversal method. This variable is that controlling the line contour (see Fig. 13·8). They have recognized that the absorption coefficient α_λ is greatest at the wavelength λ_0 for the center of the line and decreases according to a known function as the wavelength λ differs by progressively larger amounts $\Delta\lambda$ from the nominal value λ_0. Thus, the transparency of the flame is a minimum at λ_0 but increases progressively to that for the background continuum with increase in $\Delta\lambda$. The effective surface-layer thickness, whose temperature is emphasized in the determination, is chosen by the choice of $\Delta\lambda$. And, successive determinations at different values for $\Delta\lambda$ provide information about variations of temperature with depth in the flame.

Application of the Bundy and Strong [141-144] method requires the same high precision in measuring line contours that is required in determinations of kinetic temperature by Doppler broadening as discussed in Sec. 13·7. Thus, it was found necessary there to use a Fabry-Perot interferometer having a resolving power $\lambda/\delta\lambda$ of at least

Fig. 13·8. Line contour. a, Peak; b, unresolved wavelength range $\delta\lambda$, Å; and, c, background continuum.

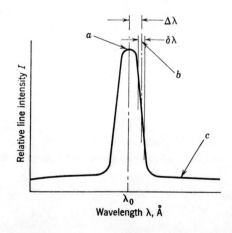

10^5, where λ is the wavelength, cm, and $\delta\lambda$ is the unresolved wavelength range, cm (see Fig. 13·8). The analysis used is somewhat complicated, and the reader is referred to the original papers of Bundy and Strong for the derivation and application of the pertinent equations. The equations describe reversals in terms of line contours and effective flame depths. Jackson [10] and Penner [44, 51, 80, 82, 83, 95, 96, 123, 124] have written excellent summaries of the Bundy and Strong method. Reading these articles may be helpful.[10, 44, 51, 80, 82, 83, 95, 96, 123, 124, 141–144]

An essential difficulty is, of course, evident in the usual procedure of observing reversals based on the average intensity over a wavelength range $\delta\lambda$ so broad as to include most of the line width. The ordinary determination made in this manner results in an average of temperature, weighted over the corresponding range of effective flame depths. This weighting thus relates to the various transparencies in the portions of the contour included in the wavelength range $\delta\lambda$.

13·24 RAPID-RESPONSE LINE-REVERSAL TECHNIQUES AND OTHER DEVELOPMENTS

The line-reversal method in its original form is applied by an iterative process. Successive visual observations are made while the background ribbon-filament-lamp temperature is altered. This continues until the reversal point is found. At temperatures below about 670°C (1238°F), the sodium D lines are not considered bright enough to be observed by the human eye (however, see also Sec. 3·2). This effects a low-temperature limit of measurement. On the other hand, at temperatures much above 2600°C (4712°F), the usual type of lamp filament cannot be operated. Apart from the time required for manual balancing, the lamp filament itself is subject to a lag time. This is the time to come to thermal equilibrium at an altered filament current. The result is that rapid changes in flame temperature cannot be followed in the usual procedure.[132, 133, 145–149]

As early as 1909, Schmidt [18] applied his somewhat similar method in the infrared bands of carbon dioxide and water vapor, at around 2.8 and 4.4 μ, respectively. In place of the human eye, he used thermal radiation-sensitive elements as the means of observation. These infrared elements reduce the low-temperature limit of observation to room temperature or below. Snelleman and Smit [150] arranged for more convenient balancing by visual observation on the screen of a cathode-ray oscilloscope. Photo elements then permitted working in the ultraviolet part of the spectrum. For temperatures above 2600°C (4712°F), Rosenthal [133] has used a three-electrode design of carbon arc. The positive crater of this arc serves as a background, and direct balancing can be performed at temperatures up to 3800°K (6380°F). Since sodium is a common contaminant in arc-electrode materials, Rosenthal advises choice of a different coloring metal for the flame. Sodium-vapor electric-discharge lamps have provided rapid-response back-grounds. Since the temperatures of carbon arcs and sodium discharges are not so well adapted to continuous ranges of adjustment, balancing may be performed with gray-wedge filters, used to effect controlled reductions in background intensity. These filters have the effect of reducing the apparent temperature of the arc or lamp. Calibration is necessary when using sodium lamps or arcs with filters (see Fig. 13·6).

Much ingenuity has been expended in devising means to avoid the slow process of manual visual balancing. Buchele,[140] for example, has developed a self-balancing line-reversal pyrometer. In this device, a magnetic drive moves the slit of the spectrograph back and forth across the sodium D lines in the spectrum. The radiation received by a pho-tomultiplier element then yields a pulsating electric output as long as unbalance persists. The difference amplitudes, with a-c amplifica-tion, are used to drive a servo-control mechanism which continu-ously adjusts the filament current in the background lamp toward the amount for balance. At a rate of change in the flame of 500°F/sec (278°C/sec), the lag time is 0.25 sec. This corresponds to a lag error of 125°F (69.5°C). A package instrument is provided, intended to be placed on one side of the flame with a mirror mounted on the opposite side. Accuracy of adjustment between the two units is not required, and each can be suspended on rubber vibration isolators. No error is caused by refraction of the light beam in intermediate gas-temperature gradients, and a separation of up to 5 ft (1.54 m) is permissible between the mirror and the main optical unit. Com-parison with thermocouple and orifice instruments has indicated agree-ment to within 60°F (33°C) for steady conditions. The minimum flame temperature, for proper functioning of the device, is 2900°R (1337°C).[140,150,151]

El Wakil,[152] Myers,[91-94,118,152] and Uyehara [91-94,118,152] have used a sodium-vapor gaseous-discharge tube emitting the sodium D lines for the background lamp. Three light paths were provided, each terminat-ing in a photo element. Two paths, one through the flame and the other around the flame, effected a difference signal when the flame temperature differed from the background temperature. The amplified output from this photo-element pair served for continuous-balancing adjustments of the background-lamp temperature. The third photo element indicated the instantaneous lamp temperature on the screen of a cathode-ray oscilloscope. Calibration was performed by replacing the test flame with a steady-burning flame whose temperature was independently measured by the conventional sodium-line-reversal method. Limitation throughout to electronic and optical components provided sufficiently rapid response to permit following the flame-temperature changes during the combustion stroke of an internal-combustion engine.[91-94, 118, 150-152]

Brevoort,[153] in work on piston internal-combustion engines, found that the combustion-chamber windows became sooted during a run. This effected a corresponding alteration in the apparent temperature of the background lamp. To correct for this source of error, he developed a set of "dirtying" curves in which the apparent background temperature was plotted against time, for operating intervals of up to 300 sec. Corry[48] has developed a nitrogen-flushed shuttered window to minimize sooting. Here, the window is bathed in clean gas under positive pressure at all times except at the moment the shutter is opened to take a reading.

Rössler[12, 100, 101, 119, 154, 155] has developed a technique for observing nonperiodic rapidly changing flame temperatures. Continuous drum-camera photographic recording locates two reversal points per cycle in a periodic variation of apparent background temperature. This cyclic variation is produced by the combination of stationary and rotating Polaroid disks. When the *planes of polarization* are *crossed*, near extinction occurs; whereas, when they are *parallel*, a maximum transmittance results. Through the range of intermediate angles, apparent background temperature is a continuous *cosine-squared* function in time. The instants of reversal are accurately resolved in this continuous range, and corresponding temperatures can be determined from the calibration curve. Modulation frequencies have thus far been limited to 50 cycles/sec, i.e., 100 reversal points per sec; however, Rössler believes that 500 cycles or 1000 points per sec are feasible.

Ribaud and Laure[20] have developed a technique roughly similar to that of Rössler.[12, 100, 101, 119, 154, 155] However, for a description, the reader is referred to their original paper.

Rössler[12, 100, 101, 119, 154, 155] has also photographed temperature patterns in rocket exhausts and at the rate of 3000 frames/sec, using 200-μ sec $(2 \times 10^{-4}\text{-sec})$ exposure times. For similar use, Zarem, Marshall, and Hauser[156] have described a rapid Kerr-cell shutter. This shutter has been applied in making a series of photographs of exploding wires. Exposure times were 5 mμ sec $(5 \times 10^{-9}$ sec$)$, and framing rates of 10^8 per sec may be attained with this technique.[12, 100, 101, 119, 154-157]

13·25 MICROWAVE METHODS

Rudlin [158] has described the use of microwave attenuation for the observation of flame temperatures. He used an oscillator frequency of 26,500 megacycles/sec (2.65×10^{10} cycles/sec) corresponding to a wavelength of 1.13 cm. Electronic *horns* served as the wave source and receiver elements. Reproducibility was to within $\pm 25°C$ ($\pm 45°F$). The pseudotemperature measured is that of the ionization temperature. This phenomenon is described in Saha's equation (see Eq. 14·2).

Drummond [160] has investigated the theory of a similar method for use at plasma temperatures of up to tens of millions of degrees.[87, 158-160]

13·26 STROBOSCOPICALLY ILLUMINATED PARTICLE METHOD

The stroboscopically illuminated particle method of Lewis and von Elbe [33-35] has been used by Anderson and Fein [161] to measure Bunsen-flame temperatures. Here, the tracks of magnesium oxide particles are illuminated by a periodically intermittent sheet of light. A photograph of the particles taken at right angles to the beam records the tracks. From the length of the particle tracks and the time interval of illumination, the particle velocity can be determined. Stream-flow theory then permits the calculation of local flame temperatures from the particle-track data. The pseudotemperature measured is the kinetic temperature.

13·27 CONCLUSION

In the present and preceding chapters, a substantial number of procedures have been described for measuring temperatures in flames. Within the scope of the array of methods, adaptations are provided for a wide variety of circumstances and objectives. The conditions include high temperatures, low temperatures, local temperatures, and rapidly changing temperatures for both luminous and clear flames. Means are available for segregating the temperature levels in the various modes of energy storage, i.e., for the measurement of pseudo-temperatures. Even when there are wide departures from equilibrium, the magnitudes of the respective pseudotemperatures are often of theoretical interest in studies on combustion processes. However, for the measurement of a temperature value which can serve as an accurate and reliable criterion of either the thermal-energy content of the gas or its ability to transmit heat to other bodies, no satisfactory means exist. Whereas there is much reason to believe that the kinetic or translational temperature does closely represent the thermal-energy content, means for measurement of this pseudotemperature tend to be cumbersome and inaccurate. On the other hand, all alternative methods have been shown to be subject to possible, and at least occasional, discrepancies of hundreds and even thousands of degrees.

The only proposal available for a reliable temperature determination in a flame is to measure at least three different pseudotemperatures. If the three determinations are independent and are found to be in agreement to within an acceptable margin, their average value can reasonably be taken as the temperature of the flame gas. If, however, one of them is found to be at a substantial departure from either of the other two, the inconsistency should be regarded as evidence that equilibrium does not exist and no true thermodynamic temperature is to be found.[34, 38, 61, 78, 162-174]

REFERENCES *

1. F. S. Dainton, *Chain Reactions,* 183 pp., Methuen & Co., London, John Wiley & Sons, New York, 1956.
2. H. S. Taylor and R. N. Pease, "Chemical Kinetics of Combustion," B. Lewis, R. N. Pease, and H. S. Taylor, "Combustion Processes," *High Speed Aerodynamics and Jet Propulsion,* **2,** nos. D1 and E1, pp. 101–197, Princeton University Press, Princeton, N. J. (1956).
3. C. N. Hinshelwood, *The Kinetics of Chemical Change,* 274 pp., Oxford at the Clarendon Press, Oxford, 1940.
4. E. Saenger, I. Bredt, and P. Goercke, "Sur l'ionisation et la luminescence dans les flammes" (Ionization and Luminescence in Flames), *Compt. rend.,* **230,** pp. 949–951 (March, 1950).
5. A. V. Engel and M. Steenbeck, "Gas- und Flammen-Temperaturmessung" (Gas- and Flame-Temperature Measurement), *Archiv für technisches Messen,* Ref. V2163-1, pp. T115–T116 (September, 1933).
6. E. Griffiths and J. H. Awbery, "The Measurement of Flame Temperatures," *Proc. Roy. Soc. London A,* **123,** pp. 401–421 (1929).
7. H. Dean Baker, N. H. Baker, and F. Freudenstein, "Preliminary Evaluation of the Thermocouple Technique for the Measurement of Instantaneous Temperatures of Unburned Gas," *Four Proposed Methods of Measuring End-Gas Properties, Appendix A,* pp. 11–25, Coordinating Research Council, New York, January, 1953.
8. H. Leidheiser, Jr. and A. T. Gwathmey, "The Catalytic Reaction of Hydrogen and Oxygen on Plane Faces of a Single Crystal of Copper," *J. Am. Chem. Soc.,* **70,** no. 3, pp. 1200–1206 (March, 1948).
9. A. H. Leah, J. Godrich, and H. R. S. Jack, "Thermal Radiation and Chemiluminescence from Explosion Flame Gases," *Nature,* **166,** p. 868 (November, 1950).
10. R. Jackson, "Temperature Measurement in Gases and Flames—Radiation Methods," *Bull. Brit. Coal Utilisation Research Assoc.,* **15,** no. 6, pp. 205–219 (June, 1951).

---

* See footnote on page 26.

11. W. A. Bone, D. M. Newitt, and D. T. A. Townend, *Gaseous Combustion at High Pressures*, 396 pp., Longmans, Green, & Co., London and New York, 1929.

12. H. Behrens and F. Rössler, "Temperaturmessungen an leuchtenden Flammen" (Temperature Measurements in Luminous Flames), *Zeitschrift für Naturforschung,* **5a,** no. 6, pp. 311–317 (1950).

13. R. T. Haslam and R. P. Russell, *Fuels and Their Combustion*, 1st ed., pp. 304–305, McGraw-Hill Book Co., New York, 1926.

14. C. E. Richardson, "The Process of Surface Combustion," *Pennsylvania Gas Association Proceedings,* pp. 3–30, April, 1916, Pennsylvania Gas Association, Easton, Pa.

15. H. N. Judyakon and V. S. Pushkin, "The Problem of Flameless Combustion," *The Engineers' Digest,* **3,** no. 8, pp. 392–394 (August, 1946); *Izvestya Akademii, Nauk, USSR,* Ser. fiz, **6,** pp. 545–553 (1945).

16. A. E. Blake, "Surface Combustion," R. F. Bacon and W. A. Hamor, *American Fuels,* Vol. II, 1st ed., pp. 1090–1094, McGraw-Hill Book Co., New York, 1922.

17. S. A. Hoenig, "Use of a Constant Current Hot Wire for the Measurement of Extreme Temperatures," *Rev. Sci. Instr.,* **29,** no. 8, pp. 704–705 (August, 1958).

18. H. Schmidt, "Prüfung der Strahlungsgesetze der Bunsenflamme" (Examination of the Radiation Laws for Flames), *Annalen der Physik,* **29,** Series 5, no. 10, pp. 971–1029 (1909).

19. H. D. Baker and G. L. Laserson, "An Investigation into the Importance of Chemiluminescent Radiation in Internal Combustion Engines," *General Discussion on Heat Transfer,* London Conference, Sec. IV, 7 pp., Institution of Mechanical Engineers, London, and American Society of Mechanical Engineers, New York, 1951.

20. G. Ribaud and Y. Laure, "Principes et technique de la mesure optique des températures des gaz incandescents" (Principles and Technique for the Optical Measurement of the Temperatures of Incandescent Gases), *Revue d'optique,* **19,** nos. 1–2, pp. 123–135 (January–February, 1940).

21. E. F. Fiock, L. O. Olsen, and P. D. Freeze, "The Use of Thermocouples in Streaming Exhaust Gas," *Third Symposium on Combustion,* pp. 655–662, Williams and Wilkins, Baltimore, 1949.

22. N. P. Bailey, "Abrupt Energy Transformation in Flowing Gases," *Trans. ASME,* **69,** no. 7, pp. 749–763, American Society of Mechanical Engineers, New York (July, 1947).

23. H. E. Alquist and D. W. Male, "Trends in Surface-Ignition Temperatures," *Wartime Report* E 4125, 7 pp., U. S. National Advisory Committee for Aeronautics, Washington (September, 1944).

24. P. G. Guest, "Ignition of Natural Gas-Air Mixtures by Heated Surfaces," *Technical Paper* 475, 59 pp., U. S. Bureau of Mines, Washington (1930).

25. A. S. Leah, C. Rounthwaite, and D. Bradley, "Some Extensions in the Use of Resistance Thermometry in the Study of Gaseous Explosions," *Phil. Mag.,* Series 7, **41,** pp. 468–477 (May, 1950); and pp. 1289–1291 (December, 1950).

26. A. S. Leah, "The Photographic Determination of Flame Temperatures in Closed-Vessel Explosions," *Phil. Mag.,* Series 7, **34,** pp. 795–803 (December, 1943).

27. A. H. Leah, J. Godrich, and H. R. S. Jack, "Thermal Radiation and Chemiluminescence from Explosion Flame Gases," *Nature,* **166,** no. 4229, pp. 868–869 (November, 1950).

28. A. S. Leah, "The Influence of Water Vapour on Flame Temperatures in Carbon-monoxide Explosions," *Phil. Mag.*, Series 7, **38**, pp. 657–672 (September, 1947).

29. W. T. David, "The Sodium Line-Reversal Method of Determining Flame Temperatures," *Engineering*, **138**, p. 475 (November, 1934).

30. W. T. David, "Temperature of Flame Gases," *Engineering*, **149**, pp. 241–242 (March, 1940).

31. W. T. David, "The Measurement of Flame Gas Temperatures," *The Engineer*, **172**, pp. 186–187 (September, 1941).

32. C. B. Daish, D. H. Fender, and A. J. Woodall, "A Note on the Use of Resistance Thermometers for Measurement of Rapidly Changing Temperatures," *Phil. Mag.*, **41**, no. 318, pp. 729–730 (July, 1950).

33. R. Klein, M. Mentser, G. von Elbe, and B. Lewis, "Determination of the Thermal Structure of a Combustion Wave by Fine Thermocouples," *J. Phys. & Colloid Chem.*, **54**, no. 6, pp. 877–884 (June, 1950).

34. B. Lewis and G. von Elbe, "Flame Temperature," American Institute of Physics, *Temperature*, pp. 707–719, Reinhold Publishing Corp., New York, 1941.

35. B. Lewis and G. von Elbe, "Stability and Structure of Flames," *J. Chem. Phys.*, **11**, no. 2, p. 75–97 (February, 1943).

36. H. Klaukins and H. G. Wolfhard, "Measurements in the Reaction Zone of a Bunsen Flame," *Proc. Roy. Soc. London A*, **193**, pp. 512–524 (1948).

37. A. G. Gaydon and H. G. Wolfhard, "Spectroscopic Studies of Low-Pressure Flames. II. Effective Translational and Rotational Temperatures from CH Bands," *Proc. Roy. Soc. London A*, **194**, pp. 169–184 (1948); and **199**, pp. 89–104 (1949).

38. A. G. Gaydon and H. G. Wolfhard, *Flames, Their Structure Radiation and Temperature*, 2nd ed., 383 pp., Chapman & Hall, London, 1960.

39. A. G. Gaydon and H. G. Wolfhard, "L'excitation du spectre de OH dans les flammes sous basse pression" (The Exitation of the OH Spectrum in Flames at Low Pressures), *Revue de l'institut français du petrole et annales des combustibles liquides*, **4**, no. 8, pp. 405–417 (August, 1947).

40. H. G. Wolfhard and W. G. Parker, "Emissivity of Small Particles in Flames," *Nature*, **162**, p. 162 (August, 1948).

41. H. G. Wolfhard and W. G. Parker, "Temperature Measurements of Flames Containing Incandescent Particles," *Proc. Phys. Soc. London B*, **62**, pp. 523–529 (1949).

42. R. Friedman, "Measurement of the Temperature Profile in a Laminar Flame," *Fourth Symposium on Combustion*, pp. 259–263, Williams and Wilkins, Baltimore, 1953.

43. R. Friedman and E. Burke, "Measurement of Temperature Distribution in a Low-Pressure Flat Flame," *J. Chem. Phys.*, **22**, no. 5, pp. 824–830 (May, 1954).

44. S. S. Penner, "Optical Methods for the Determination of Flame Temperatures. I. Two-Color and Line-Reversal Techniques. II. Reversal Methods for Nonisothermal Flames, Two-Path Method, Compensated Hot-Wire Method, Methods Based on Measurements of Line Intensities," *American J. Phys.*, **17**, no. 7, pp. 422–429 (October, 1949); and no. 8, pp. 491–500 (November, 1949).

45. K. L. Rieke, "Temperature and Gas-Analysis Surveys in the Combustion Zone of a Gas-Fired Gas-Turbine Combustor," *Paper 52-A-97* (1952); *Trans.*

ASME, **75,** no. 7, pp. 1233–1239, American Society of Mechanical Engineers, New York (October, 1953).

46. V. D. Sanders, "Review of High-Temperature Immersion Thermal Sensing Devices for In-Flight Engine Control," *Rev. Sci. Instr.,* **29,** no. 11, pp. 917–928 (November, 1958).

47. W. E. Garner, "Radiant Energy from Flames," *Ind. Eng. Chem.,* **20,** no. 10, pp. 1008–1012 (October, 1928).

48. R. T. Corry, *A Method for Detecting Chemiluminescent Radiation in an Internal Combustion Engine, and Test Results for Isooctane,* Doctoral Dissertation, 177 pp., Columbia University, New York, 1957.

49. A. F. Baldo, *The Effect of Fuel Type on Chemiluminescent Radiation in an Internal-Combustion Engine,* Doctoral Dissertation, 415 pp., Columbia University, New York, 1960.

50. C. Payne-Gaposchkin, "Astrophysical Temperatures," American Institute of Physics, *Temperature,* Vol. II, pp. 31–59, Government Printing Office, Washington (March, 1954).

51. P. J. Dyne and S. S. Penner, "Optical Methods for the Determination of Combustion Temperatures," *J. Am. Rocket Soc.,* **23,** no. 3, pp. 165–169 (May–June, 1953).

52. H. P. Broida and A. G. Gaydon, "The Mechanism of Formation of OH, CH and HCO in Flame Spectra, Using Deuterium as a Tracer," *Proc. Roy. Soc. London A,* **218,** pp. 60–69 (1953).

53. A. G. Gaydon, "Processes of Electronic Excitation in Relation to Flame Spectra," in "Energy Transfer in Hot Gases," *Natl. Bur. Standards Circ.* 523, pp. 1–8, Government Printing Office, Washington (March, 1954).

54. A. G. Gaydon, *Dissociation Energies and Spectra of Diatomic Molecules,* 239 pp., John Wiley & Sons, New York, 1948.

55. E. Sänger, P. Goercke, and I. Bredt, "Über Ionisierung und Lumineszenz in Flammen" (On Ionization and Luminescence in Flames), *Technical Memorandum* 1305, 26 pp., U. S. National Advisory Committee for Aeronautics, Washington (April, 1951).

56. L. Viaud, "Detérmination de la température moyenne dans une chambre de combustion" (Determination of the Average Temperature in a Combustion Chamber), *La recherche aéronautique,* no. 18, pp. 55–58 (November–December, 1950).

57. R. A. Gross, "Recent Advances in Gaseous Detonation," *Annual Meeting Paper* 688-58, pp. 3–4, American Rocket Society, New York, November, 1958.

58. H. Zirin, "The Temperature and Equilibrium of Hydrogen in Solar Prominences," *Astrophysical Journal,* **124,** no. 2, pp. 451–460 (September, 1956).

59. G. H. Dieke and H. M. Crosswhite, "Studies of Emission and Absorption in Flames," in "Energy Transfer in Hot Gases," *Natl. Bur. Standards Circ.* 523, pp. 39–49, Government Printing Office, Washington (March, 1954).

60. G. H. Dieke, "High Gas Temperatures," American Institute of Physics, *Temperature,* Vol. II, pp. 19–30, Government Printing Office, Washington (March, 1954).

61. A. G. Gaydon, *The Spectroscopy of Flames,* 279 pp., John Wiley & Sons, New York, 1957.

62. G. R. Harrison, R. C. Lord, and J. R. Loofbourow, *Practical Spectroscopy,* 605 pp., Prentice-Hall, Englewood Cliffs, N. J., 1948.

63. F. K. Richtmyer, E. H. Kennard, and T. Lauritsen, *Introduction to Modern Physics,* pp. 133–344, McGraw-Hill Book Co., New York, 1955.

64. G. Z. Herzberg, *Molecular Spectra and Molecular Structure.* Vol. I. *Spectra of Diatomic Molecules,* 2nd ed., 658 pp., D. Van Nostrand Co., Princeton, N. J., 1950.

65. R. W. B. Pearse and A. G. Gaydon, *The Identification of Molecular Spectra,* 2nd ed., 276 pp., John Wiley & Sons, New York, 1950.

66. W. Finkelnburg, "Conditions for Blackbody Radiation of Gases," *J. Opt. Soc. Am.,* **39,** no. 2, pp. 185–186 (February, 1949).

67. H. Edels and J. D. Craggs, "Excitation Temperatures of Hydrogen Arcs," *Proc. Phys. Soc. London A,* **64,** pp. 562–573 (1951).

68. G. H. Dieke and H. M. Crosswhite, "The Ultraviolet Bands of OH," Bur. Ordnance U.S.N. *Bumblebee Series* 87, pp. 1–118, The Johns Hopkins University, Baltimore, Md. (November, 1948).

69. D. E. Blackwell, "The Excitation Temperature of the Solar Chromosphere Determined from Molecular Spectra," in A. Beer, *Vistas in Astronomy,* Vol. I, pp. 726–732, Pergamon Press, London and New York, 1955.

70. A. V. Jones and A. W. Harrison, "Rotational Temperatures of the Auroral $N_2 +$ Bands," *Journal of Atmospheric and Terrestrial Physics,* **6,** no. 6, pp. 336–343 (June, 1955).

71. H. P. Broida, "Distributions of OH Rotational Intensities in Flames," in "Energy Transfer in Hot Gases," *Natl. Bur. Standards Circ.* 523, pp. 23–34, Government Printing Office, Washington (March, 1954).

72. W. Petrie, "The Significance of Temperatures Derived from Emission Spectra," *Amer. J. Phys.,* **16,** no. 7, pp. 378–382 (October, 1948).

73. W. Petrie, "Rotational Temperatures of Vegard-Kaplan Auroral Bands," *Phys. Rev.,* **86,** no. 5, pp. 790–791 (June, 1952).

74. W. Petrie, "Rotational Temperatures of Auroral Nitrogen Bands," *Journal of Atmospheric and Terrestrial Physics,* **4,** nos. 1 and 2, pp. 5–9 (September, 1953).

75. G. G. Shepherd and D. M. Hunten, "On the Measurement of Rotational Temperatures from Unresolved Nitrogen Bands," *Journal of Atmospheric and Terrestrial Physics,* **6,** no. 6, pp. 328–335 (June, 1955).

76. D. M. Hunten and G. G. Shepherd, "Vibrational Temperatures from Second Positive Bands," *Journal of Atmospheric and Terrestrial Physics,* **6,** no. 1, pp. 64–66 (January, 1955).

77. L. T. Earls, "Intensities in $^2II - ^2\Sigma$ Transitions in Diatomic Molecules," *Phys. Rev.,* **48,** no. 3, pp. 423–424 (September, 1935).

78. H. P. Broida, "Experimental Temperature Measurements in Flames and Hot Gases," American Institute of Physics, *Temperature,* Vol. II, pp. 265–286, Government Printing Office, Washington (March, 1954).

79. E. L. Hill and J. H. Van Vleck, "On the Quantum Mechanics of the Rotational Distortion of Molecular Spectral Terms," *Phys. Rev.,* **32,** no. 2, pp. 250–272 (August, 1928).

80. S. S. Penner, "On the Validity of Anomalous Population Temperatures in Flames," *J. Chem. Phys.,* **20,** no. 7, pp. 1175–1176 (July, 1952).

81. K. E. Shuler, "On the Validity of Spectroscopic Temperature Determinations in Flames," *J. Chem. Phys.,* **20,** no. 7, pp. 1176–1177 (July, 1952).

82. B. H. Elliot and S. S. Penner, "Effects of Temperature Gradients, Self-Absorption, and Line Shape on Apparent Rotational Temperatures of OH," *J. Chem. Phys.,* **22,** no. 1, pp. 101–105 (January, 1954).

83. S. S. Penner, M. Gilbert, and D. Weber, "Spectroscopic Studies of Low-Pressure Combustion Flames," in "Energy Transfer in Hot Gases," *Natl. Bur.*

Standards Circ. 523, pp. 35–37, Government Printing Office, Washington (March, 1954).

84. S. Silverman, "Energy Distribution of CO Molecules in CO–O_2 Flames," in "Energy Transfer in Hot Gases," *Natl. Bur. Standards Circ.* 523, pp. 51–56, Government Printing Office, Washington (March, 1954).

85. R. Herman, R. W. Rothery, and R. J. Rubin, "Line Intensities in Vibration-Rotation Bands of Diatomic Molecules," *Journal of Molecular Spectroscopy,* 2, no. 4, pp. 369–386 (August, 1953).

86. G. Lukacs and L. Herman, "Température de vibration dans le spectre de phosphorescence des bandes de Swan de la molécule C_2" (Vibrational Temperatures in the Phosphorescence Spectra of the Swan Bands for the C_2 Molecule), *Compt. rend.,* 239, no. 10, pp. 640–642 (September, 1954).

87. J. A. Smit, "The Determination of Temperature from Spectra," *Physica,* 12, nos. 9–10, pp. 683–700 (December, 1946).

88. H. P. Broida and G. T. Lalos, "Rotational Temperatures of OH in Several Flames," *J. Chem. Phys.,* 20, no. 9, pp. 1466–1471 (September, 1952).

89. J. M. Parker, "The Rotational Temperature of the Lower Solar Chromosphere," *Astrophysical Journal,* 121, no. 3, pp. 731–738 (May, 1955).

90. H. J. Kostkowski and H. P. Broida, "Spectral Absorption Method for Determining Population 'Temperatures' in Hot Gases," *J. Opt. Soc. Am.,* 46, no. 4, pp. 246–254 (April, 1956).

91. P. S. Myers, O. A. Uyehara, S. K. Chen, and N. J. Beck, "Studies of the Feasibility of Measuring Compression Temperatures from Absorption Spectra," *Four Proposed Methods of Measuring End-Gas Properties, Appendix C,* pp. 83–122, Coordinating Research Council, New York, January, 1953.

92. O. A. Uyehara, P. S. Myers, and T. J. Schweitzer, "Technical Report on Measurement of Compression Temperatures," *Progress Report on Instantaneous Temperature Measurements,* 94 pp., Coordinating Research Council, New York, December, 1955.

93. O. A. Uyehara, P. S. Myers, K. M. Watson, and L. A. Wilson, "Diesel Combustion Temperatures—The Influence of Operating Variables," *Trans. ASME,* 69, no. 5, pp. 465–477, American Society of Mechanical Engineers, New York (July, 1947).

94. P. S. Myers and O. A. Uyehara, "Flame Temperature Measurements—Electronic Solution of Temperature Equations," *S.A.E. Trans.,* Society of Automotive Engineers, 1, no. 4, pp. 592–601, 611 (October, 1947).

95. S. S. Penner, "The Emission of Radiation from Diatomic Gases. I. Approximate Calculations," *J. Appl. Phys.,* 21, no. 7, pp. 685–695 (July, 1950).

96. S. S. Penner, "The Emission of Radiation from Diatomic Gases. IV. Emissivity Calculations for CO and HCl for Nonoverlapping Rotational Lines as a Function of Temperature and Optical Density," *J. Appl. Phys.,* 23, no. 8, pp. 825–837 (August, 1952).

97. F. Hoffman and C. Tingwaldt, *Optische Pyrometrie* (Optical Pyrometry), 134 pp., Friedr. Vieweg & Sohn, Braunschweig, 1938.

98. B. Baudin, "Calcul de l'énergie rayonnée par une flamme et mesure des températures de flammes par des méthodes optiques dans le cas d'une répartition non uniforme en température et en pouvoir émissif" (Calculation of the Energy Radiated by a Flame and Measurement of the Temperatures of Flames by Optical Methods for the Case of Nonuniform Distribution of Temperature and Emissive Power), *Revue d'optique,* 35, no. 7, pp. 381–395 (July, 1956).

99. F. Kurlbaum, "Über das Reflexionsvermögen von Flammen" (On the Reflecting Power of Flames), *Physikalische Zeitschrift*, **3**, no. 15, pp. 332–334 (March, 1902).

100. F. Rössler and H. Behrens, "Bestimmung des Absorptionskoeffizienten von Russteilchen verschiedener Flammen" (Determination of the Absorption Coefficients of Soot Particles from Various Flames), *Optik*, **6**, no. 3, pp. 145–151 (March, 1950).

101. F. Rössler, "Optische Bestimmung der wahren Temperature von leuchtenden Flammen" (Optical Determination of the True Temperature of Luminous Flames), *Zeitschrift für angewandte Physik*, **2**, no. 4, pp. 161–166 (April, 1950).

102. S. Silverman, G. A. Hornbeck, and R. C. Herman, "The Infrared Emission and Absorption of the Carbon-Oxygen Flame," *J. Chem. Phys.*, **16**, pp. 155–156 (February, 1948).

103. S. Silverman, "The Determination of Flame Temperatures by Infrared Radiation," *Third Symposium on Combustion Flame and Explosion Phenomena*, pp. 498–500, Williams & Wilkins Co., Baltimore, 1949; *J. Opt. Soc. Am.*, **39**, no. 4, pp. 275–277 (April, 1949).

104. J. A. Curcio, H. S. Stewart and C. C. Petty, "A Method for the Determination of Flame Temperature from Emission in the Ultraviolet OH Band," *J. Opt. Soc. Am.*, **41**, no. 3, pp. 173–179 (March, 1951).

105. H. Graff, "Gas Temperature Measurements in Internal Combustion Engines," *The Engineers' Digest*, **4**, no. 3, pp. 67–69 (March, 1943); "Messung des Gastemperaturverlaufes in Verbrennungs Kraftmaschinen," *VDI Zeitschrift des Vereines Deutscher Ingenieure*, **86**, no. 29–30, pp. 461–466 (July, 1942).

106. J. H. Potter and R. B. Dillaway, "Investigation of Flame Temperatures in a Single Cylinder Spark-Ignition Engine," *Paper* 53-S-46, 13 pp. (1953); *Trans. ASME*, **75**, no. 7, pp. 1311–1321 (October, 1953), American Society of Mechanical Engineers, New York.

107. J. T. Agnew, "Line-Reversal Techniques in the Determination of Temperature of Gun Flash or Other Rapid Transient Phenomena," *Paper* 51-F-6, 9 pp., American Society of Mechanical Engineers, New York (1951).

108. M. F. Heidmann and R. J. Priem, "A Modified Sodium Line Reversal Technique for the Measurement of Combustion Temperatures in Rocket Engines," *Annual Meeting Paper*, 33 pp., American Society of Mechanical Engineers (December, 1952).

109. H. F. Quinn, "A Spectrophotometric Determination of Exhaust Gas Temperatures in the Pulse-Jet Engine," *Can. J. Research A*, **28**, pp. 411–432 (July, 1950).

110. V. V. Kandya, "Measurement of Flame Temperature by Means of Photoelectric Spectrometry," *Izvestiya Akademii Nauk SSSR*, Ser. fiz., **12**, no. 4, pp. 387–391 (July–August, 1948).

111. E. K. Plyler, "Infrared Radiation from a Bunsen Flame," *RP* 1860, *J. Research Natl. Bur. Standards*, **40**, no. 2, pp. 113–120 (February, 1948).

112. A. Moutet, "Détermination des températures de combustion par voie optique" (Determination of Combustion Temperatures by Optical Methods), *Revue d'optique*, **33**, no. 7, pp. 313–338 (July, 1954).

113. N. N. Sobolev, M. M. Belousov, G. M. Rodin, A. G. Sviridov, N. G. Skorobogatov, and F. S. Faizullov, "Flame Temperature of a Liquid-Fuel Jet Engine." I. (in Russian); and N. N. Sobolev, V. F. Kitaeva, G. M. Rodin, F. S. Faizulov, and A. I. Fedorov, II, *Zhurnal Tekhnicheskoi Fiziki.—Aka-*

demiya Nauk SSSR, **29**, no. 1, pp. 27–44 (January, 1959); translation, *Soviet Physics—Technical Physics*, New York, **4**, no. 1, pp. 24–37 (January, 1959).

114. A. Schack, "Strahlung von leuchtenden Flammen" (Radiation from Luminous Flames), *Zeitschrift für technische Physik*, **6**, no. 10, pp. 530–540 (1925).

115. G. Mie, "Beitrage zur Optik trüber Medien speciell kolloidal Metallösungen" (Contributions to the Optics of Absorbing Media, and Special Colloidal Suspensions of Metals), *Annalen der Physik*, **25**, Series 4, no. 3, pp. 377–445 (January, 1908).

116. H. C. Hottel and F. P. Broughton, "Determination of True Temperature and Total Radiation from Luminous Gas Flames," *Ind. Eng. Chem., Anal. Ed.*, **4**, no. 2, pp. 166–175 (April, 1932).

117. E. K. Plyler and C. J. Humphreys, "Use of Radiation from Incandescent Particles as an Indication of Flame Temperature," *RP* 2272, *J. Research Natl. Bur. Standards*, **47**, no. 6, pp. 456–460 (December, 1951).

118. O. A. Uyehara, P. S. Myers, K. M. Watson, and L. A. Wilson, "Flame-Temperature Measurements in Internal Combustion Engines," *Trans. ASME*, **68**, pp. 17–30, American Society of Mechanical Engineers, New York (January, 1946).

119. F. Rössler, "Optische Untersuchungen bei der adiabatische Verbrennung von festen Treibmitteln" (Optical Investigation of the Adiabatic Combustion of Solid Propellants), *Zeitschrift für angewandte Physik*, **6**, no. 4, pp. 175–182 (1954).

120. G. W. Bauserman, C. H. Prien, and T. Zandstra, "Determination of Transient Flame Temperatures," *Rev. Sci. Instr.*, **25**, no. 7, pp. 640–643 (July, 1954).

121. M. F. Heidmann and R. J. Priem, "Application of an Electro-Optical Two-Color Pyrometer to Measurement of Flame Temperature for Liquid Oxygen-Hydrocarbon Propellant Combination," *Technical Note* 3033, 39 pp., U. S. National Advisory Committee for Aeronautics, Washington (October, 1953).

122. M. Alentzev and N. Sobolev, "An Optical Method for Determining the Detonation Temperature of an Explosive," *Comptes rendus* (Doklady) *de l'academie des sciences de l'URSS*, **51**, no. 9, pp. 691–692 (1946).

123. S. S. Penner, "Radiation from Rocket Flames and Its Effect on Rocket Performance," *Am. J. Phys.*, **16**, no. 9, pp. 475–483 (December, 1948).

124. S. S. Penner, "A Two-Path Method for Measuring Flame Temperatures and Concentrations in Low Pressure Combustion Chambers," *J. Chem. Phys.*, **19**, no. 3, pp. 272–280 (March, 1951).

125. J. A. Sanderson, J. A. Curcio, and D. V. Estes, "A Photoelectric Pyrometer for the Measurement of Luminous Flame Temperatures," *Phys. Rev.*, **74**, p. 1221 (July, 1948).

126. J. A. Curcio and D. V. Estes, "A Photoelectric Pyrometer for the Measurement of Luminous Flame Temperatures," *Report* N-3319, 12 pp., U. S. Naval Research Laboratory, Washington (July, 1948).

127. J. H. Hett and J. B. Gilstein, "Pyrometer for Measurement of Instantaneous Temperatures of Flames," *J. Opt. Soc. Am.*, **39**, no. 11, pp. 909–911 (November, 1949).

128. J. H. Hett and J. B. Gilstein, "Instantaneous Rocket Flame Temperature Measurement," *Paper* 102-A-53, 21 pp., American Rocket Society, New York (1953).

129. F. S. Simmons and A. G. DeBell, "Photographic Pyrometry with a Color-Separation Camera," *J. Opt. Soc. Am.*, **49**, no. 7, pp. 735–736 (July, 1959).

130. F. Kurlbaum, "Über eine einfache Methode, die Temperatur leuchender Flammen zu bestimmen" (On a Simple Method for Determining the Temperatures of Luminous Flames), *Physikalische Zeitschrift*, **3**, no. 9, pp. 187–188 (1902).

131. C. Féry, "Sur la température des flammes" (On the Temperatures of Flames), *Compt. rend.*, **137**, pp. 909–912 (November, 1903).

132. H. Kohn, "Über das Wesen der Emission der in Flammen leuchenden Metalldämpfe" (On the Emission Characteristics of Radiating Metal Vapors in Flames), *Annalen der Physik*, **44**, pp. 749–782 (March, 1914).

133. G. Rosenthal, "Temperaturmessung mit Hilfe der Linienumkehrmethode" (Temperature Measurement with the Line-Reversal Method), *Archiv für technisches Messen*, Ref. V2163-2 (January, 1942).

134. M. Doncescu, "Détermination des températures de gas pendant la détente dan les moteurs à explosion" (Determination of Gas Temperatures during Expansion in Internal-Combustion Engines), *Publications scientifiques et technique du ministère de air (France)*, **69**, 63 pp., Paris (1935).

135. G. Ribaud, *Temperature des flammes* (Temperature of Flames), 43 pp., Librairie scientifique Hermann et Cie, Paris, 1930.

136. Y. Tanaka and M. Ogawa, "On the Chemiluminescence of the Sodium D Lines in the Reaction between Ozone and Sodium Vapour," *Physics Abstracts*, **59**, no. 708, p. 1007 (December, 1956).

137. F. Henning and C. Tingwaldt, "Die Temperatur der Acetylen-Sauerstoff-flamme" (The Temperature of the Oxy-Acetylene Flame), *Zeitschrift für Physik*, **48**, nos. 11 and 12, pp. 805–823 (May, 1928).

138. A. E. Hershey, "Measurement of Gas Temperature in an Internal-Combustion Engine," *Trans. ASME*, **58**, pp. 195–201, American Society of Mechanical Engineers, New York (April, 1936).

139. J. R. Arthur, D. H. Baugham, R. H. Baulk, and G. Whittingham, "The Reactions Leading to the Sodium D-Line Radiation in Flames," *Nature*, **166**, pp. 358–359 (August, 1950).

140. D. Buchele, "A Self-Balancing Line-Reversal Pyrometer," *Technical Note* 3656, 68 pp., U. S. National Advisory Committee for Aeronautics, Washington (August, 1956).

141. H. M. Strong, F. P. Bundy, and D. A. Larson, "Temperature Measurement on Complex Flames by Sodium Line Reversal and Sodium Line Intensity Contour Studies," *Third Symposium on Combustion Flame and Explosion Phenomena*, pp. 641–647, Williams and Wilkins Co., Baltimore, 1949.

142. H. M. Strong and F. P. Bundy, "Measurement of Gas Temperatures in the Exhaust Flames of Rocket Motors by Spectroscopic Methods. I.," *Phys. Rev.*, **74**, no. 9, p. 1221 (November, 1948).

143. F. P. Bundy and H. M. Strong, "Measurement of Velocity and Pressure of the Gases in Rocket Flames by Spectroscopic Methods," *Third Symposium on Combustion Flame and Explosion Phenomena*, pp. 647–654, Williams and Wilkins Co., Baltimore, 1949.

144. H. M. Strong and F. P. Bundy, "Measurement of Temperatures in Flames of Complex Structure by Resonance Line Radiation. I. General Theory and Application to Sodium Line Reversal Methods. II. Sodium Line Reversal by High-Resolution Spectroscopy. III. From Absolute Intensity Measurements at High Resolution." *J. Appl. Phys.*, **25**, no. 12, pp. 1521–1526, 1527–1530, and 1531–1537 (December, 1954).

145. A. E. Hershey and R. F. Paton, "Flame Temperatures in an Internal Combustion Engine Measured by Spectral Line Reversal," *Bulletin*, **262**, 50 pp. (1933), *University of Illinois Bulletin*, **31**, no. 9, 50 pp. (October, 1933), The University of Illinois, Engineering Experiment Station, Urbana.

146. J. G. Coutant, "Pressure-Combustion," *Southern Power and Industry*, **63**, no. 12, pp. 65–67, 96 (December, 1945).

147. S. S. Watts and J. Lloyd-Evans, "The Measurement of Flame Temperatures in a Petrol Engine by the Spectral Line-Reversal Method," *Proc. Phys. Soc. London*, **46**, pp. 444–449 (March, 1934).

148. G. M. Rassweiler and L. Withrow, "Flame Temperatures Vary with Knock and Combustion-Chamber Position," *S.A.E. Trans.*, Society of Automotive Engineers, **36**, no. 41, pp. 125–133 (April, 1935).

149. A. G. Loomis and G. St. J. Perrott, "Measurement of the Temperatures of Stationary Flames," *Ind. Eng. Chem.*, **20**, no. 10, pp. 1004–1008 (October, 1928).

150. W. Snelleman and J. A. Smit, "Photoelectric Temperature Measurement by Line Reversal," *Physica*, **21**, no. 12, pp. 946–948 (December, 1955).

151. A. G. Sviridov and N. N. Sobelov, "Measuring the Temperature of a Flame by the Spectral Line Inversion Method," *Sci. Abstr. A*, **57**, no. 681, p. 1046 (September, 1954).

152. M. M. El Wakil, P. S. Myers, and O. A. Uyehara, "An Instantaneous and Continuous Sodium-Line Reversal Pyrometer," *Paper* 50-A-94, 18 pp. (1951); *Mech. Eng.*, **73**, no. 3, p. 235 (March, 1951); *Trans. ASME*, **74**, no. 2, pp. 255–267 (February, 1952), American Society of Mechanical Engineers, New York.

153. M. J. Brevoort, "Combustion-Engine Temperatures by the Sodium Line-Reversal Method," *Technical Note* 559, 6 pp., U. S. National Advisory Committee for Aeronautics, Washington (March, 1936).

154. F. Rössler, "Temperaturmessung nach der Methode der Linienumkehrung bei kurzzeitigen aperiodischen Vorgängen" (Temperature Measurement by the Line-Reversal Method for Short-Duration Aperiodic Processes), *Zeitschrift für angewandte Physik*, **4**, no. 1, pp. 22–29 (1952).

155. F. Rössler, "Temperaturmessungen an Raketenstrahlen" (Temperature Measurements in Rocket Exhaust), *Zeitschrift für angewandte Physik*, **6**, no. 5, pp. 229–231 (1954).

156. A. M. Zarem, F. R. Marshall, and S. M. Hauser, "Millimicrosecond Kerr Cell Camera Shutter," *Rev. Sci. Instr.*, **29**, no. 11, pp. 1041–1044 (November, 1958).

157. J. G. Clouston, A. G. Gaydon, and L. I. Glass, "Temperature Measurements of Shock Waves by the Spectrum-Line Reversal Method," *Nature*, **181**, no. 4619, pp. 1325–1326 (May, 1958).

158. L. Rudlin, "Preliminary Results of a Determination of Temperatures of Flames by Means of K-Band Microwave Attenuation," *Research Memorandum* RME 51G20, 20 pp., U. S. National Advisory Committee for Aeronautics, Washington (September, 1951).

159. P. W. Kuhns, "Determination of Flame Temperatures from 2000° to 3000°K by Microwave Absorption," *Technical Note* 3254, 48 pp., U. S. National Advisory Committee for Aeronautics, Washington (August, 1954).

160. J. E. Drummond, "A Microwave Thermometer for Millions of Degrees," in H. Fisher and L. C. Mansur, *Conference on Extremely High Temperatures*, pp. 97–110, John Wiley & Sons, New York, 1958.

161. J. W. Anderson and R. S. Fein, "Measurements of Normal Burning Velocities and Flame Temperatures of Bunsen Flames," *J. Chem. Phys.*, **17**, no. 12, pp. 1268–1273 (December, 1949).

162. G. Ribaud, Y. Laure, and H. Gaudry, "The Measurement of Flame Temperatures," *J. Inst. Fuel*, **12**, no. 64, pp. S18–S30 (March, 1939).

163. E. F. Fiock, "Bibliography of Books and Published Reports on Gas Turbines, Jet Propulsion, and Rocket Power Plants," *Natl. Bur. Standards Circ.* 482, 49 pp., Government Printing Office, Washington (September, 1949).

164. W. T. Olson and E. Bernardo, "Temperature Measurements and Combustion Efficiency in Combustors for Gas-Turbine Engines," *Trans. ASME*, **70**, pp. 329–334, American Society of Mechanical Engineers, New York (May, 1948).

165. A. P. Dronov, A. G. Svirdov, and N. N. Sobolev, "Measurement of Flame Temperatures by the Method of the Relative Intensities of Spectral Lines" (in Russian), *Optika*, **5**, no. 5, pp. 490–499 (1958); *Sci. Abstr. A*, **63**, no. 745, p. 22 (January, 1960).

166. A. van Itterbeek, G. Forrez, C. G. Sluijter, and G. Vaes, "Temperature Measurements with an Acoustical Thermometer," *Bulletin de l'institute international d. froid, Annexe*, no. 1, pp. 155–164, 1958; *Sci. Abstr. A*, **63**, no. 745, p. 22 (January, 1960).

167. F. Anacker and R. Mannkopff, "A Reproducible 4000°K Black Radiator" (in German); *Zeitschrift für Physik*, **155**, no. 1, pp. 1–15 (1959); *Sci. Abstr. A*, **63**, no. 745, p. 21 (January, 1960).

168. S. S. Penner, *Quantitative Molecular Spectroscopy and Gas Emissivities*, pp. 455–531, Addison-Wesley Publishing Co., Reading and London, 1959.

169. N. N. Sobolev, S. É. Frish, N. M. Kulikova, É. N. Lotkova, G. M. Malyshev, G. M. Rodin, and A. M. Shukhtin, "Pyrometric Study of the Flame of an Oxygen-Silicon-Aluminum Fuel" (in Russian), *Zhurnal Tekhnicheskoĭ Fiziki —Akademiya Nauk SSSR*, **29**, no. 4, pp. 506–513 (April, 1959), translation, *Soviet Physics—Technical Physics*, New York, **4**, no. 4, pp. 451–456 (April, 1959).

170. B. I. Plyukhin, "Laws of the Temperature Emission of the Flame" (in Russian), *Doklady Akademii Nauk SSSR*, Ser. fiz. **131**, no. 1, pp. 68–71 (March, 1960).

171. I. M. Voskoboinikov and A. Ya. Apin, "Temperature Measurement of the Front of Detonation of Explosives" (in Russian), *Doklady Akademii Nauk SSSR*, Ser. fiz., **130**, no. 4, pp. 804–806 (February, 1960).

172. C. Veret, "Filtre à étalon interferential pour appareil de mesure de temperature de flammes" (Interferometric Etalon Filter for Apparatus for Determining the Temperatures of Flames), *Revue d'optique*, **38**, no. 7, pp. 317–344 (July, 1959).

173. F. Rössler, "Die Verteilungstemperatur von Russflammen" (The Temperature Distribution in Soot Flames), *Annalen der Physik*, **459**, Series 7, Vol. 4, nos. 6–8, pp. 396–422 (1959).

174. G. Naeser, "Optical Temperature Measurement of Luminous Hydrocarbon Flames," *J. Inst. Fuel*, **12**, no. 64, pp. S38–S41 (March, 1939).

14

ARC, PLASMA, UPPER-AIR, STELLAR, AND NUCLEAR-REACTOR TEMPERATURES

14·1 INTRODUCTION

In the preceding chapters, the principal methods and techniques of temperature-measurement have been described. In developing the various topics, these procedures have been applied to many engineering problems. The scope of the coverage has usually been limited to cases where available apparatus is well matured and where it can be hoped that such problems themselves may be of some general interest.

The present chapter is intended to outline and partially enumerate a large remaining scope of conditions and the techniques devised to cope with them. Some of the cases may be regarded as rather specialized; others are sufficiently complex to merit books in their own right. Further areas include those of unsolved problems and of controversial points. Here, lack of definite information prevents any satisfactory treatment.

14·2 ELECTRIC DISCHARGES VERSUS FLAMES

An electric spark or arc differs from a flame in the source of the energy. In a flame, energy is supplied by a chemical reaction, usually the oxidation of a fuel. In an electric discharge, such as an arc or a spark, the energy is that of electric power dissipated into heat. Charged particles, such as ions and free electrons, are accelerated in an electric field. They thus acquire kinetic energy from the electric-power source. On successive collisions with other particles, the energies of these directed motions tend to be distributed into the random pattern described by the Maxwell-Boltzmann law (see Eq. 13·1). In the collisions, the internal-energy states such as the electronic states may also be excited. Excitations then tend to the thermal pattern described by Boltzmann's law given as Eq. 12·1. However, wide departures from equilibrium commonly occur. Thus, the *electron temperature* corresponding to a Maxwell-Boltzmann velocity distribution among the free electrons may be many thousands of degrees higher than the kinetic temperature. The excitation temperatures among the internal energy states, in turn, may be higher than the kinetic temperature.[1,2]

The energy acquired by an individual particle is given by

$$K.E. = XeD \qquad (14 \cdot 1)$$

where X is the local magnitude of the electric-field intensity, dynes/esu of charge; e is the charge on the particle, i.e., the ion or free electron, esu; D is the mean free path between collisions, cm; and $K.E.$ is the acquired kinetic energy, ergs. The mean free path D can be increased almost indefinitely at high vacuo, and, by using sufficiently high differences of electric potential between electrodes, X can be made very large. Thus, the maximum energy per particle determining the possible size of the *quantum* $h\nu$ is almost without limit. In fact, for the *accelerators* used in *nuclear* studies, values measured in millions of *electron volts* are commonplace (1 electron volt = 1.6×10^{-12} erg).

On the other hand, temperatures in flames are limited to those for adiabatic combustion of fuels. One of the hottest commercial flames, that of the oxyacetylene blow torch, attains a peak temperature of around 6000°F (3580°K). Arcs and sparks, however, are not limited in this way. The temperatures attained depend merely on the amount of power dissipated in the discharge and on the concentration of the power dissipation in the arc volume. Hence, there is no theoretical limit to the temperature attainable, and magnitudes of over 50,000°K (89,540°F) have been measured.[3]

The sizes of the energy quanta in flames are limited by the reaction energies prorated over the individual pairs of combining particles. The average energy per particle can be computed as the reaction energy per mole divided by Avogadro's number (6.02×10^{23} particles per mole). Thus for a reaction energy of 100 kcal/mole, the energy per particle would be $100/(6.02 \times 10^{23})$ kcal = 0.7×10^{-11} erg = 4.3 electron volts.

Such magnitudes of energy suffice to excite the orbital-electronic states, to dissociate molecules into free atoms or complexes, and also to remove electrons from atoms. Resulting dissociation products usually have electric charges and are called ions. Free electrons also occur. However, removal of several electrons from within the same atom is not of widespread occurrence. Population densities of ions where the number of planetary electrons differs by more than one from that of the nuclear charge are relatively small in flames. In high-temperature arcs, however, not merely singly ionized atoms but doubly and triply ionized atoms may play important roles. Thus, a high-energy particle may remove one or several of the electrons from within an atom.[4]

This state of matter is sometimes described by the word *plasma*.

A plasma differs from a gas in that the neutral molecules characterizing a gas are replaced by a heterogeneous mixture of free electrons, neutral atoms, ions, and atomic nuclei with neutral molecules in declining proportions. Thus, at temperatures above 6000°K (10,340°F), the dissociation of molecules is almost complete.[5]

14·3 TEMPERATURES OF ARCS

Most of the methods described in the previous chapters for measurement of hot-gas and flame temperatures have been applied in arcs.[6]

Rudolph,[7] for example, used the fine-wire technique discussed in Secs. 8·10, 10·13, and 13·3 to measure the temperature in a *glow discharge*. He analyzed the errors expected to result from nonthermal energy exchanges between the wire and the ions, free electrons, and metastable atoms present in the arc plasma. By considering the effects of varied wire diameter, he was able to show that such errors would be acceptable. Likewise, the spectroscopic methods described in Ch. 13 have been widely used. However, in very high-temperature discharges, these methods require modification to account for the substantial ion populations which then occur.[2,3,7-19]

14·4 KINETIC TEMPERATURES OF ARCS

The Suits [20-24] velocity-of-sound technique was originally devised to measure the temperature of an electric arc (see Secs. 6·9, and 11·3 and 11·4). The pseudotemperature thus determined is the translational or kinetic temperature.

The schlieren method (see Sec. 11·11) appears particularly adaptable to the small size and transient character of most arcs and sparks. Sperling,[25] for example, has combined the use of sensitive schlieren technique with an ingenious heat-flow analysis to determine radial temperature distributions in carbon arcs. He thus found temperatures in the range from 370°K (206°F) at a 1.4-cm (0.55-in.) radial distance from the arc axis up to 4400°K (7460°F) at a 0.2-cm (0.08-in.) radius.

Schmitz [26] has applied the Mach-Zehnder-interferometer technique described in Sec. 11·10 to measure temperature patterns in carbon arcs. The values he obtained ranged from room temperature at a centimeter from the axis to a maximum of 7000°K (12,140°F).

Peters [3,27] has demonstrated that, despite the appreciable concentrations of ions and free electrons in arcs, the equations of state for ideal-gas behavior may still apply. Thus, at 10,000°K (17,540°F), he found essentially ideal behavior for pressures as high as 1000 atm. The density technique described in Secs. 8·7 and 11·2 can hence be applied in the measurement of arc temperatures.

Ecker [28] has used this principle to determine the temperature of a water-stabilized mercury arc. The pressure was directly indicated. To measure the local values of the density, he mixed a uniform concentration of the radioactive mercury isotope Hg^{203} with the mercury of the arc. In its *halflife* of 43.5 days, the radioactive component emits β and γ *radiation*. The local source intensities for such radiation were then proportional to the numbers per unit volume of the radioactive atoms. Since their numbers were in fixed proportion to the total numbers, they were in proportion to the density. To compute the gas constant R in Eqs. 6·19 to 6·21, 8·12, and 8·13, it is necessary to know the concentrations of free electrons and of the various-molecular-weight ions present in the arc gas. Saha's equation provides a means for making this determination. Thus

$$N_i = A p^{1/2} T^{1/4} e^{-E_i/2kT} \tag{14·2}$$

where N_i is the number of ions of the ith variety per unit volume, cm^{-3}; p is the pressure, atm; T is the absolute temperature, °K; e is the natural-logarithmic base; E_i is the ionization energy for the ith variety, ergs; k is Boltzmann's constant, 1.38×10^{-16} erg/°K; and the factor A includes the statistical weights.[28-33]

Since T occurs in this expression, a value must be assumed and subsequently corrected in an iterative process. The radiation is measured by a *Geiger* counter. The counter is calibrated on a uniform mixture of known Hg^{203} concentration. Only a sketch of this ingenious technique is intended to have been given here. For a full account, the reader is referred to Ecker's [28] original paper.

Using this procedure, Ecker [28] found radial temperature distributions ranging from about 6200°K (10,700°F) on the arc axis down to 1000°K (1340°F) at a distance of 1 cm.

Kenty [34,35] determined the average temperature in a mercury-vapor lamp by merely observing the vapor pressure and weighing the mercury contained in a known bulb volume. He and Karash [34] also measured this temperature by the X-ray absorption technique (see Secs. 11·12 and 11·13).

Burhorn [3,36] applied the technique of Doppler-effect line broadening (see Sec. 13·7). In addition to the other causes for line broadening, which must be considered when using this method in flames, the *Stark-effect* line broadening occurs in an arc plasma. In this phenomenon, the space-charge density arising from the populations of free electrons and ions behaves similarly to the imposed electric field used to effect line splitting in the ordinary Stark effect. The result is a calculable line broadening. Burhorn found the 4302-Å lines in the iron spectrum relatively free of this and other causes of broadening. For quantitative results, he required a spectrometer of very high resolving power, i.e., of $\lambda/\Delta\lambda = 1.5 \times 10^6$ where λ is the wavelength, μ, and $\Delta\lambda$ is the unresolved wavelength range, μ. A simultaneous observation was made of the electron temperature in this arc by using a method similar to that described by Hett and Gilstein for use with flames. Here, the intensity of the background-continuum radiation is the criterion. The Hett-Gilstein method is described in Sec. 13·21.

14·5 ELECTRON TEMPERATURES

The electron temperature in a plasma is analogous to the kinetic temperature in a gas. The kinetic temperature is based on the mean kinetic energy in translational motion of the gas molecules, when the velocity pattern accords with the Maxwell-Boltzmann law (see Eq. 13·1). The electron temperature is described by the same law where the particles are the free electrons. The spin energy of the electron is constant; hence, the only temperature is that for translational motion. Because of the small mass and the resulting high mobility for free electrons, the relaxation times are short. The likelihood of statistical equilibrium among the free electrons is correspondingly high.

Burhorn's [3,36] data indicate a close approximation to equilibrium between the electron temperature and the kinetic temperature as measured by Doppler broadening for his free-burning 6300°K (10,880°F) iron arcs. Speaking of high-pressure high-temperature arcs, Glaser [2] has noted that relaxation times among the free electrons are of the order of 10^{-13} sec and therefore that thermal equilibrium for an electron temperature is to be expected even in the most highly transient phenomena. He, however, finds that about 10^{-5} sec must elapse before equilibrium is established between the electron temperature and the kinetic temperature for the ions and neutral atoms. Bitter and Waymouth [1] note that in low-pressure discharges the electron temperature may be many thousands of degrees above the gas or ion temperature. Bayet and Guerineau [37] found electron temperatures in high-frequency discharges to be in true *Maxwellian distributions*, i.e., in accord with Eq. 13·1 at temperatures up to 35,800°K (64,000°F).[1-3, 16, 36-40]

In a vacuum electron tube, the electric current from the cathode to the plate or first grid occurs as a mass or drift motion in the *electron cloud*, i.e., *space charge*, emitted by the hot cathode. In addition to the space current flowing under the local electric-field intensity caused by the electric-potential difference between the cathode and the plate, there is the random or thermal motion of the free electrons. The electron temperature corresponds to the energy in the random motion. Here, the electron temperature is the temperature, not a pseudotemperature. Obviously, in a plasma that consists exclusively of free electrons, no other temperature can arise.

In a plane-electrode vacuum diode, the Boltzmann law describes the relation between the *plate current* and the temperature in the random motion of the electrons. For currents well below *saturation* values,

$$T = (e/k)(V + A)/(\log i + B) \tag{14.3}$$

where i is the plate current, amp; e is the electron charge, -1.6×10^{-19} coulomb; V is the (retarding) plate potential, v; k is Boltzmann's constant, 1.38×10^{-23} j/°K; T is the electron temperature, °K; and A and B are constants at any one temperature. When V plotted against $\log i$ yields a straight-line graph (for currents below the saturation value), the slope of this line is proportional to the electron temperature T. Departures from straightness in the line may be indicative of sources of error, as, for example, those due to deviations from flatness in the electrodes.

Determinations by this method have indicated that the electron temperature may differ by several hundred degrees from that of the solid-cathode material. For a full account of this technique, the reader is referred to the original papers.[41-46]

14·6 POPULATION TEMPERATURES IN ARCS

In flames, the spectroscopic measurement of temperatures is based on Boltzmann's law

$$N_1/N_2 = (g_1/g_2)e^{-(E_1 - E_2)/kT} \tag{12.1}$$

where N_1 is the number of members of a group occupying the energy state E_1; N_2 is the number occupying state E_2; E_1 and E_2 are the excitation energies for the two states, respectively, ergs; g_1 and g_2 are the a priori probabilities or statistical weights for these two states; k is Boltzmann's constant, 1.38×10^{-16} erg/°K; T is the absolute temperature, °K; and e is the natural-logarithmic base. The frequency ν of the spectral line arising from a transition between energy states E_1 and E_2 is given by

$$\nu = (E_1 - E_2)/h \tag{13.2}$$

where ν is in cycles/sec; and h is Planck's constant, 6.625×10^{-27} erg sec. The intensity of such a spectral line, as given by Eq. 13·6, is proportional to the number N_1 of energy states from which this transition can occur. In other words, the line intensity is proportional to the population density of such energy states, and the Boltzmann relationship between the population and the Kelvin temperature is the basis of the measurement. For this reason, temperatures so determined are called *population temperatures.*

The above procedure assumes that the population of atoms or molecules available to be thus excited remains essentially constant. The Boltzmann law then describes the distribution of these energy states within a fixed population of similar particles. In a high-temperature arc, however, the population is not fixed but is itself a function of the temperature.

When an atom is ionized by the removal of an electron, the electric-potential distribution is altered in the internal structure of the atom. In consequence, each of the various energy states is changed in value, and a given frequency ν, which might be the basis of measurement for a population temperature, is no longer emitted by the ionized particle. The result is that with rising temperatures the number of atoms or molecules capable of radiating the particular frequency declines. Although the proportion which is suitably excited continues to increase with rising temperatures, the total number of the excited states also enters into a decline. The effect is that the intensity of a given spectral line increases with temperature up to a certain maximum and thereafter diminishes as the temperature continues to rise.[29-33,47]

This phenomenon is illustrated by the Larenz [14,15] theoretical curves of Fig. 14·1. The initial rise with increasing temperature accords with Boltzmann's law. At the maximum, the increasing excitation is balanced by the decline due to ionization. The intensity drops off thereafter. A second peak results from the growing population of *singly ionized* particles (one electron removed). As they are reduced by *double* ionization (two electrons removed), the second curve passes through a maximum and declines. In the meantime, the third curve for the doubly ionized particles rises, passes through its maximum, and declines. Thus, successive peaks of radiant intensity correspond to a definite series of progressively higher temperatures.[14-17,36]

Bartels [16,17] and Larenz [14,15] proposed identifying the successive peaks of radiation as a means of measuring high temperatures. This procedure was carried out by van Calker and Braunisch [13] for individual spectral lines and by Busz-Peuckert and Queisser [12] for total radiation. Burhorn,[3,36] Maeckler,[3] and Peters [3,27] used this technique to plot the radial-temperature-pattern isothermals for arcs where currents ranged from 100 to 1500 amps. Measured peak temperatures exceeded $50,000°K$ ($89,540°F$).

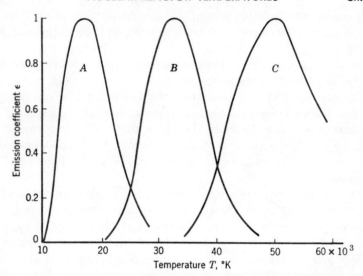

Fig. 14·1. Emission coefficient for oxygen arcs at 1 atm. A, 6046-Å line for oxygen; B, 4650-Å line for singly ionized oxygen, and C, 3347-Å line for doubly ionized oxygen. (*After R. W. Larenz, Zeitschrift für Physik,* **129,** *no. 3, 339, 1951.*)

Busz-Peuckert and Queisser [12] performed a comparison study on three argon arcs operated at different amperages. The temperature of the first arc was measured by both the spectroscopic and X-ray absorption methods, the calibration being conducted up to temperatures of about 16,000°K (28,340°F). The radiation patterns in all three arcs were recorded by blackening on the same photographic plate. Successive peaks were identified on this plate by recognizing that temperatures become progressively higher toward the centers of the arcs. Thus, the second peak was used to plot the 28,000°K (49,940°F) isothermal (see Fig. 14·1B).[12, 24]

For the argon arcs, Busz-Peuckert and Queisser [12] showed that the total-radiant intensity is a monotonic function of temperature up to about 16,000°K (28,340°F), whereas the peak-to-peak method is found to be accurate only to within about ±10 per cent. Merely a bare suggestion of the idea is intended to be indicated here. For the full theory and the various procedures, the reader is referred to the original papers.[3, 12-17]

14·7 STARK-EFFECT LINE BROADENING

Peters [3, 27] has used the Stark-effect broadening (see also Sec. 14·4) of the H_β line to determine arc temperatures. The values found ranged up to 12,000°K (21,140°F) at pressures of 1000 atm. Dickerman has used this method to measure plasma temperatures in the range from 10,000 to 20,000°K (18,000 to 36,000°R) with an estimated sensitivity to within ±5 per cent. Comparison of the measured line contour (see Fig. 13·1) with that corresponding to the theory of this cause for line broadening provides a means of calculating the ion concentration in the arc plasma. The ion concentration together with the measured value for the pressure is substituted into Saha's equation (Eq. 14·2) to compute the temperature T, °K. The pseudotemperature thus determined is the ionization temperature. Obviously, the same high resolution is required of the spectrometer as in the case of temperature determinations by the Doppler-effect broadening (see Secs. 13·7 and 14·4). For the full theory and procedure, however, the reader is referred to the body of original papers listed by Peters,[3, 27] Dickerman,[49] and others.[3, 16, 18, 27, 29, 36, 48-50]

14·8 UPPER-AIR AND STELLAR TEMPERATURES

Temperature measurement in the heavenly regions is complicated by the inaccessibility of the distant portions of the universe. Sounding balloons can ascend only to a certain limited height. Acoustic waves and searchlight beams emitted from ground stations can penetrate further. Self-propelled rockets can transcend the atmosphere altogether. However, stellar bodies and interstellar space are observable solely by the radiation they emit. Dark stars are little known and to be inferred only by their gravitational effects on visible stars and when their presence in the line of sight intercepts the view. Their temperatures are a subject for speculation. Visible stars are vast brilliantly incandescent masses. Because of their own gravitational fields, the inner cores of such masses are under great pressures and at correspondingly high densities. These densities are those of the solid state. At the prevailing internal temperatures, crystalline structure is not to be expected; however, the densities provide for effectively solid-body radiation. In fact, radiation coming from the interiors of stars is regarded as in accord with Planck's law.[50-53]

Among the outer layers, pressures are not so great, and any semblance to the solid state progressively diminishes until at the "margins" there is a merging into the extremely tenuous condition of matter characteristic of interstellar space. The vast stellar masses are sometimes described as "gaseous"; however, they consist of mixtures of free atoms, ions, atomic nuclei, free electrons, protons, neutrons, etc. This state of matter is denoted by the term *plasma*.[40, 53]

Radiation emanating from the interior of a star is partially absorbed in the outer layers. At the lower densities of the outer layers, the absorption tends to be in discontinuous spectra with well-defined absorption lines corresponding to those energy transitions possible for the constituents of this envelope. The background continua for the spectra of the outer layers are, however, also important. So much of the original continuous spectra is absorbed that the net emission from the "surface" of the star does not at all correspond to that for the internal temperatures. Such temperatures can only be determined by calculations as to what the radiation might have been before the absorption occurred.[53]

14·9 METHODS OF MEASURING STELLAR TEMPERATURES

Procedures for measuring temperatures by observing the amount and spectral distribution of the radiant energy emitted by a body have been described at various points in this volume. Chapter 4 was devoted to methods based on Planck's law for solid-body radiation. Chapters 8, 11, and 13 discussed the special problems for measurements in semi-transparent media. Both emission and absorption spectra were employed as means for indication of temperature. A method based on the broadening of spectral lines due to the Doppler effect was discussed. In the sections on arcs and sparks of the present chapter, there has been further elaboration of the population-temperature method. These modifications were shown to be necessary at the higher temperatures achieved in electric discharges. The Stark-effect line broadening due to the electric-charge densities prevalent in plasmas has been mentioned.

All of the above methods are used in the measurement of temperatures in the stellar regions; however, certain limitations in their application are imposed upon the astronomer. He cannot place apparatus on both sides of the specimen as is done, for example, in the sodium-line-reversal method; nor can he introduce coloring materials into the stellar media, such as the sodium therein employed. He must observe what he can by looking from one side only. Furthermore, he must view his source bodies through the earth's atmosphere and through the intermediate portions of interstellar space. The absorption in these regions is selective. Both the amount and the spectral distribution of the original radiation is modified. Much is known about the absorption characteristics of the earth's atmosphere, and calculated corrections are possible; however, the optical properties of the vaster distances in interstellar space are not equally well established. Color patterns and intensity ratios observed in spectra may then be attributed alternatively to the temperature of the star under consideration or to selective absorption along the optical path from the star to the measuring instrument. Much uncertainty is thus inevitable in the interpretation of results.[53-61]

14·10 SURFACE AND INTERNAL TEMPERATURES OF STARS

The sun is a star which is near enough to permit accurate measurement of its surface area and thereby determinations of its surface *brightness*. Measurements of the *solar-radiation constant*, corrected for absorption in the earth's atmosphere, lead to values of the total hemispherical radiant emission per unit area of the sun's surface. The assumption of unit emissivity, in accord with the known nonreflectivity of gaseous masses, then permits a computation of temperature by application of the Stefan-Boltzmann law (Eq. 4·1). Values found range from 5000 to 7000°K (8540 to 12,140°F) with lower values, i.e., 3800 to 5800°K (6380 to 9980°F) for the solar atmosphere.[56, 62-64]

Attempts to infer the internal temperature of a star depend on assumptions as to its structure. With a given theory as to its constitution and internal gravitational pattern, calculations can be made of the expected density and composition gradients. From them, the radial variation of the absorption coefficient is estimated. Finally, an internal temperature pattern is postulated which, after absorption of the emitted *Planckian radiation* during transmission through the successive outer layers, results in the observed surface brightness. Couteau [65] in a determination by a similar technique has obtained a value of the order of 620,000°K (1,116,000°F) for the *effective* temperature of a white-dwarf star. Kuiper [53] cites internal-temperature determinations for stars of up to 50,000,000°C (90,000,000°F).[51-53, 65]

14·11 POPULATION TEMPERATURES FOR STELLAR MEDIA

It has been noted in Sec. 14·6 that, at the temperatures attained in very intense arcs, Boltzmann's law (Eq. 12·1) no longer holds. The factor $e^{-(E_1-E_2)/kT}$ continues to describe that fraction of a given group N_2 of similar atoms that will be excited from the ground state E_2 to the energy state E_1 at the temperature T, °K. However, the number N_2 of atoms having the energy states E_1 and E_2 is reduced by ionization at progressively higher temperatures. In the temperature range 10,000 to 50,000°K (17,540 to 89,540°F), the two mechanisms have been observed to function in roughly equal importance.[29-33, 47, 62]

At the higher temperatures found for ions in the solar corona, the Boltzmann factor $e^{-(E_1-E_2)/kT}$ ceases to be important. Thus, when T is greater than 100,000°K (179,540°F), for the values of $E_1 - E_2$ corresponding to excited energy states within an atom, the ratio

$(E_1 - E_2)/kT$ becomes small because of the large values of T, and the exponential $e^{-(E_1-E_2)/kT}$ approaches unity. As such, this factor is of little further use for temperature measurement. An incident energy quantum, as supplied by electron impact at these higher temperatures, usually suffices to remove an electron from the atom. However, the ionization energy E_i required depends on the ionized state attained. Thus, Biermann's formula

$$N_{p+1}/N_p = A(T/E_i^2)e^{-E_i/kT} \qquad (14\cdot4)$$

arises where N_{p+1} is the number in the $(p+1)$th ionized state, cm^{-3}; N_p is the number in the pth ionized state, cm^{-3}; E_i is the ionization energy, ergs; k is Boltzmann's constant, 1.38×10^{-16} erg/°K; e is the natural logarithmic base; T is the temperature, °K; and A is a constant (see also Saha's equation, Eq. 14·2).[29-33, 47, 62, 63]

The energy distribution resulting in the intensity ratio I_2/I_1 for a pair of spectral lines is described by

$$I_2/I_1 = BN_2/N_1 \qquad (14\cdot5)$$

where N_1 and N_2 are the numbers of ions per cm^3 emitting the lines of intensities I_1 and I_2, respectively, w; and the coefficient B includes the effect of the Boltzmann factor.[28, 29, 31-33, 47]

Waldmeier [47] has applied this technique to measure ionization temperatures in the solar corona using pairs of iron lines at 5303 and 6374 Å (0.5303 and 0.6374 μ), respectively. The temperature patterns he observed are in the range from 400,000 to 830,000°K (719,600 to 1,494,000°F). These values are in accord with those reported for electron temperatures, which tends to support Waldmeier's view that the ionization occurs by electron impact.[47, 62, 63]

Above 1,500,000°K (2,700,000°F), the factor $e^{-E_i/kT}$ tends to approach unity. Thus, kT becomes large with respect to the ionization energies E_i, and the method becomes insensitive.[47, 62]

14·12 TEMPERATURE OF INTERSTELLAR MATTER

The regions of space between the stars and nebulae are not voids, as has sometimes been fancied, but are occupied by a dispersion of matter. The individual particles range from free electrons, protons, ions, neutral atoms, and molecules to small solid bodies. The mean densities, although varying over wide ranges, are exceedingly low; 5×10^{-22} g/cm^3 has been suggested as a possible value. The number concentration in the particles is indicated by such figures as those in the range from 10^{-2} to 10^2 hydrogen atoms per cm^3. One atom per cm^3 is sometimes regarded as a median value. The solid particles may be metallic or nonmetallic bodies but usually do not exceed around 10^{-5} cm in diameter. Energy is received from the stars, and a color temperature for the energy density of radiation has been taken as about 10,000, 15,000, or 40,000°K (17,540, 26,540, or 71,540°F). The energy is assumed to be transferred to the particles by means of the photoelectric effect. In this mechanism, radiant photons are absorbed by the atoms in the particles, and photoelectrons are ejected with energies corresponding to those of the incident photons. The electron energies are those of translatory motion and are shared in collisions among all the particles. Collisions are infrequent by ordinary standards, and translational relaxation times may be 10^4 or 10^5 years; disturbances such as photoelectric emissions are also of relatively rare occurrence. In the balance, translational equilibrium is usually assumed to prevail.[66, 67]

Energy losses occur by inelastic collisions among the electrons and atoms and the ions and molecules. Translational energy is converted to that of radiation, and the emitted photons then carry off what had been local kinetic energy to remote portions of space. Collisions between clouds of interstellar gases have also been assumed to be sources of kinetic energy.[66–68]

Kinetic temperatures have been estimated by careful but somewhat speculative calculations of the balance point between the energy-gain and energy-loss processes. Direct measurements have also been made by using the spectral-line emission at a wavelength of 21 cm. Radio-receiving circuits serve as the sensitive elements. Apparently, at this very long wavelength, scattering losses are less, and amplifiers suffice to permit indication of the weak radiant signals. A temperature of 125°K (−235°F) for interstellar matter was measured by this method.[66–70]

Although the translatory motions of the grains of solid matter are assumed to be in accord with the kinetic temperature, their internal temperatures as manifested in lattice vibrations, etc., are thought to be much lower. Estimates have been in the order of 10 to 20°K (18 to 36°R) for dielectric spheres and 30 to 100°K (54 to 180°R) for metallic spheres.[66, 67]

14·13 NEBULAE

Nebulae are described by astronomers as luminous areas in the night sky. The regions in space from which this radiation emanates are supposed to be occupied not only by gases and plasma at low densities but also by new stars in formation and in decline. Nebular structure is too complex a subject, however, for discussion here. Temperature determinations for radiation emitted from nebulae range to high values.[71-74]

14·14 UPPER-AIR TEMPERATURES

In accord with thermodynamic theory, it had long been supposed that temperatures declined with elevation in the atmosphere. Rising air currents, expanding adiabatically with the decrease in pressure, would cool and tend to maintain lower temperatures at high altitudes; this conclusion had been verified by the observations of mountain climbers. However, on the occasion of Queen Victoria's funeral in London in 1901, minute guns fired as part of the ceremony were heard distinctly in London and recognized far to the north, but the two areas of audibility were separated by a skip zone of silence. A sound wave tends to be refracted into a region of lower temperature. It was a matter of surprise, therefore, that the sound waves from the gunfire were apparently bent back to the earth as though the air at high altitudes were warmer. In succeeding decades, similar observations were reported elsewhere in Europe. Direct measurements now permit exploration of these interesting upper-air temperature patterns. However, space here will barely permit the enumeration of the ingenious techniques used.[75]

Perhaps the most direct procedure has been to mount a recording gas-temperature probe on a rocket fired to high altitudes, i.e., up to perhaps 75 km (46.6 miles). The design of such probes is discussed in Ch. 10 and need not be repeated here. Data are *telemetered* to the ground as taken, and they may also be recorded on film which is recovered when the missile returns to the earth.[76]

In the *falling-sphere method,* a strong inflatable balloon, containing instrumentation and a gas cylinder for its inflation, is discharged from a rocket at high altitude. On release, it is automatically inflated to a rigid sphere, and its internal instruments begin telemetering data indicating the rate of fall. The *drag coefficient* for the spherical body and its weight then permit local-temperature determinations from the instantaneous fall rates at the various altitudes.[77, 78]

In the *rocket-grenade* method, rockets ascending to high altitudes eject grenades which then explode at successive heights. The times of these effectively instantaneous sound-source flashes are recorded by ground photocells and by the telemetered indications of rocket-borne photocells. The positions of the explosions in space were determined by photographing the grenade flashes against the star field of the night sky. Three plate cameras were used at carefully *surveyed* locations.

The times and locations of the sound sources and the differences in arrival times of the sound waves at the ground stations permitted calculation of the velocities of sound in the space intervals between grenade explosions. From the values of the local velocity of sound, upper-air temperatures were determined.[79]

In the searchlight technique, a powerful narrow beam is projected into the night sky. A parabolic mirror is then focused on a short section of the path of this beam at successive heights. Light scattered by the air at these locations is concentrated on a photocell by the mirror. The measured scattered-light intensities are proportional to the local values of the upper-air densities, and the local temperatures are inversely proportional to the densities. However, quantitative temperature determinations must be based on sound-balloon calibration data taken at the lower altitudes accessible to such balloons (see Eq. 8·2). [80, 82]

Observations made by the various methods have confirmed the suspected cause of the phenomenon observed at the time of Queen Victoria's funeral. Upper-air temperatures are found to decline to minimum values at around 15 or 20 km (9.3 or 12.4 miles) and thereafter to rise to maxima at around 50 km (31.1 miles). Minimum values may be as low as $200°K$ ($-100°F$), whereas maxima of up to $320°K$ ($116°F$) are found.[75-82]

14·15 NUCLEAR-REACTOR TEMPERATURES

Fundamentally, the problems for *nuclear explosions* are the same as those for stellar bodies. The relatively small sizes, however, tend not to provide the opaque depths and approximations to internal equilibrium which occur, for example, with our sun. On the other hand, close-range observations are possible on a small-scale basis.

The absorption of *neutrons* is known to depend on both the thickness of the absorbing layer and on the velocities of the neutrons. This relationship permits experiments in which the mean velocity and the velocity distribution in a *neutron beam* can be investigated. Approximations to *Maxwellian velocity distributions* are found by which temperatures can be assigned to the neutron beams.[83-88]

Targets and various other solid members in nuclear apparatus are subject to radiation of high-energy particles. Consequently, thermocouples installed for the measurement of the solid-body temperatures are exposed to the effects of such radiation, and it has been a matter of concern as to whether thermoelectric emfs would be altered by *radiation damage*. Controlled experiments have, however, shown that any such effects are small, i.e., small enough ordinarily to be negligible in comparison to other errors. However, prolonged exposure may effect composition changes in certain alloys.[89-93]

14·16 GASES WITH ENTRAINED PARTICLES

Flue gases usually contain varying amounts of *fly ash*. It may be in the molten condition as globules of liquid, or it may be in semisolid particles and coarse dust. This entrained matter tends to congeal on thermometer elements inserted in the stream. Shielded aspirated units tend to become clogged, so that design and servicing arrangements must be oriented to the problem. Solid dust particles at high speeds may have serious abrasive effects as well. In common, however, with the suspended carbon particles in luminous flames and depending on their average size (see Sec. 13·19), these solid, molten, and semimolten particles may be nearly in thermal equilibrium with the gases. Hence, temperature indications usually constitute valid measurements.

In *wet steam* and in the mixtures of gasoline spray occurring in the intake manifolds of internal-combustion engines, a different problem arises. Here, the entrained particles are of liquid in coexistence with the vapor phase. If the vapor is at the saturation density, thermodynamic equilibrium will prevail and the temperatures will be the same for both the droplets and the vapor. However, in a flow process where velocities and pressures are changing, the temperatures of the droplets may lag behind those corresponding to the vapor densities. Thus, during expansions the droplets will be evaporating, and during compressions they will be growing with accumulated condensate. In either case, their temperatures will differ from those of the vapor or of the gas-vapor mixtures.[94-97]

A solid thermometer element immersed in a stream containing evaporating or condensing droplets assumes a temperature intermediate between that of the gas-vapor stream and that of the droplets. The liquid phase tends to accumulate on the surface of the thermometer elements; thus, some approximation to the *wet-bulb temperature* may be indicated.[94-97]

Bayle (see Sec. 5·15) has described a radiation technique for measuring the water-droplet temperatures of clouds in the sky. Here, opaque depths occur. Perhaps, similar technique might be attempted by a Kurlbaum-type procedure at the wavelength for maximum absorption in the semitransparent layers which occur in mechanical apparatus. However, efforts to measure liquid-vapor-mixture stream temperatures with solid thermometers have been attended by little success. Furthermore, erroneous results have been sources of disturbing confusion.[94-97]

14·17 MEASUREMENTS AT HIGH AND LOW PRESSURES

For bodies at high pressures and in vacuo, leads to thermometer elements must usually pass through the walls of a vessel, or, if radiation technique is being used, pressure resistant windows must be provided. A correspondingly extensive assortment of stuffing-box and window-mounting technique has been described, some material for which is commercially available from the Conax Corporation (Buffalo, New York).[98-105]

14·18 OTHER PROBLEMS

Temperature measurements in solar-energy furnaces, agricultural research, biological and medical studies, and almost innumerable other situations have occupied the attention of workers in these fields. Some of the problems have been illustrated at scattered points in this book. For others, unfortunately, no space has been found, leaving the reader recourse only to the references listed.[106-126]

14·19 CONCLUSION

In this chapter a number of problems have been briefly enumerated. They are mostly either beyond the scope of the book or outside the achievements of available technique. Recourse to the references will provide the reader with access to much of the information that exists and which, due to its complexity, appears impractical for any attempted inclusion in the present volume.

REFERENCES *

1. F. Bitter and J. F. Waymouth, "Radiation Temperature of a Plasma," *J. Opt. Soc. Am.*, **46**, no. 10, pp. 882–884 (October, 1956).
2. G. Glaser, "Über die Erzeugung sehr hoher Temperaturen im Hochleistungs-funken" (On the Production of Very High Temperatures in High-Power Sparks), *Zeitschrift für Naturforschung*, **6a**, no. 11, pp. 706–713 (November, 1951).
3. F. Burhorn, H. Maeckler, and T. Peters, "Temperaturmessungen am Wasser-stabilisierten Hochleistungsbogen" (Temperature Measurements in Water Stabilized Heavily Loaded Arcs), *Zeitschrift für Physik*, **131**, no. 1, pp. 28–40 (1951).
4. F. L. Mohler, "Concepts of Temperature in Electric Discharge Phenomena," American Institute of Physics, *Temperature*, pp. 734–744, Reinhold Publishing Corp., New York, 1941.

---

* See footnote on page 26.

5. R. Landshoff, "Plasma Dynamics," *Physics Today*, **12**, no. 12, pp. 18–24 (December, 1958).

6. C. W. Waidner and G. K. Burgess, "On the Temperature of the Arc," *Bulletin of the Bureau of Standards*, **1**, no. 1, pp. 109–124 (November, 1904).

7. G. Rudolph, "Temperaturmessungen in einer Glimmentladung" (Temperature Measurements in a Glow Discharge), *Zeitschrift für Physik*, **111**, nos. 7–8, pp. 523–534 (January, 1939).

8. E. M. Akimov and I. P. Malkov, "Determination of the Temperature of a Spark in Vacuum" (in Russian), *Optika i Spektroskopiya—Akademiya Nauk SSSR*, **6**, no. 1, pp. 96–98 (January, 1959); *Sci. Abstr. A*, **62**, no. 743, p. 1162 (December, 1959).

9. A. Vassy, H. Norinder, and E. Vassy, "Spectres d'étincelles sous trés haute tension dans l'air et températures de couleur" (On the Spectra and Color Temperature of Very High Voltage Sparks in Air), *Compt. rend.*, **234**, no. 20, pp. 1957–1959 (May, 1952).

10. K. N. Mochalov, A. Y. Nikiforon, and A. S. Bogonostsev, "The Problem of the Temperature of the Torch Discharge" (in Russian), *J. Exptl. Theoret. Phys. USSR*, **20**, pp. 474–477 (May, 1950).

11. Y. A. Kalashnikov and L. F. Vereshchagin, "Temperature Measurement at High Pressures by the Emission Method and Some Optical Phenomena Occurring in Gases Under these Conditions" (in Russian), *Zhurnal Tekhnicheskoi Fiziki—Akademiya Nauk SSSR*, **26**, no. 8, pp. 1802–1814 (1956); *Sci. Abstr. A*, **60**, no. 711, p. 200 (March, 1957).

12. G. Busz-Peuckert and H. J. Queisser, "Zur Bestimmung der Temperatur von Lichtbögen durch Scharzungvergleich mit einem ähnlichen Bogen bekannter Temperaturverteilung" (The Determination of the Temperature of Arcs by Photographic Blackening Comparison with a Similar Arc of Known Temperature Distribution), *Zeitschrift für Naturforschung*, **11a**, no. 6, pp. 513–514 (June, 1956).

13. J. van Calker and H. Braunisch, "Über spektroskopische Temperaturmessungen an kondensierten Funkenentladungen" (On the Spectroscopic Measurement of the Temperature of Condensed Spark Discharges), *Zeitschrift für Naturforschung*, **11a**, no. 7, pp. 612–613 (July, 1956).

14. R. W. Larenz, "Über ein Verfahren zur Messung sehr hoher Temperaturen in nahezu durchlässigen Bogensäulen" (On a Procedure for Measuring Very High Temperatures in Nearly Transparent Arcs), *Zeitschrift für Physik*, **129**, no. 3, pp. 327–342 (1951).

15. R. W. Larenz, "Temperaturmessungen in der Säule eines Gerdien-Bogens" (Measurements of Column Temperature in Gerdien Arcs), *Zeitschrift für Physik*, **129**, no. 3, pp. 343–364 (1951).

16. H. Bartels, "Der Einfluss erzwungener Übergänge und starker kontinuierlicher Emission auf die Linienkontur bei inhomogener Schicht" (The Influence of Forced Transitions and Strong Continuous Emission on the Line Contours for Inhomogeneous Layers), *Zeitschrift für Physik*, **136**, pp. 411–440 (1953).

17. H. Bartels, "Eine neue Methode zur Temperaturmessung an hochtemperierten Bogensäulen" (A New Method of Temperature Measurement in High-Temperature Arc Discharges), Parts I and II, *Zeitschrift für Physik*, **127**, no. 3, pp. 243–273 (1950); and **128**, no. 4, pp. 546–574 (1950).

18. W. Göing, "Bestimmung der radialen Temperaturverteilung von Hg-Höchstdruckbögen aus den Kuppenstrahldichten selbstumgekehrten Linien" (Meas-

urement of the Radial Temperature Variations in Very-High-Pressure Mercury Arcs from the Peak Intensities of Self-Absorbed Spectral Lines), *Zeitschrift für Physik,* **131,** no. 4, pp. 603–618 (1952).

19. W. Elenbaas, "On the Excitation Temperature the Gas Temperature and the Electron Temperature in the High-Pressure Mercury Discharge," *Philips Research Reports,* **2,** no. 1, R 33, pp. 20–41 (February, 1947).

20. C. G. Suits, "The Determination of Arc Temperature from Sound Velocity Measurements. I and II," *Physics,* **6,** no. 6, pp. 190–195 and 196–202 (June, 1935).

21. C. G. Suits, "High-Temperature Gas Measurements in Arcs," American Institute of Physics, *Temperature,* pp. 720–733, Reinhold Publishing Corp., New York, 1941.

22. C. G. Suits, "A Study of Arc Temperatures by an Optical Method," *Physics,* **6,** no. 10, pp. 315–322 (October, 1935).

23. C. G. Suits, "The Temperature of the Copper Arc," *Proceedings of the National Academy of Sciences,* **21,** no. 1, pp. 48–50 (January, 1935).

24. C. G. Suits, "The Temperature of High Pressure Arcs," *J. Appl. Phys.,* **10,** no. 10, pp. 728–729 (October, 1939).

25. J. Sperling, "Das Temperaturfeld im freien Kohlebogen" (The Temperature Field of a Free-Burning Carbon Arc), *Zeitschrift für Physik,* **129,** no. 5, pp. 269–278 (1950).

26. G. Schmitz, "Zur Temperaturverteilung im freibrennenden Kohlelichtbogen" (On the Temperature Distribution in a Free-Burning Carbon Arc), *Zeitschrift für Physik,* **126,** nos. 1 and 2, pp. 1–11 (1949).

27. T. Peters, "Temperatur- und Strahlungsmessungen am wasserstabilisierten Hochdruckbogen" (Temperature and Radiation Measurements on a Water-Stabilized High-Pressure Arc), *Zeitschrift für Physik,* **135,** no. 5, pp. 573–592 (1953).

28. G. Ecker, "Messung der Temperaturverteilung im Innern eines wandstabilisierten Bogens mit Hilfe des radioaktiven Quecksilberisotopes ^{203}Hg" (The Measurement of the Temperature Distribution within a Wall-Stabilized Arc with the Aid of the Radioactive Hg^{203} Isotope), *Zeitschrift für Physik,* **130,** no. 5, pp. 585–604 (1951).

29. O. Koch and H. Dunstadter, "Ein Beitrag zur Temperaturbestimmung im wandstabilisierten Quecksilberhochdruckbogen" (A Contribution to the Measurement of Temperature in a Wall-Stabilized High-Pressure Mercury Arc), *Zeitschrift für Physik,* **129,** no. 2, pp. 140–147 (1951).

30. J. A. Smit, "The Determination of Temperature from Spectra," *Physica,* **10,** no. 6, pp. 683–700 (December, 1946).

31. E. Sänger, P. Goercke, and I. Bredt, "On Ionization and Luminescence in Flames," *Technical Memorandum* 1305, U. S. National Advisory Committee for Aeronautics, Washington (June, 1949).

32. S. C. Brown and W. P. Allis, "Motions of Electrons and Ions in Gases," American Institute of Physics, *American Institute of Physics Handbook,* pp. 7.174–7.219, McGraw-Hill Book Co., New York, 1957.

33. F. K. Richtmyer, E. H. Kennard, and T. Lauritsen, *Introduction to Modern Physics,* pp. 158–169, 648–650, McGraw-Hill Book Co., New York, 1955.

34. C. Kenty and W. J. Karash, "X-Ray Determination of Hg Arc Temperature," *Phys. Rev.,* **78,** no. 5, pp. 625–626 (June, 1950).

35. C. Kenty, "The Temperature of the Mercury Arc," *Phys. Rev.,* **78,** no. 5, pp. 626–627 (June, 1950).

36. F. Burhorn, "Temperatur und thermisches Gleichgewicht im Eisenbogen" (The Temperature and Thermal Equilibrium in Iron Arcs), *Zeitschrift für Physik*, **140**, no. 4, pp. 440–451 (1955).

37. M. Bayet and F. Guerineau, "Determination de la 'température électronique' dans la décharge dans les gaz excités en ultra-haute fréquence" (Determination of the "Electronic Temperature" in the Discharge in Gases Excited at Ultra-High Frequency), *Compt. rend.*, **239**, no. 17, pp. 1029–1031 (October, 1954).

38. M. A. Easley and W. W. Mumford, "Electron Temperature vs Noise Temperature in Low Pressure Mercury Argon Discharges," *J. Appl. Phys.*, **22**, no. 6, pp. 846–847 (June, 1951).

39. D. Barbiere, "Energy Distribution, Drift Velocity, and Temperature of Slow Electrons in Helium and Argon," *Phys. Rev.*, **84**, pp. 653–658 (November, 1951).

40. P. L. Phatnagar, M. Krook, D. H. Menzel, and R. N. Thomas, " 'Turbulence,' Kinetic Temperature, and Electron Temperature in Stellar Atmospheres," in A. Beer, *Vistas in Astronomy*, Vol. I, pp. 296–303, Pergamon Press, London and New York, 1955.

41. R. Champeix, "Comparaison entre la température électronique et la température thermodynamique des cathodes à oxides" (Comparison between the Electron Temperature and the Thermodynamic Temperature of Oxide Cathodes), *Compt. rend.*, **230**, no. 1, pp. 64–65 (January, 1950).

42. S. Friedman and L. N. Heynick, "Circuit for the Determination of Contact Potentials and Electron Temperatures from Retarding Field Characteristics," *Rev. Sci. Instr.*, **26**, no. 1, pp. 17–19 (January, 1955).

43. T. N. Chin, "Electron Temperature in the Parallel Plane Diode," *J. Appl. Phys.*, **26**, no. 4, pp. 418–423 (April, 1955).

44. E. O. Johnson and L. Malter, "Double-Probe Method for Determination of Electron Temperatures in Steady and Time-Varying Gas Discharges," *Phys. Rev.*, **76**, no. 9, pp. 1411–1412 (November, 1949).

45. D. G. Bulyginski and D. D. Dobretsow, "Electron Temperature in Oxide (Coated) Cathodes" (in Russian), *Zhurnal Tekhnicheskoĭ Fiziki-Akademiya Nauk SSSR*, **26**, no. 5, pp. 977–984 (1956); *Sci. Abstr. A*, **60**, no. 710, p. 135 (February, 1957).

46. I. S. Solet, "Elimination of Cold-Junction Error in Thermocouple Measurements in Electron Tubes," *Rev. Sci. Instr.*, **29**, no. 1, pp. 73–74 (January, 1958).

47. M. Waldmeier, "Variationen der Koronatemperatur" (Variability of the Coronal Temperature), *Zeitschrift für Astrophysik*, **30**, no. 2, pp. 137–151 (1952).

48. W. Elenbaas, "A New Method of Determining the Temperature of a High-Pressure Discharge," *Physica*, **9**, no. 1, pp. 53–64 (January, 1942).

49. P. J. Dickerman, "The Determination of the Equilibrium Temperature of a Plasma," in H. Fisher and L. C. Mansur, *Conference on Extremely High Temperatures*, pp. 77–92, John Wiley & Sons, New York, 1958.

50. H. Griem, "Recent Developments in Line Broadening Theory for High Temperature Gases," in H. Fisher and L. C. Mansur, *Conference on Extremely High Temperatures*, pp. 93–95, John Wiley & Sons, New York, 1958.

51. K. Pilowski, "Zur Masse-Leuchtkraft-Beziehung und zur empirischen Festlegung einer Skala von effektiven Temperaturen" (An Empirical Temperature

Scale Fixed by the Mass-Luminosity Relationship), Parts I and II, *Zeitschrift für Astrophysik*, **27**, pp. 193–222 (1950); and **29**, no. 2, pp. 162–172 (1951).

52. K. Pilowski, "Über das Zustandsdiagramm der Sterne" (On the State Diagram for Stars), Parts I and II, *Zeitschrift für Astrophysik*, **37**, pp. 149–183 (1955); and **39**, pp. 95–125 (1956).

53. G. P. Kuiper, "Stellar Temperatures," American Institute of Physics, *Temperature*, pp. 395–406, Reinhold Publishing Corp., New York, 1941.

54. L. D. Kaplan, "On the Pressure Dependence of Radiative Heat Transfer in the Atmosphere," *J. Meteorology*, **9**, no. 1, pp. 1–12 (February, 1952).

55. L. D. Kaplan, "On the Calculation of Atmospheric Transmission Functions for the Infrared," *J. Meteorology*, **9**, no. 2, pp. 139–144 (April, 1952).

56. H. Kienle, "The Problem of Stellar Temperatures," in A. Beer, *Vistas in Astronomy*, Vol. II, pp. 1321–1327, Pergamon Press, London and New York, 1955.

57. D. E. Blackwell, "The Excitation Temperature of the Solar Chromosphere Determined from Molecular Spectra," in A. Beer, *Vistas in Astronomy*, Vol. I, pp. 726–732, Pergamon Press, London and New York, 1955.

58. A. R. Sandage, "Solar Excitation Temperature of V_1," *Astrophysical Journal*, **111**, no. 3, pp. 575–579 (1951).

59. A. R. Sandage and A. J. Hill, "The Solar Growth for Lines of Cr 1," *Astrophysical Journal*, **113**, pp. 525–530 (1951).

60. J. C. Pecker, "Les températures de couleur des étoiles B" (Color Temperatures of B-Stars), *Compt. rend.*, **231**, no. 17, pp. 821–823 (October, 1950).

61. C. S. Beals and R. D. Hatcher, "The Photoelectric Temperatures of the P Cygni Stars," *Can. J. Research A*, **26**, pp. 149–166 (May, 1948).

62. R. V. Williams and S. Kaufman, "The Measurement of Electron Temperature in High-Temperature Plasmas," *Proc. Phys. Soc., London*, **75**, Part 3, pp. 329–336 (March, 1960).

63. A. Unsöld, "Turbulenz und Temperatur der Sonnenchromosphäre" (Turbulence and Temperature of the Solar Chromosphere), *Zeitschrift für Naturforschung*, **7a**, no. 1, pp. 121–126 (January, 1952).

64. R. Howard, "Excitation Temperatures and Turbulent Velocities in Sunspots," *Astrophysical Journal*, **127**, no. 1, pp. 108–117 (January, 1958).

65. P. Couteau, "Sur une détermination de la température effective d'une naine blanche montrant des raies de l'hydrogène en légère émission" (A Determination of the Effective Temperature of a White-Dwarf Showing Faint H Emission Lines), *Compt. rend.*, **232**, no. 9, pp. 797–798 (February, 1951).

66. L. Spitzer, Jr. and M. P. Savedoff, "The Temperature of Interstellar Matter. I, II, and II," *Astrophysical Journal*, **107**, no. 1, pp. 6–33 (January, 1948); **109**, no. 3, pp. 337–353 (May, 1949); and **111**, no. 3, pp. 593–608 (May, 1950).

67. R. Ebert, "Temperatur des interstellaren Gases bei grossen Dichten" (The Temperature of Interstellar Gas of High Density), *Zeitschrift für Astrophysik*, **36**, no. 3, pp. 222–229 (1955).

68. M. J. Seaton, "The Kinetic Temperature of the Interstellar Gas in Regions of Neutral Hydrogen," *Annales d'astrophysique*, **18**, series B, no. 139, 18 pp. (1955).

69. H. C. van de Hulst, C. A. Muller, and J. H. Oort, "The Spiral Structure of the Outer Part of the Galactic System Derived from the Hydrogen

Emission at 21 cm Wave Length," *Bulletin of the Astronomical Institutes of the Netherlands*, **12**, no. 452, pp. 117–149 (May, 1954).

70. A. E. Salomonovich, "Radio Emission of the Moon in the 8 Millimeter Band" (in Russian), *Astronomicheskii Zhurnal-Akademkniga*, **35**, no. 1, pp. 129–139 (1958); *Sci. Abstr. A*, **61**, no. 730, p. 614 (October, 1958).

71. K. Wurm, "Die Temperatur des Crabnebel-Zentralsternes" (The Temperature of the Crab-Nebula Central Star), *Naturwissenschaften*, **38**, no. 21, pp. 496–501 (November, 1951).

72. H. Andrillat, "Températures électroniques et degrés d'excitation des nébuleuses gazeuses" (Electron Temperatures and Degrees of Excitation in Gaseous Nebulae), *Compt. rend.*, **234**, no. 1, pp. 62–64 (January, 1952).

73. H. Andrillat, "Température électronique des nébuleuses gazeuses" (Electronic Temperature of Gaseous Nebulae), *Compt. rend.*, **231**, no. 25, pp. 1432–1434 (December, 1950).

74. H. Andrillat, "Les températures électronique des nébuleuses planétaires" (Electronic Temperatures of Planetary Nebulae), "Thèses présentées à la Faculté des Science de l'Université de Paris," *Service des publications du CNRS*, *2760*, Series, no. 3633, 58 pp. (1955).

75. E. F. Cox, "Upper Atmosphere Temperatures from Remote Sound Measurements," *Am. J. Phys.*, **16**, no. 9, pp. 465–474 (December, 1948).

76. H. S. Sicinski, N. W. Spencer, and W. G. Dow, "Rocket Measurements of Upper Atmosphere Ambient Temperature and Pressure in the 30- to 75-Kilometer Region," *J. Appl. Phys.*, **25**, no. 2, pp. 161–168 (February, 1954).

77. F. L. Bartman, L. W. Chaney, L. M. Jones, and V. C. Liu, "Upper-Air Density and Temperature by the Falling-Sphere Method," *J. Appl. Phys.*, **27**, no. 7, pp. 706–712 (July, 1956).

78. L. M. Jones and F. L. Bartman, "A Simplified Falling-Sphere Method for Upper-Air Density," *Univ. Mich. Eng. Research Inst. Report* 2215-10-T, 89 pp., Ann Arbor, Mich. (June, 1956).

79. W. G. Stroud, E. A. Terhune, J. H. Venner, J. R. Walsh, and S. Weiland, "Instrumentation of the Rocket-Grenade Experiment for Measuring Atmospheric Temperature and Winds," *Rev. Sci. Instr.*, **26**, no. 5, pp. 427–432 (May, 1955).

80. L. Elterman, "Seasonal Trends of Temperature, Density, and Pressure to 67.6 Km Obtained with the Searchlight Probing Technique," *J. Geophys. Research*, **59**, no. 3, pp. 351–358 (September, 1954).

81. L. Elterman, "A Series of Stratospheric Temperature Profiles Obtained with the Searchlight Technique," *J. Geophys. Research*, **58**, no. 4, pp. 519–530 (December, 1953).

82. L. Elterman, "Seasonal Trends of Temperature, Density, and Pressure in the Stratosphere Obtained with the Searchlight-Probing Technique," *AFCRC Technical Report* 54-19, Geophysical Research Papers no. 29, 70 pp., Air Force Cambridge Research Center, Cambridge, Mass. (July, 1954).

83. M. Kuchle, "Neutron Temperature Measurements in Graphite," *Nuclear Science and Engineering*, **2**, no. 1, pp. 87–95 (February, 1957).

84. M. Kuchle, "Messung der Neutronentemperatur in Graphit" (Measurement of Neutron Temperatures in Graphite), *Zeitschrift für Naturforschung*, **11a**, no. 8 (1956).

85. D. L. Livesley, "A Note on Nuclear Temperatures at Low Excitation Energies," *Can. J. Phys.*, **33**, no. 7, pp. 391–393 (July, 1955).

86. A. Ertaud and R. Beaugé, "Mesure de la température des neutrons dans le réflecteur d'une pile à eau lourde" (Measurement of the Temperature of the Neutrons in the Reflector of a Heavy-Water Pile), *Journal de physique et le radium*, **12**, no. 5, pp. 580–584 (May, 1951).

87. D. B. Beard, "Interpretation of Experiments on Nuclear Temperatures," *Bull. Am. Phys. Soc.*, **28**, no. 7, p. 16 (December 28, 1953).

88. G. M. Branch, "Neutron Temperature Measurements in Graphite and in a Uranium-Graphite Reactor," *U. S. Atomic Energy Commission* MDDC-747, 10 pp., Washington, October, 1946.

89. A. Andrew and C. R. Davidson, "Induced Thermoelectric Potential from Radiation Damage," *Phys. Rev.*, **89**, no. 4, pp. 876–877 (February, 1953).

90. G. Barbaras, J. Farr, and J. Kuranz, "Design and Construction of Boron Coated Thermocouples for Use in Neutron Fields," *U. S. Atomic Energy Commission*, AECD-2485, 3 pp., Washington, February, 1949.

91. W. J. Sturm and R. J. Jones, "Application of Thermocouples to Target Temperature Measurement in the Internal Beam of a Cyclotron," *Rev. Sci. Instr.*, **25**, no. 4, pp. 392–393 (April, 1954).

92. R. E. Jamison and T. H. Blewitt, "Behavior of Two Types of Thermocouples under Pile Irradiation at Low Temperatures," *Rev. Sci. Instr.*, **24**, no. 6, p. 474 (June, 1953).

93. A. I. Dahl and M. S. Van Dusen, "Resistance-Temperature Relation and Thermoelectric Properties of Uranium," *RP* 1813, *J. Research Natl. Bur. Standards*, **39** (July, 1947).

94. J. C. Johnson, "Measurement of the Surface Temperature of Evaporating Water Drops," *J. Appl. Phys.*, **21**, no. 1, pp. 22–23 (January, 1950).

95. H. J. White and G. L. Gammon, "Correlation of Mixture Temperature Data Obtained from Bare Intake-Manifold Thermocouples," *Wartime Report* E5L03, 9 pp., U. S. National Advisory Committee for Aeronautics, Washington (January, 1946).

96. M. Jakob, "Local Temperature Differences as Occurring in Evaporation, Condensation and Catalytic Reaction," *Research Publications*, **2**, no. 3, pp. 159–171, Illinois Institute of Technology, Chicago (May, 1942).

97. G. M. Pound and V. K. LaMer, "Surface Tension of Small Droplets as a Function of Size from Critical Supersaturation Data," *J. Chem. Phys.*, **19**, no. 4, pp. 506–507 (April, 1951).

98. P. W. Bridgman, *The Physics of High Pressure*, p. 39, G. Bell & Sons, London, 1949.

99. H. T. Hill, "Some High-Pressure, High-Temperature Apparatus Design Considerations: Equipment for Use at 100,000 Atmospheres and 3000°C," *Rev. Sci. Instr.*, **29**, no. 4 (April, 1958).

100. T. S. Noggle, T. H. Blewitt, R. R. Coltman, and C. E. Klabunde, "Thermal-emf-Free Vacuum Seal for Electrical Lead Wires," *Rev. Sci. Instr.*, **28**, no. 6, pp. 464 (June, 1957).

101. L. Seren, "Thin Glass Window to Withstand High Pressures," *Rev. Sci. Instr.*, **19**, no. 2, p. 123 (February, 1948).

102. P. W. Bridgman, "High-Pressure Instrumentation," *Mech. Eng.*, **75**, no. 2, pp. 111–113 (February, 1953).

103. V. P. Butuzov, M. G. Gonikberg, and S. P. Smirnov, "Measurements of Melting Points of Metals Under Extremely High Pressures," *Doklady*

Akademii Nauk SSSR, **89,** pp. 651–653 (1953); *National Science Foundation* NSF-tr-76, 3 pp., Office of Technical Services, Washington (September, 1953).

104. V. P. Butuzov and M. G. Gonikberg, "Melting Temperatures of Tin and Lead at Pressures Reaching 34,000 kg/cm²," *Doklady Akamedii Nauk SSSR,* Ser. fiz., **91,** pp. 1083–1084 (1953); *National Science Foundation* NSF-tr-144, 2 pp., Office of Technical Services, Washington (September, 1953).

105. R. Aumont and J. Romand, "Quelques considérations sur la réalisation pratique d'un thermomètre à bruit de fond" (Considerations on the Practical Realization of a Background-Noise Thermometer), *Journal de physique et le radium,* **15,** no. 7–8–9, pp. 585–586 (July–August–September, 1954).

106. R. Eggert, "The Construction and Installation of Thermocouples for Biological Research," *Journal of Agricultural Research,* **72,** no. 11, pp. 341–355 (June, 1946).

107. W. M. Conn, "Accurate Temperature Measurements in Work with Solar Furnaces," *Am. J. Phys.,* **24,** no. 8, pp. 581–583 (November, 1956).

108. J. Euler, "Zur Temperatur des positiven Kraters im Graphit-Normalbogen nach McPherson" (Temperature of the Positive Crater in McPherson's Normal Graphite Arc), *Zeitschrift für angewandte Physik,* **3,** no. 7, pp. 260–263 (July, 1951).

109. M. Nicolet, "Sur la mesure des températures au voisinage du sol" (On the Measurement of Temperatures in the Neighborhood of the Ground), *Institut royal météorologique de Belgique memoires,* **32,** no. 38, pp. 3–8 (1949).

110. A. MacFayden, "A Simple Device for Recording Mean Temperatures in Confined Spaces," *Nature,* **164,** no. 4179, p. 965 (December, 1949).

111. R. B. Platt and J. N. Wolf, "General Uses and Methods of Thermistors in Temperature Investigations, with Special Reference to a Technique for High Sensitivity Contact Temperature Measurement," *Plant Physiology,* **25,** no. 3, pp. 507–512 (1950).

112. H. L. Penman and I. Long, "A Portable Thermistor Bridge for Micrometeorology among Growing Crops," *J. Sci. Instr.,* **26,** no. 3, pp. 77–80 (March, 1949).

113. E. B. Greenhill and J. R. Whitehead, "An Apparatus for Measuring Small Temperature Changes in Liquids," *J. Sci. Instr.,* **26,** no. 3, pp. 92–95 (March, 1949).

114. G. Keinath, "Temperatur-Messung und- Regelung in Härteöfen" (Temperature Measurement and Control in Hardening Furnaces), *ATM Archiv für technisches Messen,* V2172-1, T71 (June, 1938).

115. K. S. Knol, "Determinations of the Electron Temperature in Gas Discharges by Noise Measurements," *Philips Research Reports,* **6,** pp. 288–302 (August, 1951); *Sci. Abstr. A,* **54,** no. 647, p. 1022 (November, 1951).

116. H. E. Stubbs and R. G. Phillips, "High-Speed Bolometer," *Rev. Sci. Instr.,* **31,** no. 2, pp. 115–118 (February, 1960).

117. P. P. Coppola, "Techniques of Cathode Temperature Measurements as Applied to Commercial Cathode-Ray Tubes," *Rev. Sci. Instr.,* **31,** no. 2, pp. 137–143 (February, 1960).

118. R. C. Kurtzrock, "Quick Connector for Multipoint Thermocouple Assemblies," *Rev. Sci. Instr.,* **31,** no. 4, pp. 457–458 (April, 1960).

119. H. C. van de Hulst, "Density and Velocity Distribution of the Interstellar Gas," *Reviews of Modern Physics,* **30,** no. 3, pp. 913–921 (July, 1958).

120. A. H. Davis, "The Kinetic Temperature of an Atmosphere Supported by Radiation," *Astrophysical Journal*, **127**, no. 1, pp. 118–124 (January, 1958).

121. R. D. Davies, "Twenty-One-Cm Studies of Some Interstellar Clouds," *Reviews of Modern Physics*, **30**, no. 3, pp. 931–933 (July, 1958).

122. H. Späth and H. Krempl, "Temperaturbestimmungen im Funkentladungen mit Hilfe zeitlich aufgelöster Spektren" (Temperature Measurements in Spark Discharges Made with Time Resolved Spectroscopy), *Zeitschrift für angewandte Physik*, **12**, no. 1, pp. 8–16 (January, 1960).

123. I. G. Donaldson, "Temperature Errors Introduced by Temperature-Measuring Probes," *British Journal of Applied Physics*, **10**, no. 6, pp. 252–255 (June, 1959).

124. S. S. Srivasta and V. Padmanabhan, "Capacitor Thermometer for Hydrologic Investigations," *Journal of Scientific and Industrial Research B*, New Delhi, **18**, no. 8, pp. 345–346 (August, 1959).

125. P. ten Bruggencate and G. Elste, "Temperature and Turbulence in Quiescent Prominences Derived from Line-Widths" (in German), *Nachrichten der Akademie der Wissenschaften in Göttingen. Mathematische-physikalische Klasse, 2a*, no. 9, pp. 255–271 (1959).

126. American Institute of Physics, Instrument Society of America, National Bureau of Standards, *Fourth Symposium on Temperature*, March 27–31, 1961, Columbus, Ohio.

NAME INDEX

Abbey, R. L., 349, 372
Aboud, A. A., 72
Abragam, A., 392
Abrams, H., 303
Adams, F. W., 202
Addicks, L., 72
Agnew, J. T., 125, 444
Agosta, V. D., 226, 227, 233
Aiken, C. B., 114, 123
Akimoff, E. M., 466
Akobjanoff, L., 375
Alderton, G., 126
Alentzev, M., 427, 445
Alford, J. S., 231
Allen, S., 324, 329, 344
Allis, W. P., 467
Allison, W., 233
Alquist, H. E., 400, 439
Althaus, E. J., 233
Ambler, E., 392, 395, 396
Ambur, I., 120
Ames Co., W. V-B, 333
Amme, R. C., 341
Anacker, F., 448
Anderson, A. R., 303
Anderson, D. H., 119
Anderson, H. C., 231
Anderson, J. W., 437, 448
Anderson, S., 118
Anderson, W. J., 118
Andress, P. M., 69
Andrew, A., 471
Andrews, D. H., 98, 124
Andrillat, H., 470
Anglin, F., 395
Apin, A. Ya., 448
Appl, F. C., 250, 260
Archibold, E., 123

Armi, E. L., 235, 257
Armstrong, G. T., 69
Aronson, M. H., 69
Arthur, J. R., 446
Ascah, R. G., 394
Assman, 328
Aston, J. G., 394
Atkins, K. R., 392
Atkins, R. M., 198
Atlantic Pyrometers, Inc., 199
Aumont, R., 71, 472
Avogadro, 450
Awbery, J. H., 399, 438

Babcock & Wilcox Company, 339
Babiskin, J., 397
Bachman, C. H., 118
Badgley, F. I., 232
Bailey, N. P., 215, 232, 400, 439
Baimakoff, Y. B., 72
Bain, J. W., 302
Baird, 114
Baker, E. B., 92, 125
Baker, E. M., 128
Baker, H. D., 71, 128, 165, 227, 233, 326, 339, 340, 400, 405, 438
Baker, N. H., 400, 438
Baker, R. C., 304
Balaban, P., 71
Baldo, A. F., 405, 420, 441
Ball, J. J., 120
Ballard, S. S., 118
Barbaras, G., 471
Barbee, C. E., 230
Barber, C. R., 12, 29, 70, 118, 127, 395
Barber, D., 163
Barber, R., 326, 343
Barbiere, D., 468